GESTA ROMANORUM.

GESTA ROMANORUM:

OR,

ENTERTAINING MORAL STORIES;

INVENTED BY THE MONKS AS A FIRESIDE RECREATION, AND COMMONLY APPLIED IN
THEIR DISCOURSES FROM THE PULPIT: WHENCE THE MOST CELEBRATED
OF OUR OWN POETS AND OTHERS, FROM THE EARLIEST
TIMES, HAVE EXTRACTED THEIR PLOTS.

TRANSLATED FROM THE LATIN, WITH

PRELIMINARY OBSERVATIONS AND COPIOUS NOTES,

BY THE REV. CHARLES SWAN,

Late of Catharine Hall, Cambridge.

REVISED AND CORRECTED BY

WYNNARD HOOPER, B.A.,

Clare College, Cambridge.

"They" [the Monks] "might be disposed occasionally to recreate their
minds with subjects of a light and amusing nature; and what could be
more innocent or delightful than the stories of the GESTA ROMANORUM?"
DOUCE's *Illustrations of Shakespeare.*

DOVER PUBLICATIONS, INC.

This new Dover edition first published in 1959
is an unabridged and unaltered republication
of the Bohn Library Edition of 1876.

Manufactured in the United States of America

Dover Publications, Inc.
180 Varick Street
New York 14, New York

PREFACE.

———•◦•———

It is somewhat remarkable that, in spite of the great
interest attaching to the *Gesta Romanorum*, as the most
popular story book of the Middle Ages, and as the source of
much literature in that and later times, no English version
of it should have appeared until 1824, when a translation
was published in two volumes by the Rev. C. Swan. Mr.
Swan, though his translation was in many respects faulty,
kept to the original with tolerable fidelity, and only
deliberately tampered with the text once; namely, in alter-
ing the termination of Tale XXVIII., because he considered
that the story, as it stood, did not afford a good " moral."
He very often paraphrased; and where the Latin contained too bald a statement of facts, he considered himself
justified in amplifying the narrative. But this can hardly
be objected to. The stories are often told so carelessly
that a translator is bound to add something in his rendering to make them express what they were intended to
convey to the reader. An English version of a work like
the *Gesta Romanorum* should certainly not be a literal
translation.

The present edition is a reprint of Mr. Swan's, with
considerable corrections and alterations. Whenever Mr.
Swan only expanded the Latin in his translation so as to
express what was really implied in the original, I have left
his rendering untouched. But I have expunged whatever

was an unnecessary departure from the text. On the other hand, Mr. Swan had occasionally omitted sentences of importance; these have been restored to the text in the present edition. Mistakes in translation, of which there are more than might have been expected, have, of course, been corrected.

Mr. Swan's notes are sometimes erroneous and occasionally pointless. With regard to the former class, I have generally allowed them to stand, and added a correction of the mistakes. Notes of the latter class I have sometimes omitted, and those so treated will not, I think, be missed by the reader. The most valuable part of Mr. Swan's notes are his quotations from other authors illustrative of the text, in selecting which he showed more judgment than in the actual work of translation; but it is throughout evident that his knowledge of English literature, or, at all events, of writers about English literature, was greater than his acquaintance with either Latin or Greek.

A great deal has been done, since Mr. Swan wrote, towards settling the vexed questions relative to the genesis of the *Gesta*. Sir Frederick Madden, in his work on the old English versions of the *Gesta*, did a good deal towards solving the problem. But the book which has dealt with the subject in the most thorough and satisfactory manner is the work of a painstaking German, Herr Hermann Oesterley.* It is little known in England. The British Museum only possesses the first part; the authorities apparently not thinking it worth while to obtain the remainder, when it was not spontaneously offered them by the bookseller, perhaps because no one ever asked for the work. The leaves of the first part were not even cut till recently. Considering the value of Herr Oesterley's book, its absence, except in an incomplete state, from the shelves

* *Gesta Romanorum*, von H. Oesterley. Berlin, 1872.

of our great national library is strange. There is a complete copy in the University Library, Cambridge.

It is impossible to do more here than to give a brief *résumé* of Herr Oesterley's conclusions regarding the *Gesta*. To go into his proofs, except in the merest outline, would be to reproduce his book, for it contains nothing whatever but what is strictly relevant to the matter in hand. Those who are acquainted with the subject will be aware how obscure and perplexing it is. Mr. Swan's Introduction, though rather vague and rambling, is worth studying. It contains some valuable conjectures, which subsequent inquiry has shown to be sound. Warton's "Dissertation on the *Gesta Romanorum*" (*Hist. of English Poetry*,* vol. i. p. cxxxix.), as being the earliest attempt to arrive at definite conclusions as to the origin of this collection of stories, is worth reading, apart from the deservedly high authority of its author. But its inadequacy was obvious even to Warton's contemporaries. Douce's "Dissertation" (*Illustrations of Shakespeare*, p. 516) is a really useful piece of work. Although mistaken in several points, his remarks are always acute and valuable ; and he called attention to the importance of a thorough examination of the MSS. contained in the libraries of the Continent, with a view to discovering, if possible, the origin of the *Gesta*. "It is a fact," he says, "as remarkable as the obscurity which exists concerning the author of the *Gesta*, that no manuscript of this work, that can with certainty be pronounced as such, has hitherto been described. If the vast stores of manuscripts that are contained in the monastic and other libraries of Germany, Switzerland, Italy, and Spain, were examined, there is scarcely a doubt that some original of a work so often printed would be discovered." Douce's expectations have been falsified by the result of Herr Oesterley's investiga-

---

* Taylor's edition, in three volumes. 1840.

tions in this very field. It is now clearly ascertained that
no MS. corresponding to the printed collection of stories
known as the *Gesta Romanorum* exists.

Before laying before the reader a succinct account of
the facts relative to the *Gesta* with which Herr Oesterley's
work supplies us, it is necessary to say that what is known
par excellence as the *Gesta Romanorum* is a collection of
181 stories, first printed about 1473, and that this is the
collection of which the present edition is a translation.
But before the appearance of this collection there existed
a great number of MSS. all over Western Europe, no two
of which exactly resembled each other. I shall now give
some details, chiefly obtained from Herr Oesterley, concerning both printed editions and MSS.

I. Printed editions.
  A. The *editio princeps*, printed in folio by Ketelaer and
     De Leempt, at Utrecht. Date uncertain. It con-
     tains 150 (not 152, as Douce erroneously says *)
     chapters.†
        (*a*) A second edition of the *editio princeps*, printed
             by Arnold Ter Hoenen, at Cologne. Date un-
             certain. It contains 151 chapters.
  B. The Vulgate (*vulgärtext*), or second *editio princeps*,
     printed by Ulrich Zell, at Cologne. Date uncertain.
     It contains 181 chapters.
Subsequent to the Vulgate numerous editions were
printed resembling it in all essentials.

There is no doubt, according to Herr Oesterley, that all
three editions [A, (*a*), & B] appeared between 1472 and
1475.‡ He has adopted A and B as his text; A for
the first 150 chapters (except chapter 18, which is found

---

* *Illustrations*, &c., p. 532. See Oesterley, p. 266.
† In discussions on the *Gesta Romanorum* the reader must
remember that " chapter " = " story."   ‡ Oesterley, p. 267.

only in B), and B for the remainder.* His text therefore reproduces the two *editiones principes*, if such an expression is not a solecism.

C. Various editions *in English*, based on the Latin MSS. of English origin. They contain usually 44 chapters, but sometimes 43, and once 58. A few examples will suffice.

(*a*) Printed by Wynkyn de Worde, in small 4to., at London, date uncertain. It contains 43 chapters, and is a translation of MS. Harl. 5369.† In the library of St. John's College, Cambridge.

(*b*) Printed in London, 1648. Contains 44 chapters.

(*c*) London, 1689. 44 chapters.

(*d*) London [1722?]. 58 chapters (British Museum, 1456A).

These editions all have some stories in common with the Vulgate, together with many which are peculiar to themselves. I may remark that Wynkyn de Worde's edition (*a*) is the only instance we have of a printed copy exactly corresponding to a MS. of the *Gesta*.

II. Manuscripts.

The MSS. of the *Gesta* fall naturally into three groups, or families, as Herr Oesterley calls them.‡

A. *The English group;* written in Latin. Of this the best representative is MS. Harl. 2270; date, fifteenth century. It contains 102 chapters, of which 72 are found in the Vulgate.§ This is the group which Mr. Douce‖ calls the "English Gesta," and which he and others have maintained to have been com-

---

piled in imitation of the "Original Gesta," i.e. the
Gesta represented by the set of manuscripts (C)
which supplied the Vulgate.

B. *Group of Latin and German MSS.* This family is
best represented by an edition in German, printed by
John Schopser, at Augsburg, in 1489.*

C. *A group represented by the Vulgate.* The MSS. of
this group have been greatly influenced by one
another, and by entirely distinct collections of
stories; † particularly by Robert Holkot's *Moralitates.*
Stories from Gervase of Tilbury appear in some of
the younger MSS. of this group.‡ This group con-
stitutes what Douce calls the "Original Gesta."

I have here given as concise a statement as possible of
a great multiplicity of facts. The diversity existing among
the MSS. known in England, and their apparent want
of connection with the printed editions, gave rise to the
theory, upheld by Mr. Douce and combated by Mr.
Swan and others, that there were two distinct collections
of stories called *Gesta Romanorum,* one of German, the
other of English origin. The early appearance of the
Gesta in England, the fact that the Vulgate was only
printed on the Continent, as well as the local colouring of certain of the stories, were held to prove that
shortly after the compilation of the "Original Gesta" in
Germany, a similar set of stories was composed in imitation of it in England. That no copy of the "English Gesta"
was printed appeared as strange as the fact that no MS.
of the Vulgate had ever been found. As remarked above,
Mr. Douce fully expected that a careful search in the
libraries of the Continent would reveal the missing MS.

Herr Oesterley's investigations appear to show con-
clusively that, though there were not *two Gestas,* in the

---

* Oesterley, pp. 1, 245.   † *Ibid.* pp. 245, 246.   ‡ *Ibid.* p. 253.

sense intended by Douce, yet there *is* a considerable differ
ence between the MSS. of England and of the Continent,
and between each of these and the printed Vulgate. He
is of opinion that the *Gesta* was originally compiled in
England; that it rapidly passed to the Continent; was
then considerably altered, by additions and corruptions;
and that, on the invention of printing, an edition (A) containing 150 stories, selected by the editors, as they thought
best, was issued. Shortly after, an enlarged edition
(B) was issued. This last is the Vulgate. Neither A
nor B was a reproduction of any one MS.; and they were
both compiled from MSS. belonging to group C. It is
easy to understand why the "English Gesta" was never
printed. The Vulgate appeared in England before there
was time to commence printing an edition of the *Gesta*
from the MSS. of the English group, and being much
larger than even the best of these (Harl. 2270, above
referred to), speedily got possession of the field, and
rendered it superfluous to produce another *Gesta*. Probably not one man in ten thousand would know of the
existence of MSS. containing stories not in the Vulgate.
And when Wynkyn de Worde printed his edition (1510—
1515) a need for an English version had arisen, which he
met by printing a complete translation of one of the MSS.
of the English group (see p. ix.).

Herr Oesterley admits * that it is *possible* that the
Gesta was originally compiled in Germany, and thence
carried to England, and enlarged by the addition of
specially English stories, while in Germany a process of
growth was also going on. But he thinks that the
balance of probability is in favour of the view which
places the home of the *Gesta* in England. He considers
that the names of the dogs in Tale CXLII. are distinctly
English; † and that the German proverb in the moraliza-

* Oesterley, p. 266. † *Ibid.* p. 264.

tion of Tale CXLIV., on which so much stress has been laid
by the believers in the German origin of the *Gesta*, is an
addition made by the editors of the printed copies, as is
clear from an inspection of the MSS.*

Herr Oesterley's conclusions as to the author of the
Gesta are purely negative. The theory which assigns the
authorship to Berchorius, the prior of St. Eloi (Pierre
Bercheur), he treats as quite unproved. The only other
claimant put forward is Helinand; Herr Oesterley decides
against him also, and the matter is left as incapable of
settlement.†

Herr Oesterley is of opinion that the *Gesta* was compiled towards the end of the thirteenth century. It has been
urged that the collection cannot have appeared before the
death of Robert Holkot (1349), since a series of stories
found in the *Gesta* are taken from his *Moralitates*. But
even supposing these stories *were* first made known by
Holkot, this can only be used to prove that the MSS. of
the *Gesta* which contain them were written since 1349, not
that the *Gesta* was not originally compiled much earlier.‡
Herr Oesterley also urges the fact that the MSS. had, as
early as the middle of the fourteenth century, become sufficiently diversified, by a natural process of differentiation, as
to group themselves into the three families mentioned above,§
as a proof that the first or primitive MS. cannot have
appeared *later* than the early part of the fourteenth century.
For some time must have elapsed before so great a diversity
could have arisen. Moreover, Herr Oesterley mentions a
MS. written in 1326, which is obviously, from the corruptions of words, and especially of proper names, a copy of
some earlier edition.‖

Herr Oesterley's views as to the origin of the *Gesta* are

---

* Oesterley, p. 262.   † *Ibid.* pp. 254, 255.   ‡ *Ibid.* p. 256.
§ *Ibid.* p. 257. " Von jeder familie ist uns mindestens *ein* codex
aus der mitte des 14 jahrhunderts erhalten," and the rest of the page.
‖ *Ibid.* pp. 257 and fol.

necessarily only conjectures, but as such they are of considerable value. He thinks that at some early period there
were collections of stories taken from Roman history in
actual use as texts for sermons;* and that these stories
were then put together for the express purpose of being
moralized, and finally appeared under the title of *Gesta
Romanorum Moralizata*, or something similar.† Whether
this first compilation was entirely composed of classical
stories, or contained some of more modern date as well, it
is impossible to say.‡ What we now know as the *Gesta
Romanorum* arose from the moralizing of this, or some
similar work, after it had been enlarged by the addition of
a considerable number of stories relating to later times.
It would be easy to circulate a collection of stories under
the name of the "Gests of the Romans" among a people
whose ideas of history were as limited as those of our fore-
fathers in the twelfth and thirteenth centuries, even though
it had not contained a single word about Rome. The intention of the original authors of the *Gesta* was to provide
texts for moralizations. The stories themselves were of
secondary importance. Very often in the MSS. the first
words of some well-known story appear at the commencement of a chapter, and then the moralization follows
immediately. In many of the older copies some of the
stories have spaces left after them for the moralization,
the writer presumably intending to add it subsequently.§
It is not till a very late period that the stories become the
more important part, and the moralization recedes into the
background.‖ Herr Oesterley is very severe on Grässe's
rash statement that the English MSS., which are mostly
early ones, have, as a rule, no moralizations.¶

At the risk of being accused of undue repetition, I shall

---

* Oesterley, p. 260.   † *Ibid.* p. 261.
‡ *Ibid.* p. 261.   § *Ibid.* p. 261.   ‖ *Ibid.* p. 262.
¶ *Ibid.* p. 262. Grässe, *Gesta Romanorum*, ii. 302.

recapitulate the results of Herr Oesterley's labours, which have been set forth in the pages of this preface. The *Gesta* was originally composed in England, whence it rapidly passed to the Continent, at the end of the thirteenth century. By the middle of the fourteenth century there were three distinct families of MSS. of the *Gesta*. When printing was invented, one of these groups (C) was, so to speak, crystallized and hardened into the Vulgate, after which no further change took place. The Vulgate became known as *Gesta Romanorum*, and was probably supposed by each person to be identical with the work he had always heard called by that title, but which was, as we have seen, differently given by every MS.

Returning to the present edition, it is necessary to explain why the moralizations have been shortened. Mr. Swan omitted the greater part of all but a few at the commencement. As the moralizations are of no interest, except from the light they throw on the nature and origin of the *Gesta*, and as a mere translation of them is of no use for this purpose, I have left them in the abbreviated state. The reader can easily judge of their nature from the few given in full.

I have revised the translation chiefly by reference to the readings in Oesterley's edition, which is a reprint of the two first editions.* I have also frequently referred to an edition printed in folio, at Hagenau, by Henry Gran, in 1517, which is a reprint of his edition of 1508, from which Mr. Swan made his translation. The colophon of the edition of 1517 (in the British Museum) is the same, with the exception of the date, as that of Gran's edition of 1508, of which the colophon will be found at the end of the volume. The differences between the Hagenau edition and the Vulgate are very small, and would only be appreciable to the public if a literal translation were made of each.

* See above, pp. viii., ix.

Whenever the reading of the Hagenau copy is more intelligible than that of the older edition, I have adopted it. It is quite possible that Gran may have had access to MSS. which the editors of the Vulgate did not know of; and thus he may have obtained a warrant for introducing the few slight improvements he made on his predecessors' text.

I would call the reader's attention to the fact that one or two very good stories are contained in Mr. Swan's Introduction.

W. H.

LONDON, *July* 31st, 1876.

INTRODUCTION.

SECTION I.

THE History of Romantic Fabling is enveloped in much perplexity; nor is it diminished by the various conjectures which have been started and upheld. The labours of ingenuity are not always convincing; and perhaps the very fact of their plausibility leads us to mistrust. Discussion upon remote history is ever attended with difficulty; and arguments that rest upon the basis of refined deduction—that are artfully designed to pull down one system while they support another equally imaginative, may have a well-founded claim to admiration, but not upon the score of truth. It is singular how the mind loves to grasp at mystery, and to disport itself in the chaos of departed time. It springs undauntedly forward, unappalled by the numberless shadows which flit in "dim perspective" before it, and undeterred by the intricacies of the way. It would seem like a captive escaped from confinement, wantoning in the excess of unaccustomed liberty. And the more boundless the subject, the less timid we find the adventurer; the more perilous the journey, the less wary are his movements. Boldness appears to constitute success; as if, because the faint·heart never attained the fair lady, modest pretensions and unassuming merit never secured the lady TRUTH. It is a libel upon the head and the heart; and cannot be too speedily abandoned.

Of the theories already advanced, none, it seems to me, is perfect; and none, without some portion of accuracy. They each go part of the way, but stop before they touch the mark. Bishop Percy, after Mallet, attributes the invention of romance to the ancient Scalds or Bards of the North. "They believed the existence of giants and dwarfs; they entertained opinions not unlike the more modern notion of fairies; they were strongly possessed with the belief of spells and enchantments, and were fond of inventing combats with dragons and monsters."[1] Now, this is unequivocally nothing less than the entire machinery employed in all the Arabian Tales, and in every other oriental fiction. Such a coincidence no one will suppose the result of accident; nor can it for a moment be believed that the warm imaginations of the East—where Nature brightens the fancy equally with the flowers—borrowed it from the colder conceptions of the Northern bards. Many parts of the Old Testament demonstrate familiarity with spells; and Solomon (which proves a *traditional* intercourse, at least, between the Jews and other people of the East), by universal consent, has been enthroned sovereign of the Genii, and lord of the powerful Talisman. In David and Goliath, we trace the contests of knights with giants: in the adventures of Samson, perhaps, the miraculous feats attributed to the heroes of chivalry. In the apocryphal Book of Tobit, we have an angel in the room of a SAINT; enchantments, antidotes, distressed damsels, demons, and most of the other machinery of the occidental romance.[2] Parts of the Pentateuch, of Kings, &c., &c., appear to have been amplified, and rendered wild and fabulous; and were the comparison carried minutely forward, I am persuaded that the analogy would be found as striking as distinct. I mean not that this has always been the *immediate* source : I am rather inclined to suppose that certain ramifications, *direct* from the East, already dilated and improved, were more generally the origin. But Scripture, in many cases, furnished a supernatural agency without pursuing this circuitous route; as well as heroes with all the attributes of ancient romance. In the old French prose of Sir Outel, chap. xxiv., we have the following exclamations on the death of the knight Roland, which partly confirm my observation :—"Comparé à *Judas Machabeus* par ta valeur et prouesse; ressemblant à *Sanson*, et pareil à *Jonatas fils de Saul* par la fortune de sa triste morte!" The Jewish Talmud, and especially the commentary upon it, abounds with fables, composed in some respects of the materials worked up by the Scalds, but long anterior in date to their compositions, so far as they are known.

Dr. Percy contends that "old writers of chivalry appear utterly unacquainted with whatever relates to the Mahometan nations, and represent them as worshipping *idols,* or adoring a golden image of Mahomet."[3] This, I should conceive, would naturally be the case. It was the aim of Christian writers to represent the infidels in the

[1] *Reliques of Ancient English Poetry,* vol. iii. p. xiii.
[2] In the *application* of the 10th Tale, the Book of Tobit is referred to.
[3] *Rel. of Anc. Eng. Poetry, ibid.*

worst light possible. They thought them the most wretched beings in creation; and they might, therefore, artfully pervert their creed and exaggerate their vices. Most frequently, such would be the genuine result of their abhorrence: just as popular superstition pictures the "foul fiend" with horns, and cloven feet, and a hideously distorted countenance—not because it is really accredited, but because nothing is thought too vile or too fearful for the Evil One. The hostility which the crusades excited and nourished; nay, the very difference of religious feeling, would necessarily call out the whole virulence of an age not remarkable for its forbearance; and it is absurd to suppose that the intercourse so long maintained between the two continents (both previous to these expeditions, and subsequent) should not have given them a sufficient acquaintance with the Saracen belief and mode of worship. If the great Saladin required and received *knighthood* from the hands of the Christians,[1] it argued a degree of intimacy with European customs on the one side, which it would be unfair and arbitrary to deny the other.

That the Scalds added some circumstances to the original matter, and rejected others, is extremely probable. The traditions which conveyed the fable would, of course, be corrupted; not only from the mode of conveying it, but from the dissimilarity of customs and ideas among those by whom it was received. All I contend for is the original ground, upon which they and other nations have built; and this, I think I shall be able to demonstrate, purely oriental. But it is objected that, if the Northern bards had derived their systems from the East, they would have naturalized them as the Romans did the stories of Greece. It is thought that they must have adopted into their religious rites the same mythology, and have evinced as strong a similitude, as the nations of classical celebrity. There is, in truth, no basis for such an assertion to stand upon. The long intercourse between these nations, their vicinity to each other, and, more than all, the original similarity of their worship, *prepared* the Romans to receive the devotional system of a conquered country without hesitation. They understood and valued Grecian literature, and consequently found an additional motive for the reception of Grecian theology. It accorded with preconceived notions; it was, in fact, a *part* of their own. Besides, the Romans were rising in civilization, and caught at every shadow of improvement. The people of the North were totally the reverse. They were the children

---

[1] See *Gesta Dei per Francos*, p. 1152. Joinville (p. 42) is cited by Gibbon for a similar instance.

of Nature—of Nature yet unbetrothed to Art. *They* were not, therefore, prepared by anything analogous to produce a similar effect : and could but seize the most prominent features that were presented to them, upon which to engraft their own wild and terrible stories.

Warton has written a long dissertation to prove that the Arabians, who had been for some time seated on the northern coasts of Africa, and who entered Spain about the beginning of the eighth century, " disseminated those extravagant inventions which were so peculiar to their romantic and creative genius."[1] This hypothesis Bishop Percy has endeavoured to refute ; and, according to Mr. Ellis,[2] he has entirely succeeded. The argument advanced on this occasion is that, were it true, " the first French romances of chivalry would have been on Moorish, or at least Spanish subjects, whereas the most ancient stories of this kind, whether in prose or verse, whether in Italian, French, English, &c., are *chiefly* on the subjects of Charlemagne and the Paladins, or of our British Arthur, and his Knights of the Round Table, &c., being evidently borrowed from the fabulous chronicles of the supposed Archbishop Turpin, and of Jeffrey of Monmouth."[3] Something in this there may be ; but it is still clear that intercourse, of whatever kind, existing between two nations, must, to a certain degree, supply information relative to their peculiar habits and belief. That each side would hold communication with their captives, either from political motives or otherwise, is consistent with the experience of all ages ; and, surely, not every individual would be so fastidious as to repel a closer intimacy. Courtesy, humanity, intrigue, &c., would, in some few at least, open a door to an unfettered interchange of thought ; while gratitude for certain benefits might operate on others. In the course of a multifarious warfare, such things *must* occur ; the line of separation *must* occasionally be removed, and youthful hearts and minds *must*, *now and then*, however sundered by human prejudices, break down the strongest barrier that interposes between them. If this be granted, when the history of such times and such circumstances was forgotten, the literature which they had helped to disseminate would remain. The legendary tale of the sire descends unmutilated to the son ; and the fact is on record, though the occasion be obliterated. The fabulous chronicle of Turpin might *then* be drawn up ; having its superstructure on French manners, but its basis on oriental

---

[1] *Hist. of Eng. Poetry*, Diss. 1.   [2] *Specimens of Anc. Met. Romances*, vol. i. p. 31.
[3] *Rel. of Anc. Eng. Poetry*, vol. iii. p. xii. *Note.*

learning. Much time must inevitably elapse before new systems can take root; and when they do, it is imperceptibly and silently. Hence, may the hostile incursions of the Saracens have introduced *some* portion of Eastern fiction: but not *all;* for it is the common tendency of a conquered country to engraft its *own* character and customs upon those of the stronger power.

It has been observed by Ritson (whose virulent and ungentlemanly abuse of his opponents is disgusting in the extreme!) that neither the Spaniards, nor any other nations of Europe, had an opportunity of adopting literary information "from a people with whom they had no connection, but as enemies, *whose language they never understood, and whose manners they detested;* nor would even have condescended or permitted themselves to make such an adoption from a set of infidel barbarians who have invaded, ravaged, and possessed themselves of some of the best and richest provinces of Spain."[1] Much of this is in substance what has been contended against above; and that a very short period of servitude will not open the sources of a more friendly communication—in appearance at least—between nations under such circumstances, is contrary to historical fact and to human nature. The enslaved must look up to the enslaver for protection— for support; and the latter in return would enforce, under the penalty of extermination, the aid which was considered requisite. Thus, however involuntary and hateful, intercourse must be under *all* situations. But here the fact is, as Mr. Warton remarks (though Ritson pleases to overlook it), that after the irruption of the Saracens, the Spaniards neglected even the study of the Sacred Writings, for the express purpose of acquiring the Arabic. This curious passage is cited by Du Cange, whose words I shall quote at length:—

"Quod vero suprà laudatus Scriptor anonymus de Galliæ nostræ in Lingua Latina barbarie ante Caroli M. tempora, idem de Hispania post Saracenorum irruptionem testatur Alvarus : ubi neglectis et posthabitis Scripturis Sanctis, earumque sacris interpretibus, quotquot supererant Christiani, Arabum Chaldæorumque libris evolvendis incumbebant, *gentilitia eruditione præclari, Arabico eloquio sublimati, Ecclesiasticam pulchritudinem ignorantes, et Ecclesiæ flumina de Paradiso manantia, quasi vilissima contemnentes, legem suam nesciebant, et linguam propriam non advertebant Latini, ita ut ex omni Christi Collegio vix inveniretur unus in milleno hominum genere, qui salutatorias fratri posset rationaliter dirigere literas,* CUM REPERIRENTUR ABSQUE NUMERO MULTIPLICES TURBÆ, QUI ERUDITE CHALDAICAS

---

[1] *Diss. on Romance and Minstrelsy,* vol. i. pp. xx. xxi.

VERBORUM EXPLICARENT POMPAS. Quod quidem abunde firmat; quæ de Elepanto Toletano suprà diximus. Sed et inde satis arguimus unde tot voces Arabicæ in Hispanam, subinde sese intulerunt." [1]

We have, then, a complete refutation of Ritson's strongest objection ; and perhaps had not the spleen of the writer been more powerful than the good sense and feeling of the man, he never would have hazarded the remark. And if judicial astrology, medicine, and chemistry, were of Arabian origin, and introduced into Europe a century at least before the crusades ; if Pope Gerbert, or Sylvester II., who died A.D. 1003, brought the Arabic numerals into France, it is surely reasonable to suppose that these sciences, so intimately connected with magical operations (and with fictions from them) as to confer upon the possessor a title to supernatural agency, would extend their influence to the legendary stories, as well as to the manners of the West, which these very stories are admitted to describe! Yet, after all, it is not to be imagined that the introduction of Eastern invention happened at one time, or in one age; it was rather the growth of many times, and of many ages—continually, though gradually, augmenting, till it attained maturity.

The next hypothesis gives Armorica, or Bretany, as the source of romantic fiction. But to this, the same objections arise that have been started with respect to the rest. Mr. Ellis, in the introduction to his *Specimens of Early English Romances*, plausibly suggests that all are compatible. He imagines " that the scenes and characters of our romantic histories were very generally, though not exclusively, derived from the Bretons, or from the Welsh of this island; that much of the colouring, and perhaps some particular adventures, may be of Scandinavian origin, and that occasional episodes, together with part of the machinery, may have been borrowed from the Arabians." [2] Which is as much as to say, that each nation contributed *something*, and very likely they did ; but which furnished the greater part, or which originated the whole, is just as obscure as before a "reconciliation" of opinions was projected. This conciliatory system will remind the reader of Boccacio's tale of *The Three Rings*, "the question of which is yet remaining."

Another supposition attributes the chief source of romantic fiction to classical and mythological authors ; that is, to the stories of Greece and Rome, somewhat altered by modern usages. To this belief Mr. Southey [3] and Mr. Dunlop seem to incline. The latter

---

[1] Du Cange ; *Gloss. Med. Inf. Lat.* tom. 1., *Præfatio*, p. xxxii. § 31.
[2] Vol. i. p. 35.   [3] Introduction to *Amadis of Gaul*.

adds that, "after all, a great proportion of the wonders of romance must be attributed to the imagination of the authors." But when these wonders, similarly constructed, pervade the most remote countries, there must be something more than an author's imagination brought into the account. Consideration, however, is due to the idea of a classical origin; and this, blended with the rest, may help to make up a perfect system. Before I proceed to the attempt, I would advert to certain observations which Mr. Dunlop has promulgated in his *History of Fiction.* He says, "It cannot be denied, and indeed has been acknowledged by Mr. Warton, *that the fictions of the Arabians and Scalds are totally different.*" [1] Much misunderstanding would doubtless be avoided by accurate references: and if Mr. Dunlop be correct in what he asserts, it would be a pleasant thing to know the edition and page to which he alludes. In contradiction to the insinuation here thrown out, Warton says, "But as the *resemblance which the pagan Scandinavians bore to the Eastern nations in manners, monuments, opinions, and practices* IS SO VERY PERCEPTIBLE AND APPARENT, an inference arises, that their migration from the East must have happened at a period by many ages more recent, and therefore most probably about the time specified by historians." [2] And again, "These practices and opinions co-operated with kindred superstitions of *dragons, dwarfs, fairies, giants, and enchanters, which the traditions of the Gothic Scalders had already planted :* and produced that extraordinary species of composition which has been called ROMANCE." [3] In another place, indeed, he admits that there were "*but few*" of these monsters in the poetry of the most ancient Scalds; but that few is quite sufficient for the argument.

So that, one would think, Warton supplies no testimony in support of a doctrine, which I cannot help fancying may be proved altogether groundless. "Allowing the early Scaldic odes to be genuine," says Mr. Dunlop, " we find in them no *dragons, giants, magic rings, or enchanted castles.* These are only to be met with in the compositions of the bards who flourished after the native vein of Runic fabling had been enriched by the tales of the Arabians." [4] This is an extremely cautious method of writing; for while we contend that the Easterns furnished the groundwork, and fix the date, Mr. Dunlop may tell us, be it when it may, that it was subsequent to the period in which the Runic fable flourished in its

[1] Page 163. [2] Dissertation I. p. xxviii.
[3] *Hist. of Eng. Poetry*, vol. i. p. 110. [4] Vol. i. p. 164.

native purity. Let us examine, however, how far his bold assertion
may be maintained, respecting the poetical machinery adopted by the
ancient Scalds. Let us advert to EDDA,[1] a monument "tout-à-fait
unique en son espèce," as Monsieur Mallet assures us,[2] and try
whether there be not, in fact, almost the whole of what he has
rejected.

Gylfe was king of Sweden, and a celebrated magician. When a
colony of Asiatics arrived in his country (a tradition which adds
strength to *my* hypothesis) he assumed the form of an old man, and
journeyed to the city of Asgard. "Sed Asæ erant perspicaciores,
(imo ut) præviderent iter ejus, eumque *fascinatione* oculorum
exciperent. *Tunc cernebat ille altum palatium :* Tecta ejus erant
tecta aureis clypeis, ut tectum novum. Ita loquitur Diodolfius :
'Tectum ex auro micante, Parietes ex lapide, Fundamina aulæ ex
montibus fecere Asæ sagaciores.' "[3]

Here, beyond dispute, is an *enchanted castle.* And not only so,
but the common oriental practice of putting a number of questions as
the test of a person's wisdom, occurs in this very fable. "Qui est le
plus ancien ou le premier des Dieux ?" is first asked, and other
interrogatories follow, of a similar character. Then for the GIANTS
—in the Runic mythology nothing is more common. Speaking of
the formation of man, the Edda observes (I follow the French
translation of M. Mallet): "Cet homme fut appellé *Yme ;* les Géans
le nomment *Oergelmer,* et c'est de lui que toutes leurs familles descendent, comme cela est dit dans la *Voluspa:* 'Toutes les Prophétesses
viennent de Vittolfe; les sages de Vilmôde, LES GEANS de Yme,'
et dans un autre endroit : 'Des fleuves Elivages ont coulé des
goutes de venim, et il souffla un vent d'où un Géant fut formé.
De lui viennent toutes les races Gigantesques.' "[4] In this place we
have not merely an accidental notice of giants, but their full
genealogy, and a quotation from a poem still more ancient than the
Edda, introduced in support of it. Afterwards mention is made of
the *Dwarfs :* "Alors les Dieux s'etant assis sur leurs thrônes rendirent

---

[1] "The Edda was compiled, *undoubtedly* with many additions and interpolations,
from fictions and traditions in the old Runic poems, by Soemund Sigfusson, surnamed
the Learned, about the year 1057."—WARTON. But Warton has not proved his
undoubtedly; and though I do not deny the probability of interpolations, I shall not
relinquish the *giants,* &c., without further proof.

[2] *Monumens de la Mythol. et de la Poesie des Celtes,* &c., p. 13, *Pref.*

[3] "But the Asiatics were more quick-sighted; nay, they foresaw his journey, and
deceived him with their enchantments. *Then he beheld a lofty palace;* its roofs
were covered with golden shields, like a new roof. Thus Diodolfius speaks of it : 'The
Asiatics, more skilful, made the roof of shining gold, and its walls of stone; the
foundations of the hall were mountains.' "—GORANSON, *Lat. Tr. of the Edda.*
Mythologie Celtique, p. 11.

la justice et délibererent sur ce qui concernoit les NAINS. Cette
espèce de créatures s'etoit formée dans la poudre de la terre, comme
les vers naissent dans un cadavre."[1] And again of the *Fairies* and
Genii, or beings answering to them—"Les unes sont d'origine
divine, d'autres descendent des GENIES, d'autres des Nains, comme
il est dit dans ses vers : *Il y a des* FÉES *de diverse origine, quelques
unes viennent des Dieux, et d'autres des* GENIES, *d'autres des Nains.*"[2]
This fable gives a very curious account of the fairies : "Voici," says
M. Mallet, "une Théorie complette de la Féerie;" but they are
perhaps, as Bishop Percy has remarked, more analogous to the *Weird
Sisters* than to the popular notion of fairyism in the *present* day. The
ninth fable of the EDDA alludes to "LES GENIES lumineux," who are
said to be "plus brillans que le soleil; mais les *noirs* sont plus noirs
que la poix."[3] And what is this but the good and bad genii of
Eastern romance ? Thor's "vaillante ceinture, qui a le pouvoir
d'accroitre ses forces," and the "chaine magique,"[4] are equivalent
to the *enchanted ring;* nor are "le grand serpent de Midgard," with
other monsters, so unlike the oriental Dragon,[5] as to preclude any
comparison.

In short, the reader clearly distinguishes the accordance of the
Northern mythology with that of the East. I could cite many more
examples, but they are unnecessary; and if, as Mr. Dunlop imagines,
"in the Eastern Peris we may trace the origin of EUROPEAN FAIRIES,"[6]
by what possible contrivance, if he will be consistent, can he deny
to the fairies of the North that claim which he grants to the *whole
of* EUROPE ?

I shall now proceed to account for the introduction of romantic
fiction, by a channel which appears to me the most natural, and
therefore the most likely to be true. I would begin with that
period in which the persecutions of the pagan rulers drove the
primitive Christians into the East. Full of the mysterious wonders
of the Apocalypse, not less than of the miraculous records of the
Holy Gospels; imbued with all that the Old Testament narrates, and
probably anticipating similar interposition from Heaven in their own
persons; their minds wrought up by many causes to the highest
pitch of enthusiasm, and their hearts glowing with a fervour that no
other ages can boast—they were well prepared to receive the impres-

---

[1] *Mythologie Celtique*, p. 30.   [2] *Ibid*. p. 36.
[3] *Ibid*. p. 40.   [4] *Ibid*. pp. 84 and 90.
[5] The Apocryphal continuation of the Book of *Esther*, and *Bel and the* DRAGON,
seem to bespeak the prevalence of this fiction in the East at a very early period.
[6] *Hist. of Fiction*, vol. i. p. 165.

sions naturally made upon a heated fancy; and to put credit in tales
which the distress of their situation prevented them from investi-
gating, and their ignorance or credulity debarred from doubt. Hence,
with the lives of the Fathers of the Church, they interwove prodigies
of another land; and being further willing to address the prejudices
of those they might hope to convert, adorned their martyrologies
with fictitious incidents of oriental structure—even as, to conciliate
the heathen, they introduced into their religious buildings the
statues of pagan worship, dignifying them with novel names, and
serving them with novel ceremonies. Not always, indeed, was this
the process; nor the apotheosis always intentional. Succeeding
times exhibited another mode of realizing fables, if I may so speak;
and discovered another path to falsehood under the garb of truth.
The monks were accustomed to exercise themselves with declaiming
upon the merits of their patron saint. To give a new varnish to his
fame, to excite yet more powerfully either the intellects or the
devotion of the drowsy brotherhood, they added romantic fictions
of their own; and invented familiar stories, derived from an infinite
variety of sources. But because Eastern imaginations were more
splendid and captivating—because Jerusalem and the Holy Sepulchre
were in the East—because "an idle and lying horde of pilgrims and
palmers" (as Mr. Dunlop expresses it) annually brought thither fresh
subjects for credulity to feed upon, they were the most partial to
oriental conceptions. The fables which they thus constructed were
laid by, fairly transcribed, and beautifully illuminated; until, in due
time, the monastery coffers were ransacked, and the gross and
acknowledged inventions of earlier ascetics were imposed upon their
later brethren, as the undoubted and veritable history of real Fathers
and real saints.

It is well known that, in the earlier ages of Christianity, forged
gospels were put forth in imitation of the true: while the tenets of
the Persian magi were united with the doctrines of the Son of God.[1]
If this prove nothing further, it proves the facility with which
oriental dogmas were interwoven with those of the West. At a more
advanced period, other legends written in Latin, and professing to be
narratives of what actually occurred, were again transcribed, with
manifold amplifications by those into whose hands the manuscripts
might happen to fall. Metrical versions were then given; and their
popularity soon induced the narrators to step out of their immediate
walk of martyrdom, to raise the standard of chivalry in the persons

[1] See Mosheim's *Eccles. Hist.* Cent. I. and III.

of Brute, Alexander, Charlemagne, and the rest. Let it be observed that all these stories are of a similar cast; the *Lives of the Saints*, somehow or other, are always connected with the fictions of every hero of chivalry. They invariably work marvels in behalf of their votaries; they bequeath relics of surprising power—or they appear in dreams; or the utterance of their mighty names counteracts the potency of magical delusions, &c., &c., while the hero himself, treading in the steps of his canonized precursor, becomes a distinguished *religieux ;* and at last takes *his* place in the calendar—"a very, very SAINT."

If my hypothesis, therefore, be just, with the return of the exiled Christians from the East *originated* romantic fiction in Europe. But this, of course, must be taken with modifications. Time alone could mature what in its progress acquired such extensive popularity; and it seems to me one of the glaring defects of other systems, that they would represent the rise of that particular kind of fable in question to have been almost instantaneous: to have followed swift upon the incursions of the Saracens—to have sprung up mysteriously among the Scandinavians, or equally, if not more so, among the Armoricans. Whereas that which was so wide in its extent—so singular in its effects—so deeply impressed on a large portion of the globe, must inevitably have had a beginning and a middle : it must have been long crescent, before it was at the full. It is true the classical system has not all the objections which meet the other, on the score of precipitancy ; but still it accounts only for that part of romance which is evidently built upon classic ground. Much of the machinery is wholly different; and from the comparatively few allusions—from the indistinct and monstrous perversions of Grecian or Roman fable, we are sure that their knowledge was very limited. But, in fact, a union of classic traditions with oriental fiction is not only probable but certain ; yet my hypothesis still traces it to the East.[1] For it will be noticed, that Eastern conceptions invariably predominate, even where the subject is confessedly classic ; as in the stories of Alexander, Cæsar, and others. Besides, the incursions of these leaders into that quarter of the world might, as it has happened

---

[1] The process by which Ulysses preserved himself from the charms of Circe is very similar to that which occurs in the story of " Beder Prince of Persia, and Giahaure Princess of Samandal," in the *Arabian Tales ;* and the fable of the Cyclops is found in the third voyage of Sinbad the Sailor. But Homer is known to have been a great wanderer, and to have picked up much traditionary matter in the East and elsewhere. Speaking of the fable of Atalanta, Warton has observed (*Diss. on the Gest. Rom.* v. 3) that " It is not impossible that an oriental apologue might have given rise to the Grecian fable." This, I am inclined to think, has often been the case.

in similar cases, leave certain traditionary monuments of their own belief.[1] This, however, I by no means intend to urge.

When instances of those who fled, or were exiled to the East, or voluntarily settled there, are so numerous, it would be idle to weary the reader's attention, by entering into any lengthened detail. The names of Clemens of Alexandria, of Ignatius, Tertullian, and Origen, are conspicuous in the second and third centuries, with many others, who were in constant intercourse with the West; and the soft and yielding character of these times presented a plastic surface to every, even the slightest touch. In the early part of the fourth century the foundation of Constantinople,[2] which drew from Italy such a large population, would facilitate the interchange of literature; for it is not improbable that many of the Asiatics, driven from their settlements by the influx of the foreigners, would hasten to occupy the homes which the others had vacated. At all events, the new settlers in the East had friends and connexions in their fatherland, with whom it was natural, and even necessary, that there should be a certain intercourse. Towards the conclusion of the third century, when monachism was so vehemently propagated, and the East inundated with a restless class of men, who strolled about in pursuit of proselytes (not much unlike the errant-knights of a subsequent age), the position I have laid down is more clearly evinced. It would be doing injustice to my subject, if, in speaking of this singular fact, I used other language than that of the historian of the Roman empire. " The progress of the monks," says this philosophic writer, " was not less rapid, or universal, than that of Christianity itself. Every province, and at last, every city of the empire, was filled with their increasing multitude; and the bleak and barren isles, from Lerins to Lipari, that arise out of the Tuscan sea, were chosen by the Anachorets for the place of their voluntary exile. An easy and perpetual intercourse by sea and land connected the provinces of the Roman world; and the life of Hilarion displays the facility with which an indigent hermit of Palestine might *traverse Egypt, embark for Sicily, escape to Epirus, and finally settle in the island of Cyprus.* The Latin Christians embraced the religious institutions of Rome.

---

[1] There is in the British Museum, I understand, a TURKISH MS. poem, of which *Alexander the Great* is the hero. It is said to have been written in the 14th century, if not earlier.

[2] I use this term, and one or two following, with some latitude. Gibbon calls the little town of Chrysopolis, or Scutari, " *the Asiatic suburb of Constantinople:*" and the extreme approximation of the two shores, the constant and easy intercourse from and before the time of Xerxes, &c., downward, not omitting the *Asiatic population* which has been so long naturalized there, sufficiently authorize the expression.

The pilgrims, who visited Jerusalem, eagerly copied, in the most *distant climes of the earth,* the faithful model of monastic life. *The disciples of Antony spread themselves beyond the tropic, over the Christian empire of Œthiopia.*[1] The monastery of Banchor,[2] in Flintshire, which contained above two thousand brethren, dispersed a numerous colony among the barbarians of Ireland ; and Iona, one of the Hebrides, which was planted by the Irish monks, diffused over the northern regions a doubtful ray of *science and superstition.*"[3]

The roving characters of the monks, therefore, is another link of the chain by which I introduce oriental fiction into the West; and it is utterly impossible (maturely weighing the habits and propensities of this class of people) that they should not have picked up and retained the floating traditions of the countries through which they passed. " Some of the early romances," says Mr. Walker,[4] " as well as the legends of saints, were *undoubtedly* fabricated in the deep silence of the cloister. Both frequently sprung from the warmth of fancy, which religious seclusion is so well calculated to nourish ; but the former were adorned with *foreign embellishments.*" It·is exactly on this footing (though I certainly include the *latter,* that is, the legends of the saints, in the idea of foreign embellishment !) that I would place the hypothesis I have advanced ; and here Mr. Walker's opinion, that Ireland is indebted to Italy for some of her fictions, derived originally from the East, will find confirmation. They might, at the same time, have been received by way of ENGLAND, and as history testifies the fact of a colony of monks from thence, taking root in Ireland, the notion is more than probable. But in either case the *original* is the same. As further corroborative I may add, that in the ninth century Crete and Sicily were invaded and conquered by the Arabs ; who likewise entered Italy, and almost approached Rome.

I need scarcely allude to the crusades as sources of romantic fabling. They are undisputed parts of the system ; and probably, at the termination of the third expedition, toward the close of the twelfth century, this kind of writing was at its height. Chivalry was then followed with a steady devotion, which, I am inclined to think, soon afterwards abated ; and was rather the undulation of the water succeeding the tempest, than the tempest itself. The fourth and

---

[1] See Jerom. (tom. i. p. 126); Assemanni (*Bibliot. Orient.* tom. iv. p. 92, p. 857—919), and Geddes's *Church Hist. of Œthiopia,* pp. 29, 30, 31.
[2] Camden's *Britannia,* vol. i. pp. 666, 667.
[3] Gibbon's *Decline and Fall,* vol. vi. p. 245-6, ed. 1811.
[4] *Essay on the Origin of Romantic Fabling in Ireland,* p. 4. 4to.

fifth crusade followed at the distance of about twenty years; but upwards of thirty elapsed before the sixth and last. The blood and coin that had been so uselessly lavished might well conduce to satisfy the most enthusiastic crusader, and stem the torrent of popular superstition : while the surprising frenzy that had so long desolated both hemispheres, from its very intensity, was calculated to subside, and introduce a juster mode of thinking, and more rational ideas. Time, which allays all other passions, could not but temper this ; and the last of these frantic expeditions appears, to my imagination, the desperate effort of expiring fanaticism—the last violent struggle of religious persecution in the East. With the decline of chivalry, the fictions, which principally attained their celebrity during its zenith (because they had become incorporated with it; though originally independent and extraneous), would naturally cease to be regarded; and the extravagant conceptions which this institution cherished, would, when good sense resumed or assumed her proper place, necessarily fall into decay.

SECTION II.

I now hasten to the GESTA ROMANORUM; and purpose giving a brief outline of its history, with a notice of certain stories which, without reference to their own individual merit, have been raised into higher importance by furnishing the groundwork of many popular dramas. I shall also take occasion to offer a few remarks upon the translation now before the public, elucidatory of certain points which seem to require explanation.

The GESTA ROMANORUM was one of the most applauded compilations of the Middle Ages. The method of instructing by fables is a practice of remote antiquity; and has always been attended with very considerable benefit. Its great popularity encouraged the monks to adopt this medium, not only for the sake of illustrating their discourses, but of making a more durable impression upon the minds of their illiterate auditors. An abstract argument, or logical deduction (had they been capable of supplying it), would operate but faintly upon intellects rendered even more obtuse by the rude nature of their customary occupations ; while, on the other hand, an apposite story would arouse attention, and stimulate that blind and uninquiring devotion, which is so remarkably characteristic of the Middle Ages.

The work under consideration is compiled from old Latin chronicles of Roman, or rather, as Mr. Warton and Mr. Douce think, of GERMAN invention. But this idea, with all submission, derives little corroborative evidence from fact. There is one story, and I believe, *but* one, which gives any countenance to it. That a few are extracted from German authors (who may not, after all, be the *inventors*) is no more proof that the compiler was a German, than that, because some stories are found in the Roman annals, the whole book was the production of a Latin writer.

Oriental, legendary, and classical fables, heightened by circum-stances of a strong romantic cast, form the basis of this singular com-position. But the authorities cited for classical allusions are usually of the lower order. Valerius, Maximus, Macrobius, Aulus Gellius, Pliny, Seneca, Boethius, and occasionally OVID, are introduced; but they do not always contain the relation which they are intended to substantiate; and it is invariably much disguised and altered. The oriental apologues are sometimes from the romance of *Baarlam and Josaphat,* and in several instances from a Latin work entitled, *De Clericali Disciplina,* attributed to Petrus Alphonsus, a converted Jew, godson to Alphonsus I. of Arragon, after whom he was named. There is an analysis of it by Mr. Douce inserted in Mr. Ellis's *Specimens of Early English Romances.* According to the former of these gentlemen, two productions bearing the title of GESTA ROMA-NORUM, and totally distinct from each other, exist. I confess I see no good reason for the assertion. I take the later work to be the same as its predecessor, with a few additions, not so considerable by any means as Mr. Douce imagines.[1] This I shall show, by and by. Of the present performance, though it purports to relate the GESTS OF THE ROMANS, there is little that corresponds with the title. On the contrary, it comprehends "a multitude of narratives, either not historical, or in another respect, such as are totally unconnected with the Roman people, or perhaps the most preposterous misrepre-sentations of their history. To cover this deviation from the promised plan, which, by introducing a more ample variety of matter, has contributed to increase the reader's entertainment, our collector has taken care to preface almost every story with the name

[1] "In fact, the two Gestas may just as well be considered the same work, as the different versions of *The Wise Masters,* or of *Kalilah u Damnah.* The term Gesta Romanorum implies nothing more than a collection of ancient stories, many of which might be the same, but which would naturally vary in various countries according to the taste of the collector, in the same manner as different stories are introduced in the Greek *Syntipas,* the Italian *Erastus,* and English *Wise Masters.*"—DUNLOP, *Hist. of Fiction,* vol. ii. p. 170.

or reign of a Roman emperor; who, at the same time, is often a monarch that never existed, and who seldom, whether real or supposititious, has any concern with the circumstances of the narrative."[1]

The influence which this work has had on English poetry is not the least surprising fact connected with it. Not only the earlier writers of our country—Gower, Chaucer, Lydgate, Occleve, &c.—have been indebted to it, but also, as the reader will perceive in the notes, the poets of modern times. Its popularity in the reign of Queen Elizabeth is proved by many allusions in the works of that period. In an anonymous comedy, published early in the following reign, entitled *Sir Giles Goosecap*, we have: "Then for your lordship's quips and quick jests, why GESTA ROMANORUM were nothing to them."[2] In Chapman's *May-Day*,[3] a person speaking of the literary information of another character, styles him—" One that has read Marcus Aurelius, GESTA ROMANORUM, the Mirrour of Magistrates, &c. .... to be led by the nose like a blind beare that has read nothing!"[4]

The author of this popular work has been often guessed at, but nothing certain is known. Warton believes him to be Petrus Berchorius, or Pierre Bercheur, a native of Poitou; and prior of the Benedictine convent of Saint Eloi, at Paris, in the year 1362. Mr. Douce, on the other hand, contends that he is a German, because "in the Moralization to chapter 144" [Tale CXLIV. of the translated Gesta], "there is, in most of the early editions, a German proverb; and in chapter 142" [Tale CXLII.], "several German names of dogs." I apprehend, however, that these names may be found more analogous to the *Saxon;* and, at all events, Warton's idea of an interpolation is far from improbable. Mr. Douce adds, that the earliest editions of the Gesta were printed in Germany; and certainly they often bear the *name* of some place in that country. But in the first ages of the art of printing, such might be the case, without actually identifying the point where the impression was struck off. It is a fact, sufficiently well known, that copies of certain books, printed in Italy, appeared, in every respect similar, and at the same time, in many parts of Germany, the Netherlands, &c. The only observable difference was in the alteration of *names* in the title-page. Now, if this be true, the *Gesta Romanorum*, printed in Italy, and thence sent for sale to some factor

---

[1] Warton, *Dissert. on Gest. Rom.* p. vii.
[2] London. Printed for J. Windet, 1606.   [3] Act III. p. 39. 1611.   [4] Warton.

in distant parts, might have this person's name and residence affixed, not from any dishonest motive, but merely to announce the place in which they were to be sold. Such a supposition is not beyond the bounds of probability, and may be worth considering. Many copies will be found *without* date or place; and perhaps the inconvenience and difficulty which a new title-page · created, might on some occasions induce the booksellers to omit it altogether.

ENGLISH idioms and proverbial expressions are so frequent in the *Gesta Romanorum,* that they might lead to a supposition quite the reverse of Mr. Douce's idea; but I rather conceive them the necessary consequence of transcription; and that the manuscript was thought to require verbal flourishes, as well as gilded margins and illuminated initials. In like manner I account for the Saxon names of dogs [Tale CXLII.], which are quite unnecessary, and seem introduced in the most arbitrary manner. The incidents of one story [Tale CLV.] are said to occur in the bishopric of Ely. "This fact," says the writer of the Gest, "related upon the faith of many to whom it was well known, *I have myself heard,* both from the inhabitants of the place and others." The inference, therefore, is that the narrator was either an Englishman, or one well acquainted with the localities of the place he describes. If the origin of the other stories be deducible from the position laid down by Mr. Douce, then, by parity of reasoning, the writer of the tale in question was the compiler of the series—and most probably an Englishman : at all events, his work might be *prepared* in England. But this would not be conceded ; and it is only by supposing an interpolation of the story, or of part of the story, that the difficulty is to be obviated. At any rate, the circumstance itself cannot justly be adduced in *proof* either one way or the other. But whoever was the author, or *authors* (which is more probable), and wherever they were produced, it is for the most part agreed that these tales were collected as early as the commencement of the fourteenth century—if not long before. Through a period of five hundred years, they have afforded a popular entertainment : the uncultivated minds of the Middle Ages valued them as a repertory of theological information, and later times as an inexhaustible fund of dramatic incident.

Of that which is called by Mr. Douce the ENGLISH GESTA, it now remains to speak. "This work was *undoubtedly* composed in England in imitation of the other ; and therefore it will be necessary for the future to distinguish the two works by the respective appellations of the *original* and the *English Gesta*."[1] "It is natural to suppose that a work like the *original Gesta* would stimulate some person to the compilation of one that should emulate, if not altogether supersede it; and accordingly this design was accomplished at a very early period by some Englishman—in all probability, a monk."[2] The feeling on my mind with regard to this Gesta certainly is, that it was *intended* for the same work as the original: but that in the transcription, with the latitude which the *"Adam scriveners"* of old invariably allowed themselves, many alterations (miscalled improvements) were made, together with some additions. The English translations of this last compilation vary frequently from their original. For instance, in the eighteenth chapter of the MS. [*" English"*] Gesta, fol. 17, a knight falls in love with Aglaës, daughter of the Emperor POLENTIUS; but in the English translation of the story (in 1648, a thin 18mo, containing forty-four stories) this same person is styled PHILOMINUS. It forms "The fourteenth History." Now, the fact that no manuscript of this Gesta exists in any of the catalogues of continental libraries is easily accounted for, on the supposition of its being transcribed in England, and consequently confined to this country. For other nations, being in possession of an authenticated original, would have little inducement to seek after a newly fabricated copy. English verses found therein, with English proper names, and English law terms, and modes of speech (arguments on which Mr. Douce lays much stress), no more constitute another work than Horace's *Art of Poetry*, translated by Roscommon; or than Donne's *Satires*, modernized by Pope.

As the annexed tales gave occasion to some of Shakespeare's plays, and moreover are not defective in that kind of interest which is the peculiar merit of such things, I shall transcribe as many as appear in the English translation,[3] following Mr. Douce's arrangement, in order to show that the difference between the two Gestas is not so wide as this gentleman appears to imagine. Such as are of no interest, I shall omit.

[1] Douce, *Illustr. of Shakespeare*, vol. ii. p. 362.
[2] *Ibid.* p. 364.
[3] I follow a copy printed in 1703, "for R. Chiswell, B. Walford, G. Conyers, at the Ring in Little Britain, and J. W." It is a reprint of the edition of 1648, containing forty-four stories; and is rather scarce. The title-page assures us that it is "very pleasant in reading, and profitable in practice." I hope it may be found so. Amongst the late Sir M. M. Sykes's books was a Black Letter copy of the same work, printed in 1672, "by Edward Crowch for A. Crook." It is in excellent condition, which most other copies are not.

CHAPTER I.

There reigned some time in Rome a wise and mighty emperor, named Anselm, who did bear in his arms a shield of silver with five red roses; this emperor had three sons whom he loved much; he had also continual war with the king of Egypt, in which war he lost all his temporal goods except a precious tree. It fortuned after on a day that he gave battel to the same king of Egypt, wherein he was grievously wounded, nevertheless he obtained the victory, notwithstanding he had his deadly wound: wherefore while he lay at point of death, he called unto his eldest son, and said: My dear and well-beloved son, all my temporal riches are spent, and almost nothing is left me, but a precious tree, the which stands in the midst of my empire; I give to thee all that is under the earth, and above the earth of the same tree. O my reverend father (quoth he) I thank you much.

Then said the emperor, call to me my second son. Anon the eldest son greatly joying of his father's gift, called in his brother; and when he came, the emperor said, my dear son, I may not make my testament, forasmuch as I have spent all my goods, except a tree which stands in the midst of mine empire, of the which tree I bequeath to thee all that is great and small. Then answered he and said, My reverend father, I thank you much.

Then said the emperor, call to me my third son, and so it was done. And when he was come, the emperor said, My dear son, I must die of these wounds, and I have only a precious tree, of which I have given thy brethren their portion, and to thee I bequeath thy portion: for I will that thou have of the said tree all that is wet and dry. Then said his son, Father, I thank you. Soon after the emperor had made his bequest, he died. And shortly after the eldest son took possession of the tree. Now when the second son heard this, he came to him, saying, My brother, by what law or title occupy you this tree? Dear brother, quoth he, I occupy it by this title, my father gave me all that is under the earth, and above of the said tree, by reason thereof the tree is mine. Unknowing to thee, quoth the second brother, he gave unto me all that is great and small of the said tree, and therefore I have as great right in the tree as you. This hearing the third son, he came to them and said, My well-beloved brethren, it behoveth you not to strive for this tree, for I have as much right in the tree as ye, for by the law ye wot, that the last will and testament ought to stand, for of truth he gave me of the said tree all that is wet and dry, and therefore the tree by right is mine: but forasmuch as your words are of great force and mine also, my counsel is, that we be judged by reason: for it is not good nor commendable that strife or dissension should be among us. Here beside dwelleth a king full of reason, therefore to avoid strife let us go to him, and each of us lay his right before him; and as he shall judge, let us stand to his judgment: then said his brethren thy counsel is good, wherefore they went all three unto the king of reason, and each of them severally sheweth forth his right unto him, as it is said before.

When the king had heard the titles, he rehearsed them all again severally: First, saying to the eldest son thus: You say (quoth the king) that your father gave you all that is under the earth and above the earth of the said tree. And to the second brother he bequeathed all that is great and small of that tree. And to the third brother he gave all that is wet and dry.

And with that he laid the law to them, and said that this will ought to stand.

Now my dear friends, briefly I shall satisfie all your requests, and when he had thus said, he turned him unto the eldest brother, saying, My dear friend, if you list to abide the judgment of right, it behoveth you to be letten blood of the right arm. My lord (quoth he), your will shall be done. Then the king called for a discreet physician, commanding him to let him blood.

When the eldest son was letten blood, the king said unto them all three: My dear friends, where is your father buried? then answered they and said: forsooth my lord in such a place. Anon the king commanded to dig in the ground for the body, and to take a bone out of his breast, and to bury the body again: and so it was done. And when the bone was taken out, the king commanded that it should be laid in the blood of the elder brother, and it should lie till it had received kindly the blood, and then to be laid in the sun and dried, and after that it should be washt with clear water: his servants fulfilled all that he had commanded: and when they began to wash, the blood vanished clean away; when the king saw this, he said to the second son, It behoveth that thou be letten blood, as thy brother was. Then said he, My lord's will shall be fulfilled, and anon he was done unto like as his brother was in all things, and when they began to wash the bone, the blood vanished away. Then said the king to the third son, It behoveth thee to be letten blood likewise. He answered and said, My lord it pleaseth me well so to be. When the youngest brother was letten blood, and done unto in all things as the two brethren were before, then the king's servants began to wash the bone, but neither for washing nor rubbing might they do away the blood of the bone, but it ever appeared bloody: when the king saw this, he said it appeareth openly now that this blood is of the nature of the bone, thou art his true son, and the other two are bastards, I judge thee the tree for evermore.

CHAPTER II.

In Rome there dwelt sometimes a noble emperor, named Dioclesian, who loved exceedingly the vertue of charity, wherefore he desired greatly to know what fowl loved her young best, to the intent that he might thereby grow to more perfect charity; it fortuned upon a day, that the emperor rode to a forrest to take his disport, whereas he found the nest of a great bird, (called in Latin *struchio calemi*, in English an ostridge) with her young, the which young bird the emperor took with him, and closed her in a vessel of glass, the dam of this little bird followed unto the emperor's palace, and flew into the hall where her young one was. But when she saw her young one, and could not come to her, nor get her out, she returned again to the forrest, and abode there three days, and at the last she came again to the palace, bearing in her mouth a worm called *thumare*, and when she came where her young one was, she let the worm fall upon the glass, by virtue of which worm the glass brake, and the young one flew forth with her dam. When the emperor saw this, he praised much the dam of the bird, which laboured so diligently to deliver her young one.

CHAPTER IV.

"The emperor Gauterus," &c.—This is Tale CI. of the *original* Gesta; and, as the reader will see, *not* related with much variety.

CHAPTER XVIII.

In Rome some time dwelt a mighty emperor, named Philominus, who had one only daughter, who was fair and gracious in the sight of every man, who had to name Aglaes. There was also in the emperor's palace a gentle knight that loved dearly this lady. It befel after on a day, that this knight talked with this lady, and secretly uttered his desire to her. Then she said courteously, Seeing you have uttered to me the secrets of your heart, I will likewise for your love utter to you the secrets of my heart, and truly I say, that above all other I love you best. Then said the knight, I purpose to visit the Holy Land, and therefore give me your troth, that this seven years you shall take no other man, but only for my love to tarry for me so long, and if I come not again by this day seven years, then take what man you like best. And likewise I promise you that within this seven years I will take no wife. Then said she, This covenant pleaseth me well. When this was said, each of them was betrothed to other, and then this knight took his leave of the lady, and went to the Holy Land. Shortly after the emperor treated with the king of Hungary for the marriage of his daughter. Then came the king of Hungary to the emperor's palace, to see his daughter, and when he had seen her, he liked marvellous well her beauty and her behaviour, so that the emperor and the king were accorded in all things as touching the marriage, upon the condition that the damsel would consent. Then called the emperor the young lady to him, and said, O my fair daughter, I have provided for thee, that a king shall be thy husband, if thou list consent, therefore tell me what answer thou wilt give to this. Then said she to her father, It pleaseth me well: but one thing, dear father, I intreat of you, if it might please you to grant me : I have vowed to keep my virginity and not to marry these seven years; therefore, dear father, I beseech you for all the love that is between your gracious fatherhood and me, that you name no man to be my husband till these seven years be ended, and then I shall be ready in all things to fulfil your will. Then said the emperor, Sith it is so that thou hast thus vowed, I will not break thy vow, but when these seven years be expired, thou shalt have the king of Hungary to thy husband.

Then the emperor sent forth his letters to the king of Hungary, praying him if it might please him to stay seven years for the love of his daughter, and then he should speed without fail. Herewith the king was pleased and content to stay the prefixed day.

And when the seven years were ended, save a day, the young lady stood in her chamber window, and wept sore, saying, Woe and alas, as to-morrow my love promised to be with me again from the Holy Land : and also the king of Hungary to-morrow will be here to marry me, according to my father's promise : and if my love comes not at a certain hour, then am I utterly deceived of the inward love I bear to him.

When the day came, the king hasted toward the emperor, to marry his daughter, and was royally arrayed in purple. And while the king was riding on his way, there came a knight riding on his way, who said, I am of the empire of Rome, and now am lately come from the Holy Land, and I am ready to do you the best service I can. And as they rode talking by the way, it began to rain so fast, that all the king's apparel was sore wet : then said the knight, My lord ye have done foolishly, for as much as ye brought not with you your house : then said the king, Why speakest thou so ? My house is large and broad, and made of stones, and mortar, how should I bring then with me, my house ? thou speakest like a fool.

When this was said, they rode on till they came to a great deep water, and the king smote his horse with his spurs, and leapt into the water, so that he was almost drowned. When the knight saw this, and was over on the other side of the water without peril, he said to the king, Ye were in peril, and therefore ye did foolishly, because you brought not with you your bridge. Then said the king, Thou speakest strangely, my bridge is made of lime and stone, and containeth in quality more than half a mile: how should I then bear with me my bridge? therefore thou speakest foolishly. Well, said the knight, my foolishness may turn thee to wisdom. When the king had ridden a little further, he asked the knight what time of day it was. Then said the knight, If any man hath list to eat, it is time of the day to eat. Wherefore my lord, pray take a *modicum* with me, for that is no dishonour to you, but great honour to me before the states of this empire: Then said the king, I will gladly eat with thee. They sat both down in a fair vine garden, and there dined together, both the king and the knight. And when dinner was done, and that the king had washed, the knight said unto the king, My lord ye have done foolishly, for that ye brought not with you your father and mother. Then said the king, what sayest thou? My father is dead, and my mother is old, and may not travel, how should I then bring them with me? therefore to say the truth, a foolisher man than thou art did I never hear. Then said the knight, Every work is praised at the end.

When the knight had ridden a little further, and nigh to the emperor's palace, he asked leave to go from him, for he knew a nearer way to the palace, to the young lady, that he might come first, and carry her away with him. Then said the king, I pray thee tell me by what place thou purposest to ride? Then said the knight, I shall tell you the truth: this day seven years I left a net in a place, and now I purpose to visit it, and draw it to me, and if it be whole, then will I take it to me, and keep it as a precious jewel; if it be broken, then will I leave it: and when he had thus said, he took his leave of the king, and rode forth, but the king kept the broad highway.

When the emperor heard of the king's coming, he went towards him with a great company, and royally received him, causing him to shift his wet cloaths, and to put on fresh apparel. And when the emperor and the king were set at meat, the emperor welcomed him with all the chear and solace that he could. And when he had eaten, the emperor asked tydings of the king; My lord, said he, I shall tell you what I have heard this day by the way: there came a knight to me, and reverently saluted me; and anon after there fell a great rain, and greatly spoiled my apparel. And anon the knight said, Sir, ye have done foolishly, for that ye brought not with you your house. Then said the emperor, What cloathing had the knight on? A cloak, quoth the king. Then said the emperor, sure that was a wise man, for the house whereof he spake was a cloak, and therefore he said to you, that you did foolishly, because you came without your cloak, then your cloaths had not been spoiled with rain. Then said the king, when he had ridden a little further, we came to a deep water, and I smote my horse with my spurs, and I was almost drowned, but he rid through the water without any peril: then said he to me, You did foolishly, for that you brought not with you your bridge. Verily said the emperor, he saith truth, for he called the squires the bridge, that should have ridden before you, and assayed the deepness of the water. Then said the king, we rode further, and at the last he prayed me to dine with him. And when he had dined, he said, I did unwisely, because I brought not with me my father and mother. Truly said the emperor, he was a wise man, and saith [wisely] : for he called your father and mother, bread and wine, and other victual. Then said the king, we rode further, and anon after he asked me leave to go from me, and I asked earnestly whither he went : and he answered again, and said, This day seven years, I left a net in a private place, and now I will ride to see it ; and if it be broken and torn, then will I leave it, but if it be as I left it, then shall it be unto me right precious. When the emperor heard this, he cryed with a loud voice, and said, O ye my knights and servants, come ye with me speedily unto my daughter's chamber, for surely that is the net of which he spake ; and forthwith his knights and servants went unto his daughter's chamber, and found her not, for the aforesaid knight had taken her with him. And thus the king was deceived of the damsel, and he went home again to his own country ashamed.

CHAPTER XXI.

Theodosius reigned, a wise emperour, in the city of Rome, and mighty he was of power ; the which emperour had three daughters. So it liked to this emperour to know which of his daughters loved him best. And then he said to the eldest daughter, How much lovest thou me ? Forsooth, quoth she, more than I do myself. Therefore, quoth he, thou shalt be highly advanced, and married her to a rich and mighty king. Then he came to the second, and said to her, Daughter, how much lovest thou me ? As much, forsooth, said she, as I do myself. So the emperour married her to a duke. And then he said to the third daughter, How much lovest thou me ? Forsooth, quoth she, as much as ye be worthy, and no more. Then said the emperour, Daughter, sith thou lovest me no more, thou shalt not be married so richly as thy sisters. And then he married her to an earl. After this it happened that the emperour held battle against the king of Egypt. And the king drove the emperour out of the empire, in so much that the emperour had no place to abide in. So he wrote letters, ensealed with his ring, to his first daughter, that said that she loved him more than herself, for to pray her of succouring in that great need, because he was put out of his empire. And when the daughter had read these letters, she told it to the king, her husband. Then, quoth the king, it is good that we succour him in this need. I shall, quoth he, gatheren an host and help him in all that I can or may, and that will not be done without great costage. Yea, quoth she, it were sufficient if that we would grant him five knights to be in fellowship with him, while he is out of his empire. And so it was ydone indeed. And the daughter wrote again to the father, that other help might he not have but five knights of the king to be in his fellowship, at the cost of the king her husband. And when the emperour heard this, he was heavy in his heart, and said, alas ! alas ! all my trust was in her, for she said she loved me more than herself, and therefore I advanced her so high.

Then he wrote to the second that said she loved him as much as herself, and when she had read his letters, she shewed his errand to her husband, and gave him in counsel that he should find him meat and drink and clothing honestly, as for the state of such a lord during time of his need. And when this was granted, she wrote letters again to her father. The emperor was heavy with this answer, and said, Sith my two daughters have thus treated me, soothly I shall prove the third, And so he wrote to the third, that said she loved him as much as he was worthy, and prayed her of succour in his need, and told her the answer of her two sisters. So the third daughter, when she had considered the mischief of her father, she told her husband in this form: My worshipful lord, do succour me now in this great need, my father is put out of his empire and his heritage. Then spake he, What were thy will I do thereto? That ye gather a great host, quoth she, and help him to fight against his enemies. I shall fulfil thy will,' said the earl, and gathered a great host, and went with the emperour at his own costage to the battle, and had the victory, and set the emperour again in his heritage. And then said the emperour, Blessed be the hour I gat my youngest daughter: I loved her less than any of the other, and now in my need she hath succoured me, and the other have yfailed me; and therefore after my death she shall have mine empire. And so it was done indeed; for after the death of the emperour, the youngest daughter reigned in his stead, and ended peaceably. —HARL. MS. No. 7333.

This, as the reader will be aware, is the story of Lear in Shakspeare; but there were many popular tales built upon the same story.

CHAPTER XXV.

There was a powerful emperor called Andronicus, before whom a knight was wrongfully accused. When the charge could not be substantiated, his majesty proposed to him certain puzzling questions, which were to be accurately answered, under pain of death. The knight expressed himself ready to do his best. Then said the emperor, How far is heaven distant from hell? That is the first question. As far, replied he, as a sigh is from the heart.

Emperor. And how deep is the sea?
Knight. A stone's throw.
Emperor. How many flaggons of salt water are there in the sea?
Knight. Give me the number of flaggons of *fresh* water, and I will tell you.

* * * * * * * * *

Emperor. To the first question you answered, that the distance between heaven and hell, was as great as between a sigh and the heart. How can this be?
Knight. A sigh passes from the heart with the rapidity of a glance; and in like manner the soul goes from the body into a state of punishment or happiness.
Emperor. How is the depth of the sea a stone's throw?
Knight. All weight descends; and because a stone is heavy it drops to the bottom of the sea at once. Its depth is therefore a *stone's throw.*
Emperor. And how, if you knew the number of flaggons of fresh water, could you estimate the number of salt? This seems impossible.
Knight. Be good enough to try it. Begin the reckoning yourself.

* * * * * * * * *

The emperor, pleased with the knight's shrewdness, bids him go in peace.—*MS. Copy of the* GEST. ROM.

CHAPTER XXVI.

Bononius was emperor of Rome, &c., &c.
This is the same story as Tale CXXXII. of the *original* Gesta. *Overpassed by Mr. Douce.*

CHAPTER XXVII.

Antonius governed the city of Rome with great wisdom. He was exceedingly fond of the game of chess; and observing, on one occasion, that when the men were replaced in his bag as usual, the king was confounded with the inferior pieces, it led him to reflections upon the vanity of human greatness. He thereupon determines to make a triple division of his kingdom, and hasten to the Holy Land. He did so, and died in peace.

CHAPTER XXX.

The emperor Averrhoes, &c., &c.

This is the story of the knight Placidus, in Tale CX. of the original Gesta, with some variations. This also Mr. Douce has omitted to observe.

CHAPTER XXXI.

The following tale, together with Mr. Douce's remarks, I extract, *verbatim*, from the second volume of the *Illustrations of Shakespeare*. It happened in Rome, under the reign of one PLEBENS, according to the MS. It should be premised that the first part of the story resembles Tale LXIX.

"A law was made at Rome that the sentinels of the city should each night examine what was passing in all the houses, so that no private murders should be committed, nor anything done whereby the city should be endangered. It happened that an old knight named Josias had married a young and beautiful woman who, by the sweetness of her singing, attracted many persons to his house, several of whom came for the purpose of making love to her. Among these were three young men who were high in the emperor's favour. They respectively agreed with the woman for a private assignation, for which she was to receive twenty marks. She discloses the matter to her husband, but not choosing to give up the money, prevails on him to consent to the murder of the gallants, and the robbing of their persons. This is accomplished, and the bodies deposited in a cellar. The woman, mindful of the new law that had been made, sends for one of the sentinels, who was her brother, pretends that her husband had killed a man in a quarrel, and prevails on him, for a reward, to dispose of the dead body. She then delivers to him the first of the young men, whom he put into a sack, and throws into the sea. On his return to the sister, she pretends to go into the cellar to draw wine, and cries out for help. When the sentinel comes to her, she tells him that the dead man is returned. At this, he of course expresses much surprise, but putting the second body into his sack, ties a stone round its neck and plunges it into the sea. Returning once more, the woman, with additional arts, plays the same part again. Again he is deceived, and taking away the third body, carries it into a forest, makes a fire, and consumes it. During this operation he has occasion to retire, and in the mean time a knight on horseback, who was going to a tournament, passes by, and alights to warm himself at the fire. On the other's return, the knight is mistaken for the dead man, and with many bitter words thrown into the fire, horse and all.[1] The sentinel goes back to his sister, and receives the stipulated reward. A

---

[1] Setting aside the tragical part of this story, it would be susceptible of much comic effect.

hue and cry had now been made after the young men who were missing. The husband and wife engage in a quarrel, and the murder is of course discovered.

"This story has been immediately taken from *The Seven Wise Masters*, where it forms the *example* of the sixth master. The groundwork is, no doubt, oriental, and may be found, perhaps in its most ancient form, in *The little hunchbacked taylor* of *The Arabian Nights*. It was imported into Europe very early, and fell into the hands of the lively and entertaining French minstrels, who have treated it in various ways, as may be seen in Le Grand, *Fableaux et Contes*, tom. iv., where it is related five times. The several imitations of it from *The Seven Wise Masters* may be found in all the editions of Prince *Erastus*, an Italian modification[1] of the *Wise Masters*. It forms the substance of a well-constructed and entertaining story of two friars, John and Richard, who are said to have resided at Norwich, in the reign of Henry the Fifth. This is related in Heywood's *History of Women*, under the title of *The faire ladie of Norwich*,[2] and has crept into Blomefield's *History of Norfolk* in a very extraordinary manner, unaccompanied with any comment, but with the addition of the murderer's name, who is unaccountably stated to be Sir Thomas Erpingham, a well-known character.[3] In the Bodleian library there is an old English poem entitled, *A merry jest of Dane Hew, munck of Leicestre, and how he was foure times slain, and once hanged*. Printed at London, by J. Alde, in 4to, without date. This is probably the same story, which has certainly been borrowed from one of those related by the Norman minstrels."

CHAPTER XXXII.

For this chapter I am also indebted to the *Illustrations*, &c.

"Folliculus, a knight, was fond of hunting and tournaments. He had an only son, for whom three nurses were provided. Next to this child he loved his falcon and his greyhound. It happened one day that he was called to a tournament, whither his wife and domestics went also, leaving the child in the cradle, the greyhound lying by him, and the falcon on his perch. A serpent that inhabited a hole near the castle, taking advantage of the profound silence that reigned, crept from his habitation and advanced towards the cradle to devour the child. The falcon, perceiving the danger, fluttered with his wings till he awoke the dog, who instantly attacked the invader, and after a fierce conflict, in which he was sorely wounded, killed him. He then lay down on the ground to lick and heal his wounds. When the nurses returned they found the cradle overturned, the child thrown out, and the ground covered with blood, as well as the dog, who, they immediately concluded, had killed the child. Terrified at the idea of meeting the anger of the parents, they determined to escape, but in their flight fell in with their mistress, to whom they were compelled to relate the supposed murder of

---

[1] It is curious that the difference in the editions of the *Wise Masters* Mr. Douce calls a MODIFICATION; but the same kind of thing in the *Gesta* is a *distinct work*.

[2] Page 253, folio edit.

[3] "Vol. iii. p. 647. Mr. Gough speaks of it as separately printed (*Brit. Topogr.* ii. 27). It is also copied in Burton's *Unparalleled Varieties*, p. 159, edit. 1699, 12mo, and *The Gentleman's Magazine*, vol. i. p. 310. It has twice been versified: 1st, anonymously, under the title of *A hue and cry after the Priest, or, the Convent, a Tale*, 1749, 8vo; and 2ndly, by Mr. Jodrell, under that of *The Knight and the Friars*, 1785, 4to."—DOUCE. It should be added that it has been a third time versified, by Mr. Colman, in *Broad Grins*, &c.

the child by the greyhound. The knight soon arrived to hear the sad story, and, maddened with fury, rushed forward to the spot. The poor wounded and faithful animal made an effort to rise, and welcome his master with his accustomed fondness; but the enraged knight received him on the point of his sword, and he fell lifeless to the ground. On examination of the cradle the infant was found alive and unhurt, and the dead serpent lying by him. The knight now perceived what had happened, lamented bitterly over his faithful dog, and blamed himself for having depended too hastily on the words of his wife. Abandoning the profession of arms, he broke his lance in three pieces, and vowed a pilgrimage to the Holy Land, where he spent the rest of his days in peace.

"This tale is likewise borrowed by the compiler of the *Gesta*, from *The Seven Wise Masters*, and of oriental construction. It is originally in Pilpay's Fables, being that of *The Santon and the broken Pitcher*.

"There is a very extraordinary tradition in North Wales, of an incident resembling that in our story having happened to Prince Llewellyn about the year 1205. He is said to have erected a tomb over his faithful dog, still known in Carnarvonshire by the name of *Celhart's Grave*.[1] This tradition is the subject of an elegant ballad by the honourable Mr. Spencer, privately printed, in a single sheet; under the title of *Beth Gêlert, or the Grave of the Greyhound*. At Abergavenny Priory Church there is said to be the figure of an armed knight with a dog at his feet; and with this person, whoever he was, the story of *Celhart* has also been connected. But the dog, as well as other animals, is frequently found at the feet of figures on old monuments. On the whole, the subject appears not undeserving of the consideration of Welsh Antiquaries. It would be proper, however, on any such occasion, to bear in mind the numerous applications of circumstances altogether fabulous to real persons; one example of which has occurred in the story from the *Gesta* that immediately precedes the present.

"It may be thought worth adding, that Virgil's *original Gnat* resembled in its outline, as given by Donatus, the story in the *Gesta*. A shepherd there falls asleep in a marshy spot of ground; a serpent approaches, and is about to kill him. At this moment a gnat settles on the shepherd's face, stings, and awakens him. He instinctively applies his hand to the wounded part, and crushes the gnat. He soon perceives that he had destroyed his benefactor, and, as the only recompense in his power, erects a tomb to his memory."

CHAPTER XLVI.

"Some time ago in Rome there dwelt a noble emperor, of great livelihood, named Alexander, which, above all vertues loved the vertue of bounty; wherefore he ordained a law for great charity, that no man under pain of death should turn a plaice in his dish at his meat, but only eat the white side, and not the black; and if any man would attempt to do the contrary, he should suffer death without any pardon: but yet ere he dyed, he should ask three petitions of the emperor what him list (except his life) which should be granted to him.

"It befel after, upon a day, that there became an earl and his son, of a strange country, to speak with the emperor; and when the earl was set

---

[1] "Jones's *Reliques of the Welsh Bards*, p. 75, where there is an old Welsh song, or *Englyn*, on the subject."—Douce.

at meat, he was served with a plaice, and he which was an hungry and had an appetite to his meat, after he had eaten the white side, he turned the black side, and began to eat thereof : wherefore, straightway he was accused to the emperor, because he had offended against the law. Then said the emperor, Let him dye according to the law without any delay.

" When the earl's son heard that his father should die, immediately he fell down on both his knees before the emperor, and said, O my reverend lord, I most humbly intreat you, that I may dye for my father. Then said the emperor, It pleaseth me well so that one dye for the offence. Then said the earl's son, Sith it is so that I must dye, I ask the benefit of the law, that is, that I may have three petitions granted ere I dye. The emperor answered and said, Ask what thou wilt, there shall no man say thee nay.

" Then said this young knight, My lord, you have but one daughter, the which I desire of your highness * * *. The emperor granted for fulfilling of the laws, though it were against his will * * *.

" The second petition is this, I ask all thy treasure ; and immediately the emperor granted, because he would not be called a breaker of the law. And when the earl's son had received the emperor's treasure, he imparted it both to poor and to rich, by means whereof he obtained their good wills.

" My third petition is this, I ask, my lord, that all their eyes may be put out incontinent that saw my father eat the black side of the plaice. And they that saw him turn the plaice, bethought them, and said within themselves : If we acknowledge that we saw him do this trespass, then shall our eyes be put out : and therefore it is better that we hold us still ; And so there was none found that would accuse him.

" When the earl's son heard this, he said to the emperor, My lord (quoth he) ye see there is no man accuseth my father, therefore give me rightful judgment. Then said the emperor, Forasmuch as no man will acknowledge that they saw him turn the plaice, therefore I will not that thy father shall die. So thus the son saved his father's life, and after the decease of the emperor married his daughter.''

CHAPTER XLVII.

This chapter, but with less incident, is the twenty-fifth history of the old English translation, which tolerably well exemplifies the usual arbitrary method of departing from the original text. As there is little interest in the story, I pass it.

CHAPTER XLVIII.

" Selestinus reigned, a wise emperor, in Rome, and he had a fair daughter.''

*　　*　　*　　*　　*　　*　　*　　*

[It is needless to transcribe this tale (which is the origin of the *bond story* in Shakespeare's " Merchant of Venice ") because it is to be found prefixed to all the editions of the drama itself, from the *Pecorone* of Ser Giovanni Fiorentino, an Italian novelist, who wrote in 1378. It occurs also in an old English MS. preserved in the Harl. Collection, No. 7333, evidently translated from the *Gesta Romanorum* [TEMP. Hen. VI.], which Mr. Douce has given in the 1st volume of his very entertaining *Illustrations of Shakespeare*, p. 281. But as the *Tale of the Three Caskets* has not been made so public, I insert it in this place, although it forms Chapter CIX. of the MS. Gesta. *See also Note* 11.]

"Some time dwelt in Rome a mighty emperor, named Anselm, who had married the king's daughter of Jerusalem, a fair lady, and gracious in the sight of every man, but she was long time with the emperor ere she bare him any child; wherefore the nobles of the empire were very sorrowful, because their lord had no heir of his own body begotten: till at last it befell, that this Anselm walked after supper, in an evening, into his garden, and bethought himself that he had no heir, and how the king of Ampluy warred on him continually, for so much as he had no son to make defence in his absence; therefore he was sorrowful, and went to his chamber and slept. Then he thought he saw a vision in his sleep, that the morning was more clear than it was wont to be, and that the moon was much paler on the one side than on the other. And after he saw a bird of two colours, and by that bird stood two beasts, which fed that little bird with their heat. And after that came more beasts, and bowing their breasts toward the bird, went their way: then came there divers birds that sung sweetly and pleasantly, with that the emperor awaked.

"In the morning early this Anselm remembred his vision, and wondred much what it might signifie; wherefore he called to him his philosophers, and all the states of the empire, and told them his dream; charging them to tell him the signification thereof on pain of death, and if they told him the true interpretation thereof, he promised them good reward. Then said they, Dear lord, tell us your dream, and we shall declare to you what it betokens. Then the emperor told them from the beginning to the ending, as is aforesaid. When the philosophers heard this, with glad chear they answered and said, Sir, the vision that you saw betokeneth good, for the empire shall be clearer than it is.

"The moon that is more pale on the one side than on the other, betokeneth the empress, that hath lost part of her colour, through the conception of a son that she hath conceived. The little bird betokeneth the son that she shall bear. The two beasts that fed this bird, betokeneth the wise and rich men of the empire which shall obey the son. These other beasts that bowed their breasts to the bird, betoken many other nations that shall do him homage. The bird that sang so sweetly to this little bird, betokeneth the Romans, who shall rejoyce and sing because of his birth. This is the very interpretation of your dream.

"When the emperor heard this, he was right joyful. Soon after that, the empress travailed in childbirth, and was delivered of a fair son, at whose birth there was great and wonderful joy made.

"When the king of Ampluy heard this, he thought in himself thus: Lo, I have warred against the emperor all the days of my life, and now he hath a son, who when he cometh to full age, will revenge the wrong I have done against his father, therefore it is better that I send to the emperor, and beseech him of truce and peace, that the son may have nothing against me, when he cometh to manhood: when he had thus said to himself, he wrote to the emperor, beseeching him to have peace. When the emperor saw that the king of Ampluy wrote to him more for fear than for love, he wrote again to him, that if he would find good and sufficient sureties to keep the peace, and bind himself all the days of his life to do him service and homage, he would receive him to peace.

"When the king had read the tenor of the emperor's letter, he call'd his council, praying them to give him counsel how he best might do, as touching this matter. Then said they, It is good that ye obey the emperor's will and commandment in all things. For first, in that he desired of you surety for the peace; to this we answer thus, Ye have but one daughter, and the emperor one son, wherefore let a marriage be made between them, and that may be a perpetual covenant of peace. Also he asketh homage and tribute, which it is good to fulfil. Then the king sent his messengers to the emperor, saying, that he would fulfil his desire in all things, if it might please his highness, that his son and the king's daughter might be married together. All this well pleased the emperor, yet he sent again, saying, If his daughter were a clean virgin from her birth unto that day, he would consent to that marriage. Then was the king right glad, for his daughter was a clean virgin.

" Therefore, when the letters of covenant and compact were sealed, the king furnished a fair ship, wherein he might send his daughter, with many noble knights, ladies, and great riches, unto the emperor, for to have his son in marriage.

" And when they were sailing in the sea, towards Rome, a storm arose so extreamly and so horribly that the ship brake against a rock, and they were all drowned save only the young lady, which fixed her hope and heart so greatly on God, that she was saved, and about three of the clock the tempest ceased, and the lady drove forth over the waves in that broken ship which was cast up again : But a huge whale followed after, ready to devour both the ship and her. Wherefore this young lady, when night came, smote fire with a stone wherewith the ship was greatly lightned, and then the whale durst not adventure toward the ship for fear of that light. At the cock crowing, this young lady was so weary of the great tempest and trouble of sea, that she slept, and within a little while after the fire ceased, and the whale came and devoured the virgin. And when she awaked and found herself swallowed up in the whale's belly, she smote fire, and with a knife wounded the whale in many places, and when the whale felt himself wounded, according to his nature he began to swim to land.

" There was dwelling at that time in a country near by, a noble earl named Pirris, who for his recreation walking on the sea shore, saw the whale coming towards the land, wherefore he turned home again, and gathered a great many of men and women, and came thither again, and fought with the whale, and wounded him very sore, and as they smote, the maiden that was in his belly cryed with an high voice, and said, O gentle friends, have mercy and compassion on me, for I am a king's daughter, and a true virgin from the hour of my birth unto this day. When the earl heard this, he wondered greatly, and opened the side of the whale, and found the young lady, and took her out ; and when she was thus delivered, she told him forthwith whose daughter she was, and how she had lost all her goods in the sea, and how she should have been married unto the emperor's son. And when the earl heard this, he was very glad, and comforted her the more, and kept her with him till she was well refreshed. And in the mean time he sent messengers to the emperor, letting him to know how the king's daughter was saved.

" Then was the emperor right glad of her safety, and coming, had great compassion on her, saying, Ah good maiden, for the love of my son thou hast suffered much woe : nevertheless, if thou be worthy to be his wife, soon shall I prove. And when he had thus said, he caused three vessels to be brought forth : the first was made of pure gold, well beset with precious stones without, and within full of dead men's bones, and thereupon was engraven this posie : WHOSO CHUSETH ME, SHALL FIND THAT HE DESERVETH. The second vessel was made of fine silver, filled with earth and worms, the superscription was thus, WHOSO CHUSETH ME, SHALL FIND THAT HIS NATURE DESIRETH. The third vessel was made of lead, full within of precious stones, and thereupon was insculpt this posie, WHOSO CHUSETH ME, SHALL FIND THAT GOD HATH DISPOSED FOR HIM. These three vessels the emperor shewed the maiden, and said; Lo, here daughter, these be rich vessels, if thou chuse one of these, wherein is profit to thee and to others, then shalt thou have my son. And if thou chuse that wherein is no profit to thee, nor to any other, soothly thou shalt not marry him.

"When the maiden heard this, she lift up her hands to God, and said, Thou Lord, that knowest all things, grant me grace this hour so to chuse, that I may receive the emperor's son. And with that she beheld the first vessel of gold, which was engraven royally, and read the superscription: *Whoso chuseth me, shall find that he deserveth;* saying thus, Though this vessel be full precious, and made of pure gold, nevertheless I know not what is within, therefore, my dear lord, this vessel will I not chuse.

"And then she beheld the second vessel, that was of pure silver, and read the superscription, *Whoso chuseth me, shall find that his nature desireth:* Thinking thus within herself, if I chuse this vessel, what is within I know not, but well I know, there shall I find that nature desireth, and my nature desireth the lust of the flesh, and therefore this vessel will I not chuse.

"When she had seen these two vessels, and had given an answer as touching them, she beheld the third vessel of lead, and read the superscription, *Whoso chuseth me, shall find that God hath disposed:* Thinking within herself, this vessel is not very rich, nor outwardly precious, yet the superscription saith, *Whoso chuseth me, shall find that God hath disposed:* and without doubt God never disposeth any harm, therefore, by the leave of God, this vessel will I chuse.

"When the emperor heard this, he said, O fair maiden, open thy vessel, for it is full of precious stones, and see if thou hast well chosen or no. And when this young lady had opened it, she found it full of fine gold and precious stones, as the emperor had told her before. Then said the emperor, daughter, because thou hast well chosen, thou shalt marry my son. And then he appointed the wedding day; and they were married with great solemnity, and with much honour continued to their lives end."

CHAPTER XLIX.

This story is *wholly* in the original Gesta; Tale L. Not observed by Mr. Douce.

CHAPTER L.

This apologue is also in the original Gesta, with slight variations. See Tale XLV. It is noticed in the *Illustrations*, &c.

CHAPTER LI.

Is also in the original Gesta; Tale LXIV. Not observed by Mr. Douce.

CHAPTER LIV.

In the original Gesta; Tale CXX. Noticed in the *Illustrations*.

CHAPTER LVI.

In the original Gesta; Tale XX. Overlooked by Mr. Douce.

CHAPTER LXII.

This story, though not exactly the same, resembles Tale I., Tale XXVII., and part of Tale LV. But it is really Tale LXVI. *Not noticed by Mr. Douce.*

CHAPTER LXVIII.

This is the Twenty-third History of the English Translation; but being of little interest, I omit it.

CHAPTER LXX.

Is the story of Guido (and of Sir Guy, Ellis's *Specimens*, &c.), Tale CLXXI. Not observed by Mr. Douce.

CHAPTER LXXII.

Forms the latter part of Tale CI. Not observed by Mr. Douce.

CHAPTER LXXVII.

Is the Twenty-eighth History of the English Translation, but not worth transcribing. The latter part of this story is the same with Tale LXXXII. and Tale CLXXXI. Mr. Douce notices the *latter*, but it is not so similar by any means as the former.

CHAPTER LXXVIII.

" A law was made at Rome, that no man should marry for beauty, but for riches only; and that no woman should be united to a poor man, unless he should by some means acquire wealth equal to her own. A certain poor knight solicited the hand of a rich lady, but she reminded him of the law, and desired him to use the best means of complying with it, in order to effect their union. He departed in great sorrow, and after much enquiry, was informed of a rich duke, who had been blind from the day of his birth. Him he resolved to murder, and obtain his wealth; but found that he was protected in the day-time by several armed domestics, and at night by the vigilance of a faithful dog. He contrived, however, to kill the dog with an arrow, and immediately afterwards the master, with whose money he returned to the lady. He informed her that he had accomplished his purpose; and being interrogated how this had been done in so short a space of time, he related all that had happened. The lady desired, before the marriage should take place, that he would go to the spot where the duke was buried, lay himself on his tomb, listen to what he might hear, and then report it to her. The knight armed himself, and went accordingly. In the middle of the night he heard a voice saying, O duke, that liest here, what askest thou that I can do for thee? The answer was, O Jesus, thou upright judge, all that I require is vengeance for my blood unjustly spilt. The voice rejoined, Thirty years from this time thy wish shall be fulfilled. The knight, extremely terrified, returned with the news to the lady. She reflected that thirty years were a long period, and resolved on the marriage. During the whole of the above time the parties remained in perfect happiness.

" When the thirty years were nearly elapsed, the knight built a strong castle, and over one of the gates, in a conspicuous place, caused the following verses to be written :

> 'In my distress, religious aid I sought :
> But my distress relieved, I held it nought.
> The wolf was sick, a lamb he seemed to be ;
> But health restored, a wolf again we see.'

Interrogated as to the meaning of these enigmatical lines, the knight at once explained them, by relating his own story, and added, that in eight days' time the thirty years would expire. He invited all his friends to a feast at that period, and when the day was arrived, the guests placed at table, and the minstrels attuning their instruments of music, a beautiful bird flew in at the window, and began to sing with uncommon sweetness. The knight listened attentively, and said, I fear this bird prognosticates misfortune. He then took his bow, and shot an arrow into it, in presence of all the company. Instantly the castle divided into two parts, and, with the knight, his wife, and all who were in it, was precipitated to the lowest depth of the infernal regions. The story adds, that on the spot where the castle stood, there is now a spacious lake, on which no substance whatever floats, but is immediately plunged to the bottom." [1]

CHAPTER LXXIX.

"The dog and the lamp, in this story, are introduced in chap. i. of the other *Gesta*, but the tales have nothing else in common." [2]—DOUCE. But the *pure virgin* is in Tale CXV., and the thorn extracted from the lion's foot, in Tale CIV. The protection afforded by the animal resembles that in Tale CIX.—The youth's subterranean residence seems copied from the story of the third calendar in the *Arabian Nights*.

CHAPTER LXXX.

"The substance of this story," says Mr. Douce, "is incorporated with the old ballad of 'A warning Piece to England, or the Fall of Queen Eleanor.'"—*Coll. of old Ballads*, vol. i. No. xiii.

CHAPTER LXXXII.

"There dwelt some time in Rome a mighty emperor and a merciful, named Menelay, who ordained such a law, that what innocent person was taken and put in prison, if he might escape and come to the emperor's palace, he should be there safe from all manner of accusations against him in his life time. It was not long after, but it befel, that a knight was accused, wherefore he was taken and put in a strong and dark prison, where he lay a long time, and had no light but a little window, whereat scant light shone in, that lighted him to eat such simple meat as the keeper brought him : wherefore he mourned greatly, and made sorrow that he was thus fast shut up from the sight of men. Nevertheless, when the keeper was gone, there came daily a nightingale in at the window, and sung full sweetly, by whose song this woful knight was oftentimes fed with joy, and when the bird left off singing, then would she flye into the knight's bosome, and there this knight fed

---

[1] From Douce's Abridgement of the *Gesta Romanorum*.
[2] The dog is again introduced in Tale XVII.

her many a day, of the victual that God sent him. It befel after upon a day, that the knight was greatly desolate of comfort. Nevertheless, the bird that sate in his bosome fed upon kernels of nuts, and thus he said to the bird, Sweet bird, I have sustained thee many a day, what wilt thou give me now in my desolation to comfort me? Remember thy self well, how that thou art the creature of God, and so am I also, and therefore help me now in this my great need.

"When the bird heard this, she flew forth from his bosome, and tarried from him three days, but the third day she came again, brought in her mouth a precious stone, and laid it in the knight's bosom. And when she had so done, she took her flight and flew from him again. The knight marvelled at the stone, and at the bird, and forthwith he took the stone in his hand, and touched his gives and fetters therewith, and presently they fell off. And then he arose and touched the doors of the prison, and they opened, and he escaped, and ran fast to the emperor's palace. When the keeper of the prison perceived this, he blew his horn thrice, and raised up all the folk of the city, and led them forth, crying with an high voice, lo, the thief is gone, follow we him all. And with that he ran before all his fellows towards the knight. And when he came nigh him, the knight bent his bow, and shot an arrow, wherewith he smote the keeper in the lungs, and slew him, and then ran to the palace, where he found succour against the law."

CHAPTER XCIV.

The same as Tale CXXX. and Tale CXLII. Not observed by Mr. Douce.

CHAPTER XCVIII.

"In Rome some time dwelt a mighty emperor, named Martin, which for entire affection kept with him his brother's son, whom men called Fulgentius. With this Martin dwelt also a knight that was steward of the empire, and unkle unto the emperor, which envied this Fulgentius, studying day and night how he might bring the emperor and this youth at debate. Wherefore the steward on a day went to the emperor, and said, My lord (quoth he), I that am your true servant, am bound in duty to warn your highness, if I hear any thing that toucheth your honour, wherfore I have such things that I must needs utter it in secret to your majesty between us two. Then said the emperor, Good friend, say on what thee list.

"My most dear lord (quoth the steward), Fulgentius your cousin and your nigh kinsman, hath defamed you wonderfully and shamefully throughout all your whole empire, saying that your breath stinketh, and that it is death to him to serve your cup. Then the emperor was grievously displeased, and almost beside himself for anger, and said unto him thus: I pray thee good friend tell me the very truth, if that my breath stinketh as he saith. My lord (quoth the steward), ye may believe me, I never perceived a sweeter breath in my days than yours is. Then said the emperor, I pray thee good friend, tell me how I may bring this thing to good proof.

"The steward answered and said: My Lord (quoth he) ye shall right well understand the truth; for to-morrow next when he serveth you of your cup, ye shall see that he will turn away his face from you, because of your breath, and this is the most certain proof that may be had of this thing. Verily (quoth the emperor), a truer proof cannot be had of this thing. Therefore anon when the steward heard this, he went streight to Fulgentius, and took him aside, saying thus. Dear friend, thou art near kinsman and also nephew unto my lord the emperor, therefore if thou wilt be thankful unto me, I will tell thee of a fault whereof my lord the emperor complaineth oft, and thinks to put thee from him (except it be the sooner amended) and that will be a great reproof to thee. Then said this Fulgentius, Ah good Sir, for his love that died upon the cross, tell me why my lord is so sore moved with me, for I am ready to amend my fault in all that I can or may, and for to be ruled by your discreet counsel.

"Thy breath (quoth the steward) stinketh so sore, that his drink doth him no good, so grievous unto him is the stinking breath of thy mouth. Then said Fulgentius unto the steward: Truly, that perceived I never till now; but what think ye of my breath, I pray you tell me the very truth? Truly (quoth the steward) it stinketh greatly and foul. And this Fulgentius believed all that he had said, and was right sorrowful in his mind, and prayed the steward of his counsel and help in this woful case. Then said the steward unto him, If that thou wilt do my counsel, I shall bring this matter to a good conclusion, wherefore do as I shall tell thee.

"I counsel thee for the best, and also warn thee, that when thou servest my lord the emperor of his cup, that thou turn thy face away from him, so that he may not smell thy stinking breath, until the time that thou hast provided thee of some remedy therefore.

"Then was Fulgentius right glad, and sware to him that he would do by his counsel.

"Not long after it befell that this young man Fulgentius served his lord as he was wont to do, and therewith suddenly he turned his face from the lord the emperor, as the steward had taught him.

"And when the emperor perceived the avoiding of his head, he smote this young Fulgentius on the breast with his foot, and said to him thus: O thou lewd varlet; now I see well it is true that I have heard of thee, and therefore go thou anon out of my sight, that I may see thee no more in this place. And with that this young Fulgentius wept full sore, and avoided the place, and went out of his sight.

"And when this was done, the emperor called unto him his steward, and said, How may I rid this varlet from the world, that thus hath defamed me? My most dear lord (quoth the steward), right well you shall have your intent.

"For here beside, within these three miles, ye have brick-makers, which daily make great fire, for to burn brick, and also they make lime, therefore my lord, send to them this night, charge them upon pain of death, that whosoever cometh the first in the morning, saying to them thus, My lord commandeth them to fulfil his will, that they take him and cast him into the furnace, and burn him: and this night command you this Fulgentius, that he go early in the morning to your workmen, and that he ask them whether they have fulfilled your will which they were commanded, or not; and then shall they, according to your commandment, cast him into the fire, and thus shall he die an evil death.

"Surely (quoth the emperor), thy counsel is good, therefore call to me that varlet Fulgentius. And when the young man was come to the emperor's presence, he said to him thus, I charge thee upon pain of death, that thou rise early in the morning, and go to the burners of lime and brick, and that thou be with them early before the sun rise, three miles from this house, and charge them in my behalf, that they fulfil my commandment, or else they shall die a most shameful death.

"Then spake this Fulgentius. My Lord, if God send me my life, I shall fulfil your will, were it that I go to the world's end.

"When Fulgentius had this charge, he could not sleep for thought, that he must rise early to fulfil his lord's commandment. The emperor about midnight sent a messenger on horseback unto his brick-makers, commanding, that upon pain of death, that whosoever came to them first in the morning, saying unto them (as is before rehearsed) they should take him and bind him, and cast him into the fire, and burn him to the bare bones.

"The brick-makers answered and said, it should be done. Then the messenger returns home again, and told the emperor that his commandment should be diligently fulfilled.

"Early in the morning following, Fulgentius arose and prepared him towards his way, and as he went, he heard a bell ring to service, wherefore he went to hear service, and after the end of service he fell asleep, and there slept a long while so soundly, that the priest, nor none other, might awake him.

"The steward desiring inwardly to hear of his death, about two of the clock he went to the workmen, and said unto them thus. Sirs (quoth he), have ye done the emperor's commandment or no?

"The brick-makers answered him and said. No truly, we have not yet done his commandment, but it shall be done, and with that they laid hands on him. Then cried the steward, and said, Good sirs, save my life, for the emperor commanded that Fulgentius should be put to death. Then said they, the messenger told us not so, but he bad us, that whosoever came first in the morning, saying as you have said, that we should take him, and cast him into the furnace, and burn him to ashes: and with that they threw him into the fire.

"And when he was burnt, Fulgentius came to them and said: Good sirs, have you done my lord's commandment, yea, soothly, said they, and therefore go ye again to the emperor, and tell him so. Then said Fulgentius, for Christ's love tell me that commandment.

"We had a commandment said they, upon pain of death, that whosoever came to us first in the morning, and said like as thou hast said, that we should take him and cast him into the furnace: But before thee, came the steward, and therefore on him have we fulfilled the emperor's commandment, now he is burnt to the bare bones.

"When Fulgentius heard this, he thanked God, that he had so preserved him from death, therefore he took his leave of the workmen, and went again to the palace.

"When the emperor saw him, he was almost distract of his wits for anger, and thus he said. Hast thou been with the brick-makers, and fulfilled my commandment? Soothly, my gracious Lord, I have been there, but ere I came there, your commandment was fulfilled. How may that be true, quoth the emperor?

"Forsooth, said Fulgentius, the steward came to them afore me, and said that I should have said, so they took him and threw him into the furnace, and if I had come any earlier, so would they have done to me, and therefore I thank God, that he hath preserved me from death.

"Then said the emperor, tell me the truth of such questions as I shall demand of thee. Then said Fulgentius to the emperor: You never found me in any falshood, and therefore I greatly wonder why ye have ordained such a death for me? for well ye know, that I am your own brother's son.

Then said the emperor to Fulgentius : It is no wonder, for that death I ordained for thee, through counsel of the steward, because thou didst defame me throughout all my empire, saying, that my breath did stink so grievously, that it was death to thee, and in token thereof thou turnedst away thy face when thou servedst me of my cup, and that I saw with mine eyes ; and for this cause I ordained for thee such a death ; and yet thou shalt die, except I hear a better excuse.

"Then answered Fulgentius, and said ; Ah, dear lord, if it might please your highness for to hear me, I shall shew you a subtile and deceitful imagination. Say on, quoth the emperor.

"The steward (quoth Fulgentius) that is now dead, came to me and said, that ye told unto him that my breath did stink, and thereupon he counselled me, that when I served you of your cup, I should turn my face away, I take God to witness, I lie not.

"When the emperor heard this, he believed him, and said. O my nephew, now I see, through the right wise judgment of God, the steward is burnt, and his own wickedness and envy is fallen on himself, for he ordained this malice against thee, and therefore thou art much bound to Almighty God, that hath preserved thee from death.[1]

"This story may have come from the East. (See Scott's *Tales from the Arabic and Persian*, p. 53, where there is an excellent story, of similar construction.) It is likewise extremely well related in the *Contes devots, or Miracles of the Virgin* (Le Grand, *Fabliaux*, v. 74), and in other places."—DOUCE.

CHAPTER C.

The commencement of this story is in Tale CIV. Not observed by Mr. Douce.[2]

CHAPTER CI.

"In Rome dwelt some time a mighty emperor, named Manelay, which had wedded the king's daughter of Hungaria, a fair lady, and

---

[1] On this story Schiller seems to have founded his legend of "Fridolin, or the Road to the Iron Foundery," lately translated by Mr. Collier. In Schiller the cause of the youth's purposed destruction is *jealousy* malignantly excited in the mind of his master, by Robert the Huntsman.

But the termination and most of the principal circumstances of the story are similar. Here, then, arises a pretty strong inference that Mr. Douce's opinions relative to what he terms the *English Gesta* are not altogether accurate. Whence had Schiller this story, if not from the GESTA ? And if from thence, a copy of it was probably in his possession. The resemblance is too close to suppose it furnished by tradition, when there were actually several printed or MS. copies. And even in that view, it opposes the idea of an *English* origin, which is the hypothesis of Mr. Douce. Such are my sentiments ; the following is the account given by Mr. Collier. " Not long subsequent to the first publication of 'Fridolin,' it became so great a favourite throughout Germany, that it was converted into a five-act play, by Holbein, the director of the theatre at Prague ; and during the fifteen years that followed, it was represented on most of the continental stages, with great success, other authors making use of the same story. It was also set to music by C. F. Weber, master of the chapel at Berlin, and in this shape it was extremely popular. Mr. Boettiger informs us that the origin of the story is an *Alsatian tradition*, which Schiller learnt when at Manheim. The probable adherence to this *Volkssage*, as far as was at all convenient, will account for the mode in which the author has treated some incidents. We know of no similar narrative, or ballad, in English."—*Remarks on " Fridolin*," p. 37.

[2] These omissions of Mr. Douce, it is presumed, indicate a less considerable variation than he supposed ; while, at the same time, they go a great way to prove the *two* Gestas *one*.

gracious in all her works, especially she was merciful. On a time, as the emperor lay in his bed, he bethought him, that he would go and visit the Holy Land. And on the morrow he called to him the empress his wife, and his own only brother, and thus he said; Dear lady, I may not, nor will not hide from you the privities of my heart, I purpose to visit the Holy Land, wherefore I ordain thee principally to be lady and governess over all my empire, and all my people; and under thee I ordain here my brother to be thy steward, for to provide all things may be profitable to my empire and my people.

"Then said the empress, Sith it will no otherwise be, but that needs thou wilt go to visit the city of Jerusalem, I shall be in your absence as true as any turtle that hath lost her mate; for as I believe, ye shall not escape thence with your life.

"The emperor anon comforts her with fair words, and kissed her, and after that took his leave of her and all others, and went toward the city of Jerusalem.

"And anon after the emperor was gone, his brother became so proud, that he oppressed poor men and robbed rich men; and he did worse than this, for he daily stirred the empress to commit sin with him; but she ever answered again as a holy and devout woman; nevertheless this knight would not leave with this answer, but ever when he found her alone, he made his complaint to her, and stirred her by all the ways that he could to sin.

"When this lady saw that he would not cease for any answer, nor would not amend himself; when she saw her time, she called to her three or four of the worthiest men of the empire, and said to them thus: It is not unknown to you, that my lord the emperor ordained me principal governor of this empire, and also he ordained his brother to be steward under me, and that he should do nothing without my counsel, but he doth all the contrary; for he oppresseth greatly poor men, and likewise robbeth the rich men; yet he would do more than this if he might have his intent; wherefore I command you in my lord's name, that you bind him fast, and cast him into prison.

"Then said they, Soothly he hath done many evil deeds since our lord the emperor went, therefore we be ready to obey your commandments, but in this matter, you must answer for us to our lord the emperor.

"Then said she, Dread ye not, if my lord knew what he had done as well as I, he would put him to the foulest death that could be thought. Immediately these men laid hands on him, and bound him fast with iron chains, and put him in prison, where he lay long time after, till at the last it fortuned, there came tidings that the emperor was coming home, and had obtained great renown and victory. When his brother heard of his coming, he said, Would to God my brother might not find me in prison, for if he do, he will enquire the cause of my imprisonment of the empress, and she will tell him all the truth how I moved her to commit sin, and so for her I shall have no favour of my brother, but lose my life; this know I well: therefore it shall not be so. Then sent he a messenger unto the empress, praying her that she would vouchsafe to come to the prison-door, that he might speak a word or two with her.

"The empress came to him, and enquired of him what he would have. He answered and said, O lady, have mercy upon me, for if the emperor my brother find me in prison, then shall I die without any remedy.

"Then said the empress, If I might know that thou wouldst be a good man, and leave thy folly, thou shouldest find grace. Then did he promise her assuredly to be true, and to amend all his trespass. When he had thus promised, the empress deliver'd him anon, and made him to be bathed and shaven, and apparelled him worthily, according to his state, and then she said thus to him; Now, good brother, take thy steed, and come with me, that we may meet my lord. He answered and said, Lady, I am ready to fulfil your will and commandment in all things; and then the empress took him with her, and many other knights, and so rode forth to meet the emperor: and as they rode together by the way, they saw a great hart run before them, wherefore every man, with such hounds as they had, chased him on horseback; so that with the empress was left no creature, save only the emperor's brother, who seeing that no man was there but they two, thus he said unto the empress; Lo, lady, here is beside a private forrest, and long it is ago that I spake to thee of love.

"Then said the empress, Ah fool, what may this be? Yesterday I delivered thee out of prison upon thy promise, in hope of amendment, and now thou art returned to thy folly again; wherefore I say unto thee, as I have said before. Then said he, if thou wilt not consent unto me, I shall hang thee here upon a tree in this forrest, where no man shall find thee, and so shalt thou die an evil death. The empress answered meekly, and said, Though thou smite off my head, or put me to death with all manner of torments, thou shalt never have my consent to such a sin.

"When he heard this, he unclothed her all save her smock, and hanged her up by the hair upon a tree, and tied her steed before her, and so rode to his fellows, and told them that a great host of men met him, and took the empress away from him, and when he had told them this, they made all great sorrow.

"It befell on the third day after, there came an earl to hunt in that forrest, and as he rode beating the bushes, he unkennelled a fox, whom his hounds followed fast, till they came near the tree where the empress hanged. And when the dogs smelt the savour of the empress, they left the fox, and ran towards the tree as fast as they could.

"The earl seeing this, wondred greatly, and spurring his horse, followed them till he came where the empress hanged. When the earl saw her thus hanging, he marvelled greatly, forasmuch as she was right fair and beautiful to behold; wherefore he said unto her in this manner-wise: O woman, who art thou? and of what country? and wherefore hangest thou here in this manner?

"The empress that was not yet fully dead, but at point ready to die, answered and said, I am, quoth she, a strange woman, and am come out of a far country, but how I came hither, God knoweth. Then answered the earl and said, Whose horse is this that standest by thee bound to this tree? Then answered the lady and said, that it was hers. When the earl heard this, he saw well that she was a gentlewoman, and come of noble lineage, wherefore he was the rather moved with pity, and said unto her: O fair lady, thou seemest of gentle blood, and therefore I purpose to deliver thee from this mischief, if thou wilt promise to go with me, and nourish my fair young daughter, and teach her at home in my castle, for I have no child but only her, and if thou keep her well thou shalt have a good reward for thy labour. Then said she: As far forth as I can or may, I shall fulfil your intent. And when she had thus promised him, he took her down off the tree, and led her home to his castle, and gave her the keeping of his daughter that he loved so much, and she was cherished so well, that she lay every night in the earl's chamber, and his daughter with her: and in the chamber every night there burned a lamp, which hanged between the empresses bed and the earl's bed. This lady behaved herself so gently, that she was beloved of every creature. There was at that time in the earl's house a steward, which much loved this empress, and often spake to her of his love. But she answered him again and said, Know ye, dear friend, for a certainty, that I will never love any man in such manner-wise, but only him whom I am greatly bound to love by God's commandment.

"Then said the steward, Then thou wilt not consent unto me? Sir (quoth she), what need you any more to ask such things? The vow that I have made, I will truly keep, and hold by the grace of God.

"And when the steward heard this, he went his way in great wrath and anger, thinking within himself, if I may, I shall be revenged on thee.

"It befel upon a night within a short time after, that the earl's chamber door was forgotten, and left unshut, which the steward had anon perceived: and when they were all asleep, he went and espied by the light of the lamp where the empress and the young maiden lay together, and with that he drew out his knife, and cut the throat of the earl's daughter and put the knife into the empresses hand, she being asleep, and nothing knowing thereof, to the intent, that when the Earl awaked he should think that she had cut his daughter's throat, and so would she be put to a shameful death for his mischievous deed.* And when the damsel was thus slain, and the bloody knife in the empresses hand, the countess awaked out of her sleep, and saw by the light of the lamp the bloody knife in the empresses hand, wherefore she was almost out of her wits, and said to the earl, O my lord, behold in yonder lady's hand a wonderful thing.

"The earl awaked, and looked toward the empresses bed; and saw the bloody knife, as the countess had said: wherefore he was greatly moved, and cried to her, and said, Awake, woman, out of thy sleep, what thing is this that I see in thy hand? Then the empress through his cry awaked out of her sleep, and in her waking the knife fell out of her hand, and with that she looked by her, and found the earl's daughter dead by her side, and all the bed besprinkled with blood, wherefore with an high voice she cried, and said, Alas! alas! and wo is me, my lord's daughter is slain.

"Then cried the countess unto the earl with a piteous voice, and said, O my lord, let this devilish woman be put to the foulest death that can be thought, which thus hath slain our only child.

"Then when the countess had said thus to the earl, he said to the empress in this wise; The high God knoweth that thou, mischievous woman, hast slain my daughter with thine own hands, for I saw the bloody knife in thy hand, and therefore thou shalt die a foul death. Then said the earl in this wise: O thou woman, were it not I dread God greatly, I should cleave thy body with my sword in two parts, for I delivered thee from hanging, and now thou hast slain my daughter; nevertheless, for me thou shalt have no harm, therefore go thy way out of this city, without any delay, for if I find thee here after this day, thou shalt die a most cruel death.

"Then arose this woful empress, and put on her cloaths, and after leap'd on her palfrey, and rode toward the east alone without any safe conduct; and as she rode thus, mourning by the way, she espied on the

---

* This incident will remind the reader of a similar one in *Macbeth*.

left side of the way a pair of gallows, and seven officers leading a man to be hanged, wherefore she was moved with great pity, and smote her horse with her stick, and rode to them, praying that she might redeem that misdoer if he might be saved from death by any means.

"Then said they, Lady, it pleaseth us well that you redeem him. Anon the empress accorded with them and paid his ransom, and he was delivered.

" Then said she to him: Now, my good friend, be true unto me till thou die, sith I have delivered thee from death.

" On my soul (quoth he) I promise you ever to be true. And when he had thus said, he followed the lady still, till they came nigh a city, and then said the empress to him: Good friend (quoth she), go forth thy way afore me into the city, and see thou take up for us an honest lodging, for there I purpose to rest awhile. Her man went forth as she commanded, and took up her a good lodging, and an honest, where she abode a long time. When the men of the city perceived her beauty, they wondred greatly; wherefore many of them craved of her unlawful love, but all was in vain, for they might not speed in any wise.

" It fortuned after upon a day, that there came a ship full of merchandise, and arrived in the haven of that city. When the lady heard this, she said unto her servant: Go to the ship, and see if there be any cloth for my use.

" Her servant went forth to the ship whereas he found many very fine cloths: wherefore he pray'd the master of the ship, that he would come to the city and speak with his lady. The master granted him, and so the servant came home to his lady before, and warned her of the coming of the master of the ship. Soon after the master of the ship came and saluted her courteously, and the lady received him according to his degree, praying him that she might have for her money such cloth as might be profitable for her wearing. Then he granted that she should have any thing that liked her, and soon they were agreed, wherefore the servant went immediately again with the master of the ship for the cloth. And when they were both within on ship-board, the master said to the lady's servant: My dear friend, to thee I would open my mind, if I might trust to thee, and if thou help me, thou shalt have of me a great reward.

" Then answered he and said : I shall (quoth he) be sworn to thee to keep thy counsel, and fulfil thine intent as far forth as I can.

" Then said the master of the ship, I love thy lady more than I can tell thee, for her beauty and feature is so excellent, that I would give for the love of her all the gold that I have : and if I may obtain the love of her through thy help, I will give thee whatsoever thou wilt desire of me.

" Then said the lady's servant, tell me by what means I may best help thee. Then said the master of the ship, go home to thy lady again, and tell her, that I will not deliver to thee the cloth except she come herself; and do thou but bring her to my ship, and if the wind be good and fit, then I purpose to lead her away. Thy counsel is good, quoth the lady's servant, therefore give me some reward, and I shall fulfil thy desire.

" Now when he had received his reward, he went again to the lady, and told her, that by no means the master of the ship would deliver him the cloth, except she came to him herself.

" The lady believed her servant, and went to the ship. Now when she was within the ship-board, her servant abode without.

" When the master saw that she was within the ship, and the wind
was good, he drew up the sail and sailed forth.

" When the lady perceived this, thus she said to the master: O master
(quoth she), what treason is this thou hast done to me? The master
answered and said: certainly it is so, that I must needs * * * * espouse
thee. O good sir, quoth she, I have made a vow, that I shall never do
such a thing * * * * Soothly (quoth he), if you will not grant me with
your good will, I will cast you out into the midst of the sea, and there
shall ye die an evil death: If it be so (quoth she), that I must needs consent, or else die, first I pray thee to prepare a private place in the end of
the ship, whereas I may fulfil thine intent ere I die, and also I pray thee,
that I may say my prayers unto the father of heaven, that he may have
mercy on me.

" The master believed her, wherefore he did ordain her a cabbin in
the end of the ship, wherein she kneeled down on both her knees and
made her prayers, saying on this wise: O thou my Lord God, thou hast
kept me from my youth in cleanness, keep me now * * * * * so that I
may ever serve thee with a clean heart and mind, and let not this wicked
man prevail with me, nor any other the like wickedness come nigh me.
When she had ended her prayers, there arose suddenly a great tempest
in the sea, so that the ship all brast, and all that were therein perished,
save the lady; and she caught a cable and saved herself, and the master
caught a board of the ship and saved himself likewise; nevertheless, she
knew not of him, nor he of her, for they were driven to divers coasts.
The lady landed in her own empire near to a rich city, wherein she was
honourably received, and she lived so holy a life, that God gave her
grace and power to heal sick folk of all manner of diseases; wherefore
there came much people to her, both crooked, blind, and lame, and every
man through the grace of God and her good endeavour was healed,
wherefore her name was known thro' diuers regions. Nevertheless, she
was not known as the empress. At the same time the emperor's brother,
that had hanged her before by the hair, was smitten with a foul leprosie.
The knight that slew the earl's daughter, and put the bloody knife in her
hand, was blind, deaf, and had the palsie. The thief that betrayed her
to the master of the ship, was lame and full of the cramp, and the master
of the ship distraught of his wits.

" When the emperor heard that so holy a woman was in the city, he
called his brother, and said to him thus: Go we, dear brother, unto this
holy woman that is dwelling in this city, that she may heal thee of thy
leprosie. Would to God, O noble brother (quoth he), that I were healed.
Anon the emperor with his brother went toward the city. Then when
the citizens heard of his coming, they received him honourably with pro-
cession and all provision befitting his estate. And then the emperor
enquired of the citizens, if any such holy woman were among them, that
could heal sick folk of their diseases. The citizens answered and said,
that such an one there was. Now at the same time was come to the
same city, the knight that slew the earl's daughter, and the thief which
she saved from the gallows, and the master of the ship, to be healed of
their diseases.

" Then was the empress called forth before the emperor, but she
muffled her face as well as she could, that the emperor her husband
should not know her, and when she had so done, she saluted him with
great reverence, as appertained to his state; and again he in like
manner, saying thus: O good lady, if thou list of thy kindness to heal
my brother of his leprosie, ask of me what you will, and I shall grant it
thee for thy reward.

" When the empress heard this, she looked about her, and saw there the emperor's brother, a foul leper; she saw there also the knight that slew the earl's daughter, blind and deaf, the thief that she saved from the gallows lame, and also the master of the ship distraught out of his wits, and all were come to her to be healed of their maladies, and knew her not; but though they knew her not, she knew them well. Then said she unto the emperor thus: My reverend lord, though you would give me all your empire, I cannot heal your brother, nor none of these other, except they acknowledge openly what great evil they have done.

" When the emperor heard this, he turned him towards his brother, and said unto him : Brother, acknowledge openly thy sin before all these men, that thou mayest be healed of thy sickness. Then anon he began to tell how he had led his life, but he told not how he had hanged the empress in the forrest by the hair of the head most despitefully.

" When he had acknowledged all that him list, the empress replied, and said : Soothly, my lord, I would gladly lay unto him my medicine, but I wot right well it is in vain, for he hath not made a full confession.

" The emperor hearing this, he turned towards his brother, and said in this wise : What evil, sorrow, or other unhappy wretchedness is in thee ? Seest thou not how that thou art a foul leper ? therefore acknowledge thy sin truly, that thou mayest be whole, or else avoid my company for evermore.

" Ah my lord (quoth he), I may not tell my life openly, except I be sure of thy grace. What hast thou trespassed against me, said the emperor ? Then answered his brother, and said : Mine offence against thee is grievous, and therefore I heartily ask thee forgiveness. The emperor thought not on the empress, forasmuch as he supposed she had been dead many years before; therefore he commanded his brother to tell forth wherein he had offended him, and he should be forgiven.

" When the emperor had thus forgiven his brother, he began to tell openly how he had desired the empress to commit adultery with him, and because she denied, he had hanged her by the hair, in the forrest, on such a day.

" When the emperor heard this, he was almost beside himself, and in his rage he said thus : O thou wretched creature, the vengeance of God is fallen upon thee, and were it not that I have pardoned thee, thou shouldest die the most shameful death that could be thought.

" Then said the knight that slew the earl's daughter, I wot not quoth he, what lady you mean, but I wot that my lord found on a time such a lady hanging in the forrest, and brought her home to his castle, and he took her, and gave her his daughter to keep, and I provoked her as much as I could to sin with me, but she would in no wise consent to me; wherefore I slew the earl's daughter that lay with her, and when I had so done, I put the bloody knife in the lady's hand, that the earl should think that she had slain his daughter with her own hand, and then she was exiled thence, but where she became I wot not.

" Then said the thief, I wot not of what lady you mean; but well I wot, that seven officers were leading me to the gallows, and such a lady came riding by, and bought me of them, and then went I with her, and betrayed her unto the master of the ship.

" Such a lady (quoth the master of the ship), received I, and when we were in the midst of the sea, I would have lain with her, but she kneeled down to her prayers, and anon there arose such a tempest, that the ship all to brast, and all therein was drowned, save she and I, but afterward what befell of her I wot not.

" Then cried the empress with a loud voice, and said : Soothly dear friends, ye do now truly confess and declare the truth, wherefore I will now apply my medicine, and anon they received their healths.

" When the lady the empress had thus done, she uncovered her face to the emperor, and he forthwith knew her, and ran to her, and embraced her in his arms, and kissed her oftentimes, and for joy he wept bitterly : saying, Blessed be God, now I have found that I desired. And when he had thus said, he led her home to the palace with great joy ; and after, when it pleased Almighty God, they ended both their lives in peace and rest."

" Occleve has related this story in verse, from the present work (MS. Reg. 17 D. vi.), and it is also to be found in the *Patrañas* of Timonida (Patr. 21). The outline has been borrowed from one of the *Contes devots*, or miracles of the Virgin Mary.[1] The incident of the bloody knife occurs likewise in Chaucer's *Man of Law's Tale*, and in a story related by Gower, *Confessio Amantis*, fol. 32."—DOUCE.

A few additional remarks upon the stories to follow, for which indulgence is bespoke, shall close, what I fear the reader may be disposed to consider, as toilsome a march as the doughty knights of old experienced in gaining access to some enchanted castle. But let me whisper in his ear that the distressed damsels whom his intrepidity shall relieve are most of them passing fair and gentle. He cannot display resolution in a better cause ; and if (*de gustibus non est disputandum !*) their beauty sometimes disappoint · his expectations, let him remember that adoration has been offered them by past ages of heroic spirits : that bards, whose names are familiar in our mouths as household words, have condescended to adopt them ; and, therefore, that they possess an undoubted claim to public consideration, if not on the ground of their own intrinsic excellence.

Much of the merit of these fables consists in the curious and interesting light which they throw upon a period necessarily involved in great obscurity. The fictions are strongly and vividly delineated ; and the reader feels himself hurried back into the romantic scenes of chivalrous emprize, and busily mingling in the commotions of camp and court. The fantastic regulations of many of the tales accord with historical notices of chivalry ; in which the most ridiculous commands were imposed and executed. The sports of the field, united with the pursuit of wild adventure : love, and war, and devotion ; absurd penances for unimaginable crimes, and carelessness

[1] See Vincent of Beauvais, *Spec. Theol.* Let. viii. cap. 90, 91.

for the commission of enormous ones, form no small part of the present compilation. Every natural phenomenon is a miracle; and construed as best may serve the interests, or accord with the prejudices of the party. The first object is to espouse some ineffably fair daughter : whose affections are disposed of, not according to the common *excellent* system of policy, or power, or wealth, but by the simple and singularly efficacious method of resolving certain mysteries; in expounding riddles, or in compliance with some inexplicable vow. If this should be considered no very favourable account of what the reader may look for, it should be remembered that the tales in question are faithful representations of other days, and that the character with which the period is impressed tolerates and justifies many absurdities. Yet are we not to suppose everything absurd which now appears so. The progress of civilization has introduced a vast number of unnecessary refinements, at which our ancestors would laugh; perhaps more boisterously, but with as much regard to *justice* as their politer descendants exhibit at the inartificial character of earlier times.

Ignorance is always credulous; and therefore, in considering the probability or improbability of the fable, we must consider how it was calculated to impress those for whom it was invented, or to whom it was told. If the narrator suited his contrivance to the understanding, and communicated pleasure to the imagination, of *his* readers or auditors, he possessed the requisite ingenuity; and his merit was proportionably great. We ought not to make our own the standard of others' judgments; much less ought we to impose our own age and nation as the criterion of past times and foreign countries. Comparatively secluded as the monks at all times were, their views of life must necessarily have been confined also : and their simplicity would easily be duped by those who were interested in deceiving them. From the pulpit, whence it would appear that their stories were delivered, the opportunity of adding new fictions, for the purpose of illustrating new positions, would be irresistible; and here we trace the source of many of the strained allusions which so repeatedly occur. The good old custom likewise, of enlivening a winter's evening by the relation of *fabliaux*, accompanied, no doubt, by *moral and mystical applications*, gives us a delightful picture of the social intercourse and familiarity of remote times; but discovers to us another incentive to extravagant fancy and high-flown conceit. The attention of their hearers could only be riveted by the marvellous; and that which was barely *probable*, from the constant recurrence of extravagant fiction—from the itching ears, which opened only to the wildest exaggeration, naturally became no longer acceptable, because taste was vitiated, and the imagination overwrought. All these circumstances require consideration in forming a judgment of the ensuing tales. They certainly vary in point of merit; but many of them are eminently beautiful. Some display a rich vein of pathos; and there are passages of deep poetic interest. In the description of manners, however, they are unrivalled; and my aim has been, to render passages of this kind with all fidelity; while, in the diction, I have adhered as closely as possible to that simplicity of style which forms the principal charm of ancient narrative.

In perusing the conversational parts, the reader who has pored over illuminated manuscripts will recall subjects to which they apply. He will recollect fair ladies glittering in every colour of the rainbow, chattering from a window to grotesque-looking gentlemen with pink feathers drooping from immense hats; and misshapen shoes, vying in the longitude of their peaks with a barber's pole: he will be reminded of grim-visaged emperors ornamented with royal beards and projecting jaws—in short, he will distinguish the whole of what these volumes delineate. There is in the British Museum a beautiful manuscript of the *Romant de la Rose*, which will, in most respects, exemplify my observations.

It would appear that hospitality was a never-failing virtue; and the eagerness with which pilgrims and wayfaring persons were invited to share the repast and partake the couch of the friendly citizen, or to occupy the castle of the knight, is a pleasing trait in the character of the times. But it will be thought that wisdom was a scarce commodity, when three prudential maxims were valued at a thousand florins. [See Tale CIII.] Considering the result, they were cheaply purchased; although, in these days, when advice is much oftener given than paid for—even with thanks, the price may be deemed somewhat of the highest.

The many stories on the subject of adultery seem to indicate a bad moral state of society at the time they were written; and it is to be feared that the lawless feeling which chivalry in its decline exhibited, affords an unhappy confirmation. Whether the fact of the monks levelling much of their satire against the fair sex is also corroborative, or whether it proceed from that impotence of mind which, being itself fretted by circumstance, would gladly efface or deteriorate whatever is the object of its unavailing wishes, I do not take upon me to decide.

It is necessary that I should advertise the reader of what he will not fail to perceive, that the tales are not always perfect in every part; nor are the positions laid down at the commencement always remembered. This may result from ignorant transcribers having omitted some passages, and interpolated others: and such a supposition accounts, as I observed before, for the numerous variations which appear in various copies, as well as for the introduction of certain expressions that have been considered arguments in behalf of their origin. That they have been collected from all countries, and at many times, I have no doubt. Some appear of Italian construction, a few German, but the greater part oriental. The absolute power of the emperors, who sport with life and death in the most capricious and extraordinary manner—the constant introduction of the leprosy and crucifixion, amply confirm their connection with the East.

"It may not be thought impertinent to close this discourse with a remark on the MORALIZATIONS subjoined to the stories of the GESTA ROMANORUM. This was an age of vision and mystery: and every work was believed to contain a double, or secondary, meaning. Nothing escaped this eccentric spirit of refinement and abstraction; and, together with the Bible, as we have seen, not only the general history of ancient times was explained allegorically, but even the poetical fictions of the classics were made to signify the great truths of religion, with a degree of boldness, and a want of discrimination, which, in another age, would have acquired the character of the most profane levity, if not of absolute impiety, and can only be defended from the simplicity of the state of knowledge which then prevailed.

"Thus, God creating man of clay, animated with the vital principle of respiration, was the story of Prometheus, who formed a man of similar materials, to which he communicated life by fire stolen from heaven. Christ twice born, of His Father, God, and of His mother, Mary, was prefigured by Bacchus, who was first born of Semele, and afterwards of Jupiter. And as Minerva sprung from the brain of Jupiter, so Christ proceeded from God without a mother. Christ born of the Virgin Mary was expressed in the fable of Danäe shut within a tower, through the covering of which Jupiter descended in a shower of gold, and begat Perseus. Actæon, killed by his own hounds, was a type of the persecution and death of our Saviour. The poet Lycophron relates that Hercules, in returning from the adventure of the golden fleece, was shipwrecked; and that, being devoured by a monstrous fish, he was disgorged alive on the shore after three days. Here was an obvious symbol of Christ's resurrection. John Waleys, an English Franciscan of the thirteenth century, in his moral exposition of Ovid's Metamorphoses, affords many other instances equally ridiculous ; and who forgot that he was describing a more heterogeneous chaos, than that which makes so conspicuous a figure in his author's exordium, and which combines, amid the monstrous and indigested aggregate of its unnatural associations,

————Sine pondere habentia pondus.[1]

" At length, compositions professedly allegorical, with which that age abounded, were resolved into allegories for which they were never intended. In the famous ROMAUNT OF THE ROSE, written about the year 1310, the poet couches the difficulties of an ardent lover in attaining the object of his passion, under the allegory of a rose, which is gathered in a delicious but almost inaccessible garden. The theologists proved this rose to be the white rose of Jericho, the new Jerusalem, a state of grace, divine wisdom, the holy Virgin, or eternal beatitude, at none of which obstinate heretics can ever arrive. The chemists pretended that it was the philosopher's stone ; the civilians, that it was the most consummate point of equitable decision; and the physicians, that it was the infallible panacea. In a word, other professions, in the most elaborate commentaries, explained away the lover's rose into the mysteries of their own respective science. In conformity to this practice, Tasso allegorized his own poem; and a flimsy structure of morality was raised on the chimerical conceptions of Ariosto's ORLANDO. In the year 1557, a translation of a part of Amadis de Gaule appeared in France; with a learned preface, developing the valuable stores of profound instruction, concealed under the naked letters of the old romances, which were discernible only to the intelligent, and totally unperceived by common readers ; who, instead of plucking the fruit, were obliged to rest contented with *la simple* FLEUR *de la Lecture litterale*. Even Spenser, at a later period, could not indulge his native impulse to descriptions of chivalry, without framing such a story, as conveyed, under the *dark conceit* of ideal champions, a set of historic transactions, and an exemplification of the nature of the twelve moral virtues. He presents his fantastic queen with a rich romantic mirror, which shewed the wondrous achievements of her magnificent ancestry :—

[1] *Met.* lib. i. 20.

‘And thou, O fairest princess under sky,
In this fayre mirrour maist behold thy face,
And thine own realms in lond of Faëry,
And in this antique image thy great ancestry.’[1]

"It was not, however, solely from an unmeaning and a wanton spirit of refinement that the fashion of resolving everything into allegory, so universally prevailed. The same apology may be offered for cabalistical interpreters, both of the classics and of the old romances. The former, not willing that those books should be quite exploded which contained the ancient mythology, laboured to reconcile the apparent absurdities of the pagan system to the Christian mysteries, by demonstrating a figurative resemblance. The latter, as true learning began to dawn, with a view of supporting for a while the expiring credit of giants and magicians, were compelled to palliate those monstrous incredibilities, by a bold attempt to unravel the mystic web which had been wove by fairy hands, and by shewing that truth was hid under the gorgeous veil of Gothic invention."[2]

[1] B. ii. Introd. St. vi.

[2] WARTON, *Introductory Disser.* See *Hist. of E. Poetry*, vol. iii. p. xciv. *et seq.* I cannot omit observing here, that in the opinions which I have hazarded, I am led by no presumptuous feeling to condemn those who think differently. I deprecate every suspicion to the contrary. While I am anxious to elucidate and establish my own sentiments, I retain the utmost respect and deference for those whose research, judgment, critical acumen, and ability, there is little merit in frankly avowing. And I take this opportunity of acknowledging the assistance I have derived from the invaluable labours of Mr. Douce and Mr. Ellis—not to mention a fund of information from Mr. Warton, which the reader will readily observe. The latter writer, whose inaccuracies have been the theme of every pen, it seems to me, has not been justly appreciated. That he is frequently incorrect is certain; but he is blamed by those who have not repaired his deficiencies, while they have forgot the difficulty of his undertaking, and the impossibility of preventing typographical errors in a work of such extent. A slight blunder, which I should think must have been unintentional (*Isumbras* for *Ippotis*), causes Ritson to accuse him of an "*infamous lie!*" See *Diss. on Romance and Minstrelsy; passim.*

OUTLINES OF THE TALES.

———◦◇◦———

GESTA ROMANORUM.

———◆———

TALE I.

OF LOVE.

POMPEY* was a wise and powerful king. He had an only
daughter, remarkable for her beauty, of whom he was
extremely fond. He committed her to the custody of five
soldiers; and charged them, under the heaviest penalties,
to preserve her from every possible injury. The soldiers
were on guard night and day; and before the door of her
bed-chamber they suspended a burning lamp, that the
approach of an intruder might be the more easily detected.
And they kept a dog, whose bark was loud and piercing,
to rouse them from sleep. From all these circumstances,
it would appear that every precaution had been taken:
but, unhappily, the lady panted for the pleasures of the
world. As she was one day looking abroad, a certain duke
passed by, who regarded her with impure and improper

---

* The fair reader who has not condescended to notice my *pro-
legomena* (and I hope the suspicion is not treasonable!) may require
to be informed that "GESTA ROMANORUM" supplies a very inadequate
idea of the contents of these volumes. The Romans have little to do
in the matter, and *King Pompey* must not be confounded with Pompey
the Great, though they are unquestionably meant for the same person.
Such blunders are perpetual.

feelings. Observing her beauty, and ascertaining that she was the reputed heir to the throne, he became enamoured, and made her many promises to obtain her consent; which she, hoping much from his words, gave, and straightway slew the dog, put out the lamp, and rising by night, fled with the duke. In the morning, however, inquiries were set on foot. Now, there was at that time in the king's palace * a champion of remarkable prowess, who ever did battle for justice in that realm. When he understood the contempt which the lady had exhibited towards her parent, he armed himself, and hastened after the fugitives. A battle speedily ensued, in which the champion triumphed, and decapitated the seducer on the spot. The lady he conveyed back to the palace; but being refused admittance to the presence of her father, thenceforward she passed her time in bitterly bewailing her misdeeds. It happened that a wise person in the emperor's court heard of her repentance. On all occasions when his services were required, he had proved himself an active mediator between majesty and its offenders; and being now moved with compassion, he reconciled her to her indignant parent, and betrothed her to a powerful nobleman. After this she received many and diverse gifts from her father. In the first place he presented to her a tunic, which extended to the heel, composed of the finest and richest woof, having the following inscription:—" I have forgiven thee, see that thou add not to thy offence." From the king also she received a golden coronet, bearing the legend, " Thy dignity is from me." The champion, who had conquered in her behalf, gave a ring, on which was sculptured, " I have loved thee, learn thou to love." The mediator also bestowed a ring, inscribed as follows, " What have I done? How much? Why?" Another ring was presented by the king's son; and there was engraved upon it, " Thou art noble, despise not thy nobility." Her own brother bestowed a similar gift, of which the motto ran thus:—" Approach; fear not—I am thy brother." Her husband likewise added a golden signet, which confirmed his wife in the inheritance of his

---

* [Whether the *Rex* here spoken of is identical with the *Imperator* or not, it is impossible to discover. The confusion becomes still worse further on.—ED.]

goods, and bore this superscription, "Now thou art espoused, sin no more."

The lady received these various presents, and kept them as long as she lived. She succeeded in regaining the favour of those whose affections her former conduct had alienated, and closed her days in peace.*

APPLICATION.

My beloved, the king is our heavenly Father, who hath drawn away His children from the jaws of the devil by the sufferings of His blessed Son. He is the King of kings, and Lord of lords. *Deut.* xxxii.: "Is He not thy Father who hath obtained thee by conquest, made, and established thee?" The only daughter is the rational soul, which is delivered to five soldiers, that is, to the five senses, to guard; being armed by virtues received in baptism. These senses are sight, hearing, &c., which have in charge to preserve it from the devil, the world, and the flesh. The burning lamp is the will, subjected in all things to the control of God, and which in good works should shine out brilliantly, dispersing the gloom of sin. The barking dog is conscience, which has to struggle against error; but, alas! the soul, desirous of gazing upon the objects of this world, looks abroad as often as it acts contrary to the divine command; and then is willingly seduced by a duke—that is, by the infernal ravisher. And thus the lamp of good works is extinguished, and the dog of conscience destroyed: and thus the soul follows the devil in the dark night of sin. These things, when our champion had heard, namely, GOD—because "there is no other that fights for us, but only Thou, our God"—instantly He combats with that wicked misleader the devil, gains a victory, and leads the soul to the palace of the heavenly King. The wise mediator is CHRIST; as the apostle says, 1 *Tim.* ii.: "There is one mediator between God and man, the Man Christ Jesus." The son of the king is CHRIST. So the psalmist

---

* "The latter part of this story is evidently oriental. The feudal manners, in a book which professes to record the achievements of the Roman people, are remarkable in the introductory circumstances. But of this mixture we shall see many striking instances."—WARTON.

witnesses—"Thou art my son, this day have I begotten
thee." Christ is also our brother. *Gen.* xxxvii.: "He is
our brother." And He is our spouse, according to that of
Hosea ii.: "I will marry thee in faithfulness." Again,
"Thou shalt be the spouse of my blood." By Him, we are
reconciled to our heavenly Father, and restored to peace.
"For He is our peace, who hath made both one."—*Ephes.* ii.
From Him we received the aforesaid gifts: first, a cloak
descending to the ankle—that is, His most precious skin; *
and said to be of delicate texture, because it was woven
with stripes, blood, bruises, and other various instances of
malice. Of which texture, nothing more is meant than
this—"I have forgiven thee," because I have *redeemed*
thee; "see that thou add not to thy offence." "Go," said
our Lord, "and sin no more." This is the vest of Joseph
—the garment dyed in the blood of a goat.—*Gen.* xxxvii.
That same Christ our King gave to us an all-glorious
crown; that is, when He submitted to be crowned for our
sakes. And of a truth, "Thy dignity is from me"—even
from that crown. *John* xix.: "Jesus went forth, bearing
the crown of thorns." Christ is our champion, who gave us
a ring—that is, the hole in His right hand; and we ourselves may perceive how faithfully it is written—"I have
loved thee, learn thou to love." *Rev.* i.: "Christ our mediator
loved us, and washed us from our sins in His blood." He
gave us another ring, which is the puncture in his left
hand, where we see written, "What have I done? How
much? Why?"—"What have I done?" I have despoiled
myself, receiving the form of a servant. "How much?"
I have made God man. "Why?" To redeem the lost.
Concerning these three—*Zachary* xiii.: "What are the
wounds in the middle of thy hands? And He answered,
saying, I am wounded by these men in their house, who
loved me." Christ is our brother, and son of the eternal
King. He gave us a third ring—to wit, the hole in His

---

* Attempts, like the present, to strain everything into an allegory,
are very frequent in these "mystical and moral applications." It
for this reason, among others, that I thought it right to abridge them;
for while the reader's patience was exhausted, his feelings would
revolt as well at the absurdity as at the apparent impiety of the
allusion.

right foot; and what can be understood by it except, "Thou art noble, despise not thy nobility"? In like manner, Christ is our *brother-german*. And He gave us a fourth ring, the puncture in his left foot, on which is written, "Approach; fear not—I am thy brother." Christ is also our *spouse;* He gave us a signet, with which He confirmed our inheritance: that is, the wound made in His side by the spear, on account of the great love with which He loved us. And what can this signify but "Thou art now joined to me through mercy; sin no more."

Let us study, my beloved, to keep these gifts uninjured, that we may be able to exclaim, as in *St. Matthew*, "Lord, thou gavest to me five talents;" and thus, unquestionably, we shall reign in the bosom of bliss. That we may be thought worthy the Father, Son, &c.

TALE II.

OF MERCY.

The Emperor Titus made a law, that whosoever provided not for his parents should be condemned to death. It happened that there were two brethren, descended from the same father. One of them had a son, who discovered his uncle in the greatest indigence; and immediately, in compliance with the law, but in opposition to the will of his father, administered to his wants. Thereupon the father expelled him from his house. Notwithstanding, he still maintained his poor uncle, and supplied him with every requisite. By and by, the uncle became rich and the father indigent. Now, when the son beheld the altered circumstances of his parent, he liberally supported him also, to the great indignation of his uncle, who drove him from his house and said,* "Formerly, when I was poor, thou gavest me support, in opposition to thy father; for which I constituted thee my heir, in the place of a

---

* [There is an anacoluthon in the Latin text: "Et ideo a societate avunculi est expulsus, *dicensque ei*, &c."—Ed.]

son. But an ungrateful son ought not to obtain an inheritance; and rather than such, we should adopt a stranger. Therefore, since *thou* hast been ungrateful to thy father in maintaining me contrary to his command, thou shalt never possess my inheritance." The son thus answered his uncle: "No one can be punished for executing what the law commands and compels. Now, the law of nature obliges children to assist their parents in necessity, and especially to honour them: therefore, I cannot justly be deprived of the inheritance."

APPLICATION.

My beloved, the two brothers are the Son of God and the world, which both proceed from one heavenly Father. The first, begotten; the second, created. Between them, from the beginning, discord arose, and continues to this day; so that he who is the friend of the one is an enemy to the other. According to *St. James* iv.: "Whosoever would become the friend of this world shall be accounted an enemy to God." The only son is every Christian, who is the progeny of Christ, because he is descended from Him by faith. Therefore, we should not feed fat the world with pride, avarice, and other vices, if we would be the children of God. And if our desires are contrary, too surely we shall be excluded from the family of Christ, and lose our heavenly inheritance. If we maintain and cherish Christ by works of love and of piety, the world indeed will abhor us—but better is it to be at enmity with the world than forego an inheritance in heaven.

TALE III.

OF JUST JUDGMENT.

A CERTAIN emperor decreed, that if any woman were taken in adultery, she should be cast headlong from a very high precipice. It chanced that a woman, convicted of the crime, was immediately conveyed to the place of punishment, and thrown down. But she received no injury in the fall. They therefore brought her back to the judgment-seat; and when the judge perceived that she was unharmed, he commanded that she should again be led to the precipice, and the sentence effectually executed. The woman, however, addressing the judge, said, "My Lord, if you command this, you will act contrary to the law, which punishes not twice for the same fault. I have already been cast down as a convicted adultress, but God miraculously preserved me. Therefore, I ought not to be subjected to it again." The judge answered, "Thou hast well said; go in peace:" and thus was the woman saved.

APPLICATION.

My beloved, the emperor is God, who made a law that if any one polluted the soul (which is the spouse of Christ) by the commission of any mortal sin, he should be precipitated from a high mountain—that is, from heaven; as befel our first parent, Adam. But God, by the sufferings of His Son, hath preserved us. When man sins, God does not instantly condemn him, because His mercy is infinite; but " by grace we are saved," and not cast headlong into hell.

TALE IV.

OF JUSTICE.

DURING the reign of Cæsar a law was enacted, that if a man maltreated a woman, and overcame her by violence, it should remain with the aggrieved party, whether the person so offending should be put to death, or married to her, without a portion. Now, it fell out that a certain fellow violated two women upon the same night; the one of whom sought to put him to death, and the other to be married to him. The violator was apprehended and brought before the judge, to answer respecting the two women, according to law. The first woman insisting upon

her right, desired his death ; while the second claimed
him for her husband.   The first woman said, " It cannot
be denied that the law ordains that I should obtain my
wish."   The other replied, " In like manner the law raises
its voice for me.   But because my demand is of less
importance, and more charitable, I doubt not but that
sentence will be given in my favour."   Both women complained, and both required the enforcement of the law.
When either side had been heard, the judge ordered that
the second woman should obtain the man for her husband.
And so it was done.

APPLICATION.

My beloved, the emperor, who framed the law, is our
Lord Jesus Christ.   The violator, any sinner, who violates
two females, that is, Justice and Mercy, which are both
the daughters of God.   The violator is brought before the
Judge, when the soul separates from the body.   The first
woman, that is, Justice, alleges against the sinner that by
law he is subject to eternal death : but the other, that is,
Divine Mercy, alleges that by contrition and confession
he may be saved.   Therefore, let us study to please God.

TALE V.

OF FIDELITY.

THE subject of a certain king fell into the hands of pirates,
and wrote to his father for ransom.   But the father would
not redeem him ; so the youth wasted away in prison.
Now, he who detained him in chains had a daughter of
great beauty and virtue.   She was at this time in her
twentieth year, and frequently visited the young man
with the hope of alleviating his griefs.   But he was too
disconsolate to hearken.   It one day fell out that, while
the damsel was with him, the youth said to her, " Oh, that
you would try to set me free, kind maiden ! "   She replied,

"But how am I to effect it? Thy father, thine own father, will not ransom thee; on what ground then should I, a stranger, attempt it? And suppose that I were induced to do so, I should incur the wrath of my parent, because thine denies the price of thy redemption. Nevertheless, on one condition thou shalt be liberated." "Kind damsel," returned he, "impose what thou wilt; so that it be possible, I will accomplish it." "Promise, then," said she, "to marry me, whenever an opportunity may occur." "I promise," said the youth, joyfully, "and plight thee a faith that shall never be broken." The girl straightway set him free from his bonds, without her father's knowledge, and fled with him to his own country. When they arrived, the father of the youth welcomed him, and said, "Son, I am overjoyed at thy return; but who is the lady under thy escort?" He replied, "It is the daughter of a king, to whom I am betrothed." The father returned, "On pain of losing thy inheritance, I charge thee, marry her not." "My father," exclaimed the youth, "what hast thou said? My obligations to her are greater than they are to you; for when imprisoned and fettered by my enemy, I implored you to ransom me; but you would not. Now, she not only released me from prison, but from deadly peril—and, therefore, I am resolved to marry her." The father answered, "Son, I tell thee that thou canst not confide in her, and consequently ought not to espouse her. She deceived her own father, when she liberated thee from prison; for this did her father lose the price of thy ransom. Therefore, I am of opinion that thou canst not confide in her, and consequently ought not to espouse her. Besides, there is another reason. It is true she liberated thee, but it was for the gratification of her passions, and in order to oblige thee to marry her. And, since an unworthy passion was the source of thy liberty, I think that she ought not to be thy wife." When the lady heard such reasons assigned, she answered, "To your first objection, that I deceived my own parent, I reply that it is not true. He deceives who takes away or diminishes a certain good. But my father is so rich that he needs not any addition. When, therefore, I had maturely weighed this matter, I procured the young man's freedom. And if my father had received a ransom for him, he had been but little richer; while you would have been utterly impoverished. Now, in acting thus, I have served you, who refused the ransom, and have done no injury to my parent. As for your last objection, that an unworthy passion urged me to do this, I assert that it is false. Feelings of such a nature arise either from great personal beauty, or from wealth, or honours; or finally, from a robust appearance. None of which qualities your son possessed. For imprisonment had destroyed his beauty; and he had not sufficient wealth even to effect his liberation; while much anxiety had worn away his strength, and left him emaciated and sickly. Therefore, compassion rather persuaded me to free him." When the father had heard this, he could object nothing more. So his son married the lady with very great pomp, and closed his life in peace.*

APPLICATION.

My beloved, the son captured by pirates is the whole human race, led by the sin of our first parent into the prison of the devil—that is, into his power. The father who

---

* The deliverance of the youth by the lady resembles the 236th Night of the Arabian Tales.—The *Gest* is mentioned by Warton as the *second* tale in his analysis; and two or three other variations occur. What edition he followed I know not. I have examined five. The sentiment conveyed by this tale (p. 9), that she who has deceived her father will deceive her husband, is thus expressed by Shakspeare:—

> "Look to her, Moor; have a quick eye to see;
> *She has deceived her father, and may thee.*"
> *Othello*, Act i. Sc. 3.

In an 18mo edition of the GESTA ROMANORUM, published at Leyden, 1555, there is prefixed to the fourth tale, by way of argument, the following remarkable passage: "Justitia nempe et misericordia Deorum maximè est: *ad quos non possumus expeditius et proprius accedere, quàm his ducibus.*" This is *literally* what Shakspeare makes Portia observe in the "*Merchant of Venice*":—

> "But Mercy is above this sceptered sway,
>   *   *   *   *   *
> *It is an attribute of God Himself;*
> *And earthly power doth then show likest God's,*
> *When mercy seasons justice.*"—Act iv. Sc. 1.

would not redeem him is the world, which aids not man's escape from the evil one, but rather loves to detain him in thraldom. The daughter who visited him in prison is the Divinity of Christ united to the soul; who sympathized with the human species—and who, after His passion, descended into hell and freed us from the chains of the devil. But the celestial Father had no occasion for wealth, because He is infinitely rich and good. Therefore Christ, moved with compassion, came down from heaven to visit us, and took upon Himself our form, and required no more than to be united in the closest bonds with man. So *Hosea* ii.: "I will marry her to me in faithfulness." But our father, the world, whom many obey, ever murmurs and objects to this. "If thou unitest thyself to God, thou shalt lose my inheritance"—that is, the inheritance of this world; because it is "impossible to serve God and mammon." *Matt.* vi.: "He who shall leave father, or mother, or wife, or country for my sake, he shall receive an hundredfold, and possess everlasting life." Which may Jesus Christ, the Son of the living God, vouchsafe to bestow upon us; who with the Father, and the Holy Ghost, liveth and reigneth for ever and ever. Amen.

TALE VI.

OF FOLLOWING REASON.

A CERTAIN emperor, no less tyrannical than powerful, espoused a very beautiful girl, the daughter of a king. After the ceremony was concluded, each solemnly vowed that the death of the one should be followed by the voluntary destruction of the other. It happened once that the emperor went into a far country, and continued there a long time. Being desirous to prove the fidelity of his wife, he directed a messenger to inform her that he was dead. When this intelligence was communicated, she remembered the oath which had been administered, and precipitated herself from a lofty mountain, with an intention to die. But she received little injury, and in a short space was restored to health. Then once again she desired to throw herself from the mountain, and so die. Her father understanding this, forbade obedience to the mandate and oath prescribed by her husband. Still, as she seemed anxious to comply with them, the father said, "Since you refuse assent to my request, depart at once from my presence." But she replied, " I will not do that; and I will prove, by good reasons, my right to remain. When an oath is sworn, ought it not to be faithfully maintained ? I have sworn to my husband that I would destroy myself, if I survived him : therefore, it is no crime to fulfil my vow, and I ought not to be driven from your palace. Moreover, no one should be punished for that which is commendable. Now, since man and woman are one flesh, according to the laws of God, it is commendable for a wife to perish with her husband. On which account, there was a law in India, that a wife after the decease of her lord should burn herself, as evidence of her grief and love ; or else be deposited alive in his sepulchre. And therefore I think that I do no wrong to kill myself for the love of my husband." The father answered, " When you said that you were bound by an oath to act thus, you should have remembered that such an obligation is not binding, because its end is deprivation of life. An oath should always be consistent with reason ; and therefore yours being unreasonable is of no force. As for the other argument, that it is praiseworthy in a wife to die with her husband, it avails you not. For although they are one in the body, united by carnal affections, yet they are two persons in soul, and are really and substantially different. Therefore, neither does this afford any resource." When the lady heard these words, she could argue no further, but complied with the request of her parent. She refrained from soliciting destruction ; but though apprized of her husband's existence soon after, she would not return to him.

APPLICATION.

My beloved, the emperor is the devil. The girl is the soul created in the likeness of God, but by sin espoused to the evil one. Wherefore, in the commission of sin, there is a covenant established, namely, that if a man die in sin and in remote parts—that is, in hell—it is previously agreed upon by his own pride, that the sinning soul should cast itself from a high mountain—that is, from heaven down to hell : and thus it was, before the advent of our Saviour. But He, by His passion, reinstated it in health. Notwithstanding, the soul still desires to precipitate itself, as often as it acts against the divine command. But God, who is our Father, would not willingly that we should fall, but had rather, by contrition and confession, receive us wholly to Himself, and bind us so firmly to Him, that with Him we might enjoy everlasting life.

TALE VII.

OF THE ENVY OF BAD MEN TOWARDS THE GOOD.

WHEN Diocletian was emperor, there was a certain noble soldier who had two sons, whom he entirely and truly loved. The younger of them married a harlot, without the knowledge of his father, and the infamy of this proceeding overwhelmed him with the greatest grief. He sternly banished him from his presence, and left him to the rebukes of conscience, and to the agonies of approaching want. A beautiful child was born to him, and he was reduced to great distress. In this situation he despatched a messenger to his parent, to supplicate relief ; and when his wretchedness was made known, it moved him to compassion, and he forgave him all. After their reconciliation, the son entrusted to his father's protection the child that the harlot bore him, and it was taken to his house and educated as his own. But when the elder brother heard what had happened, he was exceedingly wroth, and said to his father, " Thou art mad, and I will prove it by satisfactory reasons. He is mad who fosters and adopts a son by whom he has been grievously wronged. Now, my brother, whose son that child is, did you great injury when he espoused a harlot contrary to your will. Therefore, I am persuaded that you are mad—for you both protect the

child, and are at peace with him." Here the father answered, " Son, I am reconciled to thy brother, in consequence of his own contrition, and the urgent entreaties of
his friends.   Therefore, it becomes me to love my recovered
son more than you; because you have often offended me,
but never sought a reconciliation : and since you have not
humbly acknowledged your transgressions, you are more
ungrateful than your brother has been, whom you would
have me banish from my house. You ought rather to
rejoice that he is reconciled to me. But because you have
exhibited so much ingratitude, you shall not receive the
inheritance designed for you. It shall be given to your
brother." And so it was done.*

APPLICATION.

My beloved, by this father we are to understand
our heavenly Father; by the two sons, the angelic and
human nature. The human nature was united with a
harlot—that is, with iniquity, when it ate the fatal apple,
contrary to the divine injunction. Wherefore it was
banished by the heavenly Father. The son of the harlot
is mankind, which had perished in its perverseness but for
the paternal regard. And it is described as sickly, because
being the fruit of sin, it is placed in a valley of tears.
As in *Gen.* iii.; " By the sweat of thy brow shalt thou
eat bread." But he, by the passion of Christ, is reconciled
to God the Father, and fully established by the good
offices and prayers of holy men, who daily pour forth their
petitions to Heaven, for all the world. So the Psalmist :
" They ask that which they desire." But the other
brother, namely, the devil (who is the father of ingratitude), continually attacks us, and murmurs at our reconciliation; alleging that we ought not to obtain our
heavenly inheritance because of original sin. But doubtless, if we live a holy and pure life in this world, his
allegations will nothing avail; nay, we shall obtain his
portion—that is, the place which he has lost in heaven.

* " This story, but with a difference of circumstance, ends like the
beautiful apologue of the Prodigal Son."—WARTON.

TALE VIII.

OF FALSE ALLEGATIONS.

WHEN the Emperor Leo reigned, his chief pleasure consisted in seeing beautiful women. Wherefore he caused three images to be made, to which he dedicated a stately temple, and commanded all his subjects to worship them. The first image stretched out its hand over the people, and upon one of its fingers was placed a golden ring bearing the following device: "*My finger is generous; behold this ring.*" The second image had a golden beard, and on its brow was written, "*I have a beard: if any one be beardless, let him come to me, and I will give him one.*" The third image had a golden cloak and purple tunic, and on its breast appeared these words, in large golden characters, "*I fear no one.*" These three images were fabricated of stone. Now, when they had been erected according to the command of the emperor, he ordained that whosoever conveyed away either the ring, or golden beard, or cloak, should be doomed to the most disgraceful death. It so chanced that a certain fellow entering the temple, perceived the ring upon the finger of the first image, which he immediately drew off. He then went to the second, and took away the golden beard. Last of all, he came to the third image, and when he had removed the cloak he departed from the temple. The people, seeing their images despoiled, presently communicated the robbery to the emperor. The transgressor was summoned before him, and charged with pilfering from the images, contrary to the edict. But he replied, "My Lord, suffer me to speak. When I entered the temple, the first image extended towards me its finger with the golden ring—as if it had said, 'Here, take the ring.' Yet, not merely because the finger was held forth to me, would I have received it; but, by and by, I read the superscription, which said, 'My finger is *generous*—take the ring.' At once I understood that it was the statue's pleasure to bestow it upon me, and therefore I took it. Afterwards, I approached the second image with the golden beard;

and I communed with my own heart, and said, 'The author of this statue never had such a beard, for I have seen him repeatedly; and the creature ought, beyond question, to be inferior to the Creator. Therefore, it is fitting and necessary to take away the beard.' But although he offered not the smallest opposition, yet I was unwilling to carry it off, until I distinctly perceived, 'I have a beard : if any one be beardless, let him come to me, and I will give him one.' I am beardless, as your Majesty may see, and therefore, for two especial reasons, took away the beard. The first was, that he should look more like his author, and not grow too proud of his golden beard. Secondly, that by these means I might protect my own bald pate. Again, I came to the third image, which bore a golden cloak. I took away the cloak, because, being of metal, in the winter time it is extremely cold; and the image itself is made of stone. Now, stone is naturally cold; and if it had retained the golden cloak it would have been adding cold to cold, which were a bad thing for the image. Also, if it had possessed this cloak in summer, it would have proved too heavy and warm for the season. However, I should not have borne it away even for these causes, if there had not been written upon the breast, 'I fear nobody.' For I discovered in that vaunt such intolerable arrogance, that I took away the cloak, merely to humble it." "Fair sir," replied the emperor, " does not the law say expressly that the images shall not be robbed, nor the ornaments upon them molested on any pretence? You have impudently taken away that which did not belong to you, and therefore I determine that you be instantly suspended on a gallows." And so it was done. (1)

APPLICATION.

My beloved, that emperor is our Lord Jesus Christ. The three images are three sorts of men, in whom God takes pleasure—as it is written, "Thy delight is in the sons of men." If we live piously and uprightly, God will remain with us. By the first image with extended hand, we may conceive the poor and simple of this world; who, if they have business in the halls of princes and noblemen, will prevail but little unless the hand is put forth to present a gift. Gifts blind the eyes of a judge. But if it should be asked of such a one, or of his servants, " Why fleecest thou the poor?" it is instantly replied, " Can I not receive with a good conscience what is voluntarily presented? If I took not the offering, people would say I was besotted; and therefore, to curb their tongues, I take it." By the second image we are to understand the rich of the world, who, by the grace of God, are exalted to great wealth. So the Psalmist: " Thou raisest the poor out of the mire, and they are accused before their rivals." Some wretched man hath a golden beard—that is, greater riches than his father had; and straightway we oppress him, either with a legal pretext or without. A just man is overborne and robbed; for they say, " We are bald," that is, we are poor; and it is fitting that he divide his riches with us: nay, he is often murdered for his property. " Covetousness," says St. Paul to Timothy, " is the root of all evil." By the third image with the golden cloak, we are to understand men raised to great dignities. Such are the prelates and princes of the earth, who are appointed to preserve the law, to cultivate virtue, and to root out vice. Wherefore evil-doers, who refuse to submit to necessary discipline, lift themselves up, and conspire against their ecclesiastical governors and superiors, saying, " We will not have him to reign over us."—*St. Luke.* The Jews seeing Christ performing miracles, and proving that they had sinned against the law, immediately contrive his death. But these conspirators, and the like to them, shall die the death. Therefore, let us diligently study to correct what is amiss in this life present, that we may, &c.

[From hence the morals have been abridged, and merely the chief heads of them given.]

TALE IX.

OF DEPRAVITY CONQUERED BY MILDNESS.

ALEXANDER was a renowned and prudent emperor. He married the daughter of the King of Syria, and had by her a beautiful son. The boy grew, but coming to man's estate, he conspired against his father, and continually sought his death. This conduct surprised the emperor, and conversing with the empress, he said, " Fair wife, tell me, I pray thee, without reserve, hast thou ever forsaken me for another ? "—" My Lord," answered his wife, " what is the purport of your question ? "—" Your son," said he, " seeks my life. It amazes me; and if he were mine he could not do it."—" Heaven can witness," returned the lady, " that I am innocent. He is truly your son, but to what end he pursues your destruction, I cannot surmise." The emperor, satisfied on this point, spoke to his son with the utmost mildness. " My dear son," said he, " I am your father; by my means you came into the world, and will succeed me on the throne. Why then do you desire my death? I have ever loved and cared for you, and my possessions are not less yours than mine. Cease, I conjure you, from such an iniquitous pursuit ; and curtail not the few brief hours that are assigned me." Nevertheless the son disregarded his father's entreaties, and every succeeding day discovered fresh proofs of a hard and depraved heart ; sometimes endeavouring to slay him in public, and sometimes resorting to secret assassination. When the father became aware of this, he retired into a very secluded apartment, and took with him his son. Presenting a naked sword, he said, " Take this weapon, and now hesitate not to put a speedy end to the existence of thy parent ; for it will be esteemed less shameful to be slain by my own son, quietly and in secret, than to be exposed to the uproar and observation of the people." The son, struck with the enormity of what he purposed, cast aside the extended sword, and falling upon his knees, wept aloud. " Oh, my father," said he, " I have done thee wrong—open and notorious wrong—and am no more worthy to be called thy son. Yet forgive me, dearest father, and once again restore me to thy forfeited love. From henceforth I will be indeed thy son, and in all things execute thy pleasure." When the overjoyed parent heard this, he fell upon his neck, and kissed him. "Oh, my beloved son, be faithful and affectionate, and thou shalt find a fond and indulgent father." He then clothed him in gorgeous apparel, and brought him to the banqueting-chamber, where he was sumptuously feasted with all the nobles of his empire. The emperor lived a short time after this, and finished his career in peace.

APPLICATION.

My beloved, the emperor is our Lord Jesus Christ, the Son of God. He who seeks the life of his father is any bad Christian who is made a legitimate child of God, by the virtues of baptism. The mother of the boy is the holy Church, through which our baptismal vows are received; and through which also the perverse sinner, removed from God by manifold offences, seeks the death of Christ, who is Himself the father, as appears from *Deut.* xxxii. : "Is He not thy father," &c. Therefore the Christian attempts to destroy Christ, as often as he departs from the law of God. Again, Christ leads us into the desert of this world, and there, not only offers His breast to the drawn sword—but has actually died for our sins. Wherefore, remembering His love, and the sources of our own security, we ought to resist sin, and serve Him faithfully. The father delivered to his son the instrument of death : so God gives to you a sword—that is, free will, either to receive His grace and love, or to reject them. Do thou therefore act as the son did : cast from thee the sword of iniquity and malice.

TALE X.

OF THE MANAGEMENT OF THE SOUL.

THE Emperor Vespasian lived a long time without children; but at last, by the counsel of certain wise men, he espoused a beautiful girl, brought to him from a distant country. He afterwards travelled with her into foreign lands, and there became father of a son. In the course of time, he wished to revisit his own kingdom; but his wife obstinately refused to comply, and said, "If you leave me, I will kill myself." The emperor, therefore, in this dilemma, constructed two rings; and upon the jewels with which they were richly ornamented, he sculptured images possessing very singular virtues. One bore an effigy of Memory; and the other an effigy of Oblivion. They were placed upon the apex of each ring; and that which represented oblivion he bestowed upon his wife. The other he retained himself; and as their love had been, such was the power of the rings. The wife presently forgot her husband, and the husband cared but little for the memory of his wife. Seeing, therefore, that his object was achieved, he departed joyfully to his own dominions, and never afterwards returned to the lady. So he ended his days in peace.

APPLICATION.

My beloved, by the emperor understand the human soul, which ought to return·to its own country—that is, to heaven, by which path alone it can arrive at security. Therefore the Psalmist says—"Save me, O God," &c. The wife is our body, which holds the soul in sensual delights, that encumber and bar its passage to that eternal life, where the empire and hope of the soul is. And why does it so impede it? Because the flesh rebels against the spirit, and the spirit wars against the flesh. Do ye, therefore, as the emperor did; make two rings—the rings of memory and forgetfulness, which are prayer and fasting; for both are effective. In most countries, a ring upon the woman's finger is a token of her marriage; and when a man resigns himself to prayer and fasting, it is evidence of his being the bride of Christ. Prayer is the ring of memory, for the apostle enjoins us to "pray without ceasing." Man, therefore, makes use of periodical prayer, that God may remember his desires; while angels themselves present and aid the petition, as we read in the Book of Tobit. Fasting may be called the ring of oblivion, because it withdraws from and forgets the enticements of the flesh, that there may be no obstruction in its progress to God. Let us then study to preserve these rings and merit everlasting life.

TALE XI.

OF THE POISON OF SIN.

ALEXANDER was a prince of great power, and a disciple of Aristotle, who instructed him in every branch of learning. The Queen of the North having heard of his proficiency, nourished her daughter from the cradle upon a certain kind of deadly poison; and when she grew up, she was considered so beautiful, that the sight of her alone affected many with madness. The queen sent her to Alexander to espouse. He had no sooner beheld her, than he became violently enamoured, and with much eagerness desired to possess her; but Aristotle observing his weakness, said— "Do not touch her, for if you do, you will certainly perish. She has been nurtured upon the most deleterious food, which I will prove to you immediately. Here is a malefactor, who is already condemned to death. He shall be united to her, and you will soon see the truth of what I advance." Accordingly the culprit was brought without delay to the girl; and scarcely had he touched her lips, before his whole frame was impregnated with poison, and he expired. Alexander, glad at his escape from such imminent destruction, bestowed all thanks on his instructor, and returned the girl to her mother.*

* "This story is founded on the twenty-eighth chapter of Aristotle's SECRETUM SECRETORUM: in which a queen of India is

My beloved, any good Christian strong and powerful in
virtues communicated at his baptism, may be called Alexander.   He is strong and powerful as long as he preserves
his purity from the contamination of the devil, the world,
and the flesh.   The Queen of the North is a superfluity of
the things of life, which sometimes destroys the spirit, and
generally the body.   The envenomed beauty is Luxury
and Gluttony, which feed men with delicacies, that are
poison to the soul.   Aristotle is thy conscience, or reason,
which reproves and opposes the union that would undo
the soul.   The malefactor is a perverse man, disobedient
to his God, and more diligent in pursuing his own carnal
delights than the divine commands.   He enfolds his sins
in a close embrace, by whose deadly touch he is spiritually
destroyed.   So the Book of Wisdom: "He who touches
pitch shall be defiled by it."   Let us then study to live
honestly and uprightly, in order that we may attain to
everlasting life.

TALE XII.

OF BAD EXAMPLE.

IN the reign of Otho there was a certain slippery priest,
who created much disturbance among his parishioners,
and many were extremely scandalized.   One of them, in
particular, always absented himself from Mass, when it
fell to the priest's turn to celebrate it.   Now, it happened on
a festival day, during the time of Mass, that as this person

said to have treacherously sent to Alexander, among other costly
presents, the pretended testimonies of her friendship, a girl of exquisite beauty, who having been fed with serpents from her infancy,
partook of their nature.   If I recollect right, in Pliny there are
accounts of nations whose natural food was poison.   Mithridates,
king of Pontus, the land of venomous herbs, and the country of the
sorceress Medea, was supposed to eat poison.   Sir John Mandeville's
Travels, I believe, will afford other instances."—WARTON.

[Mr. O. Wendell Holmes has made use of this weird notion in his
novel, "Elsie Venner."—ED.]

was walking alone through a meadow, a sudden thirst
came upon him; insomuch that he was persuaded, unless
present relief could be obtained, he should die. In this
extremity, continuing his walk, he discovered a rivulet of
the purest water, of which he copiously drank. But the
more he drank, the more violent became his thirst. Surprised at so unusual an occurrence, he said to himself, "I
will find out the source of this rivulet, and there satisfy
my thirst." As he proceeded, an old man of majestic
appearance met him, and said, "My friend, where are you
going?" The other answered, "I am oppressed by an
excessive drought, surpassing even belief. I discovered a
little stream of water, and drank of it plentifully; but the
more I drank, the more I thirsted. So I am endeavouring
to find its source, that I may drink there, and, if it be
possible, deliver myself from the torment." The old man
pointed with his finger. "There," said he, "is the spring-
head of the rivulet. But tell me, mine honest friend, why
are you not at church, and with other good Christians
hearing Mass?" The man answered, "Truly, master, our
priest leads such an execrable life, that I think it utterly
impossible he should celebrate it so as to please God." To
which the old man returned, "Suppose what you say is
true. Observe this fountain, from which so much excellent water issues, and from which you have lately
drunk." He looked in the direction pointed out, and
beheld a putrid dog with its mouth wide open, and its
teeth black and decayed, through which the whole fountain gushed in a surprising manner. The man regarded
the stream with great terror and confusion of mind,
ardently desirous of quenching his thirst, but apprehensive
of poison from the fetid and loathsome carcase, with
which, to all appearance, the water was imbued. "Be
not afraid," said the old man, regarding his repugnance,
"because thou hast already drank of the rivulet; drink
again, it will not harm thee." Encouraged by these
assurances, and impelled by the intensity of his thirst,
he partook of it once more, and instantly recovered from
the drought. "Oh, master!" cried he, "never man drank
of such delicious water." The old man answered, "See
now; as this water, gushing through the mouth of a

putrid dog, is neither polluted nor loses aught of its
natural taste or colour, so is the celebration of Mass by a
worthless minister. And therefore, though the vices of
such men may displease and disgust, yet should you not
forsake the duties of which they are the appointed organ."
Saying these words, the old man disappeared; and what
the other had seen he communicated to his neighbours,
and ever after punctually attended Mass. He brought
this unstable and transitory life to a good end, and passed
from that which is corruptible to inherit incorruption.
Which may our Lord Jesus Christ, the Son of Mary,
grant to all.

APPLICATION.

My beloved, the emperor is God, in whose kingdom,
that is, in the world, there is an evil priest; namely, every
perverse Christian. For as the priest provides for the
spiritual welfare of his parishioners, so the Christian is
required to watch over and preserve the spiritual gifts
communicated in baptism. The bad priest, through the
influence of a bad example, causes many to separate from
the community; and, therefore, St. Gregory well says
that "as often as he does an ill action, he loses a soul."
In like manner, the bad Christian occasions the condemna-
tion of multitudes by the attraction of wicked examples
and enticing words. If any of you to whom I now speak
have been so deluded, act like the parishioner in our story.
Walk across the meadows, that is, through the world,
until you find one whom your soul esteems and loves—to
wit, that old man, who is Christ, revealed by actions of
benevolence and mercy. But, in the first place, drink of
the rivulet, although it should not immediately extinguish
your thirst. That rivulet is baptism, which alone is able
to quench the drought occasioned by original sin. Yet,
should the evil nature of that origin prevail, and you fall
again into error, then seek out the fountain and there
drink. For that fountain is our Lord Jesus Christ, as He
witnesses of Himself: "I am a fountain of living water,
springing up into eternal life."—*John* iv. The streams or
veins of that fountain are the words of Scripture, which

too frequently issue from the mouth of a putrid dog; that is, of an evil preacher. If it should be asked why the spring of pure water is made to flow through the rank jaws of a dog, rather than through those of any other animal, it is answered, that Scripture more usually compares it with a priest than with anything else; and as in a dog there are four excellent qualities, described in the following couplet :—

> " In cane bis bina sunt; et lingua medicina,
> Naris odoratus, amor integer, atque latratus."

[In a dog there are four things: a medicinal tongue; * a distinguishing nose; an unshaken love, and unremitting watchfulness.]

So priests, who would be useful in their station, ought diligently to cultivate these four properties. *First*, that their tongue possess the power of a physician in healing the sick in heart, and probing the wounds of sin; being careful, at the same time, that too rough a treatment does not exacerbate rather than cure: for it is the nature of dogs to *lick* the body's wounds. *Secondly*, as a dog, by keenness of scent, distinguishes a fox from a hare, so a priest, by the quickness of his perception in auricular disclosures, should discover what portion of them appertains to the cunning of the fox—that is, to heretical and sophistical perverseness; what to internal struggles and timorous apprehensions, arising from the detestation of evil or hopelessness of pardon; and what to the unbroken ferocity of the wolf or lion, originating in a haughty contempt of consequences; with other gradations of a like character. *Thirdly*, as the dog is of all animals the most faithful, and ready in defence of his master or his family, so priests also should show themselves staunch advocates for the Catholic Faith; and zealous for the everlasting salvation, not of their parishioners alone, but of every denomination of true Christians, according to the words of our Lord, *John* x. : " A good shepherd lays down his life for his sheep." Also, *John* i. : " Christ laid down His life

* Lovel, in his *Panzoologico-mineralogia*, has enumerated all the rare properties which ancient medicine attributed to dogs; but what particular virtue the *tongue* was held to possess, does not appear. Lovel's work must have been one of immense labour; yet it is very useless.

for us." And we, in humble imitation of our divine Master, ought to lay down our lives for our brethren. *Fourthly*, as a dog by barking betrays the approach of thieves, and permits not the property of his master to be invaded, so the faithful priest is the watch-dog of the great King: one who by his bark, that is, his preaching and his watchfulness, ceases not to defeat the schemes and machinations of the devil against his Lord's treasury, that is, the soul of his neighbour, which our Lord Jesus Christ has redeemed with the mighty ransom of His precious blood.

TALE XIII.

OF INORDINATE LOVE.

A CERTAIN emperor was strongly attached to a beautiful wife. In the first year of their marriage, she was delivered of a son, upon whom she doated with extravagant fondness. When the child had completed its third year, the king died; for whose death great lamentation was made through the whole kingdom. The queen bewailed him bitterly; and, after his remains were deposited in the royal sepulchre, took up her residence in another part of the country, accompanied by her son. This child became the object of an affection so violent, that no consideration could induce her to leave him; and they invariably occupied the same bed, even till the boy had attained his eighteenth year. Now, when the devil perceived the irregular attachment of the mother, and the filial return exhibited by the son, he insinuated black and unnatural thoughts into their minds; and from time to time repeating his detestable solicitations, finally overthrew them. The queen became pregnant; and the unhappy son, filled with the deepest horror, and writhing beneath the most intolerable agony, quitted the kingdom, and never was heard of again. In due time the queen was delivered of a lovely female, whom her eyes no sooner beheld, than—(mark, ye who dream that one dereliction from virtue may be tried with impunity—mark!) desperate at the remembrance of her fearful crime, and apprehensive of detection, she snatched up a knife that lay beside her, and plunged it into the infant's breast. Not content with this exhibition of maternal inhumanity, she cut it directly across the throat, from whence the blood rapidly gushed forth, and falling upon the palm of her left hand, dis- tinctly impressed four circular lines, which no human power could erase. Terrified, not less at the singular consequence of her guilt than at the guilt itself, she carefully concealed this awful and mysterious evidence, and dedicated herself for life to the service of the blessed Virgin. Yet, though penitent for what she had done, and regularly every fifteenth morning duly confessed, she scrupulously avoided any disclosure relating to that horrid transaction. She distributed alms with the most unbounded liberality; and the people, experiencing her kindness and benevolence, evinced towards her the greatest respect and love.

It happened on a certain night, as her confessor knelt at his devotions, repeating five times aloud the " Ave Maria," that the blessed Virgin herself appeared to him, and said, " I am the Virgin Mary, and have an important communication to make to thee." The confessor, full of joy, answered, " Oh, dear Lady, wherein can thy servant please thee ? " She replied, " The queen of this kingdom will confess herself to you; but there is one sin she has committed, which shame and horror will not permit her to disclose. On the morrow she will come to you; tell her from me, that her alms and her prayers have been accepted in the sight of my Son; I command her, there- fore, to confess that crime which she secretly committed in her chamber—for, alas! she slew her daughter. I have entreated for her, and her sin is forgiven, if she will confess it. But if she yield no attention to your words, bid her lay aside the cover upon her left hand; and on her palm you will read the crime she refuses to acknow- ledge. If she deny this also, take it off by force." When she had thus spoken, the blessed Virgin disappeared. In the morning, the queen with great humility was shrieved of all her sins—that one excepted. After she had uttered as much as she chose, the confessor said, "Madam, and dear daughter, people are very inquisitive to know for what strange reason you constantly wear that cover upon your left hand. Let me see it, I beseech you, that I may ascertain why it is concealed, and whether the concealment be pleasing to God." The queen answered, "Sir, my hand is diseased, and therefore I cannot show it." Hearing this, the confessor caught hold of her arm, and notwithstanding her resistance, drew off the cover. "Lady," said he, "fear not; the blessed Virgin Mary loves you; and it is she who hath commanded me to do this." When the hand was uncovered, there appeared four circles of blood. In the first circle there were four letters in the form of a C; in the second, four D's; in the third, four M's; and in the fourth, four R's. Upon the outward edge of the circles, in the manner of a seal, a blood-coloured writing was distinguishable, containing the legend beneath. First, of the letter C,—which was interpreted, "*Casu cecidisti carne cæcata*," [Blinded by the flesh thou hast fallen.] The letter D, "*Dæmoni dedisti dona donata*," [The gifts that were bestowed on thee thou hast given to the devil.] The letter M, "*Monstrat manifestè manus maculata*," [The stain upon thy hand discovers thee.] The letter R, "*Recedet rubigo, regina rogata*," [When the queen is interrogated the red marks will vanish.] The lady beholding this, fell at the confessor's feet, and with many tears meekly related her dreadful offences. Then being entirely and truly penitent, she was absolved; and a very few days afterwards, slept in the Lord. Her death was long lamented by the whole state.*

APPLICATION.

My beloved, the emperor is Jesus Christ, who married a beautiful girl, that is, our human nature, when He became incarnate. But first He was betrothed to her, when the Father, speaking to the Son and Holy Ghost, said—"Let us make man in our own image, after our

* "This story is in the SPECULUM HISTORIALE of Vincent of Beauvais, who wrote about the year 1250."—WARTON.

likeness." Our Lord had a fair child, that is to say, the *soul* made free from all spot by His Passion, and by virtue of baptism. That soul is slain in us by sin. Do you ask how? I will tell you. By giving ourselves up to carnal delights, whose fruit is death. The blood on the hand is sin, which tenaciously clings to us: as it is said, "**My** soul is ever in my own hands"—that is, whether it does well or ill is as openly apparent as if it were placed in the hands for the inspection and sentence of the Supreme Judge.

[There are two moralizations to this story; but there is nothing in either worth examination.]

TALE XIV.

OF HONOURING PARENTS.

IN the reign of the Emperor Dorotheus a decree was passed that children should support their parents. There was, at that time, in the kingdom, a certain soldier, who had espoused a very fair and virtuous woman, by whom he had a son. It happened that the soldier went upon a journey, was made prisoner, and very rigidly confined. Immediately he wrote to his wife and son for ransom. The intelligence communicated great uneasiness to the former, who wept so bitterly that she became blind. Whereupon the son said to his mother, "I will hasten to my father, and release him from prison." The mother answered, "Thou shalt not go; for thou art my only son —even the half of my soul,* and it may happen to thee as it has done to him. Hadst thou rather ransom thy absent parent than protect her who is with thee, and presses thee to her affectionate arms? Is not the possession of one thing better than the expectation of two?† Thou art

---

* "Animæ dimidium meæ." This phrase is met with frequently in these volumes, and would almost lead one to suspect that the Author was acquainted with Horace (Carm. i. 3).

[See also Carm. ii. 17, 5. Pythagoras is said to have spoken of a friend of his as ἥμισυ τῆς ψυχῆς.—ED.]

† The Latin text is, "Quotiens ita est quòd aliquid est æquale duobus ei qui est præsens; magis est adhærendum." Literally, "How

my son as well as thy father's; and, I am present, while he is absent. I conclude, therefore, that you ought by no means to forsake me though to redeem your father." The son very properly answered, "Although I am thy son, yet he is my father. He is abroad and surrounded by the merciless; but thou art at home, protected and cherished by loving friends. He is a captive, but thou art free—blind, indeed; but he perhaps sees not the light of heaven, and pours forth unheeded groans in the gloom of a loathsome dungeon oppressed with chains, with wounds, and misery. Therefore it is my determination to go to him and redeem him." The son did so; and every one applauded and honoured him for the indefatigable industry with which he achieved his father's liberation.

APPLICATION.

My beloved, the emperor is our heavenly Father, who imposes upon sons the duty of maintaining and obeying their parents. But who is our father and mother? Christ is our father, as we read in *Deut.* 32. His affection for us partakes more of this than of the maternal character. You know that when the son transgresses, the father corrects him somewhat harshly, even with stripes and blows; while the doating mother soothes and coaxes her favourite into humour. Christ permits us to be scourged, because of our many failings; on the contrary, our mother, the world, promises us infinite pleasures and lascivious enjoyments. Christ forsakes us, and goes into a far country, as it is written in the Psalms, "I am made a stranger by my brethren." Christ is still bound and in prison; not indeed by Himself, but by those who are the members of His Church; for so says the apostle to the Hebrews. "Whosoever lives in any mortal sin is cast into the prison of

often does it happen that one thing is valued as much as two by him who is present: [or, by him who has it in possession:] It is therefore to be adhered to the most." The sense answers to the English proverb, "A bird in the hand is worth two in the bush."

[I have examined several of the printed copies in the British Museum, in hopes of finding *cui* in some one of them, as a variant for *qui* in this passage, but without success. *Cui* could be translated with much less difficulty than *qui*, which is awkward in the extreme.—Ed.]

the devil;" but our Father wills that we labour for his redemption. *Luke* 9 : " Let the dead bury their dead," said our blessed Lord; "but go thou, and preach the kingdom of God,"—and this is to redeem Christ. For whosoever powerfully preaches the word of God, advantages his brother, and in him redeems Christ. *Matt.* 25 : " That which you have done to the least of these my followers, ye have also done unto me." But the mother, that is, the world, will not permit a man to follow Christ into exile and poverty, but detains him with diverse arguments. " I cannot," she says, " endure a life of abstinence and privation which I must necessarily submit to, if you repent and turn after Christ." Thus it is with whatsoever she proposes to man's acceptance : but do not comply with her wishes. She is blind indeed, for she exclaims, " Let us enjoy the good things of life, and speedily use the universe like as in youth ;" but, my beloved, if you are good and grateful sons, thus answer your worldly minded mother : " My father is the source of my being—that is, of my soul; and all things which I possess are his free gift." Therefore, I advise you not to desire length of years, which may approach in suffering, poverty, and blindness ; for then the world will flee you, how much soever you cling to it. No longer than you can be serviceable will you be valued.* Remember this, and study to amend your lives with all diligence ; that so you may come eventually to everlasting life. To which may God lead us, who lives, &c.

* The sentiment here expressed, implies a greater knowledge of the world than we should have looked for in an ascetic; but we frequently meet with a shrewd reflection, when least prepared for it —as the forest-ranger finds the "cowslip, violet, and the primrose pale," ornamenting the wildest and most sequestered nooks. Old Burton has a passage so similar, both in thought and expression, that I cannot forbear affixing it at foot : " Our estate and *bene esse* ebbs and flows with our commodity ; and as we are endowed or enriched, so we are beloved or esteemed : it lasts no longer than our wealth ; when that is gone, and the object removed, farewell friendship : as long as bounty, good cheer, and rewards were to be hoped, friends enough ; they were tied to thee by the teeth, and would follow thee as crows do a carcase : but when thy goods are gone and spent, the lamp of their love is out; and thou shalt be contemned, scorned, hated, injured."—*Anatomy of Melancholy*, vol. ii. p. 169.

TALE XV.

OF THE LIFE OF ALEXIUS, SON OF THE SENATOR EUFEMIAN.*

In the reign of one of the Roman emperors † lived a
youth, named Alexius, the son of Eufemian, a noble
Roman, at that time the chief ornament of the emperor's
court. He was attended by a band of three thousand
youths, girded with golden zones, and habited in silken
vestures. Eufemian was well known for his charity. He
daily maintained three tables, to which the widow and
the orphan were ever welcome. Their necessities were
often supplied by his own person; and at the ninth hour,
in company with other devout men, he sat down to dinner.
His wife, whose name was Abael, was as religious and
charitable as himself. But there is ever some bitterness
mixed up with the draught of human joy; and in the
midst of so much splendour, the want of a successor was
long a source of unavailing affliction. At length their
prayers were heard; Heaven, in its benevolence, blessed
them with a son, who was carefully instructed in all the
polite learning of the period. Arriving at the age of
manhood, he proved himself an acute and solid reasoner.
But reason is no barrier against love; he became attached
to a lady of the blood-royal, and was united to her. On
the very evening of their nuptials, when the clamour of
the feast had subsided, the pious youth commenced a
theological disquisition, and strove with much force and
earnestness to impress his bride with the fear and love of
God. When he had concluded, recommending her to preserve the same modesty of demeanour for which she had
always been distinguished, he consigned to her care his
gold ring, and the clasp ‡ of the sword-belt which usually
begirt him. "Take charge of these vanities," said he, "for

* It is proper to warn the reader that this tale is somewhat
periphrastically translated.
† Before the close of the tale we find it was in the reign of *two*.
‡ The Latin is *caput;* if it mean not this, I know not what it
means.

I abjure them ; and as long as it shall please God, keep them in remembrance of me : may the Almighty guide us." He then provided a sum of money, and going down to the sea-coast, secretly embarked in a ship bound for Laodicea. From thence he proceeded to Edessa,* a city of Syria. It was here that the image of our Lord Jesus Christ, wrought upon linen by supernatural hands, was preserved. On reaching this place he distributed whatever he had brought with him to the poor ; and putting on a worn and tattered garment, joined himself to a number of mendicants who sat in the porch of the temple dedicated to the Virgin Mary. He now constantly solicited alms ; but of all that he received, only the smallest portion was retained—an unbounded charity leading him to bestow the residue upon his more needy, or more covetous brethren.

The father of Alexius, however, was overwhelmed with sorrow at the inexplicable departure of his son ; and despatched his servants in pursuit of him to various parts of the world. These servants were very diligent in their inquiries ; and it chanced that certain of them came to the city of Edessa, and were recognized by Alexius ; but, pertinaciously concealing himself under the garb of want and misery, he passed unknown and unsuspected. The men, little aware who was experiencing their bounty, conferred large alms upon the paupers amongst whom he sojourned ; and his heart silently but gratefully acknowledged the benefaction : " I thank thee, O my God, that thou hast thought good to dispense thine alms by the hands of my own servants."

On this unsuccessful issue of their search, the messengers returned ; and when the intelligence of their failure reached his mother, she shut herself up in a remote chamber, and there gave utterance to her griefs. She slept upon the ground, with sackcloth only for a covering ; and solemnly vowed never to change her way of life until she recovered her lost son. The bride said to her father-in-law, " Until I hear tidings from my sweet husband I will remain with you." In the mean time, Alexius remained a

* It has also borne the names of Antiochia, Callirrhoë, Justinopolis —and *Rhoas*, said to have been built by Nimrod.

beggar in the porch of St. Mary's church for the space of seventeen years; until at length the image of the Virgin, which stood within the sacred edifice, said to the warden, "Cause that man of God to enter the sanctuary: for he is worthy of the kingdom of heaven, upon whom the spirit of God rests. His prayer ascends like incense to the throne of grace." But since the warden knew not of whom she spake, she said once more, "It is the man who sits at the entrance of the porch." The warden then went out quickly, and brought him into the church. Now, a circumstance of this extraordinary nature soon attracted remark; and the veneration with which they began to consider Alexius, approached almost to adoration. But he despised human glory, and entering a ship, set sail for Tarsus,* in Cilicia; but the providence of God so ordered, that a violent tempest carried them into a Roman port. Alexius, informed of this circumstance, said within himself, "I will hasten to my father's house; no one will know me, and it is better that I prove burthensome to him, than to another." As he proceeded, he met his father coming from the palace, surrounded by a large concourse of dependants, and immediately he shouted after him, "Servant of God, command a poor and desolate stranger to be conveyed into your house, and fed with the crumbs which fall from the table: so shall the Lord have pity on the wanderer you love." The father, out of love to his son, gave him into the charge of his followers, and appropriated to him a room in his house. He supplied him with meat from his own table, and appointed one who was accustomed to attend upon himself to serve him. But Alexius discontinued not the fervency of his devotion, and macerated his body with fasts and other austerities. And though the pampered servants derided him, and frequently emptied their household utensils on his head, his patience was always invincible. In this manner, for seventeen years under his own father's roof, his life was spent; but at last, perceiving by the spirit that his end approached, he procured ink and paper, and recorded the narrative of his life. Now, on the succeeding Sunday, after the solemnization of

---

* Tarsus is the capital of Cilicia, called by the Turks *Tersis*.

Mass, a voice echoing like thunder among the mountains, was heard through the city. It said, "Come unto me, all ye that labour, and I will give you rest." The people, terrified and awe-struck, fell upon their faces; when a second time the voice exclaimed, "Seek out a man of God to offer a prayer for the iniquity of Rome." Search was accordingly made, but no such man could be found; and the same voice waxing louder, and breathing as it were with the mingled blast of ten thousand thousand trumpets, again spoke, "Search in the house of Eufemian." Then the Emperors Arcadius and Honorius,* in conjunction with the Pontiff Innocent, proceeded towards the house to which the words of the Invisible directed them, and as they approached, the servant who attended upon Alexius came running to his master, and cried, "What think you, my Lord? Is not the mendicant stranger a man of exemplary life?" Eufemian, following up the suggestion, hastened to his chamber and found him extended upon the bed. Life had already passed, but his countenance retained a dazzling emanation of glory, like the countenance of a cherub in its own pure and beatified element. A paper occupied the right hand, which Eufemian would have borne away, but he was unable to extricate it from the grasp of the dead man. Leaving him, therefore, he returned to the emperors and the pontiff, and related what he had seen. They were astonished, and entering the apartment exclaimed, "Sinners though we are, we direct the helm of State, and provide for the well-being of the pastoral government. Give us, then, the paper, that we may know what it contains." Immediately the pontiff drew near, and put his hand upon the scroll which the deceased yet firmly grasped,—and he instantly relaxed his hold. It was read to the people; and when the father, Eufemian, heard its contents, he was paralyzed with grief. His strength deserted him, and he staggered and fell. Returning to himself a little, he rent his garment, plucked off the silver hairs of his head, and tore the venerable beard that swept his unhappy bosom. He even inflicted

---

* Are we to suppose that the *one* emperor had been succeeded by the *two*, since the commencement of the tale? The *Pontiff* Innocent seems *supererogatory*.

severe wounds upon himself, and falling upon the dead body, cried, "Alas! my son—my son! why hast thou laid up for me such deadly anguish? Why, for so many years, hast thou endured a bitterness which death itself cannot exceed? Wretched man that I am, he who should have been the guardian of my increasing infirmities, and the hope and the honour of my age, lies upon this miserable pallet, and speaks not. Oh! where is consolation to be found?" At this instant, like an enraged and wounded lioness breaking through the toils with which the hunters had encompassed her, the poor broken-hearted Abael, who had followed in the press, rushed desperately forward. Her garments were torn, and hanging about her in shreds; her hair dishevelled and flying; her eyes, wild and sparkling with the violence of emotion, were raised piteously to heaven. With that strength which frenzy sometimes supplies, she burst through the multitude who struggled to detain her; and approaching the body of her deceased child, said, or rather shrieked, in a heart-piercing accent, "I will pass; I will look upon my soul's only comfort. Did not this dried fountain suckle him? Have not these withered arms supported him? Hath he not slept—ah! not such sleep as this!—while I have watched him? Oh, my child!" Saying this, she threw her emaciated form upon the unconscious object of her solicitude; and again giving vent to her sorrows, exclaimed, "My own dear boy! light of the dimmed eyes that will soon close upon all, since thou art gone—why hast thou wrought this? why wast thou so inhuman? Thou didst see our tears—thou didst hearken to our groans—yet camest not forward to abate them! The slaves scoffed at and injured thee, but thou wert patient—too, too patient." Again and again the unfortunate mother prostrated herself upon the body; one while clasping him in her arms, at another, passing her hand reverently over his seraphic features. Now, she impressed a kiss upon the cold cheek and eyelids which her tears had moistened—and now bending over him, muttered something in a low and inaudible voice. Suddenly turning to the spectators, she said, "Weep, I pray ye, weep: ye who are regarding the agonies of a bereaved parent—have ye no tear to spare her? Abiding together for seventeen years, I knew him not! not him, my beloved and beautiful! They taunted him, and showered their unmanly blows upon his enduring head. Oh! who will again bring tears to my burning eyelids? Who—who will bear a part in my misery?"

The wife, whom Alexius had married and quitted on the evening of their nuptials, had been borne along by the congregating populace; but distress, until now, had held her silent.* As Abael ceased, she sprung forward and cried, " *Thou*, miserable! what then am I? Woe is me! to-day I am desolate; to-day I am all a widow! Now, there is none for whom I may look—none whom I may yet expect, although he come not. Where shall mine eye see gladness? The glass of my joy is broken †—shivered —shivered: my hope is extinct; and grief is all the portion of my widowhood." The multitude, penetrated by the various calamities of which they were witnesses, sympathized with the sufferers, and wept aloud.

By command of the pontiff and the two emperors, the body was deposited on a sumptuous bier, and brought into the middle of the city. Proclamation was made that the man of God was discovered, whom they had before sought in vain; and every one crowded to the bier. Now, if any infirm person touched the hallowed corpse, instantly he was strengthened. The blind received their sight; those who were possessed of devils were set free, and all the sick, be the disorder what it might, when they had once come in contact with the body, were made whole. These miraculous effects attracted the attention of the emperors and the pontiff. They determined to support the bier; and when they had done so, they were sanctified by the holiness which proceeded from the corse. They then scattered great abundance of gold and silver about the streets, that the people's natural cupidity might draw them aside, and the bier be carried forward to the church; but, strange to say, careless of all else, they pressed yet the more vehemently to touch it. At length, after great exertions, he was brought to the church of St. Boniface the

---

* The reader will not perhaps comprehend much occasion for the lady's sorrow.

† The monk is not often so poetical.

Martyr; and there, for the space of seven days, they tarried, praising God. They constructed a monument, glittering with gold and precious stones, and here, with the greatest reverence, placed the body of their Saint. Even from the very monument, so sweet an odour of sanctity broke forth, that it seemed to be entirely filled with the most fragrant aroma. He died about the year of our Lord CCCXXVIII. (2)

APPLICATION.

My beloved, Eufemian is any man of this world who hath a darling son, for whose advantage he labours day and night. He obtains a wife for him, that is, the vanity of the world, which he delights in as in a bride; nay, the world's vanities are often more to a man than the most virtuous wife—for life is sacrificed to the one, but, alas! how seldom to the other! The mother is the world itself, which greatly values her worldly-minded children. But the good son, like the blessed Alexius, is more studious to please God than his parents, remembering that it is said, " He who forsakes land or houses, or father, or mother, or wife, for my sake, shall receive an hundredfold, and possess eternal life." Alexius enters a ship, &c. The ship is our holy Church, by which we ought to enter, if we would obtain everlasting happiness. We must likewise lay aside gorgeous raiment—that is, the pomps of world; and associate with the poor—that is, the poor in spirit. The warden, who conducted him into the church, is a prudent confessor, whose duty it is to instruct the sinner, and lead him to a knowledge of the sacred Scriptures, by which the soul may pass unharmed to immortality. But sometimes tempests arise, and hurry a man to his own country, as it happened to Alexius. The temptations of the Evil One are symbolized by these tempests, which turn the voyager from his settled course, and prevent a life of goodness. If, therefore, you feel that you are subject to certain temptations, follow the example of the holy Alexius. Assume the dress of a pilgrim—that is, take the qualities necessary for the pilgrimage of this life, and disguise yourself from your carnal and worldly father, and become a man of God. But if it fall out that, when such a one aspires to a life of penitence, his parents lament, and decry their child's contempt of the world, and his voluntary choice of poverty for the love of God—still, it is safer to displease them than Heaven. Obtain, therefore, a fair piece of paper, which is a good conscience, on which inscribe your life ; and then, the High Priest with the emperors will draw near—that is, Christ with a multitude of angels—and convey your soul to the church of St. Boniface—that is, to eternal life, where all sanctity (or joy) abounds.

TALE XVI.

OF AN EXEMPLARY LIFE.

WE read of a certain Roman emperor, who built a magnificent palace. In digging the foundation, the workmen discovered a golden sarcophagus, ornamented with three circlets, on which were inscribed, " I have expended—I have given—I have kept—I have possessed—I do possess —I have lost—I am punished. What I formerly expended, I have ; what I gave away, I have." * The emperor, on seeing this, called to him the nobles of his empire, and said, " Go, and consider among ye what this superscription signifies." The noblemen replied, " Sire, the meaning is, that an emperor, who reigned before your majesty, wished to leave an example for the imitation of his suc-

---

* From hence, in all probability, Robert Byrkes derived the quaint epitaph, which is to be found, according to Gough, in Doncaster church, "new cut" upon his tomb in Roman capitals :—

> " Howe: Howe: who is heare:
> I, Robin of Doncaster, and Margaret my feare.
> *That I spent, that I had :*
> *That I gave, that I have :*
> That I left, that I lost.
> A.D. 1579.
> Quod Robertus Byrkes,
> who in this worlde
> did reygne thre
> score yeares and seaven,
> and yet lived not one."

cessors. He therefore wrote, 'I have expended,'—that is, my life; judging some, admonishing others, and governing to the best of my ability. 'I have given,'—that is, equipments to my soldiers, and supplies to the needy; to every one according to his desert. 'I have kept,'—that is, exact justice; showing mercy to the indigent, and yielding to the labourer his hire. 'I have possessed,'—that is, a generous and true heart; recompensing faithfully those who have done me service, and exhibiting at all times a kind and affable exterior. 'I do possess,'—that is, a hand to bestow, to protect, and to punish. 'I have lost,'—that is, my folly; I have lost the friendship of my foes, and the lascivious indulgences of the flesh. 'I am punished,'—that is, in hell; because I believed not in one eternal God, and put no faith in the redemption." *   *   *   *

The emperor hearing this, ever after regulated himself and his subjects with greater wisdom, and finished his life in peace.

APPLICATION.

My beloved, the emperor is any Christian, whose duty it is to raise a fair structure—that is, a heart prepared for the reception of God. If he dig deep, led onward by sincere contrition for past offences, he will find a golden sarcophagus—that is, a mind gilded with virtue and full of the divine grace. Three golden circlets will ornament it, and these are faith, hope, and charity. But what is written there? In the first place, "I have expended." Tell me, my beloved, what have you expended? The good Christian may reply, "Body and soul in the service of God." Whosoever of you thus expends his life, will secure the rewards of eternity. The second legend saith, "I have kept." Tell me, my beloved, what have you kept? The good Christian may answer, "A broken and

---

* The story seems here to be defective. "What I expended, I have; what I gave away, I have," receives no explanation. It may be filled up thus: "What I expended, I have," that is, having expended my property with judgment, I have received various benefits which remain to me in my posterity. "What I gave away, I have," that is, my donations have procured for me the thanks of the poor, and the blessing of heaven.

contrite spirit." The third inscription says, "I have given." Tell me, my beloved, what have you given? The good Christian may reply, "My whole heart to God." *Et sic de cæteris.*

TALE XVII.

OF A PERFECT LIFE.

An emperor decreed that whoever wished to serve him should obtain his wish, conditionally that he struck three times upon the palace gate, by which those within might understand that he wished to take service. Now, there was a certain poor man in the Roman empire, called Guido; who, on hearing the mode by which admission to the emperor's service was to be attained, thus thought—"I am a poor fellow, of low descent; it is better for me to serve and acquire wealth than to live in independence and starve." So he proceeded to the palace, and according to the edict, gave three blows upon the gate. The porter immediately opened it, and brought him in. He was introduced and made his obeisance to the emperor, who said, "What seek you, my friend?" Guido replied, "I wish to serve your majesty." "And for what office may you be fit?" returned the emperor. "I can serve, with tolerable expertness, in six capacities," said Guido. "First, I can act as body-guard to the prince; I can make his bed, dress his food, and wash his feet. Secondly, I can watch when others sleep, and sleep when others watch. Thirdly, I can drink good drink, and tell whether it be good or not. Fourthly, I can invite company to a festival for my master's honour. Fifthly, I can make a fire without the least smoke, which will warm all that approach it. Sixthly, I can teach people the way to the Holy Land, from whence they will return in excellent health." "By my faith," said the emperor, "these are fine matters, and will be useful on many occasions. Thou shalt stay with me, and serve me first as body-guard. In each department

thou shalt remain a full year." Guido expressed himself
content; and every night made ready the emperor's bed,
washed the linen, and occasionally changed it. Then he
lay down at the entrance of the chamber, armed at all
points. He likewise provided a dog, whose barking
might warn him of any danger. Once every week * he
washed the emperor's feet, and in all respects ministered so
faithfully and manfully, that not the least fault was
found with him. The emperor, therefore, was well
pleased; and at the expiration of the year made him
his seneschal, preparatory to the fulfilment of the second
office, which was to watch. Then Guido commenced his
operations; and during the whole summer collected a
variety of stores, and watched with great assiduity the
fittest opportunities. So that on the approach of winter,
when others, who had wasted the proper season, began to
labour and lay up, he took his ease, and thus completed
the service of the second year. When the emperor perceived his diligence and sagacity, he called to him his
chief butler, and said, "Friend, put into my cup some of
the best wine, mingled with must and vinegar,† and give
it to Guido to taste; for that is his third ministry, namely,
to taste good drink, and pronounce upon its qualities."
The butler did as he was commanded. When Guido had
tasted, he said, "It was good; it is good; it will be good.
That is, the must which is new will be good when it is
older; the old wine is good, at present; and the vinegar
was good formerly." When the emperor saw that he had
such a sound judgment of the beverage, he said, "Go now
through town and country, and invite all my friends to a
festival; for Christmas is at hand: herein shall consist

---

* [Semel omni ebdomada. Mr. Swan translates this "every
night," being apparently shocked at the scanty use made by the
emperor of soap and water.—ED.]

† *Must* is new wine. "Vinum igitur *mustum*, quomodo Cato
loquitur, idem est, quod *novum*, sive οἶνος μοσχίδιος. Nonius: *Mustum*,
non solum vinum, verùm novellum quicquid est, rectè dicitur."

Vinegar, Lat. acetum. "Optimum et laudatissimum acetum a
Romanis habebatur Ægyptum, quod acrimoniam quidem habebat
multam, sed mixtam tamen dulcedine aliqua, quæ asperitatem tollerit,
nec horrorem gustandi injiceret."—*Facciol*. The vinegar spoken of
in the text was probably sweetened.

your fourth ministry." Guido instantly set out; but instead of executing the orders he had received, he invited none but the emperor's enemies; thus, on Christmas Eve, his court was filled with them. When he observed this, he was exceedingly perturbed, and calling Guido to him, said, "How is this? Did you not say that you knew what men to ask to my table?" He answered, "Surely, my Lord." "And said I not," returned the emperor, very much provoked, "said I not that thou wert to invite my *friends?* How comes it that thou hast assembled only my enemies?" "My Lord," replied Guido, "suffer me to speak. At all seasons, and at all hours, your friends may visit you, and they are received with pleasure; but it is not so with your enemies. From which reflection I persuaded myself that a conciliating behaviour and a good dinner would convert your inveterate enemies into warm friends." This was really the case; before the feast concluded they all became cordial partisans, and as long as they lived remained faithful to their sovereign. The emperor, therefore, was much delighted, and cried, "Blessed be God, my enemies are now my friends! Execute thy fifth ministry, and make both for them and me a fire that shall burn without smoke." Guido replied, "It shall be done immediately," and he thus performed his promise. In the heat of summer, he dried a quantity of green wood in the sun: having done this, he made a fire with it that blazed and sparkled, but threw out no smoke; so that the emperor and his friends warmed themselves without inconvenience. He was now directed to perform his last service, and promised great honours and wealth on completing it also, equally to the satisfaction of his master. "My Lord," said Guido, "whoever would travel to the Holy Land must follow me to the seaside." Accordingly, proclamation being made, men, women, and children in immense crowds hastened after him. When they arrived at the appointed place, Guido said, "My friends, do you observe in the sea the same things which I do?" They answered, "We know not that." "Then," continued he, "do you perceive in the midst of the waves an immense rock? Lift up your eyes and look." They replied, "Master, we see it well enough, but do not understand why you ask us." "Know," said he, "that in this rock there is a sort of bird continually sitting on her nest, in which are seven eggs. While she is thus employed the sea is tranquil; but if she happen to quit her nest, storm and tempest immediately succeed; insomuch that they who would venture upon the ocean are certain to be cast away. On the other hand, as long as she sits upon the eggs, whoever goes to sea will go and return in safety." "But," said they, "how shall we ascertain when the bird is on her nest, and when she is not?" He replied, "She never quits her nest except on some particular emergency. For there is another bird, exceedingly hostile to her, and labouring day and night to defile her nest and break the eggs. Now, the bird of the nest, when she sees her eggs broken and her nest fouled, instantly flies away possessed with the greatest grief; then the sea rages, and the winds become very boisterous. At that time you ought especially to avoid putting out of port." The people made answer, "But, master, what remedy is there for this? How shall we prevent the unfriendly bird from approaching the other's nest, and so pass safely over the waters?" "There is nothing," returned Guido, "which this unfriendly bird so much abhors as the blood of a lamb. Sprinkle, therefore, with this blood the inside and the outside of the nest, and as long as one single drop remains it will never approach it: the bird of the nest will sit; the sea will continue calm; and you will pass and repass with perfect safety." When they had heard this, they took the blood of the lamb, and sprinkled it as he had said. They then passed securely to the Holy Land; and the emperor, seeing that Guido had fulfilled every ministry with wisdom, promoted him to a great military command, and bestowed on him immense riches.*

APPLICATION.

My beloved, the emperor is our heavenly Father, who decreed that whosoever struck thrice upon the gate—

* There are several popular stories not unlike the present, but they will probably occur to the memory of most readers.

that is, who prayed, fasted, and gave alms—should become a soldier of the Church militant, and finally attain everlasting life. Guido is any poor man, who in baptism begins his ministry. The first office is to serve Christ, and prepare the heart for virtue. The second is to watch: "For ye know not at what hour the Son of Man cometh." The third, to taste of penitence; which *was* good to the saints who live eternally in heaven; and it *is* good, because it brings us to that blessed situation. Lastly, it *will* be good, when the resurrection is come, and we are summoned to receive a crown of glory. The fourth ministry is to invite Christ's enemies to become His friends, and inherit eternal life: for He "came not to call the righteous, but sinners to repentance." The fifth is to light the fire of charity, which shall burn free from all impure and improper feelings. The sixth, to teach the way to the Holy Land—that is, to heaven. The sea, over which men must be conveyed, is the world. The rock, in the midst of it, is the human form, or rather the heart, on which a bird cowers; that is, the Holy Spirit. The seven eggs are seven gifts of the Spirit. If the Spirit leave us the devil defiles the nest, and destroys those good gifts. The blood of the lamb is Christ's blood, shed for our salvation, with which we ought ever to be sprinkled; that is, ever to retain it in memory.*

---

* There is a curious defence of transubstantiation in this moral; and we may admire its ingenuity while we reprobate the absurd doctrine it is designed to advocate.

"You ask," says the writer of the *Gest*, "by what means bread may be converted into the real body of Christ. Observe how the mother nourishes her child. If she hunger and want milk, the infant, deprived of its proper sustenance, languishes and dies. But if, in her greatest extremity, she drink but the lees of wine, those lees, taken by the mouth, become changed into blood, and supply milk and nutriment to the child. If nature, then, exert so much power over the woman, how much more shall the virtue of the sacramental rite, operating by the mouth of the priest (that is, by the words of Christ proceeding from his mouth), convert bread into flesh, and wine into blood?"

TALE XVIII.

OF VENIAL SIN.

A CERTAIN soldier, called Julian, unwittingly killed his parents.* For being of noble birth, and addicted, as youth frequently is, to the sports of the field, a stag which he hotly pursued suddenly turned round and addressed him : " Thou who pursuest me so fiercely shalt be the destruction of thy parents." These words greatly alarmed Julian, who feared their accomplishment even while he disavowed the probability. Leaving, therefore, his amusement, he went privately into a distant country, and enrolled himself in the bands of a certain chieftain. His conduct, as well in war as in peace, merited so highly from the prince he served, that he created him a knight, and gave him the widow of a castellan† in marriage, with her castle as a dowry.

All this while, the parents of Julian bewailed the departure of their son, and diligently sought for him in all places. At length they arrived at the castle, and in Julian's absence were introduced to his wife, who asked them what they were. They communicated without reserve the occasion of their search, and their sorrow for an only child. Convinced by this explanation that they were her husband's parents (for he had often conversed with her about them, and detailed the strange occurrence which induced him to flee his country), she received them very kindly; and in consideration of the love she bore her husband, put them into her own bed, and commanded another to be prepared elsewhere for herself. Now, early in the morning, the lady castellan went to her devotions. In the mean time Julian returning home, hastened, according to custom, to the chamber of his wife, imagining that she had not yet risen. Fearful of awaking her, he

---

* [This story is remarkable for its resemblance in several respects to that of Œdipus, to which legend the Greek dramatists were indebted for some of their finest conceptions.—ED.]

† The castellan was a military guardian of a castle and of the same dignity as the viscount. (See Du Cange.)

softly entered the apartment, and perceiving two persons
in bed, instantly concluded that his wife was disloyal.
Without a moment's pause, he unsheathed his sabre, and
slew both. Then he hurried from the chamber, and accidentally took the direction in which the church lay, and
by which his wife had proceeded not long before. On the
threshold of the sacred building he distinguished her, and
struck with the utmost amazement, inquired whom they
were that had taken possession of his bed. She replied
that they were his parents; who, after long and wearisome
search in pursuit of him, arrived at his castle the last
evening. The intelligence was as a thunderbolt to
Julian; and unable to contain himself he burst into an
agony of tears. "Oh!" he exclaimed, "lives there in the
world so forlorn a wretch as I am? This accursed hand
has murdered my parents, and fulfilled the horrible prediction which I have struggled to avoid. Dearest wife,
pardon my fatal suspicions, and receive my last farewell;
for never will I know rest, until I am satisfied that God
has forgiven me." His wife answered, "Wilt thou abandon me then, my beloved, and leave me alone and widowed?
No—I have been the participator of thy happiness, and
now will participate thy grief." Julian opposed not, and
they departed together towards a large river, that flowed
at no great distance, and where many had perished. In
this place they built and endowed a hospital, where they
abode in the truest contrition of heart. They always
ferried over those who wished to cross the river, and
received great numbers of poor people within the place.
Many years glided by, and, at last, on a very cold night,
about the mid-hour, as Julian slept, overpowered with
fatigue, a lamentable voice seemed to call his name, and
beg him in dolorous accents to take the speaker across the
river. He instantly got up, and found a man covered
with the leprosy, perishing for very cold. He brought
him into the house, and lighted a fire to warm him; but
he could not be made warm. That he might omit no
possible means of cherishing the leper, he carried him into
his own bed, and endeavoured by the heat of his body to
restore him. After a while, he who seemed sick, and cold,
and leprous, appeared enveloped in an immortal splendour:

and waving his light wings, seemed ready to mount up
into heaven. Turning a look of the utmost benignity
upon his wondering host, he said, "Julian, the Lord hath
sent me to thee, to announce the acceptance of thy contrition. Before long both thou and thy partner will sleep in
the Lord." So saying, the angelic messenger disappeared.
Julian and his wife, after a short time fully occupied in
good works, died in peace. (3)

APPLICATION.

My beloved, the knight Julian is any good Christian
prelate, who ought manfully to war against the devil, the
world, and the flesh; and to hunt—that is, to acquire
souls for the service of God. He should flee from the
world, and he will then receive the lady castellan in
marriage—that is, divine grace. The parents are the
vanities of this life, which pursue a man everywhere:
these parents must be slain with the sabre of repentance.
The river is the Holy Scriptures; and the hospital by its
side is prayer, fasting, and alms-giving.

TALE XIX.

OF THE SIN OF PRIDE.

WE read in the Roman annals (i.e. *Gesta Romanorum*) of
a prince called Pompey. He was united to the daughter
of a nobleman, whose name was Cæsar. It was agreed between them to bring the whole world into subjection; and
with this view Pompey gave instructions to his associate
to possess himself of certain distant fortresses: for the
latter being a young man, it became him to be most active.
In the mean while, Pompey, as the chief person of the
commonwealth, endeavoured to guard it against the
machinations of their enemies; and appointed a particular
day for the return of Cæsar—in failure of which, he was
to be deprived of his citizenship for ever.* Five years

* [The mixture of romance and history throughout this tale is
wonderful, not to say ludicrous. The belief that "Pompey the Great"

were allowed him; and Cæsar, assembling a large army, marched rapidly into the country he was about to attack. But the inhabitants being warlike, he was unable to subdue them in the specified time. Caring, therefore, to offend Pompey less than to relinquish his conquests, he continued abroad considerably beyond the five years; and was consequently banished the empire. When Cæsar had concluded the campaign he turned towards Rome, marching with his forces across a river, distinguished by the name of Rubicon. Here a phantom of immense stature, standing in the middle of the water, opposed his passage. It said, " Cæsar, if your purpose be the welfare of the state—pass on; but if not, beware how you advance another step." Cæsar replied, " I have long fought for, and am still prepared to undergo every hardship in defence of Rome; of which I take the gods whom I worship to be my witnesses." As he said this, the phantom vanished. Cæsar then spurred his war-horse and crossed the river; but having effected his passage, he paused on the opposite bank:—" I have rashly promised peace," said he; " for in this case, I must relinquish my just right." From that hour he pursued Pompey with the utmost virulence, even to the death; and was himself slain afterwards by a band of conspirators.*

APPLICATION.

My beloved, by Pompey understand the Creator of all things; Cæsar signifies Adam, who was the first man. His daughter is the soul, betrothed to God. Adam was

was a sovereign Prince of Rome is only one of the strange delusions which existed during the period somewhat loosely known as "the Middle Ages."—Ed.]

* This story is evidently built upon a confused tradition of Cæsar and Pompey. "It was impossible," says Warton, "that the Roman History could pass through the dark ages without being infected with many romantic corruptions. Indeed, the Roman was almost the only ancient history which the readers of those ages knew: and what related even to Pagan Rome, the parent of the modern papal metropolis of Christianity, was regarded with a superstitious veneration and often magnified with miraculous additions."—*Diss. on the Gesta Romanorum*, vol. i. p. cl.

placed in Paradise to cultivate and to guard it; but not fulfilling the condition imposed upon him, like Cæsar, he was expelled his native country. The Rubicon is baptism, by which mankind re-enters a state of blessedness.

TALE XX.

OF TRIBULATION AND ANGUISH.

IN the reign of the Emperor Conrad, there lived a certain count, called Leopold, who for some cause, fearing the indignation of his master, fled with his wife into the woods, and concealed himself in a miserable hovel. By chance the emperor hunted there; and being carried away by the heat of the chace, lost himself in the woods, and was benighted. Wandering about in various directions, he came at length to the cottage where the count dwelt, and requested shelter. Now, his hostess being at that time pregnant, and near the moment of her travail, prepared, though with some difficulty, a meal, and brought whatever he required. The same night she was delivered of a son. While the emperor slept, a voice broke upon his ear, which seemed to say, "Take, Take, Take." He arose immediately, and with considerable alarm said to himself, "What can that voice mean? 'Take! Take! Take!' What am I to take?" He reflected upon the singularity of this for a short space, and then fell asleep. But a second time the voice addressed him, crying out, "Restore, Restore, Restore." He awoke in very great sorrow. "What is all this?" thought he. "First, I was to 'Take, Take, Take,' and there is nothing for me to take. Just now the same voice exclaimed, 'Restore, Restore, Restore,' and what can I restore when I have taken nothing?" Unable to explain the mystery, he again slept; and the third time the voice spoke. "Fly, Fly, Fly," it said, "for a child is now born, who shall become thy son-in-law." These words created great perplexity in the emperor; and getting up very early in the morning, he sought out two of his squires, and said, "Go and force away that child from its mother; cleave it in twain, and bring its heart to me." The terrified squires obeyed, and snatched away the child as it hung at its mother's breast. But observing its very great beauty, they were moved to compassion, and placed it upon the branch of a tree, to rescue it from the wild beasts; and then killing a hare, they conveyed its heart to the emperor.* Soon after this, a duke travelling in the forest, passed by, and hearing the cry of an infant, searched about; and discovering it, placed it, unknown to any one, in the folds of his garment. Having no child himself, he conveyed it to his wife, bade her nourish it as their own, and gave it the name of Henry. The boy grew up, handsome in person and extremely eloquent; so that he became a general favourite. Now, the emperor, remarking the extraordinary quickness of the youth, desired his foster-father to send him to court; where he resided a length of time. But the great estimation in which he was held by all ranks of people, caused the emperor to repent what he had done; and to fear lest he should aspire to the throne, or probably be the same whom, as the child, he had commanded his squires to destroy. Wishing to secure himself from every possible turn of fortune, he wrote a letter with his own hand to the queen to the following purport: "I command you, on pain of death, as soon as this letter reaches you, to put the young man to death." When it was completed, he went by some accident into a church, and seating himself upon a bench, fell asleep. The letter had been enclosed in a purse, which hung loosely from his girdle; and a certain priest of the place, impelled by an ungovernable curiosity, opened the purse and read the purposed wickedness. Filled with horror and indignation, he cunningly erased the passage commanding the youth's death, and wrote instead, "Give him our daughter in marriage." The writing was conveyed to the queen, who finding the emperor's signature, and the impression of the royal signet, called together the princes of the empire, and celebrated their

* [This circumstance is a part of several well-known stories. See, in particular, Lockhart's Spanish Ballads, "The Escape of Gayferos."—Ed.]

nuptials with great pomp. When this was communicated to the emperor he was greatly afflicted, but when he heard the whole chain of miraculous interposition from the two squires, the duke, and the priest, he saw that he must resign himself to the dispensations of God. And, therefore, sending for the young man, he confirmed his marriage, and appointed him heir to his kingdom.*

APPLICATION.

My beloved, the emperor is God the Father; who, angry with our first parents, drove them from Paradise into the woods, and desolate places of life. The child who was born is Jesus Christ, whom many persecute; but who will finally triumph over all His enemies. The squires are the divine power and grace operating upon the heart. The child is placed in a tree—that is, in the Church; and the duke, who preserved it, is any good prelate. The slain hare is our carnal affections, which ought to be destroyed. The letter which the emperor wrote with his own hand is every evil imagination which possesses the heart. For then Christ is in danger of being destroyed. The priest who preserved the youth is any discreet minister, who by means of the Sacred Writings mollifies the asperities of the human soul, and betroths it to Heaven.

---

* "This story is told by Caxton in the GOLDEN LEGENDE, under he life of Pelagian the Pope, entitled '*Here foloweth the lyf of Saynt Pelagyen the pope, with many other hystoryes and gestys of the Lombardes, and of Machomete, with other cronycles.*' The Gesta Longobadorum are fertile in legendary matter, and furnished Jacobus de Voragine. Caxton's original, with many marvellous histories. Caxton, from the *estis of the Lombardis*, gives a wonderful account of a pestilence in Italy, under the reign of king Gilbert."—WARTON. The GOLDEN LEGENDE enters somewhat into the life of the Emperor Henry after he came to the throne. Amongst other matters, he "put out of his countree all the juglers and gave to poor people all y^t was wont to be given to mynstrelles."—Fol. ccclxii.

TALE XXI.

OF OVERREACHING AND CONSPIRACY, AND OF CAUTION OPPOSED TO THEM.

JUSTIN records that the Lacedæmonians conspired against their king; and prevailing, banished him. It happened that a king of the Persians plotted the destruction of the same state, and prepared to besiege Lacedæmon with a large army. The exile, though smarting beneath the wrongs accumulated on him by his own subjects, could not but have regard for the land of his nativity. Having ascertained, therefore, the hostile designs of the Persian monarch against the Lacedæmonians, he reflected by what means he might securely forewarn them of the impending danger. Accordingly, taking up his tablets, he communicated his discovery, and explained how they might best resist and defeat their enemies.

When he had written, he enveloped the whole in wax, and finding a trustworthy messenger, despatched him to the chiefs of the state. On inspection of the tablets, no writing could be distinguished; for the entire surface of the wax discovered not the slightest impression. This naturally gave rise to much discussion, and each delivered his opinion as to the intent and further disposal of the tablets. But the mystery none of them could unravel. Now, it chanced that a sister of the Lacedæmonian king, understanding their perplexity, requested permission to inspect them. Her desire was admitted; she commenced a minute investigation, and assisted by that peculiar shrewdness which women frequently display in emergencies, raised the wax, and a portion of the writing became manifest. She had now a clue, and proceeding in her work, gradually removed the waxen covering and exhibited the legend at full. The nobles of the council, thus pre-monished, rejoiced exceedingly; took the necessary steps, and secured themselves against the menaced siege.*

* [This story is told by Herodotus (vii. 239), and has suffered fewer mutilations than some of the other stories which are founded

My beloved, the king is Christ, who is banished by human depravity from His right. Nevertheless, He so loved us, as to contrive a means of freeing us from the attacks of our enemy the devil.

TALE XXII.

OF WORLDLY FEAR.

AUGUSTINE tells us that, when the Egyptians formerly deified Isis and Serapis, they proceeded in this manner. First, they made a law that whosoever declared them to be mortal, or so much as spoke of their birth, should be put to an ignominious death. Then they erected two images; and that the aforesaid law should be strictly observed, they placed near them, in every temple dedicated to their honour, another of diminutive form, having a forefinger laid upon its lips,—to indicate that silence was indispensably required of those who entered their temples. In this way they endeavoured to repress the promulgation of truth.

My beloved, these Egyptians are all worldly-minded men, who would deify and worship their vices, while they sedulously hide truth from the heart. The smaller image is fear of the world, which is ever instrumental in the suppression of truth.

on history. The king who employed the device was Demaratus; so far from being "wronged" by his subjects, he was exiled for persistent misconduct, and was strongly suspected of actual treachery. Herodotus remarks that it is doubtful whether it was good-will or a feeling of malicious joy which induced him to send the information to his countrymen. Gorgo, who detected the meaning of the tablets, was not the "sister of the king," but his wife, the king being the famous Leonidas.—ED.]

TALE XXIII.

OF SPIRITUAL MEDICINE.

SAINT AUGUSTINE relates that an ancient custom formerly prevailed, in compliance with which emperors, after death, were laid upon a funeral pile and burnt; and their ashes deposited in a certain lofty place. But it happened that one of them died whose heart resisted the impression of fire. This circumstance created the utmost astonishment, and all the rhetoricians, and other wise men of every province, were summoned to one place. The question was then proposed to them, and they thus answered: "The emperor died by poison, and through the influence of the latent venom his heart cannot be consumed." When this was understood, they drew the heart from the fire, and covered it with *theriaque*,* and immediately the poison was expelled. The heart, being returned to the flames, was soon reduced to ashes.

APPLICATION.

My beloved, men are thus in a spiritual sense. The heart is impoisoned, and then the fire of the Holy Ghost will not touch it. The *theriaque* is repentance, which removes all transgressions.

TALE XXIV.

OF THE SUGGESTIONS OF THE DEVIL.

THERE was a celebrated magician, who had a very beautiful garden, in which grew flowers of the most fragrant smell, and fruits of the most delicious flavour. In short, nothing on earth could exceed it. But he invariably refused

* Theriaque is an antidote: "Tyriacum, antidotum pro thericum, quod vulgo *theriaque* dicimus."—Du Cange. See Note (4) at the end of the volume.

admittance to all except to fools, or such as were his enemies. When suffered to pass in, however, their wonder was extreme ; and they straightway implored to be allowed to remain. But the magician would grant this boon to no one who did not give up his inheritance to him. The fools, of course, believing it to be Paradise, while they themselves were the chosen and happy possessors of the land, gave not another thought to the future. The consequence was that, one night, finding them asleep, the magician cut them off ; and thus, through the instrumentality of a factitious Eden, perpetrated the foulest enormities. (5)

APPLICATION.

My beloved, the magician is the world. It supplies what is called wealth ; and this, when men have obtained, they close their hand upon it, and believe themselves rich. Presently they open their hands, and the treasure has disappeared.*

* Gay appears to have taken the idea of his 42nd Fable from the moral of this tale. "Talis ponit scutellam," says the Latin, "et nihil ponit intus : interim fabulatur et trufat et ludificat circumstantes : posteà quœrit quid est ibi ; et apparent denarii. Distribuit et dat circumstantibus. Accipiunt gratanter ; et cum clauserint manus, credentes se habere denarium : posteà aperientes manus nihil inveniunt." [Such a one lays down a dish, but he puts nothing in it. In the mean time he prates, cheats, and mocks the spectators. Presently he inquires what is there? and a number of pennies appear, which he distributes to the standers-by. They receive them gratefully, close their hands, and believe that they hold them fast. By and by they open their hands and find nothing.]

"Trick after trick deludes the train.
He shakes his bag, and shows all fair,
His fingers spread, and nothing there,
Then bids it rain with showers of gold ;
And now his ivory eggs are told.
*   *   *   *   *
A purse she to a thief exposed ;
At once his ready fingers closed.
He opes his fist, the treasure's fled,
He sees a halter in its stead."

Gay's *Fables,* ed. 1727.

TALE XXV.

OF INGRATITUDE.

A CERTAIN noble lady suffered many injuries from a tyrannical king, who laid waste her domains. When the particulars of it were communicated to her, her tears flowed fast, and her heart was oppressed with bitterness. It happened that a pilgrim visited her, and remained there for some time. Observing the poverty to which she had been reduced, and feeling compassion for her distresses, he offered to make war in her defence, on condition that, if he fell in battle, his staff and scrip should be retained in her private chamber, as a memorial of his valour, and of her gratitude. She faithfully promised compliance with his wishes; and the pilgrim, hastening to attack the tyrant, obtained a splendid victory. But, in the heat of the contest, he was himself mortally wounded. The lady, aware of this, did as she promised : the staff and scrip were suspended in her chamber. Now, when it was known that she had recovered all her lost possessions, three kings made large preparations to address, and, as they hoped, incline her to become the wife of one of them. The lady, forewarned of the intended honour, adorned herself with great care, and walked forth to meet them. They were received according to their dignity ; and whilst they remained with her, she fell into some perplexity, and said to herself, " If these three kings enter my chamber, it will disgrace me to suffer the pilgrim's staff and scrip to remain there." She commanded them to be taken away ; and thus forget her vows, and plainly evinced her ingratitude.

APPLICATION.

My beloved, the lady is the human soul, and the tyrant is the devil, who spoils us of our heavenly inheritance. The pilgrim is Christ, who fights for and redeems us ; but, forgetful of His services, we receive the devil, the world, and the flesh, into the chamber of our souls, and put away the memorials of our Saviour's love.

TALE XXVI.

OF HUMILITY.

THERE was a queen who dishonoured herself with a servant, and bore him a son. This son, on arriving at years of maturity, practised every description of wickedness, and conducted himself with the greatest insolence toward the prince, his reputed father. The prince, unable to account for such perversion of mind, interrogated the mother as to the legitimacy of her child; and finding, by her reluctant confession, that he was not his son, though loth to deprive him of the kingdom, he ordained that his dress, for the time to come, should be of a different texture and colour; one side to be composed of the most ordinary materials, and the other of the most valuable: so that when he looked upon the baser portion, his pride might be abated, and the vicious propensities, in which he had indulged, relinquished; on the other hand, when he surveyed the more gorgeous part, his hopes might be raised, and his spirit animated to goodness. By this judicious device, he became remarkable for humility, and ever after abandoned his dishonest life.

APPLICATION.

My beloved, the queen is any one who commits a mortal sin. The worthless side of the garment is our fleshly substance; the other is the soul, by which man is classed with the beings of heaven, and aspires to an immortal existence.

TALE XXVII.

OF JUST RECOMPENSE.

A VERY rich and powerful emperor had an only daughter of uncommon beauty. She was consigned to the care of five soldiers, who were commanded to be constantly in arms; and every day a stated sum was paid them out of the king's treasury. This emperor had a seneschal whom he greatly favoured; and a valuable but ferocious dog, which it was necessary to confine with triple chains, since it killed all it could seize. It happened that, as the emperor lay in bed, he formed a resolution to proceed to the Holy Land; and in the morning, when he arose, sent for the seneschal, and said, "I am about to undertake an expedition to Palestine; to your vigilance I commit my only daughter, with the soldiers of her guard. The dog, likewise, which I specially value, I entrust to your care; and, on pain of instant death, let there be no deficiency in attendance upon my daughter. You shall supply the soldiers with all that they require; but observe that the dog is securely chained, and fed sparingly, so that his ferocity may abate." The seneschal approved of all the emperor's injunctions, and promised faithfully to comply with them; instead of which he acted in direct opposition. The dog was fed with the most unsuitable food, and not guarded as he ought to have been. He denied the necessaries of life to the lady, and robbed the soldiers of their pay, who, being needy and unemployed, roamed over the country in great distress. As for the poor girl, forsaken and destitute, she passed from her chamber into the court-yard of the hall which she occupied, and there wandered up and down in sorrow and tears. Now, the dog, whose savage nature improper aliment had augmented, burst by a sudden and violent movement from the bonds that enchained him, and tore her limb from limb. When this afflicting circumstance was known in the kingdom, it excited universal regret. When the emperor heard of his daughter's death, he was deeply moved. The seneschal was summoned before him, and asked why the lady had been left unprovided for, the soldiers unpaid, and the dog improperly fed, contrary to his express command. But the man was unable to answer, and offered not the least excuse. The torturers, therefore, were called in; he was bound hand and and foot, and thrown into a fiery furnace. The emperor's decree gave satisfaction to the whole empire.*

* This is the twenty-sixth chapter in Warton's Analysis.

APPLICATION.

My beloved, the emperor is our Lord Jesus Christ; the fair daughter is the human soul; the five soldiers are the five senses; and the dog is carnal affections, which disturb and slay the spirit. The triple chain is love to God—the fear of offending Him, and shame when we have done so. The seneschal is any man to whom the care of the senses and the guardianship of the soul is committed.

TALE XXVIII.

OF THE EXECRABLE DEVICES OF OLD WOMEN.

In the kingdom of a certain empress there lived a knight, who was happily espoused to a noble, chaste, and beautiful wife. It happened that he was called upon to take a long journey, and previous to his departure he said to the lady, "I leave you no guard but your own discretion; I believe it to be wholly sufficient." He then embarked with his attendants. She meanwhile continued at her own mansion, in the daily practice of every virtue. A short period had elapsed, when the urgent entreaties of a neighbour prevailed with her to appear at a festival; where, amongst other guests, was a youth, upon whom the excellence and beauty of the lady made a deep impression. He became violently enamoured of her, and despatched various emissaries to declare his passion, and win her to approve his suit. But the virtuous lady received his advances with the utmost scorn. This untoward repulse greatly disconcerted the youth, and his health daily declined. Nevertheless he visited the lady oft, which availed him nothing; he was still despised. It chanced that on one occasion he went sorrowfully towards the church; and, upon the way, an old woman accosted him, who by pretended sanctity had long obtained an undue share of reverence and regard. She demanded the cause of the youth's apparent uneasiness. "It will nothing profit me to tell thee," said he. "But," replied the old woman, "as long as the sick man hides his malady from the physician he cannot be cured: discover the wound, and it is not impossible but a remedy may be found. With the aid of Heaven I will restore you to health." Thus urged, the youth made known to her his love for the lady. "Is that all?" said the beldam—"return to your home, I will find a medicine that shall presently relieve you." Confiding in her assurances, he went his way and the other hers.

It seems she possessed a little dog, which she obliged to fast for two successive days; on the third, she made bread of the flour of mustard, and placed it before the pining animal. As soon as it had tasted the bread, the pungent bitterness caused the water to spring into its eyes, and the whole of that day tears flowed copiously from them. The old woman, accompanied by her dog, posted to the house of the lady whom the young man loved; and the opinion entertained of her sanctity secured her an honourable and gracious reception. As they sat together, the lady noticed the weeping dog, and was curious to ascertain the cause. The crone told her not to inquire, for that it involved a calamity too dreadful to communicate. Such a remark, naturally enough, excited still more the curiosity of the fair questioner, and she earnestly pressed her to detail the story. This was what the old hag wanted; she said, "That little dog was my daughter—too good and excellent for this world. She was beloved by a young man, who, thrown into despair by her cruelty, perished for her love. My daughter, as a punishment for her hard-hearted conduct, was suddenly changed into the little dog respecting which you inquire." Saying these words, a few crocodile tears started into her eyes; and she continued, " Alas! how often does this mute memorial recall my lost daughter, once so beautiful and virtuous: now—oh, what is she now? degraded from the state of humanity, she exists only to pine away in wretchedness, and waste her life in tears. She can receive no comfort; and they who would administer it can but weep for her distresses, which surely are without a parallel." The lady, astonished and terrified at what she heard, secretly exclaimed—"Alas! I too am beloved; and he who loves me is in like manner at the point of death"—and then, instigated by her fears, discovered the whole circumstance to the old woman, who immediately answered 'Beautiful lady, do not disregard the anguish of this young man: look upon my unhappy daughter, and be warned in time. As she is, you may be." "Oh!" returned the credulous lady, "my good mother, counsel me; what would you have me do? Not for worlds would I become as she is." "Why, then," answered the treacherous old woman, "send directly for the youth, and give him the love he covets." The lady said, "May I entreat your holiness to fetch him: there might be some scandal circulated if another went." "My dear daughter," said she, "I suffer with you, and will presently bring him hither." She arose and returned with him; and thus the youth obtained his mistress. And so, through the old woman's means, the lady was led to adultery.*

APPLICATION.

My beloved, the knight is Christ; the wife is the soul, to which God gave free will. It is invited to the feast of carnal pleasures, where a youth—that is, the vanity of the world—becomes enamoured of it. The old woman is the devil; the dog, the hope of a long life, and the presumptuous belief of God's clemency, which lead us to deceive and soothe the soul.

TALE XXIX.

OF CORRUPT JUDGMENT.

An emperor established a law that every judge convicted of a partial administration of justice should undergo the

* The demon-hunter in Boccaccio is brought to mind by this story. There the lady's apprehensions "grew so powerfully on her, that to prevent the like heavy doom from falling on her, she studied (and therein bestowed all the night season) how to change her hatred into kind love, which at length she fully obtained."—*Decameron*, 5th Day, Nov. 8. The same story occurs in the 12th chapter of Alphonsus, *De Clericali Disciplina.* It appears in an English garb amongst a collection of Æsop's Fables, published in 1658. Mr. Ellis, or rather Mr. Douce in his Analysis of Alphonsus (see *Ancient Metrical Romances*), has not noticed this translation.

[Mr. Swan thought fit to alter the termination of this story, by making the husband return suddenly and kill his wife and her lover. This, he thought, "afforded a better moral." I have omitted his interpolation.—ED.]

severest penalties. It happened that a certain judge, bribed by a large sum, gave a notoriously corrupt decision. This circumstance reaching the ears of the emperor, he commanded him to be flayed. The sentence was immediately executed, and the skin of the culprit nailed upon the seat of judgment, as an awful warning to others to avoid a similar offence. The emperor afterwards bestowed the same dignity upon the son of the deceased judge, and on presenting the appointment, said, " Thou wilt sit, to administer justice, upon the skin of thy delinquent sire : should any one incite thee to do evil, remember his fate ; look down upon thy father's skin, lest his fate befal thee."

APPLICATION.

My beloved, the emperor is Christ ; the unjust judge is any evil man, who ought to be flayed—that is, stripped of all bad dispositions and humours. The skin nailed to the seat of judgment is Christ's passion, which is a memorial to us of what our conduct should be.

———

TALE XXX.

OF OFFENCE AND JUDGMENT.

A CERTAIN king determined on the occasion of some victory to appoint three especial honours, and an equal number of disagreeable accompaniments. The first of the honours was that the people should meet the conqueror with acclamations and every other testimony of pleasure. The second, that all the captives, bound hand and foot, should attend the victor's chariot. The third honour was that, enwrapped in the tunic of Jupiter, he should sit upon a triumphal car, drawn by four white horses, and be thus brought to the capital. But lest these exalted rewards should swell the heart, and make the favourite of fortune forget his birth and mortal character, three causes of annoyance were attached to them. First, a slave sat on his right hand in the chariot—which served to hint that

poverty and unmerited degradation were no bars to the
subsequent attainment of the highest dignities.   The
second annoyance was that the slave should inflict upon
him several severe blows, to abate the haughtiness which
the applause of his countrymen might tend to excite—at
the same time saying to him, " Nosce te ipsum " (that is,
know thyself), " and permit not thy exaltation to render
thee proud.   Look behind thee, and remember that thou
art mortal."   The third annoyance was this, that free
licence was given, upon that day of triumph, to utter the
most galling reproaches, and the most cutting sarcasms,
against the victor while enjoying his triumph.*

APPLICATION.

My beloved, the emperor is our heavenly Father; and
the conqueror our Lord Jesus Christ, who has obtained a
glorious victory over sin.   The first honour typifies His
entry into Jerusalem, when the people shouted, " Hosanna
to the Son of David."   The second, those enslaved by sin.
The third, Christ's divinity.   The four white horses are
the four Evangelists.   The slave is the worst of the two
robbers crucified with our Lord.   The second grievance is
the blows He received; and the third, the indignities with
which He was overwhelmed.

TALE XXXI.

OF THE RIGOUR OF DEATH.

WE read that at the death of Alexander a golden sepulchre was constructed, and that a number of philosophers

* Privileges of this kind were permitted to the Roman slaves, on
the celebration of their Saturnalia. Horace gives us an example
(Sat. ii. 7, 5):—

> " Age, libertate Decembri,
> (Quando ita majores voluerunt) utere : narra."

Davus spares not his master; and in all probability, many a long-
treasured grudge would, on these occasions, be vented in the bitterest
sarcasms.

assembled round it. One said—"Yesterday, Alexander made a treasure of gold; and now gold makes a treasure of him." Another observed—"Yesterday, the whole world was not enough to satiate his ambition; to-day, three or four ells of cloth are more than sufficient." A third said —"Yesterday, Alexander commanded the people; to-day, the people command him." Another said—"Yesterday, Alexander could enfranchise thousands; to-day, he cannot avoid the spear of death." Another remarked—"Yesterday, he pressed the earth; to-day, it oppresses him." "Yesterday," continued another, "all men feared Alexander; to-day, men repute him nothing." Another said, "Yesterday, Alexander had a multitude of friends; to-day, not one. Another said, "Yesterday, Alexander led on an army; to-day, that army bears him to the grave."

APPLICATION.

My beloved, any one may be called Alexander who is rich and worldly-minded; and to him may the observations of the philosopher be truly applied.

TALE XXXII.

OF GOOD INSPIRATION.

SENECA mentions that in poisoned bodies, on account of the malignancy and coldness of the poison, no worm will engender; but if the body be struck with lightning, in a few days it will be full of them.*

* Seneca's observations are singular: "Illud æquè inter annotanda ponas licet, quòd et hominum, et cœterorum animalium quæ icta sunt, caput spectat ad exitum fulminis: quòd omnium percussarum arborum contra fulmina hastulæ surgunt. Quid, quòd malorum serpentium, et aliorum animalium, quibus mortifera vis inest, cum fulmine icta sunt, venenum omne consumitur? Unde, inquit scis? *In venenatis corporibus vermis non nascitur. Fulmine ictâ, intra paucos dies verminant.*"— Nat. Quæst. lib. ii. 31.

APPLICATION.

My beloved, men are poisoned by sin, and then they produce no worm, that is, no virtue; but struck with lightning, that is, *by the grace of God*, they are fruitful in good works.

TALE XXXIII.

OF HANGING.

VALERIUS tells us that a man named Paletinus one day burst into a flood of tears, and calling his son and his neighbours around him, said, "Alas! alas! I have now growing in my garden a fatal tree, on which my first poor wife hung herself, then my second, and after that my third. Have I not therefore cause for the wretchedness I exhibit?" "Truly," said one who was called Arrius, "I marvel that you should weep at such an unusual instance of good fortune! Give me, I pray you, two or three sprigs of that gentle tree, which I will divide with my neighbours, and thereby afford every man an opportunity of indulging the laudable wishes of his spouse." Paletinus complied with his friend's request, and ever after found this remarkable tree the most productive part of his estate.*

APPLICATION.

My beloved, the tree is the cross of Christ. The man's three wives are pride, lusts of the heart, and lusts of the eyes, which ought to be thus suspended and destroyed. He who solicited a part of the tree is any good Christian.

---

* This curious anecdote is recorded by Cicero, in his second book, "De Oratore," from whom, probably, Valerius Maximus copied it, if it be in his work. I cannot find it.

"Salsa sunt etiam, quæ habent suspicionem ridiculi absconditam; quo in genere est illud Siculi, cum familiaris quidam quereretur, quod diceret, uxorem suam suspendisse se de ficu. *Amabo te*, inquit, *da mihi ex istâ arbore, quos seram, surculos.*"—Lib. ii. 278.

TALE XXXIV.

OF CONSIDERATION OF LIFE.

WE read that Alexander the Great was the disciple of Aristotle, from whose instructions he derived the greatest advantage. Amongst other important matters, he inquired of his master what would profit himself, and at the same time be serviceable to others. Aristotle answered, "My son, hear with attention; and if you retain my counsel, you will arrive at the greatest honours. There are seven distinct points to be regarded. First, that you do not overcharge the balance. Secondly, that you do not feed a fire with the sword. Thirdly, gird not at the crown; nor, Fourthly, eat the heart of a little bird. Fifthly, when you have once commenced a proper undertaking, never turn from it. Sixthly, walk not in the high-road; and, Seventhly, do not allow a prating swallow to possess your eaves." The king carefully considered the meaning of these enigmatical directions; and, observing them, experienced their utility in his subsequent life.*

APPLICATION.

My beloved, the balance is human life; do not overcharge it, but weigh everything accurately, and deliberate upon what you do. As in the fable of the vulture. A vulture swooping upon her prey, struck it with her talons. After it was killed, she first endeavoured to carry off the whole; but finding this beyond her power, she tore off as much as she could fly away with, and left the remainder behind. "Do not feed a fire with the sword,"—that is, provoke not anger with sharp words. "Gird not at the crown,"—that is, respect the established laws. "Eat not

* "This, I think, is from the SECRETA SECRETORUM. Aristotle, for two reasons, was a popular character in the dark ages. He was the father of their philosophy; and had been the preceptor of Alexander the Great, one of the principal heroes of romance. Nor was Aristotle himself without his romantic history; in which he falls in love with a queen of Greece, who quickly confutes his subtlest syllogisms."
—WARTON.

the heart of a little bird," which being weak and timid, becomes not the condition of a Christian man. "When you have commenced a befitting design, do not turn from it,"—and especially, having begun repentance, persevere to the end. A viper, wishing to espouse a kind of eel called the lamprey, was rejected by the latter, because of the poison it conveyed. The viper, determining to carry its object, retired to a secret place and cast up the venom; but after the nuptials were solemnized, went back to the place where the virus was deposited, and resumed the whole. In like manner do all sinners. They are awhile penitent, but soon return to their vomit—that is to their sins. "Walk not by the high-road,"—which is the road of death. "Permit not a prating swallow to possess your eaves,"—that is, suffer not sin to dwell upon thy heart.

TALE XXXV.

OF PEACE, REFORMATION, ETC.

In the Roman annals we read that it was customary, when peace was established between noblemen who had been at variance, to ascend a lofty mountain, and take with them a lamb, which they sacrificed in pledge of complete re-union; thereby intimating, that as they then poured forth the blood of the lamb, so should his blood be poured forth, who infringed the smallest article of that solemn compact.

APPLICATION.

My beloved, the noblemen are God and man; and the lamb is Christ.

TALE XXXVI.

OF THE COURSE OF HUMAN LIFE.

WE are told of a certain king who, beyond all other things, wished to make himself acquainted with the nature of man. Now, in a remote part of his kingdom, there dwelt a famous philosopher, by whose great science many surprising mysteries were expounded. When the king heard of his celebrity, he despatched a messenger to him to command his immediate appearance at court. The philosopher willingly complied with the king's wish. On his reaching the palace, the royal inquirer thus addressed him: "Master, I have heard much of your extraordinary wisdom, and profound research into natural phenomena. I would myself bear testimony to the truth of the general report. In the first place, tell me what is man?" The philosopher answered, "Man is a wretched thing : this is his beginning, middle, and end. There is no truth so apparent; and therefore Job said, ' Man that is born of a woman is full of miseries.' Look upon him at his birth ; he is poor and powerless. In the middle period of his life, you will find the world attacking him, narrowing his comforts, and contributing to the eternal reprobation of his soul. If you review the end, you will mark the earth opening to receive him ! And then, O king ! what becomes of the pomp of your regal establishment—of the pride of your worldly glory ?" "Master," said the king, "I will ask you four questions, which if you resolve well and wisely, I will elevate you to wealth and honour. My first demand is, What is man? My second, What is he like ? The third, Where is he? and the fourth, With whom is he associated?" The philosopher replied,* "At your first question, my lord, I cannot but laugh. You ask, ' What is man ?' Why, what is he but the slave of death—the guest of the place he dwells in—a traveller hastily journeying to a distant land ! He is a slave, because he is subject to the hand

---

* [The speech here begun by the philosopher is not completed, and gradually becomes nothing more than a moralization. Perhaps a part of the original is lost, and the speech has become confused and blended with the moralization.—ED.]

of the tomb; death fetters him, sweeps off from the scene even the memorials of his name, and causes his days to drop away, like the leaves in autumn. But according to his desert will he be rewarded or punished. Again, man is the ' guest of the place he dwells in,' for he lingers a few short hours, and then oblivion covers him as with a garment. He is also a 'a traveller journeying to a distant land.' He passes on, sleepless and watchful, with scarce a moment given him to snatch the means of subsistence, and discharge the relative duties of his station. Death hurries him away. How much, therefore, are we called upon to provide every requisite for the journey—that is, the virtues which beseem and support the Christian. To your second question, 'What is man like?' I answer that he resembles a sheet of ice, which the heat of noon certainly and rapidly dissolves. Thus man, mixed up of gross and elementary particles, by the fervour of his own infirmities, quickly falls into corruption. Moreover, he is like an apple hanging upon its parent stem. The exterior is fair, and promises a rich maturity—but there is a worm preying silently within : ere long it drops to the earth, perforated and rotten at the core.* Whence, then, arises human pride? The third query is, ' Where is man?' I reply, in a state of multifarious war, for he has to contend against the world, the flesh, and the devil. Your fourth demand was, ' With whom is he associated ? ' With seven troublesome companions, which continually beset and torment him. These are, hunger, thirst, heat, cold, weariness, infirmity, and death. Arm, therefore, the soul against the devil, the world, and the flesh, whose wars are divers seductive temptations. Various preparations are needful for an effectual resistance. The flesh tempts us with voluptuousness ; the world, by the gratifications of vanity ; and the devil, by the suggestions of pride. If, then, the flesh tempt thee, remember that, though the day and the hour be unknown, it must soon return into its primitive dust ; and, remember yet more, that eternal punishment awaits

---

* " An evil soul, producing holy witness,
　Is like a villain with a smiling cheek;
　A goodly apple rotten at the heart."
　　　　Shakespeare, *Merch. of Venice*, Act i. Sc. 3.

thy dereliction from virtue. So, in the second chapter of the Book of Wisdom, 'Our body shall become dust and ashes.' It follows that, after these passages of mortal life, oblivion shall be our portion—we and our deeds alike shall be forgotten. The recollection of this will often oppose a barrier to temptation, and prevent its clinging with fatal tenacity to the heart. If the vanity of the world allure thee, reflect upon its ingratitude, and thou wilt be little desirous of becoming bound to it. And though thou shouldst dedicate thy whole life to its service, it will permit thee to carry off nothing but thy sins. This may be exemplified by the fable of the partridge. A partridge, anxious for the safety of her young, on the approach of a sportsman, ran before him, feigning herself wounded, in order to draw him from her nest. The sportsman, crediting this appearance, eagerly followed. But she lured him on, until he had entirely lost sight of the nest, and then rapidly flew away. Thus the sportsman, deceived by the bird's artifice, obtained only his labour for his pains.* So it is with the world. The sportsman who approaches the nest is the good Christian, who acquires food and clothing by the sweat of his brow. The world calls, and holds out the temptation, which his frailty cannot resist. She tells him that if he follow her, he will attain the desire of his heart. Thus he is gradually removed from works of goodness, and follows the vanities of this world. Death comes and bears on his pale steed the deceived and miserable man, since he neither has those worldly goods he sought nor the fruit of good works. See how the world rewards its votaries! † So, in the second chapter of James, " The whole world is placed in evil ; is composed of the pride of life," &c. In the third place, if the devil tempt thee, remember Christ's sorrows and sufferings—a thought which pride cannot surely resist. " Put

---

* This fable of the partridge is popular; but it seems more applicable to the *lapwing*.

† Here is a remarkable coincidence or plagiarism. Pope has given a complete and literal version of the passage in this moral.

" Ecce quomodo mundus suis servitoribus reddit mercedem."

" *See how the world its veterans rewards !* "

Moral Essays, " On the Character of Women."

on," says the apostle, "the whole armour of God, that ye
may stand fast." Solinus * tells us (speaking of the wonders of the world) that Alexander had a certain horse
which he called Bucephalus. When this animal was
armed, and prepared for battle, he would permit no one
but Alexander to mount; and if another attempted it, he
presently threw him. But in the trappings of peace, he
made no resistance, mount him who would. Thus a man,
armed by the passion of our Lord, receives none into his
heart but God; and if the temptations of the devil strive
to sit there, they are cast violently down. Without this
armour, it is open to every temptation. Let us then study
to clothe ourselves with virtue, that we may at length
come to the glory of God.

TALE XXXVII.

OF LIFTING UP THE MIND TO HEAVEN.

PLINY † mentions the story of an eagle that had built her
nest upon a lofty rock, whose young a kind of serpent
called *Perna* ‡ attempted to destroy. But finding that
they were beyond her reach, she stationed herself to wind-
ward and emitted a large quantity of poisonous matter, so
as to infect the atmosphere and poison the young birds.
But the eagle, led by the unerring power of instinct, took
this precaution. She fetched a peculiar sort of stone called
Achates,§ which she deposited in that quarter of the nest

* Solinus wrote *De Mirabilibus Mundi*. He was a Latin
grammarian; but the period in which he flourished is doubtful.
Moreri says his work was entitled *Polyhistor*, "qui est un recueil
des choses les plus mémorables qu'on voit en divers païs."
† This story does not appear in Pliny.
‡ There is no such monster in Pliny. He uses the word for a
scion or graft, book 17, c. x., and it also signifies a kind of shell-fish,
according to Basil.—FABER.
§ Achates is the Latin name for agate. "Found it was first in
Sicilie, near unto a river called likewise Achates; but afterwards in
many other places." "People are persuaded that it availeth much
against the sting of venomous spiders and scorpions: which propertie

which was opposite to the wind; and the stone, by virtue of certain occult properties which it possessed, prevented the malicious intentions of the serpent from taking effect.

APPLICATION.

My beloved, the eagle is any man of quick perception and aspiring mind. The young birds are good works, which the devil—that is, the serpent—endeavours to destroy by temptation. The rock on which the eagle built is Christ.

TALE XXXVIII.

OF THE PRECAUTION NECESSARY TO PREVENT ERROR.

In the reign of the Emperor Henry II., a certain city was besieged by its enemies. Before they had reached its walls a dove alighted in the city, around whose neck a letter was suspended, which bore the following inscription:— "The generation of dogs is at hand; it will prove a quarrelsome breed; procure aid, and defend yourselves resolutely against it."

APPLICATION.

My beloved, the dove is the Holy Spirit, which thus descended on Christ.

could very well believe to be in the Sicilian agaths, for that so soone as scorpions come within the aire, and breath of the said province of Sicilie, as venomous as they bee otherwise, they die thereupon." "In Persia, they are persuaded, that a perfume of agathes turneth away tempests and all extraordinarie impressions of the aire, as also staieth the violent streame and rage of rivers. But to know which be proper for this purpose, they use to cast them into a cauldron of seething water: for if they coole the same, it is an argument that they bee right."—Pliny, *Nat. Hist.* xxxvii. 10.

TALE XXXIX.

OF RECONCILIATION BETWEEN GOD AND MAN.

THE Roman annals say, such discord existed between two brothers, that one of them maliciously laid waste the lands of the other. The Emperor Julius * having heard of this, determined to punish the offender capitally. The latter, therefore, understanding what was meditated, went to the brother whom he had injured, and besought forgiveness; at the same time requesting that he would screen him from the emperor's vengeance. But they who were present at the interview rebuked him, and declared that he deserved punishment, not pardon. To which he from whom forgiveness was asked made the following reply: "That prince is not worthy of regard who in war assumes the gentleness of a lamb, but in peace puts on the ferocity of a lion.† Although my brother should not incline towards me, yet will I endeavour to conciliate him. For the injury he did me is sufficiently avenged now that he is asking for pardon." And thus he restored peace between the enraged emperor and his brother.

APPLICATION.

My beloved, these two brothers are the sons of God and man; between whom there is discord as often as man commits a mortal sin. The emperor is God.

* "We must not forget that there was the romance of *Julius Cæsar*. And I believe Antony and Cleopatra were more known characters in the dark ages than is commonly supposed. Shakspeare is thought to have formed his play on this story from North's translation of Amyot's unauthentic French Plutarch, published at London in 1579."

From such sources, in all probability, the monks derived the little they knew of the GESTA ROMANORUM.

† "In peace, there's nothing so becomes a man,
  As modest stillness and humility:
  But when the blast of war blows in our ears,
  Then imitate the action of the tiger."
  SHAKESPEARE, *Hen. V.* Act iii. Sc. 1.

TALE XL.

OF THE MEASURE OF TEMPTATION, AND OF SKILL.

MACROBIUS relates * that a certain knight, in consequence of something he had witnessed, suspected his wife of transferring her affections from himself to another. He interrogated her on the subject, but she firmly denied it. Not satisfied with her asseverations, the knight inquired for a cunning clerk; and having found such as he wanted, he proposed to him the question which disturbed his rest. The clerk answered, "Unless I am permitted to see and converse with the lady, I cannot take upon me to decide." "I pray you, then," said the knight, "dine with me to-day, and I will give you the opportunity you require." Accordingly the clerk went to the knight's house to dinner. The meal being concluded, our clerk entered into conversation with the suspected lady, and spoke to her on various topics. This done, he took hold of her hand; and, as if accidentally, pressed his finger upon her pulse. Then, in a careless tone, adverting to the person whom she was presumed to love, her pulse immediately quickened to a surprising degree, and acquired a feverish heat. By and by the clerk mentioned her husband, and spoke of him in much the same way as he had done of the other; when the motion of her pulse abated, and its heat was entirely lost. Whereby he plainly perceived that her affections were alienated; and, moreover, that they were placed upon the very person respecting whom she had been accused. Thus, by the management of a learned clerk, the knight ascertained the truth of his suspicion.

APPLICATION.

My beloved, the knight is Christ, who, having warred in our behalf against the devil, was joined to the soul in baptism, which is emblemed by the wife. That wife too often regards another—that is, the world. As the motion of the pulse revealed the lady's attachment, so does the beating of the heart our love of worldly vanities.

* Macrobius, I believe, furnishes no relation resembling the present: nor is it likely, perhaps.

TALE XLI.

OF THE CONQUESTS AND CHARITY OF OUR LORD.

Cosdras, king of the Athenians,* having declared war against the Dorians, assembled an army, and despatched messengers to the oracle of Apollo, to ascertain the fortune of the engagement. The god answered that, unless he himself fell by the sword of the enemy, he should not win the battle. The Dorians, also, understanding the response of the oracle, strictly enjoined their soldiers to spare the life of Cosdras; but the king, disguising himself, cut his way into the heart of the hostile army. One of their soldiers seeing this, pierced him to the heart with a lance. Thus, by the sacrifice of his own life, he rescued his people from the hands of their enemies, and his death was bewailed not less by the adverse host than by his own subjects.

APPLICATION.

My beloved, thus did our blessed Lord, by the predetermined counsel of God, die to liberate mankind from their worst enemies. As Cosdras changed his regal state for the humiliating garb of a servant, so did Christ put on mortality, and by His death triumphed over our demoniacal foes.

TALE XLII.

OF WANT OF CHARITY.

Valerius records † that he once saw in the city of Rome a very lofty column, on which were inscribed four letters, three times repeated—three P's, three S's, three R's, and

---

* By *Cosdras* is meant Codrus, the last king of Athens. See Justin ii. ch. 6 and 7.

[It is curious that the Greek history of the Gesta should be so much more accurate than its Roman history. Comp. the story of Demaratus, Tale XXI.—Ed.]

† There is no foundation in Valerius Maximus for this story.

three F's. When the letters had attracted attention, he exclaimed, " Woe, woe; I see confusion to the city." The nobles, hearing what had been done, said to him, " Master, let us understand thy conceit." He answered, " The meaning of the inscription is this: ' Pater patriæ perditur.' [The father of his country is lost.] ' Sapientia secum sustollitur.' [Wisdom has departed with him.] ' Ruunt reges Romæ.' [The kings of Rome perish.] 'Ferro, flamma, fame.'" [By the sword, by fire, by famine.] The event afterwards fully approved the veracity of the prediction.

APPLICATION.

My beloved, spiritually speaking, the father of his country is charity, which is the result of love to God; when that is lost, wisdom also departs. Hence, the kings of the earth fall; and the sword, fire, and dearth devour mankind.

TALE XLIII.

OF CHRIST, WHO, BY HIS PASSION, DELIVERED US FROM HELL.

IN the middle of Rome there was once an immense chasm, which no human efforts could fill up. The gods being questioned relative to this extraordinary circumstance, made answer that, unless a man could be found who would voluntarily commit himself to the gulf, it would remain unclosed for ever. Proclamations were sent forth, signifying that he who was willing to offer himself a sacrifice for the good of his country should appear — but not a man ventured to declare himself. At length Marcus Aurelius * said, " If ye will permit me to live as I please during the space of one whole year, I will cheerfully surrender myself, at the end of it, to the yawning chasm."

* Marcus Curtius was the name of the youth who devoted himself, according to Roman history. The condition upon which the sacrifice was to be performed is purely monastic.

The Romans assented with joy, and Aurelius indulged for that year in every wish of his heart. Then, mounting a noble steed, he rode furiously into the abyss, which immediately closed over him.

APPLICATION.

My beloved, Rome is the world, in the centre of which, before the nativity of Christ, was the gulf of hell, yawning for our immortal souls. Christ plunged into it, and by so doing ransomed the human race.

TALE XLIV.

OF ENVY.

Before Tiberius ascended the throne, he was remarkable for his wisdom. His eloquence was brilliant, and his military operations invariably successful. But when he became emperor his nature seemed to have undergone a perfect revolution. All martial enterprises were abandoned, and the nation groaned beneath his relentless and persevering tyranny. He put to death his own sons, and therefore it was not to be expected that he should spare those of others. The patricians threatened, and the people cursed him. Formerly he had been noted for temperance, but now he showed himself the most intemperate of a dissolute age; insomuch that he obtained the surname of Bacchus.* It happened that a certain artificer fabricated a plate of glass, which, being exhibited to the emperor, he attempted, but ineffectually, to break it. It bent, however, beneath his efforts, and the artificer, applying a hammer and working upon the glass as upon copper, presently restored it to its level. Tiberius inquired by what art this was effected; and the other replied that it was a secret

----

* The orgies of Tiberius might qualify him for this title; but it does not appear that it was ever conferred. Seneca said pleasantly of this emperor, that "he never was drunk but once; and that once was all his life."

not to be disclosed. Immediately he was ordered to the block, the emperor alleging that if such an art should be practised, gold and silver would be reckoned as nothing.*

APPLICATION.

My beloved, Tiberius is any man who in poverty is humble and virtuous, but raised to affluence forgets every honest feeling. The artificer is any poor man who presents the rich with unacceptable gifts.

* " This piece of history, which appears also in Cornelius Agrippa DE VANITATE SCIENTIARUM, is taken from Pliny, or rather from his transcriber Isidore.[1] Pliny, in relating this story, says that the temperature of glass, so as to render it flexible, was discovered under the reign of Tiberius.

" In the same chapter Pliny observes that glass is susceptible of all colours. 'Fit et album, et murrhenum, aut hyacinthos sapphirosque imitatum, et omnibus aliis coloribus. Nec est alia nunc materia sequacior, aut etiam *picturæ accommodatior*. Maximus tamen honor in candido.'[2] But the Romans, as the last sentence partly proves, probably never used any coloured glass for windows. The first notice of windows of a church made of coloured glass occurs in Chronicles quoted by Muratori. In the year 802 a pope built a church at Rome, and 'fenestras ex vitro diversis coloribus conclusit atque decoravit.' And in 856 he produces 'fenestra vero vitreis coloribus,' &c. This, however, was a sort of Mosaic in glass. To express figures in glass, or what we now call the art of painting in glass, was a very different work: and I believe I can show it was brought from Constantinople to Rome before the tenth century, with other ornamental arts. Guicciardini, who wrote about 1560, in his *Descrittione de tutti Paesi Bassi*, ascribes the invention of baking colours in glass for church-windows to the Netherlanders; but he does not mention the period, and I think he must be mistaken. It is certain that this art owed much to the laborious and mechanical genius of the Germans; and, in particular, their deep researches and experiments in chemistry, which they cultivated in the dark ages with the most indefatigable assiduity, must have greatly assisted its operations. I could give very early anecdotes of this art in England."
—WARTON.

[1] Isidore was a favourite repertory of the Middle Ages.
[2] PLINY, *Nat. Hist.* xxxvi. 26.

TALE XLV.

OF THE GOOD, WHO ALONE WILL ENTER THE KINGDOM OF HEAVEN.

THERE was a wise and rich king who possessed a beloved, but not a loving wife. She had three illegitimate sons, who proved ungrateful and rebellious to their reputed parent.* In due time she brought forth another son, whose legitimacy was undisputed; and after arriving at a good old age, he died, and was buried in the royal sepulchre of his fathers. But the death of the old king caused great strife amongst his surviving sons, about the right of succession. All of them advanced a claim, and none would relinquish it to the other; the three first presuming upon their priority in birth, and the last upon his legitimacy. In this strait, they agreed to refer the absolute decision of their cause to a certain honourable knight of the late king. When this person, therefore, heard their difference, he said, "Follow my advice, and it will greatly benefit you. Draw from its sepulchre the body of the deceased monarch; prepare, each of you, a bow and single shaft, and whosoever transfixes the heart of his father shall obtain the kingdom." The counsel was approved, the body was taken from its repository and bound to a tree. The arrow of the first son wounded the king's right hand—on which, as if the contest were determined, they proclaimed him heir to the throne. But the second arrow went nearer, and entered the mouth; so that he, too, considered himself the undoubted lord of the kingdom. However, the third perforated the heart itself, and consequently imagined that his claim was fully decided, and his succession sure. It now came to the turn of the fourth and last son to shoot? but he broke forth into a lamentable cry, and with eyes swimming in tears, said, "Oh! my poor father; have I then lived to see you the victim of an impious contest—

---

* It is stated in the first book of Herodotus that the Persians considered a rebellious son undoubtedly illegitimate. This is another strong proof of the oriental structure of these stories. See Tales IX. and XXVI.

thine own offspring lacerate thy unconscious clay ?—Far, oh! far be it from me to strike thy venerated form, whether living or dead." No sooner had he uttered these words, than the nobles of the realm, together with the whole people, unanimously elected him to the throne; and depriving the three barbarous wretches of their rank and wealth, expelled them for ever from the kingdom.*

APPLICATION.

My beloved, that wise and rich king is the King of kings and Lord of lords, who joined Himself to our flesh, as to a beloved wife. But going after other gods, it forgot the love due to Him in return, and brought forth by an illicit connection, three sons, viz. Pagans, Jews, and Heretics. The first wounded the right hand—that is, the doctrine of Christ by persecutions. The second, the mouth—when they gave Christ vinegar and gall to drink; and the third wounded, and continue to wound, the *heart* —while they strive, by every sophistical objection, to deceive the faithful. The fourth son is any good Christian.

TALE XLVI.

OF MORTAL SINS.

JULIUS relates that in the month of May a certain man entered a grove, in which stood seven beautiful trees in leaf. The leaves so much attracted him, that he collected more than he had strength to carry. On this, three men came to his assistance, who led away both the man and the load beneath which he laboured. As he went out he fell into a deep pit, and the extreme weight upon his shoulders sank him to the very bottom. The same author

---

* This tale, containing an appeal to natural affection, in all probability takes its rise from the judgment of Solomon. But whether or not, the analogy is sufficiently striking to betray its Eastern derivation.

also relates, in his history of animals, that if, after a crow had built her nest, you wished to hinder her from hatching her eggs, place between the bark and the tree a quantity of pounded glass; * and as long as it remained in that situation, she would never bring off her young.

APPLICATION.

My beloved, the grove is the world, wherein are many trees, pleasant indeed to the eye, but putting forth only mortal sins. With these man loads himself. The three men who brought assistance, are the devil, the world, and the flesh: the pit is hell. Again, the crow is the devil; the nest the heart; which he too frequently inhabits. The pounded glass is the remembrance of our latter end, the tree is the soul, and the bark is the human body.

TALE XLVII.

OF THREE KINGS.

A DANISH king had the greatest reverence for the three Eastern potentates † whom the star led to Jerusalem on the nativity of our blessed Lord; and he was usually in the habit of invoking them to his aid upon any dilemma. The pious king set out with a great company to Cologne, where the bodies of these sainted kings are preserved with great splendour, taking with him three golden crowns, constructed after a wonderful and royal fashion. Besides this, he distributed more than six thousand marks to the church and to the poor, thus leaving an example of faith to his people. As he returned to his own dominions, he fell into a deep sleep; and dreamt that he beheld the three kings bearing upon their heads the crowns he had lately pre-

----

* *Cineres; ashes* of glass.

† We have here a curious instance of the anomalous introduction of saints. The three Magi one would have thought not exactly fitted for the Christian calendar.

sented, from whence issued a dazzling lustre. Each appeared to address him in turn. The first and the older of the three said, "My brother, thou hast happily arrived hither, and happily shalt thou return." The next said, "Thou hast offered much, but more shalt thou carry back with thee." The third said, "My brother, thou art faithful: therefore with us shalt thou conjointly reign in heaven at the end of twenty-three years." Then the elder presented to him a pyx * filled with gold—"Receive," said he, "a treasury of wisdom, by which thou wilt judge thy people with equity." The second presented a pyx of myrrh, and said, "Receive the myrrh of prudence, which will bridle the deceitful workings of the flesh: for he best governs who is master of himself." The third brought a pyx full of frankincense, saying, "Receive the frank-incense of devotion and clemency; for thus shalt thou relieve and soothe the wretched. And as the dew moistens the herbage and promotes a large increase of fertility, so the clemency of a king lifts him to the stars." † The sleeping monarch, surprised at the distinctness and singularity of his vision, suddenly awoke, and found the pyxes, with their rich contents, deposited by his side. Returning to his own kingdom, he devoutly fulfilled the purport of his dream, and on the conclusion of the period foretold, he was worthy to possess an everlasting throne.

APPLICATION.

My beloved, the Danish king is any good Christian who brings three crowns to three holy kings—that is, to the Father, Son, and Holy Ghost. These crowns are

* Pyx is properly a *box*. "πυξίς, ἀπὸ πύξος quod nomen buxum significat, unde et pyxidem *buxulum* Itali vocant."—FAB. THES. The Roman Catholics put the Host into this kind of box.

† The Latin original is as follows: "Sicut ros herbam irrigat ut crescat; sic dulcis clementia regis usque ad sydera provehit et exaltat," which coincides remarkably with a passage in the "*Merchant of Venice*":—

> "The quality of mercy is not strained;
> *It droppeth, as the gentle rain from heaven,*
> *Upon the place beneath.*"—Act iii. Sc. 1.

faith, hope, and charity. The pyx of gold is a heart full of virtues; that of myrrh typifies repentance; and the pyx of frankincense denotes the grace of God.

TALE XLVIII.

OF THE END OF SINNERS.

DIONYSIUS records that when Perillus desired to become an artificer of Phalaris, a cruel and tyrannical king who depopulated the kingdom of Agrigentum, and was guilty of many dreadful excesses, he presented to him, already too well skilled in cruelty, a brazen bull, which he had just constructed. In one of its sides there was a secret door, by which those who were sentenced should enter and be burnt to death. The idea was that the sounds produced by the agony of the sufferer confined within should resemble the roaring of a bull; and thus, while nothing human struck the ear, the mind should be unimpressed by a feeling of mercy. The king highly applauded the invention, and said, "Friend, the value of thy industry is yet untried: more cruel even than the people account me, thou thyself shalt be the first victim." Indeed, there is no law more equitable than that "the artificer of death should perish by his own devices," as Ovid * has observed.

APPLICATION.

My beloved, the sufferer is any evil-worker who will finally suffer for the exertion of his iniquitous practices.

* ———"Neque enim lex æquior ulla,
Quàm necis artifices arte perire suâ."
De Arte Amandi.

[The edition from which Mr. Swan translated read Quidius here, and he allowed this manifest error to stand. It is easy to see how it crept into the text. Q and O are very much alike in Black Letter, and v of course appeared as u. All the best editions, except that printed at Hagenau in 1817, read Ouidius.—ED.]

TALE XLIX.

OF THE ILLUSIONS OF THE DEVIL.

PAULUS, the historian of the Longobardi,* relates that Conan, king of the Hungarians, was besieging a castle in the town of Julius,† called Sondat. Rosimila, the duchess of that place, had four sons and two daughters. When she perceived that Conan was a wonderfully handsome man, she sent him a secret message, saying, "If you will take me to wife I will surrender the castle to you." The king acquiesced and the castle was given up; but the sons, indignant at the treacherous conduct of their mother, fled together. Conan, however, adhering to his promise, married the duchess on the following day. But the next morning after the nuptials, he delivered her to twelve Hungarian soldiers, to be publicly abused and mocked; and on the third day, he commanded her to be stabbed, and transfixed from the throat downward, observing, "that a wife who betrayed her country to gratify her evil passions, ought to possess such a husband."

APPLICATION.

My beloved, Conan is the devil, who besieged a castle, that is, the human heart. Rosimila is any woman who wanders from the path of rectitude. The children are those virtues which leave the breast when evil enters; and the Hungarian soldiers are the vices into which it falls.

* "Paulus, that is, Paulus Diaconus, the *historian of the Longobards*, is quoted. He was chancellor of Desiderius, the last king of the Lombards; with whom he was taken captive by Charlemagne. The history here referred to is entitled GESTA LONGOBARDORUM."—WARTON.

† Warton calls it "*Foro-Juli*," because the Latin is "*in foro Julii*." In all probability the same place is meant as in the following extract from the old play of *Promos ad Cassandra*:—"In the cytie of JULIO (sometime under the dominion of Corvinus, king of *Hungarie*, and *Boemia*)," &c. 1578.

[The name of the town here spoken of is Forum Julii (compare our *Market* Drayton, *Market* Bosworth, &c.), and consequently Warton is more nearly right in his writing of it than Mr. Swan. There were two towns of this name, one the modern Fréjus near the mouth of the Argens, in the south of France, the other (Cividad di Friuli) about forty miles north-west from Trieste.—ED.]

TALE L.

OF PRAISE DUE TO A JUST JUDGE.

VALERIUS informs us that the Emperor Zelongus made a law
by which, if any one abused a virgin, he should lose both
his eyes. It happened that his only son trespassed in this
manner with the daughter of a certain widow, who immediately hastened into the presence of the emperor, and
spoke thus : " My Lord, you have righteously decreed
that he who defiles a virgin shall lose his sight. You
only son has dishonoured my daughter ; command him to
be punished." These words greatly distressed the emperor,
but he gave instant orders respecting the punishment of
his son. On this, two noblemen observed : " The young
man is your only child, and heir to the throne : it were
impious if for this he should lose his eyes." The emperor
answered, " Is it not evident to you that I myself ordained
this very law ? disgraceful as the occasion is, it may break
my heart, but not my resolution. My son has been the
first to transgress the law, and therefore shall be the first
to undergo the penalty." " Sire," said the nobleman,
" let us implore you, for the sake of Heaven, to forgive the
errors of your child." Somewhat subdued by the urgency
of their entreaties, the emperor, after a moment's pause,
said, " My friends, listen to me : my eyes are the eyes of
my son ; and his are in like manner mine. Pluck out,
therefore, my right eye, and let him surrender his left ;
thus, the law will be satisfied." The paternal affection of
the emperor was indulged, and the whole kingdom extolled
the prudence and justice of their prince.*

* Zaleucus, not Zelongus, was the name of the king who performed
this striking act of justice. It is thus told by Valerius Maximus :
" Zaleucus, urbe Locrensium à se saluberrimis atque utilissimis legibus
munita, cum filius ejus adulterii crimine damnatus, secundum jus ab
ipso constitutum, utroque oculo carere deberet, ac tota civitas in
honorem patris pœnæ necessitatem adolescentulo remitteret, ali-
quamdiu repugnavit. Ad ultimum precibus populi evictus, suo prius,
deinde filii oculi eruto, usum videndi utrique reliquit. Ita debitum
supplicii modum legi reddidit, æquitatis admirabili temperamento,
se inter misericordem patrem et justum legislatorem partitus."—
Lib. vi. c. 5, Ex. 3.

[Zaleucus was not a " king" but a lawgiver of the Locrians.—ED.]

APPLICATION.

My beloved, the emperor is Christ; the eyes are divine grace and eternal happiness, which he who sinned would have totally lost, had not the compassion and consequent sufferings of the Son of God meliorated the condign punishment.

TALE LI.

OF EXTORTION.

JOSEPHUS mentions that Tiberius Cæsar, when asked why the governors of provinces remained so long in office, answered by a fable. " I have seen," said he, " an infirm man covered with ulcers, grievously tormented by a swarm of flies. When I was going to drive them away for him with a flap, he said to me, ' The means by which you think to relieve me would, in effect, promote tenfold suffering. For by driving away the flies now saturated with my blood, I should afford an opportunity to those that were empty and hungry to supply their place. And who doubts that the biting of a hungry insect is not ten thousand times more painful than that of one completely gorged—unless the person attacked be stone, and not flesh.' " *

APPLICATION.

My beloved, governors who are already enriched by plunder are less likely to continue their oppression than they who are poor and needy.

* I have met with a similar story in a modern book of fables under the following form :—

" One hot day in summer, a boar, covered with wounds, threw himself beneath the shadow of a large tree, where he was grievously tormented by innumerable swarms of flies. A fox, who was passing by, drew near, and good-naturedly offered to drive away the obnoxious insects. ' Let them alone, my friend,' said the boar; ' these flies are glutted, and unable to do me much further injury. But if they are driven off, others will supply their places, and at this rate, I shall not have a drop of blood left in my body.' "

[This story is only slightly varied from that in Aristotle's *Rhetoric*, bk. ii. ch. 20, p. 1393.—ED.]

TALE LII.

OF FIDELITY.

VALERIUS* records that Fabius redeemed certain captives by the promise of a sum of money; which when the senate refused to confirm, he sold all the property he possessed, and with the produce paid down the stipulated sum, caring less to be poor in lands than poor in honesty.

APPLICATION.

My beloved, Fabius is Christ, who, at the expense of life, ransomed mankind from eternal death.

TALE LIII.

OF GOOD RULERS, WHO ARE NOT TO BE CHANGED.

VALERIUS MAXIMUS † states that, when all the Syracusans desired the death of Dionysius, king of Sicily, a single

---

* The occasion of this noble proceeding is thus detailed:—"Captivos ab Annibale interposita pactione nummorum receperat. Qui cum à senatu non præstarentur, misso in Urbem filio, fundum, quem unicum possidebat, vendidit, ejusque pretium Annibali protinus numeravit. Si ad calculos revocetur, parvum, utpote septem jugeribus, et hoc in Pupinia addictis, redactum: si animo erogantis, omni pecunia majus. Se enim patrimonii, quam patriam fidei, inopem esse maluit: eo quidem majore commendatione, quod proni studii certius indicium est supra vires niti, quam viribus ex facili uti. Alter enim quod potest, præstat: alter etiam plus quam potest."—*Valerius Maximus*, lib. iv. c. 8, Ex. 1.

The *Fabius* of whom this is told is FABIUS MAXIMUS.

† The anecdote is thus recorded by the historian: "Senectutis ultimæ quædam, Syracusanis omnibus Dionysii tyranni exitum, propter nimiam morum acerbitatem et intolerabilia onera, votis expetentibus, sola quotidie matutino tempore deos, ut incolumis ac sibi superstes esset, orabat. Quod ubi is cognovit, non debitam sibi admiratus benevolentiam, arcessit eam, et *quid ita hoc, aut quo suo merito faceret*, interrogavit. Tum illa, *certa est*, inquit, *ratio propositi mei, puella enim, cum gravem tyrannum haberemus, carere eo cupiebam: quo interfecto, aliquanto tetrior arcem occupavit. Ejus quoque finiri dominationem magni*

woman, of great age, every morning entreated the gods to continue his life beyond hers. Dionysius, surprised at this solitary exception, inquired the reason. She answered, " When I was a girl, and governed by a tyrant, I wished for his removal, and presently we obtained a worse instead. Having got rid of him, a worse still succeeded; and therefore, under the justifiable apprehension that your place may be filled up by yet a worse, I pray earnestly for your longer continuance." * Dionysius, hearing this, gave her no farther trouble.†

APPLICATION.

My beloved, be not desirous of change. God is merciful and gracious—be content with His government.

æstimabam: tertium te superioribus importuniorem habere cœpimus rectorem. Itaque timens, ne, si tu fueris absumptus, deterior in locum tuum succedat, caput meam pro tua salute devoveo. Tam facetam audaciam Dionysius punire erubuit."—*Val. Max.* lib. vi. c. 2, Ex. 2.

This must remind the reader of Æsop's fable of the frogs who desired a king. *Which* is the original? It occurs among some translated *Dutch* fables, by De Witt, under the title, of *A Woman praying for the long Life of Dionysius the Tyrant.* See the Appendix.

* The sentiment is similar to that of Shakspeare :—

" And makes us rather bear those ills we have,
Than fly to others that we know not of."

Hamlet, Act iii. Sc. 1.

† This tale has been copied in a story cited by Mr. Douce in his *Illustrations of Shakespeare*, vol. ii. p. 541, and dated about the reign of Henry III.

" Quidam abbas dedit monachis suis tria fercula. Dixerunt monachi, Iste parum dat nobis. Rogemus Deum ut cito moriatur. Et sive ex hac causa, sive ex alia, mortuus est. Substitutus est alius, qui eis tamen dedit *duo* fercula. Irati monachi contristati dixerunt, Nunc magis est orandum, quia unum ferculum subtractum est, Deus subtrahat ei vitam suam. Tandem mortuus est. Substitutus est tertius, qui *duo fercula* subtrahat. Irati monachi dixerunt, Iste pessimus est inter omnes, quia fame nos interfecit ; rogemus Deum quod cito moriatur. Dixit unus monachus, Rogo Deum quod det ei vitam longam, et manu teneat eum nobis. Alii admirati quærebant quare hoc diceret: qui ait, *Vide quod primus fuit malus, secundus pejor, iste pessimus; timeo quod cum mortuus fuerit alius pejor succedit qui penitus nos fame perimet.* Unde solet dici, *Seilde comed se betere.*" [Seldom comes a better.]

TALE LIV.

OF A CELESTIAL KINGDOM.

THE Emperor Frederic II. constructed a curious marble
gate at the entrance of Capua. It stood above a fountain
of running water ; and upon it the statues of the emperor
and two of his judges were sculptured. In a half circle
over the head of the right-hand judge was inscribed as
follows : " He who regards his own safety and innocence,
let him enter here."   Similarly over the head of the left-
hand judge appeared this scroll, " Banishment or imprisonment is the doom of the envious."   In a semicircle over
the emperor's head was written, " Those whom I made
miserable, I recompensed."   In like manner, above the
gate was inscribed, " In Cæsar's reign I became the
guardian of the kingdom." *

APPLICATION.

My beloved, the emperor is God ; the marble gate is
the Church, which is placed above a running fountain—
that is, above the world, which fleets like a water-course.
The judges indicate Mary, the mother of Jesus, and John
the Evangelist.

TALE LV.

OF THE REVOCATION OF A BANISHED SINNER.

A CERTAIN great king had a handsome son, who proved
himself, on all occasions, wise, bold, and courteous. The
same king had four daughters also, whose names were
Justice, Truth, Mercy, and Peace. Now, the king, being

* "I wonder there are not more romances extant on the lives of the
Roman emperors in Germany ; many of whom, to say no more, were
famous in the crusades. There is a romance in old German rhyme,
called TEUERDANK, on Maximilian the First, written by Melchior
Pfinzing, his chaplain. Printed at Nuremberg in 1517."—WARTON.

very desirous of procuring for his son a suitable partner,
despatched a messenger in search of a beautiful virgin, to
whom he should be united. At last, the daughter of the
King of Jerusalem was selected, and married to the young
prince, who was much struck with the beauty of his bride.
At this time there was in the court a servant whom the
king's son principally trusted, and to whom he had confided the care of one of his provinces. This man, in return
for the benefits accumulated upon him, seduced the lady,
and wasted the country over which he was placed. When
the husband, therefore, knew of his wife's infidelity, he
was overwhelmed with sorrow, and repudiated her with
the loss of every honour. Thus circumstanced, she fell
into extreme poverty; and, reduced to despair by the
wretchedness of her condition, walked from place to place
begging her bread, and wishing for the death that came
not to her relief. But at length the husband, compassionating her distress, sent messengers to recall her to his
court. " Come, lady," they said, " come in perfect safety.
Thy lord wishes thy return; fear nothing." Yet she
refused, and exclaimed, " Tell my lord that I would willingly come to him, but I am unable to do so. If he asks
why, say, in compliance with an imperious law. If a man
marry, and his wife prove an adultress, he shall give her a
writing of divorcement; but from that hour, she can be no
longer his wife. To me such a writing has been given—
for, alas! I am an adultress; therefore, it is impossible for
me to return to my lord." " But," replied the messengers,
" our lord is greater than the law which he made himself:
and since he is disposed to show mercy towards you, we
repeat that you may properly comply with his wishes,
secure from further punishment or reproach." " How
shall I know that?" said the lady; " if my beloved would
assure me of it; if he would deign to come and kiss me
with the kiss of his lip, then should I feel certain of
favour."

When the messengers communicated to the prince what
had passed between them and his afflicted wife, he called
together the noblemen of his kingdom, and deliberated
upon the measures it became him to adopt. After mature
reflection, they determined that some man of experience

and judgment should be sent to persuade her to return. But they who answered this description refused to undertake the office; and the husband, in his extremity, despatched once more a messenger, whom he commissioned to speak thus: "What can I do for you? There is not a man in my dominions who will execute my wishes!" These words increased the anguish of the unfortunate lady, and she wept bitterly. Her condition was related to the prince, and he earnestly besought his father to give him permission to bring back his wife, and to assuage her sorrows. The king acquiesced—"Go," said he, "go now in thy might, and reinstate her in the seat from which she has fallen." The messengers were then ordered to return and apprize her of the purposed visit. But the prince's elder sister, that is to say, JUSTICE, understanding what was meditated, hastened to her father, and said, "My Lord, thou art just. You decided rightly concerning that harlot. You properly sanctioned the writing of divorcement, whereby she could no longer be my brother's wife; therefore, to the law let her appeal. And if, in violation of justice, you act thus, be assured that I will no longer be accounted your daughter." The second sister, who was called TRUTH, then said, "My father, she has spoken truly. You have adjudged this woman an adultress: if you permit her to return, you destroy the very essence of truth, and therefore I, too, will no more fulfil the offices of a daughter." But the third sister, called MERCY, hearing what had been said by the other two, exclaimed, "Oh, my Lord, I also am thy daughter: forgive the offence of this repentant woman. If thou wilt not, thou abandonest Mercy, and she will never again acknowledge thee her father." The fourth sister, whose name was PEACE, terrified at the discord between her parent and sisters, desired to leave the country, and fled.

Justice and Truth, however, relinquished not their purpose; and, putting into their father's hands a naked sword, said, "My Lord, we present to you the sword of Justice. Take it, and strike the harlot who has wronged our brother." But Mercy, rushing forward, snatched the weapon from their grasp. "Enough, enough," cried she; "long have you reigned, and your inclinations have been your only law. Now forbear; it is fit that my wishes should sometimes be listened to. Remember that I, too, am the daughter of the king." To this Justice made answer, " Thou hast said well : we *have* reigned long : and long will we preserve our authority. But since there is this discord, call our brother, who is wise in all things; and let him judge between us." The proposal was assented to. They showed him the grounds of their altercation, and explained how Justice and Truth pertinaciously demanded the infliction of the law, while Mercy sought a free forgiveness. " My beloved sisters," said the prince, " I am little satisfied with the flight of my sister Peace, whom your unbeseeming strife has banished. This ought not to be, and shall not. And as for my adulterous wife, I am prepared to undergo her punishment myself." " If this be your determination," observed Justice, " we cannot oppose you, my brother." Then turning towards Mercy, he said, " Use your endeavour to restore my wife. But should I receive her, and she again falls, do you design to renew your intercession?" " Not," said the other, " unless she be truly penitent." The prince then conducted back his sister Peace, and caused each of the others to embrace her, in turn. Concord being thus re-established, he hastened to his erring wife. She was received with every honour, and ended her days in peace.

APPLICATION.

My beloved, the king is our heavenly Father; the son is Christ; and the wife is the soul, made impure by connection with the devil.

TALE LVI.

OF REMEMBERING DEATH.

A CERTAIN prince derived great pleasure from the chase. It happened, on one occasion, that a merchant accidentally pursued the same path; and observing the beauty, affability, and splendour of the prince, he said in his heart,

"Oh, ye heavenly powers! that man has received too many favours. He is handsome, bold, and graceful; and even his very retinue are equipped with splendour and comfort." Under the impression of such feelings, he addressed himself to one of the attendants. "My friend," said he, "tell me who your master is?" "He is," replied the other, "the despotic lord of an extensive territory; his treasury is filled with silver and gold; and his slaves are exceedingly numerous." "God has been bountiful to him," said the merchant; "he is more beautiful than any one I ever beheld; and he is as wise as any I have met with." Now, the person with whom he conversed related to his master all that the merchant had said; and as the prince turned homeward about the hour of vespers, he besought the merchant to tarry there all night. The entreaty of a potentate is a command; and the merchant, therefore, though with some reluctance, returned to the city. When he had entered the palace, the prodigious display of wealth, the number of beautiful halls, ornamented in every part with gold, surprised and delighted him. But supper-time approached, and the merchant, by express command of the prince, was seated next his wife. This honour, and her beauty and gracious manner, so enraptured the poor tradesman, that he secretly exclaimed, "Oh, Heaven! the prince possesses everything that his heart wishes; he has a beautiful wife, fair daughters, and brave sons. His family establishment is too extensive." As he thus thought, the meat was placed before him; but what was his consternation to observe that it was deposited in the skull of a human being, and served from thence to the prince and his guests on silver dishes. Horror-struck at what he saw, the merchant said to himself, "Alas, I fear I shall lose my head in this place!"

In the mean time the lady of the mansion comforted him as much as she could. The night passed on, and he was shown into a bed-chamber hung round with cauldrons; and in one corner of the room several lights were burning. As soon as he had entered, the door was fastened without; and the merchant was left alone in the chamber. Casting his eyes around him, he distinguished in the corner where the light was two dead men hanging by the arms from the ceiling. This shocking circumstance so agonized him, that he was incapable of enjoying repose. In the morning he got up. "Alas!" cried he, "they will assuredly hang me by the side of these murdered wretches." When the prince had risen, he commanded the merchant to be brought into his presence. "Friend," said he, "what portion of my family establishment best pleases you?" The man answered, "I am well pleased with everything, my Lord, except that my food was served to me out of a human head—a sight so sickening that I could touch nothing. And when I would have slept, my repose was destroyed by the terrific objects which were exhibited to me. And, therefore, for the love of God, suffer me to depart." "Friend," replied the prince, "the head out of which you were served, and which stood exactly opposite to my wife— my beautiful but wicked wife!—is the head of a certain duke. I will tell you why it was there. He whom I have punished in so exemplary a manner, I perceived in the act of dishonouring my bed. Instantly prompted by an uncontrollable desire of vengeance, I separated his head from his body. To remind the woman of her shame, each day I command this memento to be placed before her, in the hope that her repentance and punishment may equal her crime. A son of the deceased duke slew two of my kindred, whose bodies you observed hanging in the chamber which had been appropriated to you. Every day I punctually visit their corpses, to keep alive the fury which ought to animate me to revenge their deaths. And recalling the adultery of my wife, and the miserable slaughter of my kindred, I feel that there is no joy reserved for me in this world. Now, then, go in peace, and in future judge not of the life of any man until you know more of its true nature." The merchant gladly availed himself of the permission to depart; and returned with greater satisfaction to the toils of traffic.*

* "Caxton has the history of Albrone, a king of the Lombards, who having conquered another king, 'lade awaye wyth hym Rosamounde his wyf in captyvyte, but after he took hyr to hys wyfe, and he dyde make a cuppe of the skulle of that kynge, and closed in fyne

APPLICATION.

My beloved, the prince is intended to represent any good Christian, whose wife is the soul that sins, and being punished, remembers its iniquity and amends. The adulterer is the devil; to cut off his head is to destroy our vices. The slain kinsmen of the prince are love to God and to our neighbour, which the sin of our first parent annihilated. The merchant is any good prelate or confessor, to whom the truth should always be exposed.

———

TALE LVII.

OF PERFECT LIFE.

WHEN Titus was emperor of Rome, he made a decree that the natal day of his first-born son should be held sacred; and that whosoever violated it by any kind of labour should be put to death. This edict being promulgated, he called Virgil, the learned man,* to him, and said, " Good friend, I

golde and syluer, and dranke out of it.' "—*Gold. Leg.* f. ccclxxxvii. a. edit. 1493. This is an historical fact, and may be found in Gibbon's *Decline and Fall of the Roman Empire,* vol. viii. page 129. 1811. " This, by the way, is the old Italian tragedy of Messer Giovanni Rucellai, planned on the model of the antients, and acted in the Rucellai Gardens, at Florence, before Leo the Tenth and his Court in the year 1516. Davenant has also a tragedy on the same subject, called ALBOVINE, *King of the Lombards, his Tragedy.*

" A most sanguinary scene in Shakespeare's TITUS ANDRONICUS, an incident in Dryden's, or Boccace's TANCRED and SIGISMONDA, and the catastrophe of the beautiful metrical romance of the LADY OF FAGUEL, are founded on the same horrid ideas of inhuman retaliation and savage revenge: but in the last two pieces, the circumstances are so ingeniously imagined, as to lose a considerable degree of their atrocity, and to be productive of the most pathetic and interesting situations." —WARTON.

[Tale CXLIII. terminates with a similar piece of advice to that given in this.—ED.]

* The Latin original says, *Magistrum Virgilium,* Master Virgil, signifying one skilful in the occult sciences.

" This story is in the old black-lettered history of the Necromancer Virgil, in Mr. Garrick's collection.

have established a certain law, but as offences may frequently be committed without being discovered by the ministers of justice, I desire you to frame some curious piece of art, which may reveal to me every transgressor of the law." Virgil replied, "Sire, your will shall be accomplished." He straightway constructed a magic statue, and caused it to be erected in the midst of the city. By virtue of the secret powers with which it was invested, it communicated to the emperor whatever offences were committed in secret on that day. And thus, by the accusation of the statue, an infinite number of persons were convicted. Now, there was a certain carpenter, called Focus, who pursued his occupation every day alike. Once, as he lay in bed, his thoughts turned upon the accusations of the statue, and the multitudes which it had caused to perish. In the morning he clothed himself, and proceeded to the statue, which he addressed in the following manner : " O statue ! statue ! because of thy informations, many of our citizens have been apprehended and slain. I vow to my God that, if thou accusest me, I will break thy head." Having so said, he returned home. About the first hour, the emperor, as he was wont, despatched sundry messengers to the statue, to inquire if the edict had been strictly complied with. After they had arrived, and delivered the emperor's pleasure, the statue exclaimed, " Friends, look up; what see ye written upon my forehead?" They

"Vincent of Beauvais relates many wonderful things, *mirabiliter actitata*, done by the poet Virgil, whom he represents as a magician. Among others, he says that Virgil fabricated those brazen statues at Rome, called *Salvacio Romæ*, which were the gods of the provinces conquered by the Romans. Every one of these statues held in its hand a bell, framed by magic; and when any province was meditating a revolt, the statue or idol of that country struck his bell."—WARTON.

The following ingenious hypothesis may explain the cause of the necromancy so universally attributed to Virgil during the dark ages:—

"*Maium* illum, avum Virgilii, exemplaria vitæ omnia *Magum* vocant. At cùm ejus filia, Virgilii mater, juxta omnes *Maia* dicta sit : omninò Maiæ pater fuit Maius, non Magus : indeque ortum existimo, ut Virgilius *magicis artibus imbutus fuisse creditus sit* ab Elinando monacho aliisque sequioris seculi scriptoribus : quòd et Eclogâ septimâ magica quædam sacra descripsisset, et peritus esset multarum artium, et præcipuè avum habuisse MAGUM diceretur."—*Hist. P. Virg. Mar. à Car. Ruæo.*

looked, and beheld three sentences which ran thus : " Times are altered. Men grow worse. He who speaks truth will have his head broken." " Go," said the statue, " declare to his majesty what you have seen and read." The messengers obeyed, and detailed the circumstances as they had happened.

The emperor, therefore, commanded his guard to arm, and march to the place on which the statue was erected ; and he further ordered that, if any one presumed to molest it, they should bind him hand and foot, and drag him into his presence. The soldiers approached the statue and said, " Our emperor wills you to declare who have broken the law, and who they were that threatened you." The statue made answer, " Seize Focus the carpenter ! Every day he violates the law and, moreover, menaces me." Immediately Focus was apprehended, and conducted to the emperor, who said, " Friend, what do I hear of thee? Why dost thou break my law?" " My Lord," answered Focus, " I cannot keep it ! for I am obliged to obtain every day eight pennies, which, without incessant labour, I have not the means of acquiring." " And why eight pennies?" said the emperor. " Every day through the year," returned the carpenter, " I am bound to repay two pennies which I borrowed in my youth ; two I lend ; two I lose ; and two I spend." " You must make this more clear," said the emperor. " My Lord," he replied, " listen to me. I am bound, each day, to repay two pennies to my father ; for, when I was a boy, my father expended upon me daily the like sum. Now he is poor, and needs my assistance, and therefore I return what I borrowed formerly. Two other pennies I lend to my son, who is pursuing his studies ; in order that if, by any chance, I should fall into poverty, he may restore the loan, just as I have done to his grandfather. Again, I lose two pennies every day on my wife ; for she is contradictious, wilful, and passionate. Now, because of this disposition, I account whatsoever is given to her entirely lost. Lastly, two other pennies I expend upon myself in meat and drink. I cannot do with less ; nor can I obtain them without unremitting labour. You now know the truth ; and, I pray you, give a righteous judgment." " Friend," said the emperor, " thou hast answered well.

Go, and labour earnestly in thy calling." Soon after this the emperor died, and Focus the carpenter, on account of his singular wisdom, was elected in his stead, by the unanimous choice of the whole nation. He governed as wisely as he had lived ; and at his death, his picture, bearing on the head eight pennies, was reposited among the effigies of the deceased emperors.

APPLICATION.

My beloved, the emperor is God, who appointed Sunday as a day of rest. By Virgil is typified the Holy Spirit, which ordains a preacher to declare men's virtues and vices. Focus is any good Christian who labours diligently in his vocation, and performs faithfully every relative duty.

TALE LVIII.

OF CONFESSION.

A CERTAIN king, named Asmodeus, established an ordinance, by which every malefactor taken and brought before the judge should, if he distinctly declared three truths, against which no exception could be taken, obtain his life and property. It chanced that a certain soldier transgressed the law and fled. He hid himself in a forest, and there committed many atrocities, despoiling and slaying whomsoever he could lay his hands upon. When the judge of the district ascertained his haunt, he ordered the forest to be surrounded, and the soldier to be seized and brought bound to the seat of judgment. " You know the law," said the judge. " I do," returned the other : "if I declare three unquestionable truths, I shall be free ; but if not, I must die." " True," replied the judge : "take then advantage of the law's clemency, or this very day you shall not taste food until you are hanged." "Cause silence to be kept," said the soldier. His wish being complied with, he proceeded in the following manner :—" The first truth is this : I protest before ye all, that from my youth up I have been a bad man." The judge, hearing this, said to the bystanders, "He says true?" They answered, "Else, he had not now been in this situation." "Go on, then," said the judge; "what is the second truth?" "I like not," exclaimed he, "the dangerous situation in which I stand." "Certainly," said the judge, "we may credit thee. Now then for the third truth, and thou hast saved thy life." "Why," he replied, "if I once get out of this confounded place, I will never willingly re-enter it." "Amen," said the judge, "thy wit hath preserved thee; go in peace." And thus he was saved.

APPLICATION.

My beloved, the emperor is Christ. The soldier is any sinner; the judge is a wise confessor. If the sinner confess the truth in such a manner as not even demons can object, he shall be saved—that is, if he confess and repent.

———

TALE LIX.

OF TOO MUCH PRIDE ; AND HOW THE PROUD ARE FRE-
QUENTLY COMPELLED TO ENDURE SOME NOTABLE
HUMILIATION.

WHEN Jovinian was emperor, he possessed very great power; and as he lay in bed reflecting upon the extent of his dominions, his heart was elated to an extraordinary degree. "Is there," he impiously asked, "is there any other god than me?" Amid such thoughts he fell asleep.

In the morning he reviewed his troops, and said, "My friends, after breakfast we will hunt." Preparations being made accordingly, he set out with a large retinue. During the chase, the emperor felt such extreme oppression from the heat, that he believed his very existence depended upon a cold bath. As he anxiously looked around, he discovered a sheet of water at no great distance. "Remain here," said he to his guard, "until I have refreshed myself in yonder stream." Then spurring his steed, he rode hastily to the edge of the water. Alighting, he divested himself of his apparel, and experienced the greatest pleasure from its invigorating freshness and coolness. But whilst he was thus employed, a person similar to him in every respect—in countenance and gesture—arrayed himself unperceived in the emperor's dress, and then mounting his horse, rode off to the attendants. The resemblance to the sovereign was such, that no doubt was entertained of the reality; and when the sport was over command was issued for their return to the palace.

Jovinian, however, having quitted the water, sought in every possible direction for his horse and clothes, and to his utter astonishment could find neither. Vexed beyond measure at the circumstance (for he was completely naked, and saw no one near to assist him), he began to reflect upon what course he should pursue. "Miserable man that I am," said he, "to what a strait am I reduced! There is, I remember, a knight residing close by, whom I have promoted to a military post; I will go to him, and command his attendance and service. I will then ride on to the palace and strictly investigate the cause of this extraordinary conduct." Jovinian proceeded, naked and ashamed, to the castle of the aforesaid knight, and beat loudly at the gate. The porter inquired the cause of the knocking. "Open the gate," said the enraged emperor, "and you will see whom I am." The gate was opened; and the porter, struck with the strange appearance he exhibited, replied, "In the name of all that is marvellous, what are you?" "I am," said he, "Jovinian, your emperor; go to your lord, and command him from me to supply the wants of his sovereign. I have lost both horse and clothes." "Thou liest, infamous ribald!" shouted the porter; "just before thy approach, the Emperor Jovinian, accompanied by the officers of his household, entered the palace. My lord both went and returned with him; and but even now sat with him at meat. But because thou hast called thyself the emperor, my lord shall know of thy presumption." The porter entered, and related what had passed. Jovinian was introduced, but the knight retained not the slightest recollection of his master, although the emperor remembered him. "Who are you?" said the former, "and what is your name?" "I am the Emperor Jovinian," rejoined he; "canst thou have forgotten me? At such a time I promoted thee to a military command." "Why, thou most audacious scoundrel," said the knight, "darest thou call thyself the emperor? I rode with him myself to the palace, from whence I am this moment returned. But thy impudence shall not go without its reward. Flog him," said he, turning to his servants, "flog him soundly, and drive him away." This sentence was immediately executed, and the poor emperor, bursting into a convulsion of tears, exclaimed, "Oh, my God, is it possible that one whom I have so much honoured and exalted should do this? Not content with pretending ignorance of my person, he orders these merciless villains to abuse me!" He next thought within himself, "There is a certain duke, one of my privy councillors, to whom I will make known my calamity. At least, he will enable me to return decently to the palace." To him, therefore, Jovinian proceeded, and the gate was opened at his knock. But the porter, beholding a naked man, exclaimed in the greatest amaze, "Friend, who are you, and why come you here in such a guise?" He replied, "I am your emperor; I have accidentally lost my clothes and my horse, and I have come for succour to your lord. I beg you, therefore, to do me this errand to the duke." The porter, more and more astonished, entered the hall, and communicated the strange intelligence which he had received. "Bring him in," said the duke. He was brought in, but neither did he recognize the person of the emperor. "What art thou?" he asked. "I am the emperor," replied Jovinian, "and I have promoted thee to riches and honour, since I made thee a duke and one of my councillors." "Poor mad wretch," said the duke, "a short time since I returned from the palace, where I left the very emperor thou assumest to be. But since thou hast claimed such rank, thou shalt not escape unpunished. Carry him to prison, and feed him with bread and water." The command was no sooner delivered than obeyed; and the following day his naked body was submitted to the lash, and he was again cast into the dungeon.

Thus afflicted, he gave himself up to the wretchedness of his untoward condition. In the agony of his heart, he said, " What shall I do? Oh, what will be my destiny? I am loaded with the coarsest contumely, and exposed to the malicious observation of my people. It were better to hasten immediately to my palace, and there discover myself—my servants will know me; and even if they do not my wife will know me!" Escaping, therefore, from his confinement, he approached the palace and beat upon the gate. "Who art thou?" said the porter. "It is strange," replied the aggrieved emperor, "it is strange that thou shouldest not know me; thou, who hast served me so long!" "Served *thee!*" returned the porter indignantly, "thou liest abominably. I have served none but the emperor." "Why," said the other, "thou knowest that I am he. Yet, though you disregard my words, go, I implore you, to the empress; communicate what I will tell thee, and by these signs bid her send the imperial robes, of which some rogue has deprived me. The signs I tell thee of are known to none but to ourselves." "In verity," said the porter, "thou art mad: at this very moment my lord sits at table with the empress herself. Nevertheless, out of regard for thy singular merits, I will intimate thy declaration within; and rest assured, thou wilt presently find thyself most royally beaten." The porter went accordingly, and related what he had heard. But the empress became very sorrowful, and said, "Oh, my lord, what am I to think? The most hidden passages of our lives are revealed by an obscene fellow at the gate, and repeated to me by the porter, on the strength of which he declares himself the emperor and my espoused lord!" When the fictitious monarch was apprised of this, he commanded him to be brought in. He had no sooner entered than a large dog, which couched upon the hearth, and had been much cherished by him, flew at his throat, and, but for timely prevention, would have killed him. A falcon, also, seated upon her perch, no sooner beheld him, than she broke her jesses * and flew out of the hall. Then the pretended emperor, addressing those who stood about him,

---

* Jesses are the leather straps with which a hawk was confined.

said, "My friends, hear what I will ask of yon ribald.
Who are you? and what do you want?" "These questions," said the suffering man, "are very strange. You
know I am the emperor and master of this place." The
other, turning to the nobles who sat or stood at the table,
continued, "Tell me, on your allegiance, which of us two
is your lord and master?" "Your majesty asks us an easy
thing," replied they, "and need not to remind us of our
allegiance. That obscene wretch we have never before
seen. You alone are he, whom we have known from
childhood; and we entreat that this fellow may be severely
punished, as a warning to others how they give scope to
their mad presumption." Then turning to the empress,
the usurper said, "Tell me, my lady, on the faith you have
sworn, do you know this man who calls himself thy lord
and emperor?" She answered, "My lord, how can you
ask such a question? Have I not known thee more than
thirty years, and borne thee many children? Yet, at one
thing I do admire. How can this fellow have acquired
so intimate a knowledge of what has passed between us?"

The pretended emperor made no reply, but addressing
the real one, said, "Friend, how darest thou to call thyself
emperor? We sentence thee, for this unexampled impudence, to be drawn, without loss of time, at the tail of a
horse. And if thou utterest the same words again, thou
shalt be doomed to an ignominious death." He then commanded his guards to see the sentence put in force, but to
preserve his life. The unfortunate emperor was now
almost distracted; and urged by his despair, wished vehemently for death. "Why was I born?" he exclaimed.
"My friends shun me; and my wife and children will not
acknowledge me. But there is my confessor, still. To
him will I go; perhaps he will recollect me, because he
has often received my confessions." He went accordingly,
and knocked at the window of his cell. "Who is there?"
said the confessor. "The emperor Jovinian," was the
reply; "open the window, and I will speak to thee." The
window was opened; but no sooner had he looked out than
he closed it again in great haste. "Depart from me," said
he, "accursed thing: thou art not the emperor, but the
devil incarnate." This completed the miseries of the per-

secuted man; and he tore his hair, and plucked up his beard by the roots. "Woe is me!" he cried, "for what strange doom am I reserved?" At this crisis, the impious words which, in the arrogance of his heart, he had uttered, crossed his recollection. Immediately he beat again at the window of the confessor's cell, and exclaimed, "For the love of Him who was suspended from the cross, hear my confession with the window closed." The recluse said, "I will do this with pleasure;" and then Jovinian acquainted him with every particular of his past life; and principally how he had lifted himself up against his Maker, saying that he believed there was no other god but himself.

The confession made, and absolution given, the recluse opened the window, and directly knew him. "Blessed be the most high God," said he, "now do I know thee. I have here a few garments: clothe thyself, and go to the palace. I trust that they also will recognize thee." The emperor did as the confessor directed. The porter opened the gate, and made a low obeisance to him. "Dost thou know me?" said he. "Very well, my lord!" replied the menial; "but I marvel that I did not observe you go out." Entering the hall of his mansion, Jovinian was received by all with a profound reverence. The strange emperor was at that time in another apartment with the queen; and a certain knight came out of the chamber, looked narrowly at Jovinian, and returning to the supposed emperor, said, "My lord, there is one in the hall to whom everybody bends; he so much resembles you, that we know not which is the emperor." Hearing this, the usurper said to the empress, "Go and see if you know him." She went, and returned greatly surprised at what she saw. "Oh, my lord," said she, "I declare to you that I know not whom to trust." "Then," returned he, "I will go and determine you." When he had entered the hall, he took Jovinian by the hand and placed him near him. Addressing the assembly, he said, "By the oaths you have taken, declare which of us is your emperor." The empress answered, "It is incumbent on me to speak first; but Heaven is my witness that I am unable to determine which is he." And so said all. Then the feigned emperor spoke thus, "My friends, hearken! That man is your king and your lord.

He exalted himself to the disparagement of his Maker; and God, therefore, scourged and hid him from your knowledge. I am the angel that watches over his soul, and I have guarded his kingdom while he was undergoing his penance. But his repentance removes the rod; he has now made ample satisfaction, and again let your obedience wait upon him. Commend yourselves to the protection of Heaven." So saying, he disappeared. The emperor gave thanks to God, and lived happily, and finished his days in peace. (6)

APPLICATION.

My beloved, the emperor represents any one whom the pride and vanity of life wholly engross. The knight to whom Jovinian first applied is Reason; which ever disclaims the pomps and fooleries of life. The duke is conscience; the savage dog is the flesh, which alarms the falcon, that is, divine grace. The wife is the human soul; the clothes in which the emperor was at last arrayed are the virtues that befit the true sovereign, that is, the good Christian.

TALE LX.

OF AVARICE AND ITS SUBTLETY.

A CERTAIN king had an only daughter, remarkable for the beauty and dignity of her person. She was called Rosamond; and, at the early age of ten years, she proved so swift a runner, that she invariably attained the goal before her competitor. The king caused it to be proclaimed that whosoever should surpass his daughter in speed should marry her, and succeed to the throne: but in the event of a failure he should lose his head. And even with the heavy penalty before them, numbers permitted themselves to be buoyed up by the hope of success to attempt, and to perish in the attempt. But it happened that a poor man, called Abibas, inhabited that country, who thus communed with himself: "I am very poor, and of a base extraction;

if I may overcome this lady and marry her, not only shall I be promoted myself, but all who are of my blood." But wiser than the rest, he took the three following precautions. First, he framed a curious garland of roses, of which he had ascertained that the lady was devotedly fond. Then, he procured a zone of the finest silk, from a conviction that most damsels were partial to this sort of clothing. And, lastly, he bought a silken bag, in which he deposited a golden ball bearing the following inscription: "Whosoever plays with me shall never satiate of play." These three things he placed in his bosom, and knocked at the palace gate. The porter inquired his business; and he stated his wish in the usual form.

It happened that the princess herself stood at a window close by, and heard Abibas express his intention to run with her. Observing that he was poor, and his attire threadbare and rent, she despised him from her very heart, and said, "Lo! what poor wretch is this with whom I have to contend?" However, she prepared to run; and everything being in readiness, they commenced the race. Abibas would have been left at a considerable distance; but taking the garland of roses from its repository, he skilfully threw it down before her, on which the maiden stooped, picked it up, and placed it on her head. Delighted with the odour and beauty of the flowers, she paused to examine it; and Abibas took advantage of her forgetfulness and advanced rapidly towards the goal. This awoke her to a recollection of what was going forward, and crying aloud, "Never shall the daughter of a prince be united to this miserable clown," she threw the garland from her into a deep well, and rushed onward like a whirlwind. In a few moments she overtook the youth, and extending her hand, struck him upon the shoulder, exclaiming, "Stop, foolish thing; hopest thou to marry a princess?" Just as she was on the point of repassing him, he drew forth the silken girdle, and cast it at her feet. The temptation again proved too strong for her resolution, and she stooped to gather it. Overjoyed at the beauty of its texture, she must bind it round her waist; and whilst she did this, Abibas had recovered more ground than he had lost. As soon as the fair racer perceived the consequences of her folly, she burst into a flood of tears, and rending the zone asunder, hurried on.   Having again overtaken her adversary, she seized him by the arm, striking him smartly at the same time : " Fool, thou shalt *not* marry me ; " and immediately she ran faster than before.   Abibas, when he . saw this, waited until she was near the goal, and then threw at her feet the bag with the golden ball.   It was impossible to forbear picking it up ; and equally impossible not to open it and peep at its contents.   She did so ; but reading the inscription, " Who plays with me shall never satiate of playing," she played so much and so long, that Abibas came first to the goal and married her.*

APPLICATION.

My beloved, the king is Christ; the daughter is the soul, and Abibas is the devil, who provides various seductions to draw us from the goal of heaven.

————

TALE LXI.

OF REFLECTION.

THE Emperor Claudius had an only daughter who was incomparably beautiful.   As he lay in bed, he reflected seriously upon the best mode of disposing of her.   "If," thought he, " I should marry her to a rich fool, it will occasion her death.   But if I bestow her upon a wise man, although he be poor, his own wit will procure him riches." †

Now, it happened that there dwelt in the city a phi-

———

* " This is evidently a Gothic innovation of the classical tale of Atalanta.   But it is not impossible that an oriental apologue might have given rise to the Grecian fable."—WARTON.

The story of Atalanta I consider to be the origin of many subsequent fables.   Amongst these, the "Hare and the Tortoise" may be noticed.

† It was a maxim of Themistocles that his daughter had better marry a man without an estate, than an estate without a man.

losopher called Socrates, whom the king very greatly esteemed. This person was sent for, and thus addressed, "My good friend, I design to espouse you to my only daughter." Socrates, overjoyed at the proposal, expressed his gratitude as he best could. "But," continued the emperor, "take her with this condition : that if she die first, you shall not survive her." The philosopher assented ; the nuptials were solemnized with great splendour, and for a length of time their happiness was uninterrupted.

But at last she sickened, and her death was hourly expected. This deeply afflicted Socrates, and he retired into a neighbouring forest and gave free course to his alarm. Whilst he was thus occupied, it chanced that King Alexander * hunted in the same forest; and that a soldier of his guard discerned the philosopher, and rode up to him. "Who art thou?" asked the soldier. "I am," replied he, "the servant of my master ; and he who is the servant of my master is the lord of thine." "How?" cried the other, "there is not a greater person in the universe than he whom I serve. But since you are pleased to say otherwise, I will presently lead you to him ; and we will hear who thy lord is." Accordingly, he was brought before Alexander. "Friend," said the king, "concerning whom dost thou say that his servant is my master?" The philosopher answered, "My master is reason ; *his* servant is the will. Now, dost thou not govern thy kingdom according to the dictates of thy will? Therefore, thy will is thy master. But the will is the servant of my master. So that what I said is true, and thou canst not disprove it." Alexander, wondering at the man's wit, candidly answered in the affirmative, and ever after ruled both himself and his kingdom by the laws of reason.

Socrates, however, entered farther into the forest, and wept bitterly over the expected decease of his wife. In the midst of his distress he was accosted by an old man who inhabited that part of the wood. "Master," said he, "why art thou afflicted?" "Alas!" answered the other,

* The introduction of Alexander the Great, Socrates, and a Roman emperor, is a strange jumble of times and persons.

"I have espoused the daughter of an emperor upon the condition that if she die I should die with her: she is now on the point of death, and my life therefore will certainly be required." "What!" said the old man, "grievest thou for this? Take my counsel, and thou shalt be safe enough. Thy wife is of royal descent; let her besmear her breast with some of her father's blood. Then, do thou search in the depths of this forest, where thou wilt find three herbs: of one of them make a beverage and administer it to her; the other two beat into a plaster, and apply it to the afflicted part. If my instructions are exactly attended to, she will be restored to perfect health." Socrates did as he was directed; and his wife presently recovered. When the emperor knew how he had striven to find a remedy for his wife's disorder, he loaded him with riches and honours.*

APPLICATION.

My beloved, the emperor is our Lord Jesus Christ; the daughter is the soul, given to man on condition that, should it be destroyed by sin, he also should lose eternal life. The priest is the Church, where health and safety may be found. The old man is a wise confessor, and Alexander is the world.

TALE LXII.

OF THE BEAUTY OF A FAITHFUL MIND.

WHEN Salus was emperor, there lived a very beautiful woman, whose name was Florentina. She was so remarkably handsome that three kings sought her love, by one of whom she was abused. This occasioned a war between them, and great numbers of men fell on both sides. But

---

* The latter part of this apologue is in Alphonsus, *De Clericali Disciplina*. It is the last of the Latin copy; but not noticed in Mr. Douce's analysis, as occurring in the GESTA.

the nobles, unwilling to see so much waste of blood, inter-
fered, and addressing the emperor, bade him observe that,
unless a stop were put to the virulent animosity which
divided them, the whole kingdom would be annihilated.
The emperor, duly considering what had been said,
directed letters, impressed with the royal signet, to be
sent to the fair occasion of the war; by which, without
delay, she was commanded to appear before him. A
herald bore the mandate, but before he could deliver it
she died. The herald, therefore, returned, and the emperor, very much regretting that he had lost sight of so
beautiful a woman, caused all the best artists in the
kingdom to be summoned into his presence. When they
were assembled, he spoke as follows: " My friends, the
reason that I have sent for you is this. There was a very
beautiful woman, named Florentina, for whose love a
great number of men have lost their lives. She died
before I had an opportunity of seeing her. Do ye go,
therefore; paint her to the life, as she was in all her
beauty. Thus shall I discover wherefore so many were
sacrificed." The artists answered, " Your majesty wishes
a thing which is very difficult to execute. Her beauty
was so surpassing, that not all the artists in the world,
save one, would be able to do her justice; and he hides
himself amongst the mountains. But he alone can perfectly fulfil your desires." On receiving this information,
messengers were despatched in pursuit of him. He was
soon found, and brought before the curious monarch, who
commanded him to paint Florentina as she appeared when
living; and if he did it, his reward should be royal.
" Your request is extremely difficult," said the painter;
" nevertheless, cause all the beautiful women in your
kingdom to come before me for an hour at least, and I
will do as you desire." The emperor complied, and made
them stand in his presence. From these the artist selected
four, and permitted the rest to return home. Then he
commenced his labours. First, he laid on a coat of red
colour; and whatever was exquisitely beautiful in the
four women, *that* he copied in his painting. In this
manner it received its completion; and when the emperor
beheld it, he said, " Oh, Florentina, had you lived to

eternity, you ought to have loved that painter who has represented you in so much beauty."

My beloved, the emperor is God; the beautiful Florentina is the soul ; the three kings, the devil, the world, and the flesh. The nobles are the patriarchs and prophets, who were the mediators between God and man. The painters are the angels and men, amongst whom there was found no one who would rescue the soul from death. The artist who came from the mountains is Christ. The red colour is blood; the four women are existence, growth, feeling, and understanding.

TALE LXIII.

OF THE PLEASURES OF THIS WORLD.

THE Emperor Vespasian had a daughter called Agläes, whose loveliness was greater than that of all other women. It happened that as she stood opposite to him on a certain occasion, he considered her very attentively, and then addressed her as follows : "My beloved daughter, thy beauty merits a loftier title than thou hast yet received. I will change thy name; henceforward, be thou called the LADY OF COMFORT, in sign that whosoever looks upon thee in sorrow may depart in joy."

Now, the emperor possessed, near his palace, a delicious garden, in which he frequently walked. Proclamation was made that whosoever wished to marry his daughter should come to the palace, and remain in this garden the space of three or four days ; when they quitted it, the ceremony should take place. Immense crowds were allured by the apparently easy terms of the notice; they entered the garden, but were never again seen. Not one of them returned. But a certain knight, who dwelt in some remote country, hearing of the conditions by which the daughter of a great king might be espoused, came to the gate of the palace and demanded entrance. On being introduced to the emperor, he spoke thus: "I hear it commonly reported, my Lord, that whoever enters your garden shall espouse your daughter. For this purpose I come." "Enter, then," said the emperor; "on thy return thou shall marry her." "But," added the knight, "I solicit one boon of your majesty. Before I enter the garden, I would entreat an opportunity of conversing a short time with the lady." "I have no objection to that," said the emperor. She was called, and the knight accosted her in these words: "Fair damsel, thou hast been called the *Lady of Comfort*, because every one who enters thy presence sorrowful returns contented and happy. I, therefore, approach thee sad and desolate—give me the means to leave thee in happiness: many have entered the garden, but never any reappeared. If the same chance happen to me—alas! that I should have sought thee in marriage." "I will tell thee the truth," said the lady, "and convert thy unhappiness into pleasure. In that garden there is an enormous lion, which devours every one who enters with the hope of marrying me. Arm thyself, therefore, cap-a-pie, and smear your armour with gum. As soon as you have entered the garden the lion will rush toward you; attack him manfully, and when you are weary, leave him. Then will he instantly seize you by the arm or leg; but in so doing, the gum will adhere to his teeth, and he will be unable to hurt you. As soon as you perceive this, unsheath your sword and separate his head from his body. Besides the ferocious animal I have described, there is another danger to be overcome. There is but one entrance, and so intricate are the labyrinths, that egress is nearly impossible without assistance. But here also I will befriend you. Take this ball of thread, and attach one of the ends to the gate as you enter, and, retaining the line, pass into the garden. But, as you love your life, beware that you lose not the thread." *

The knight exactly observed all these instructions. Having armed himself, he entered the garden; and the

---

* A fine moral, which might be oftener remembered with advantage. The Gospel is to the Christian what the ball of thread was to the knight: pity that it should so frequently be lost!

lion, with open mouth, rushed forward to devour him. He defended himself resolutely; and when his strength failed, he leapt a few paces back. Then, as the lady had said, the lion seized upon the knight's arm; but, since his teeth were clogged with gum, he did him no injury, and the sword presently put an end to the combat. Unhappily, however, while exulting over his victory, he let go the thread, and in great tribulation wandered about the garden for three days, diligently seeking the lost clue. Towards night he discovered it, and with no small joy hastened back to the gate. Then, loosening the thread, he bent his way to the presence of the emperor; and in due time the LADY OF COMFORT became his wife.*

APPLICATION.

My beloved, the emperor is Christ; the Lady of Comfort is the kingdom of heaven. The garden is the world; the lion, the devil. The ball of thread represents baptism, by which we enter into the world.

TALE LXIV.

OF THE INCARNATION OF OUR LORD.

A CERTAIN king was remarkable for three qualities. Firstly, he was stronger in body than all men; secondly, he was wiser; and lastly, more beautiful. He lived a long time unmarried; and his counsellors would persuade him to take a wife. "My friends," said he, "it is clear to you that I am rich and powerful enough; and therefore want not wealth. Go, then, through town and country, and seek me out a beautiful and wise virgin; and if ye can find such a one, however poor she may be, I will marry her." The command was obeyed; they proceeded on their search,

---

* "Here seems to be an allusion to MEDEA'S history."—WARTON. It is surely more analogous to the story of the Minotaur, and the clue furnished by Ariadne to her lover. Warton should have explained the resemblance he has fancied.

until at last they discovered a lady of royal extraction with the qualifications desired. But the king was not so easily satisfied, and determined to put her wisdom to the test. He sent to the lady by a herald a piece of linen cloth, three inches square; and bade her contrive to make for him a shirt exactly fitted to his body. " Then," added he, " she shall be my wife." The messenger, thus commissioned, departed on his errand, and respectfully presented the cloth, with the request of the king. " How can I comply with it," exclaimed the lady, " when the cloth is but three inches square? It is impossible to make a shirt of that; but bring me a vessel in which I may work, and I promise to make the shirt long enough for the body." The messenger returned with the reply of the virgin, and the king immediately sent a sumptuous vessel, by means of which she extended the cloth to the required size, and completed the shirt. Whereupon the wise king married her.

APPLICATION.

My beloved, the king is God; the virgin, the mother of Christ; who was also the chosen vessel. By the messenger is meant Gabriel; the cloth is the grace of God, which, by proper care and labour, is made sufficient for man's salvation.

TALE LXV.

OF THE CURE OF THE SOUL.

A KING once undertook a journey from one state to another. After much travel, he came to a certain cross, which was covered with inscriptions. On one side was written, " Oh, king, if you ride this way, you yourself will find good entertainment, but your horse will get nothing to eat." On another part appeared as follows: " If you ride this road, your horse will be admirably attended to, but you will get nothing for yourself." Again, on a third place was inscribed: " If you walk this path, you will find entertainment both for yourself and horse ; but before you depart, you will be miserably beaten." On a fourth part of the cross it was said : " If you walk this way, they will serve you diligently, but they will detain your horse, and oblige you to proceed the rest of your journey on foot." When the king had read the inscriptions, he began to consider which of the evils he should choose. He determined at length upon the first ; " For," said he, " I shall fare very well myself, though my horse starve ; and the night will soon pass away." On this, he struck the spurs into his horse ; and arrived at the castle of a knight, who entreated him courteously, but gave his steed little or nothing. In the morning he rode on to his own palace, and related all that he had seen.*

APPLICATION.

My beloved, the king is any good Christian, who journeys for the safety of his soul. The horse which he rides is the body, composed of the four elements. The cross is conscience, which points out the way, and explains the consequences attending it.

TALE LXVI.

OF CONSTANCY.

THERE once lived a king who had a beautiful and beloved daughter. After his death she succeeded to the throne, but, being young and unprotected, a certain tyrannical duke came to her, and, by means of large promises, won her to dishonour. When his iniquitous purpose was accomplished, the girl wept bitterly ; and soon after the tyrant expelled her from the inheritance. Thus reduced from the splendours of royalty to the lowest state of wretchedness, she solicited alms of the passengers. It

---

* [Compare the story of " Lubim Czarewich and the Winged Wolf" in *Russian Popular Tales*, p. 1, where the hero is offered the choice between three roads in terms almost identical with the text. —ED.]

happened that as she sat weeping by the wayside, a certain knight passed by, and observing her great beauty, became enamoured of her. "Fair lady," said he, "what are you?" "I am," replied the weeping girl, "the only daughter of a king; after whose death a tyrant seduced and abused me, and then deprived me of my inheritance." "Well," returned the knight, "are you willing to marry me?" "Oh, my Lord!" exclaimed she, "I desire it beyond anything that could happen." "Then plight me your faith," said the knight; "promise to receive no one for your husband but me, and I will make war upon the tyrant, and reinstate you in your possessions. But if I fall in the conflict, I entreat you to retain my bloody arms under your care, in testimony of affection; that in case any one hereafter shall desire your love, you may enter the chamber in which the arms hang, and may thus be reminded of the proof I have given of my attachment and devotion to your service." "I promise faithfully," returned she, "to comply with your wishes: but, oh! may your life be safe!" The knight therefore armed himself, and proceeded to engage the tyrant, who had heard of his intention, and prepared for the attack. The knight, however, overcame him, and cut off his head: but, receiving a mortal wound, he died on the third day. The lady bewailed his death, and hung up his bloody armour in her chamber. She visited it frequently, and washed it with bitter tears. Many noblemen sought to espouse her, and made magnificent promises; but invariably before returning an answer she entered the chamber, and, surveying the bloody armour steadfastly, exclaimed, amid abundance of tears, "Oh, thou, who devotedst thyself to death for one so unworthy, and restoredst me my kingdom!—far be it from me to abjure my plighted faith." Then returning to those who sought her love, she declared her resolution never to unite herself with another. When they heard this they departed; and thus she remained single to the end of her life.*

* See Tale XXV., which differs but little from this.
[Mr. D. G. Rossetti has used this tale and the twenty-fifth as the groundwork of his beautiful poem, "The Staff and Scrip" (Rossetti's *Poems*, p. 47).—ED.]

My beloved, the king is our heavenly Father; and the daughter is the soul seduced by the devil. The wayside is the world. The soldier who rode past is the Son of God; the bloody armour is His death and passion.

TALE LXVII.

OF EXCUSES WHICH ARE NOT TO BE ADMITTED IN EXTREME CASES.

THE Emperor Maximian was renowned for the wisdom of his government. In his reign there lived two knights, the one wise and the other foolish, but who had a mutual regard for each other. "Let us make an agreement," said the wise knight, "which will be advantageous to both." The other assented, and, by the direction of his friend, proceeded to draw blood from his right arm. "I," said the latter, "will drink of thy blood, and thou of mine; so that neither in prosperity nor in adversity shall our covenant be broken, and whatsoever the one gains, shall be divided by the other." The foolish knight agreed; and they ratified the treaty by a draught of each other's blood. After this they both dwelt in the same mansion. Now, the lord of the country had two cities, one of which was built on the summit of a lofty mountain. Since all who went to it would possess great wealth, and remain there for life, the path to this city was narrow and stony, and about midway three knights with a large army were stationed. The custom was that whosoever passed should do battle, or lose his life, with everything that he possessed. In that city the emperor appointed a seneschal, who received without exception all who entered, and ministered to them according to their condition. But the other city was built in a valley under the mountain, the way to which was perfectly level and pleasant. Three soldiers dwelt there, who cheerfully received whosoever came, and served them according to their pleasure. In this city also a seneschal was placed, but he ordered all who approached to be thrown into prison, and on the coming of the judge to be condemned.

The wise knight said to his companion, " My friend, let us go through the world as other knights are wont to do,* and seek our fortune." His friend acquiesced; they set out upon their travels, and presently came to a place where two roads met. " See," said the wise knight, " here are two roads. The one leads to the noblest city in the world, and if we go thither, we shall obtain whatsoever our hearts desire. But the other path conducts to a city which is built in a valley; if we venture there, we shall be thrown into prison, and afterwards crucified. I advise, therefore, that we avoid this road, and pursue the other." " My friend," replied the foolish knight, " I heard long ago of these two cities; but the way to that upon the mountain is very narrow and dangerous, because of the soldiers who attack those that enter; nay, they frequently rob and murder them. But the other way is open and broad; and the soldiers who are stationed there receive passengers with hospitality, and supply them with all things necessary. This is sufficiently manifest; I see it, and had rather believe my own eyes than you." " It is true," returned his companion, " one way is difficult to walk along, but the other is infinitely worse at the end: ignominy and crucifixion will certainly be our doom. But fear you to walk the strait road, on account of a battle, or because of robbers? you, who are a soldier, and therefore in duty bound to fight valiantly! However, if you will go with me the way I desire, I promise to precede you in the attack; and be assured with your aid we shall overcome every obstacle." " I protest to you," said the

---

* " Sicut cæteri milites." Here we discover those features of chivalry, so admirably ridiculed by Cervantes. But, in times of oppression, when every one followed

> " the simple plan,
> That he may take who has the power,
> And he may keep who can,"

the wandering hero, ever ready to risk his life in defence of the injured, was governed by a noble and useful institution.

other, "I will not go your way, but will take mine own."
"Well," replied the wise knight, "since I have pledged
you my word, and drank your blood in token of fidelity, I
will proceed with you, though against my better judgment." So they both went the same path.

The progress was extremely pleasant till they reached
the station of the three soldiers, who honourably and magnificently entertained them. And here the foolish knight
said to the wise one, "Friend, did I not tell thee how
comfortable this way would be found; in all which the
other is deficient?" "If the end be well," replied he,
"all is well;* but I do not hope it." With the three
soldiers they tarried some time; insomuch that the
seneschal of the city, hearing that two knights, contrary
to royal prohibition, were approaching, sent out troops to
apprehend them. The foolish knight he commanded to
be bound hand and foot, and thrown into a pit, but the
other he imprisoned. Now, when the judge arrived, the
malefactors were all brought before him, and among the
rest our two knights—the wiser of whom thus spoke : "My
Lord, I complain of my comrade, who is the occasion of
my death. I declared to him the law of this city, and the
danger to which we were exposed, but he would not listen
to my words, nor abide by my counsels. 'I will trust my
eyes,' said he, 'rather than you.' Now, because I had
taken an oath never to forsake him in prosperity or in
adversity, I accompanied him hither. But ought I therefore to die? Pronounce a just judgment." Then the
foolish knight addressed the judge: "He is himself the
cause of my death. For every one knows that he is
reckoned wise, and I am naturally a fool. Ought he then
so lightly to have surrendered his wisdom to my folly?
And had he not done so, I should have returned to go the
way which he went, even for the solemn oath which I had
sworn. And therefore, since he is wise, and I am foolish,
he is the occasion of my death." The judge, hearing this,
spoke to both, but to the wise knight first : "Thou who
art wise, since thou didst listen so heedlessly to his folly

* "Si finis bonus est, totum bonum erit." This gives us the
origin, probably, of the proverb, "*All's well that ends well.*" "Finis
coronat opus" is of a similar character.

and followedst him, and thou, foolish man, since thou
didst not credit his word, but acted out thine own folly, ye
shall both be suspended on the cross this very day." Thus
it was done.

My beloved, the emperor is Christ; the two knights,
body and soul; of which the last is the wise one. In
baptism they were united. They drank blood; that is,
the blood in the veins prevents their separation, and preserves life. The two ways are penitence and the world's
glory. The way of penitence is narrow, but the other is
broad and alluring. The city on the mountain is heaven;
that in the valley is hell. The three soldiers are the
world, the flesh, and the devil, &c., &c.

TALE LXVIII.

OF MAINTAINING TRUTH TO THE LAST.

In the reign of Gordian, there was a certain noble soldier
who had a fair but vicious wife. It happened that her
husband having occasion to travel, the lady sent for her
gallant. Now, one of her handmaids, it seems, was skilful
in interpreting the song of birds; and in the court of the
castle there were three cocks.* During the night, while
the gallant was with his mistress, the first cock began to
crow. The lady heard it, and said to her servant, " Dear
friend, what says yonder cock?" She replied, " That you
are grossly injuring your husband." "Then," said the lady,
" kill that cock without delay." They did so; but soon
after the second cock crew, and the lady repeated her
question. "Madam," said the handmaid, "he says "My

---

* The interpretation of the language of birds is clearly an oriental
fiction; several instances of which are furnished by the Arabian
Tales. It has since been made the vehicle of many instructive fables.
See *Spectator*, vol. vii. No. 512, which is copied from the "Story of
the two Owls," in the *Turkish Tales.*

companion died for revealing the truth, and for the same cause, I am prepared to die.'" "Kill him," cried the lady, —which they did. After this, the third cock crew. "What says he?" asked she again. "Hear, see, and say nothing, if you would live in peace." "Oh, oh!" said the lady, "*don't* kill him." And her orders were obeyed.

APPLICATION.

My beloved, the emperor is God; the soldier, Christ; and the wife, the soul. The gallant is the devil. The handmaid is conscience. The first cock is our Saviour, who was put to death; the second is the martyrs; and the third is a preacher who ought to be earnest in declaring the truth, but, being deterred by menaces, is afraid to utter it.

TALE LXIX.

OF CHASTITY.

The Emperor Gallus employed a singularly skilful carpenter in the erection of a magnificent palace. At that period, a certain knight lived who had a very beautiful daughter; and who, perceiving the extraordinary sagacity of the artificer, determined to give him the lady in marriage. Calling him, therefore, he said, "My good friend, ask of me what you will; so that it be possible, I will do it, provided you marry my daughter." The other assented, and the nuptial rites were celebrated accordingly. Then the mother of the lady said to the carpenter, "My son, since you have become one of our family, I will bestow upon you a curious shirt. It possesses this singular property, that as long as you and your wife are faithful to each other, it will neither be rent, nor worn, nor stained. But if—which Heaven forbid!—either of you prove unfaithful, instantly it will lose its virtue." The carpenter, very happy in what he heard, took the shirt, and returned great thanks for the gift.

A short while afterward, the carpenter being sent for to superintend the building of the emperor's palace, took with him the valuable present which he had received. He continued absent until the structure was complete; and numbers, observing how much he laboured, admired the freshness and spotless purity of his shirt. Even the emperor condescended to notice it, and said to him, " My master, how is it that in despite of your laborious occupation, and the constant use of your shirt, it still preserves its colour and beauty?" " You must know, my Lord," said he, " that as long as my wife and I continue faithful to each other, my shirt retains its original whiteness and beauty; but if either of us forget our matrimonial vows, it will sully like any other cloth." A soldier, overhearing this, thought within himself, " If I can I will make you wash your shirt." Wherefore, without giving any cause of suspicion to the carpenter, he secretly hastened to his house, and solicited his wife to dishonour. She received him with an appearance of pleasure, and seemed to be entirely influenced by the same feelings. " But," added she, " in this place we are exposed to observation; come with me, and I will conduct you into a private chamber." He followed her, and closing the door, she said, " Wait here awhile; I will return presently." Thus she did every day, all the time supplying him only with bread and water. Without regard to his urgency, she compelled him to endure this humiliating treatment; and before long, two other soldiers came to her from the emperor's court, with the same evil views. In like manner, she decoyed them into the chamber, and fed them with bread and water.

The sudden disappearance, however, of the three soldiers gave rise to much inquiry; and the carpenter, on the completion of his labours, received the stipulated sum, and returned to his own home. His virtuous wife met him with joy, and looking upon the spotless shirt, exclaimed, " Blessed be God! our truth is made apparent—there is not a single stain upon the shirt." To which he replied, " My beloved, during the progress of the building, three soldiers, one after another, came to ask questions about the shirt. I related the fact, and since that time nothing has been heard of them." The lady smiled, and said, " The soldiers respecting whom you feel anxious thought me a fit subject for their improper solicitation, and came hither with the vilest intent. I decoyed them into a remote chamber, and have fed them with bread and water." The carpenter, delighted with this proof of his wife's fidelity, spared their lives, and liberated them; and he and his wife lived happily for the rest of their lives.

APPLICATION.

My beloved, the emperor is God; the palace is the human heart. The knight who married his daughter to the carpenter is Christ; the carpenter is any good Christian, and the mother is the Church. The shirt is faith; the three soldiers are pride, lusts of the eyes, and lusts of the heart.

TALE LXX.

OF THE COMPUNCTIONS OF A FAITHFUL MIND.

A CERTAIN king had a beautiful and wise daughter, whom he was desirous of marrying. But she had sworn never to unite herself to any but upon three conditions. First, he was to state accurately how many feet there were in the length, breadth, and depth of the four elements. Secondly, he was to change the north wind. And thirdly, he was to carry fire in his bosom without injury. When the king, therefore, understood his daughter's resolution, he proclaimed it through the kingdom, and promised to give her in marriage to whomsoever performed the conditions. Many endeavoured, but failed; until at length a certain knight from foreign parts heard of the girl's oath. He hastened to the palace, conveying with him a single attendant, and an extremely fiery horse. On being admitted into the king's presence, he said, " I am desirous of espousing your majesty's daughter, and I am prepared to solve the questions which have been proposed." The king assented, and the soldier, calling his servant, commanded him to lie upon the earth. And when he was thus laid, his master measured his length from one extremity to the other. When he had done this, he said to the king, " My Lord, your first question is resolved ; I find in the four elements scarcely seven feet." " How ? " replied the king. " What has this to do with the four elements ? " " My Lord," answered the soldier, " every man, as well as every animal, is composed of the four elements." "Amen," said the king, " you have proved this very satisfactorily. Now then for the second condition, which is to change the wind." Immediately he caused his horse to be brought into the area of the court, and there administered a potion, by which the animal was made perfectly quiet. This done, he turned his horse's head towards the east, and said, " Observe, my Lord, the wind is changed from north to east." " How ? " answered the king, " what is this to the wind ? " " Sire," returned the soldier, " is it not obvious to your wisdom that the life of every animal consists in his breath, which is air ? As long as he raged fiercely, so long was he in the north. But when I had given him the potion I turned him toward the east, so that he is ready to bear his burden." " This also," said the king, " you have well proved ; go on to the third." " My Lord," replied the soldier, " this, so please you, I will perform before all your court." Then, taking up a handful of burning coals, he deposited them in his bosom, without injury to his flesh. " Truly," exclaimed the king, " you have done very well in these matters : but tell me, how happens it that you are unhurt by the fire." " It was not," returned the soldier, " by any power of my own, but by virtue of a singular stone, which I always carry about with me. And whosoever possesses this stone is able to resist the hottest fire." The king, satisfied that the conditions had been accurately complied with, gave orders for his marriage with the lady. He loaded him with riches and honours, and they both ended their days in the greatest happiness.

APPLICATION.

My beloved, the king is our Lord Jesus Christ. The daughter is the human soul. To measure the elements is to subdue the lusts of the flesh. The fiery horse is any sinner, whom repentance changes. The fire in the bosom is luxury, pride, avarice, &c., and the stone is a true and lively faith in Christ.

TALE LXXI.

OF AN ETERNAL RECOMPENSE.

A KING made a great feast, and despatched messengers with invitations, in which the guests were promised not only a magnificent entertainment, but considerable wealth. When the messengers had gone through town and country, executing everywhere the commands of their king, it happened that there dwelt in a certain city two men, of whom one was valiant and robustly made, but blind; while the other was lame and feeble, but his sight was excellent. Said the blind man to the lame, "My friend, ours is a hard case; for it is spread far and near that the king gives a great feast, at which every man will receive not only abundance of food, but much wealth; and thou art lame, while I am blind: how then shall we get to the feast?" "Take my counsel," replied the lame man, "and we will obtain a share both of the dinner and wealth." "Verily," answered the other, "I will follow any counsel that may benefit me." "Well, then," returned the lame man, "thou art stout of heart, and robust of body, and therefore thou shalt carry me on thy back who am lame and weak, and I will guide you, since I have good sight; by this means we shall reach the festival and secure the reward." "Be it as thou hast said," replied he of the legs; "get upon my back immediately." He did so; the lame man pointed the way, and the other carried him. They arrived at the feast, and received the same recompense as the rest.*

APPLICATION.

My beloved, the king is our Lord Jesus Christ, who prepared the feast of eternal life. The blind man is the

---

* This fable has crept into our story-books.

powerful of this world, who are blind to their future safety. The lame man is any devout person, who has nothing in common with the man of the world, but sees the kingdom which is to come.*

TALE LXXII.

OF THE DESTRUCTION OF UNGRATEFUL MEN.

A CERTAIN king had an only son, whom he ardently loved. When the boy arrived at man's estate, day after day he solicited his father to resign the kingdom, and deliver to himself the sovereign power. " My dear son," said the king, " if I were satisfied that you would treat me honourably and kindly during the remainder of my life, I should have no objection to relinquish the throne to you." The son answered, " My Lord, I will bind myself by an oath, before all the noblemen of the empire, to do in every respect as a son ought to do. Be confident that I will show greater honour to you than to myself." The old king trusted to his assurances, and resigned the supreme command. But no sooner was the son crowned, and seated on the throne of his ancestors, than his heart underwent a total change. For a few years he gave due honour to his indulgent parent, but after that entirely neglected him. This unexpected and unmerited treatment naturally exasperated the old king, and he began to complain to the wise men of the empire that his son had broken the contract. They, therefore, having always loved the father, reproved the son for his ingratitude. But the new king spurned them from him with fury; imprisoned his father in a castle, and permitted not the smallest access to him. Here he often endured the extremity of hunger, and every other species of wretchedness.

* The latter part of this *moralization* recommends " fideliter viris ecclesiasticis *decimas dare. Si* hæc feceritis nos viri religiosi tenemur vobis viam salutis ostendere quomodo poteritis ad vitam eternam pervenire." The monks never forgot this—" If you pay us, we will show you the way; else, find it out yourself." Such was the burden of their song.

It happened that the king himself once passed the night in the same castle; and the father sent to him the following message:—" Oh, my son, pity thy old father who gave up everything to thee. I suffer thirst and hunger; and deprived of all comfort—even of wine to cheer me in my infirmity—I draw out my life." " I know not," said the king, " that there is wine in this castle." He was told that there were five casks reposited in that place, but that without his permission the seneschal refused to draw wine from them. " Suffer me, my dear son," said the unhappy father, " suffer me at least to recruit my wasted form with the first of these casks." The son refused, alleging that it was new, and therefore prejudicial to old men. " Then," said the old man, " give me the second cask." " I will not do that," answered the king, " because it is kept for my own drinking, and for the young noble-men who attend me." " Yet you will surely permit me to take the third," continued his father; " No," replied the other; " it is very strong, and you are so weak and infirm that it would kill you." " The fourth cask, then?" said he, " give me that." " It is sour, and would do you much injury." " But," urged the father, " there is a fifth, allow me to retain it." " Oh," said the king, " it is nothing but dregs; the noblemen would charge me with having slain thee in case thou wert permitted to drink of it." The poor father, hearing excuses like these, went away very sorrowful; but secretly wrote letters to the noblemen, declaring how he had been treated, and imploring them to relieve him from the misery he was compelled to endure. His ill-usage excited their pity and indignation; they restored the father, and threw the son into prison, where he died.*

APPLICATION.

My beloved, the king is Christ; and the son is any bad Christian.

* Our nursery-books contain a story not unlike the present. A father resigns his estates to an ungrateful son, and is driven into the garret, and left to neglect and poverty. The grandson pities, and by a pointed speech—hardly characteristic of a child—reproves, and touches his parent's heart.

TALE LXXIII.

OF AVARICE, WHICH MAKES MANY BLIND.

A CERTAIN king of Rome decreed that every blind man should annually receive a hundred shillings. It happened that twenty-three associates came into the city and entered a tavern to drink. They remained there seven days, both eating and drinking; but when they would reckon with the tavern-keeper, they had not sufficient money to defray the expense of what they had consumed. "Friends," quoth mine host, "here be wanting a hundred shillings. I tell you, of a certainty, ye go not hence till ye have paid the uttermost farthing." This rather startled the revellers, who, turning to one another, exclaimed, "What shall we do? We cannot pay so large a sum." At length one of them observed, "Listen to me; I will give you the best advice. The king of this country has decreed that whosoever is blind shall receive from his treasury one hundred shillings. Let us then cast lots, and upon whomsoever the lot falls, we will deprive him of sight, and send him to the king for the promised benevolence. Thus we shall depart in peace." They all agreed that the counsel was excellent; and casting lots, the chance fell upon the contriver of the expedient; whose eyes they immediately put out. He was then led to the palace. Arriving at the gate, they knocked and were admitted by the porter, who inquired their business. The blind man answered, "I am one entitled, from my deficiency of sight, to the benefit of the royal donation." "Well," said the porter, "I will inform the seneschal." He went accordingly; but the wary seneschal first determined to examine his exterior before he delivered the money. He did so, and then asked what he wanted. "A hundred shillings," replied he, "which the law gives to every blind man." "My friend," said the seneschal, "if I am not greatly mistaken, I saw you yesterday in a tavern with both eyes perfect. You misinterpret the law. It relates to those who, by some natural infirmity, or by accident, become blind—and against which there was no defence. Such the law protects and relieves. But you voluntarily surrendered your eyes; you drank away your money in a tavern, and planned this deceit. Seek, therefore, consolation and relief in the same place, for you shall not get a halfpenny here." The blind man then retired in great confusion from the palace.

APPLICATION.

My beloved, the law in the story is the law of God. He who errs by natural infirmity, or through the temptations of the devil, and repents, is forgiven. But if any one, from pure malice, shall commit sin and fall into despair, he can scarcely, if at all, be pardoned. The tavern-keeper is the devil.

TALE LXXIV.

OF FORESIGHT AND CARE.

A KING had an only son, whom he tenderly loved. He caused a golden apple to be made at an immense expense; and shortly after its fabrication he sickened. Finding his end approach, he called to him his son, and spoke after the following manner:—"My dear son, I shall not recover from the sickness under which I suffer, and on my blessing I charge you, travel through town and country, and take with you the golden apple which I caused to be made; find out the greatest fool, and deliver to him that apple from me." The son faithfully promised to execute his parent's wish; and the king, turning himself toward the wall, resigned his spirit. A splendid funeral was prepared, and after the interment the son set out upon his travels, with the apple in his possession.

He traversed many countries and kingdoms, and found abundance of fools, but none whom he thought quite worthy of the apple. At last he entered a certain province, and approached its principal city. Observing the king, very magnificently attended, riding through the streets, he asked various questions respecting the person he saw, and especially of the institutions of the country. He was answered that, according to their custom, the throne was annually vacated; and that the late possessor, deprived of every honour, was driven into banishment, where he died in obscurity and poverty. The traveller, hearing this account, exclaimed, " *This* is the man ; I have found him whom I sought;" and immediately hastening to the palace, he bent his knee, and cried, " Hail, oh king! my deceased father bequeathed to you this golden apple in his last will." The king received the gift and said, " My friend, how can this be ? Your royal parent knew nothing of me, nor have I ever performed any service to him. Why, then, hath he left me so valuable a present?" "The king, my Lord," replied he, " bequeathed it not more to you than to another; but on his blessing, he charged me to bestow it upon the greatest fool that I could find. And I have now travelled through various kingdoms and countries, but nowhere have I discovered so exquisite a fool and madman. Therefore, according to my sire's command, I resign the apple to your most gracious majesty." " But," said the king, " on what account do you take me for so great a fool?" " I will tell you, my Lord," returned the other. " You are king for one year; and then, doomed to poverty and exile, you perish most miserably. I declare to you, I do not believe that there is in the whole world such an instance of egregious folly. For would any but a fool choose so short a time of splendour for an end so calamitous?" " Why," replied the king, " you are doubtless right; and therefore, while I yet reign, I will prepare for my future existence. I will send the greater portion of my wealth into a remote land, upon which I may live in comfort, when I am driven into exile." He did so; and for a number of years enjoyed great prosperity, and ended his life in peace.

APPLICATION.

My beloved, the king who bequeathed a golden apple to fools is God. That apple is the world. The king who

reigned for a year is any man who lives in this world
(considered with respect to futurity) but as a single hour.
Let us then make provision for the future.

———

TALE LXXV.

OF WORLDLY ANXIETY.

THERE formerly lived a king who had three fair daughters.
He married them to three dukes; but, unhappily, all their
husbands died in the space of one year.   The king, being
made acquainted with this circumstance, would have had
his daughters marry again, and calling the first into his
presence he said, "My dear daughter, your husband is
dead; I will therefore unite you to another."   But she
would by no means consent, and assigned for it this reason:
"If I marry again, I should love my second husband
equally with the first; perhaps more, or it might be less.
This ought not to be; for my first husband possessed my
earliest affection—my virgin troth.   Therefore the second
ought not to be loved so well.   But I might love him more,
and this would increase the evil: on the other hand, if I
loved him less, there would exist only contention between
us.   So that I resolve never to be espoused again."   The
king, satisfied with what he heard, called another of his
daughters, and proposed the same thing to her as to her
eldest sister.   She replied, "My Lord, I also decline this
matter.   For should I comply, it must be either for riches,
or power, or beauty.   Now, of riches I have quite enough;
my friends are sufficiently numerous to defend me; and as
for beauty, I do not believe there was so beautiful a person
in the world as my late husband.   Therefore, I too resolve
upon a single state."   The king then applied to the third
daughter, and she gave the following reasons for refusing
his request:—"If," said she, "I marry, my husband must
desire me either for my beauty or my wealth.   Now, it cannot be for the former, because I am not beautiful; then, it
must be for the latter, and true love never existed which

was founded upon mercenary feelings. When wealth flies, love flies with it.* Therefore, I would on no account marry again. Moreover, the Sacred Writings say that a husband and wife are one body but two souls; therefore, the body of my husband is my body, and the converse. Every day I visit the sepulchre of my deceased lord, and he is ever present to my mind. For all these causes, I determine to remain as I am." The king, pleased with the virtuous resolutions of his daughters, solicited them no more.

APPLICATION.

My beloved, the king is God. The three daughters are the soul, which image the Holy Trinity. For God said, "Let us make man in *our image;*" therefore the Trinity in unity is typified by the soul, and the soul represented by three persons. The three dukes are the devil, the world, and the flesh; when they die, that is, when the soul repents of her sins, do not again be united to them.

TALE LXXVI.

OF CONCORD.

Two physicians once resided in a city, who were admirably skilled in medicine; insomuch that all the sick who took their prescriptions were healed, and it thence became a question with the inhabitants which of them was the best. After a while, a dispute arose between them upon this point. Said one, "My friend, why should discord or envy or anger separate us? Let us make the trial, and whosoever is inferior in skill shall serve the other." "But how," replied his friend, "is this to be brought about?" The first physician answered, "Hear me. I will pluck out your eyes, without doing you the smallest injury, and lay them

* When Poverty comes in at the door, Love flies out at the window.—ENGLISH PROVERB.

before you on the table; and when you desire it, I will replace them as perfect and serviceable as they were before. If, in like manner, you can perform this, we will then be esteemed equal, and walk as brethren through the world. But, remember, he who fails in the attempt shall become the servant of the other." "I am well pleased," returned his fellow, "to do as you say." Whereupon, he who made the proposition took out his instruments and extracted the eyes, besmearing the sockets and the outer part of the lids with a certain rich ointment. "My dear friend," said he, "what do you perceive?" "Of a surety," cried the other, "I see nothing. I want the use of my eyes, but I feel no pain from their loss. I pray you, however, restore them to their places as you promised." "Willingly," said his friend. He again touched the inner and outer part of the lids with the ointment, and then, with much precision, inserted the balls into their sockets. "How do you see now?" asked he. "Excellently," returned the other, "nor do I feel the least pain." "Well, then," continued the first, "it now remains for you to treat me in a similar manner."* "I am ready," said the latter. And accordingly taking the instruments, as the first had done, he smeared the upper and under parts of the eye with a peculiar ointment, drew out the eyes and placed them upon the table. The patient felt no pain; but added, "I wish you would hasten to restore them." The operator cheerfully complied; but as he prepared his implements, a crow entered by an open window, and seeing the eyes upon the table, snatched one of them up, and flew away with it. The physician, vexed at what had happened, said to himself, "If I do not restore the eye to my companion, I must become his slave." At that moment a goat, browsing at no great distance, attracted his observation. Instantly he ran to it, drew out one of its eyes, and put it into the place of the lost orb. "My dear friend," exclaimed the operator, "how do things appear to you?" "Neither in extracting nor in replacing," he answered, "did I suffer the least pain; but—bless me!—one eye looks up to the trees!" "Ah!"

---

* A foolish physician. If the other succeeded, he acknowledged his superiority, or equality, at least; if not, he lost his eyes. At all events, he could gain nothing by the experiment.

replied the first, " this is the very perfection of medicine. Neither of us is superior; henceforward we will be friends, as we are equals; and banish far off that spirit of contention which has destroyed our peace." They lived from this time in the greatest amity.

APPLICATION.

My beloved, the two physicians are the new and the old law. Thus the Jews and Christians contend: the extracted eyes denote those parts of the old law which Christians retain. The crow is the devil; and the goat's eye typifies those ceremonies of the Jews to which they attach so much importance, and by which they are not able to discern the truth.*

TALE LXXVII.

OF RICHES, WHICH ARE NOT TO BE COVETED.

A CERTAIN king had two daughters, one of whom was extremely beautiful, and very much beloved. The other, however, was of a dark, unprepossessing complexion, and hated as much as her sister was esteemed. This difference in their appearance caused the king to give them characteristic names. He called the first Rosamunda,† that is, the fragrant rose; and the second, Gratiaplena, or the full of grace.

A herald was commanded to proclaim that all men should come to him, and he would give his daughters to

---

* This is to see the beam in a neighbour's eye, and forget that in their own. The Catholic ceremonies are open to the same censure, and are equally prejudicial in their consequences.

† Or *Rosa mundi*, rose of the world. There are two monkish Latin verses inscribed over the unfortunate paramour of Henry II. which may find a place here:—

"Hic jacet in tumba ROSA MUNDI, non ROSAMUNDA;
"Non redolet, sed olet, quæ redolere solet."—CAMDEN.

those who were worthy. But whoever got the beautiful girl to wife should have nothing but her beauty; and he who selected the dark girl should succeed him to the throne. Multitudes flocked to the summons; but every one still clung to the fair lady, and not even the temptation of a kingdom could induce any one to espouse the other. Gratiaplena wept bitterly at her unhappy fate. " My daughter," said the king, "why are you so grievously afflicted?" "Oh, my father," returned she, "no one visits or speaks kindly to me; all pay their attentions to my sister, and despise me." "Why, my dear daughter," said the father, "do you not know that whosoever marries you will possess the crown?" The lady dried her tears, and was marvellously comforted.

Not long after a king entered the royal palace, and, seeing the great beauty of Rosamunda, desired her in marriage. The king, her father, consented, and she was espoused with great joy. But the other daughter remained many years unbetrothed. At last a certain poor nobleman, very wisely reflecting that though the girl was abominably ugly yet she was rich, determined to marry her. He therefore went to the king, and solicited his consent; who, glad enough at the proposal, cheerfully bestowed her upon him; and after his decease, bequeathed him the kingdom.

APPLICATION.

My beloved, the king is our Lord Jesus Christ; Rosamunda is the world, which every one loves. The other daughter, Gratiaplena, so abhorred by the world, is poverty. But the poor in spirit will receive the kingdom of heaven.

TALE LXXVIII.

OF THE CONSTANCY OF LOVE.

THE beautiful daughter of a certain king was betrothed to a noble duke, by whom she had very handsome children. The duke died, and was greatly bewailed by the whole state. After his death her friends earnestly solicited the lady to marry a second time, alleging that her youth and beauty required it. But she answered, "I will never marry again. My departed lord was so good and kind; he loved me so truly, that I verily believe I shall not live much longer. And if it were possible that I could forget what he has been, where shall I find another? Admitting that I should marry, perhaps my second husband would also precede me to the grave? Why, then, my grief would be awakened the second time, and my afflictions be as heavy as before! Moreover, if he were a bad man, it would indeed be torture to remember him who was good, while one so inferior had succeeded him. I am therefore determined to remain as I am." *

APPLICATION.

My beloved, the king is God; the daughter the soul, betrothed to our Lord Jesus Christ.

TALE LXXIX.

OF PRESUMPTION.

THERE was a certain king who had a singular partiality for little dogs that barked loudly; so much so, indeed, that they usually rested in his lap. Being long accustomed to eat and sleep in this situation, they would scarcely do either elsewhere: seeming to take great pleasure in looking at him, and putting their paws upon his neck; and thus the king got much amusement from their antics. Now, it happened that an ass, who noticed this familiarity, thought to himself, "If I should sing and dance before the king, and put my feet round his neck, he would feed me also upon the greatest dainties, and suffer me to rest in his lap." Accordingly, quitting his stable, he entered

* See Tale LXXV., which is similar both in structure and reasoning.

the hall, and running up to the king, raised his clumsy feet with difficulty around the royal neck. The servants, not understanding the ass's courteous intention, imagined that he was mad; and pulling him away, belaboured him soundly. He was then led back to the stable.*

APPLICATION.

My beloved, the king is Christ; the barking dogs are zealous preachers. The ass is any one who, without the necessary qualifications, presumes to take upon himself the interpretation of the word of God.

TALE LXXX.

OF THE CUNNING OF THE DEVIL, AND OF THE SECRET JUDGMENTS OF GOD.

THERE formerly lived a hermit, who in a remote cave passed night and day in the service of God. At no great distance from his cell a shepherd tended his flock. It happened that this person one day fell into a deep sleep, and in the mean time a robber, perceiving his carelessness, carried off his sheep. When the keeper awoke and discovered the theft, he began to swear in good set terms that he had lost his sheep; and where they were conveyed was totally beyond his knowledge. Now, the lord of the flock, when he heard this, was filled with rage, and commanded him to be put to death. This gave great umbrage to the hermit before mentioned. "Oh, Heaven," said he to himself, "seest thou this deed? the innocent suffers for the guilty: why permittest thou such things? If thus injustice triumph, why do I remain here? I will again enter the world, and do as other men do."

With these feelings he quitted his hermitage, and returned into the world; but God willed not that he should

---

* We have here a new version of an Æsopian fable.

be lost : an angel in the form of a man was commissioned
to join him. Accordingly, crossing the hermit's path, he
thus accosted him—" My friend, where are you going ? "
" I go," said the other, " to the city before us." " I will
accompany you," replied the angel; " I am a messenger
from heaven, and come to be the associate of your way."
They walked on together towards the city. When they
had entered, they entreated for the love of God * harbourage during the night at the house of a certain knight,
who received them with cheerfulness, and entertained
them with much magnificence. The knight had an only
son lying in the cradle, whom he exceedingly loved.
After supper, their bed-chamber was sumptuously decorated; and the angel retired with the hermit to rest. But
about the middle of the night the former got up and
strangled the sleeping infant. The hermit, horror-struck
at what he witnessed, said within himself, " Never can
this be an angel of God : the good knight gave him everything that was necessary; he had but this poor innocent,
and this strange companion of mine has strangled him."
Yet he was afraid to reprove him.

In the morning both arose and went forward to another
city, in which they were honourably entertained at the
house of one of the inhabitants. This person possessed
a superb golden cup which he highly valued ; and which,
during the night, the angel purloined. The hermit
thought, " Verily, this is one of the lost angels ; our host
has treated us well, and yet he has robbed him." But
still he held his peace, for his apprehension was extreme.
On the morrow they continued their journey ; and as they
walked they came to a certain river, over which a bridge
was thrown ; they ascended the bridge, and about mid-way
a poor man met them. " My friend," said the angel to
him, " show us the way to yonder city." The pilgrim
turned, and pointed with his finger to the road they were
to take; but as he turned, the angel seized him by the
shoulders, and precipitated him into the stream below.
At this the terrors of the hermit were again aroused—
" It is the devil," exclaimed he internally—" it is the

* The common mode of supplication, and will be frequently
noticed in these volumes.

devil, and no good angel! What evil had the poor man done that he should be drowned?" He would now have gladly departed alone; but was afraid to give utterance to the thoughts of his heart. About the hour of vespers they reached a city, in which they again sought shelter for the night; but the master of the house to whom they applied sharply refused it. "For the love of Heaven," said the angel, "afford us a shelter, lest we fall a prey to the wolves and other wild beasts." The man pointed to a stye—"That," said he, "is inhabited by pigs; if it please you to lie there, you may—but to no other place will I admit you." "If we can do no better," returned the angel, "we must accept your ungracious offer." They did so; and in the morning the angel, calling their host, said, "My friend, I give you this cup;" and he presented to him the stolen goblet. The hermit, more and more astonished at what he saw, said to himself, "Now I am certain this is the devil. The good man who received us with all kindness he despoiled, and gives the plunder to this fellow who refused us a lodging." Turning to the angel, he exclaimed, "I will travel with you no longer. I commend you to God." "Dear friend," answered the angel, "first hear me, and then go thy way. When thou wert in thy hermitage, the owner of the flock unjustly put to death his servant. True it is he died innocently, but he had formerly done deeds for which he deserved to die. God allowed him to be slain, to enable him to escape the future consequences of those former sins of which he had not repented. But the guilty man who stole the sheep will suffer eternally, while the owner of the flock will repair, by alms and good works, that which he ignorantly committed. As for the son of the hospitable knight, whom I strangled in the cradle, know that before the boy was born he performed numerous works of charity and mercy, but afterwards grew parsimonious and covetous, in order to enrich the child, of which he was inordinately fond. This was the cause of its death; and now its distressed parent again is become a devout Christian. Then, for the cup which I purloined from him who received us so kindly, know that before the cup was made, there was not a more abstemious person in the world; but afterwards he took such pleasure in it, and drank from it so often, that he was intoxicated twice or thrice during the day. I took away the cup, and he has turned to his former sobriety. Again, I cast the pilgrim into the river; and know that he whom I drowned was a good Christian, but had he proceeded much further, he would have fallen into a mortal sin. Now he is saved, and reigns in celestial glory. Then, that I bestowed the cup upon the inhospitable citizen, know nothing is done without reason. He suffered us to occupy the swine-house, and I gave him a valuable consideration. But *he* will hereafter reign in hell. Put a guard, therefore, on thy lips, and detract not from the Almighty. For He knoweth all things." The hermit, hearing this, fell at the feet of the angel and entreated pardon. He returned to his hermitage, and became a good and pious Christian. (7)

TALE LXXXI.

OF THE WONDERFUL DISPENSATIONS OF PROVIDENCE, AND OF THE RISE OF POPE GREGORY.

THE Emperor Marcus had an only son and daughter, to whom he was extremely attached. When he was much advanced in years, he was seized with a grievous sickness; and seeing his end approach, summoned into his presence the chief nobles of his empire. "My friends," said he, "know that this day my spirit will return to the God who gave it. All my concern resides in an only daughter, whom I have not yet bestowed in marriage. Therefore, do thou, my son and heir, upon my blessing, provide for her an honourable and befitting husband; and as long as thou livest, value her as thine own self." Saying these words, he turned toward the wall, and his spirit fled. The state made great lamentation, and interred him with much magnificence.

The young emperor commenced his reign with great

wisdom, and in all that related to his sister strictly
fulfilled his father's dying injunction. He seated her in
the same chair with him at table, and assigned to her a
separate couch in the same apartment that he occupied
himself. Here began their unhappiness. Tempted by
the devil, he gave way to the most horrible desires ; and
finally, in spite of the pleading of the wretched girl,
violated every law both human and divine. Her tears,
if tears could have retrieved the ignominy, had been
enough : she wept bitterly, and refused all comfort ;
although the emperor attempted to console her, and
evinced the excess of grief and love. About the middle
of the year, as they sat at table, the brother narrowly
scrutinized his sister's looks. "My beloved sister," said
he, "why dost thou change colour ? the upper part of
thine eyelids darken." "No wonder," she returned, "for
I bear the weight of thy most fearful wickedness."
Hearing this, the emperor felt his spirit sink within
him, and turning round, wept very bitterly. "Perish,"
said he, "the evil day that I was born ; what is to be
done ?" "My brother," said the lady, "hear me ; we are
not, alas, the first who have grievously offended God.
There is, as you well know, a certain ancient knight, one
of the most approved counsellors of our late father : call
him hither, and, under the seal of confession, let us tell
him the whole sad story ; he will give us counsel how we
may make atonement to God, and avoid disgrace before
the world." The emperor assented—"but," said he,
"let us study in the first place to be reconciled to God."
They were then both confessed, and their contrition was
perfect as sincere. Afterwards sending for the knight,
they revealed amid a flood of tears their crime. "My
lord," he replied, "since ye are reconciled to God, hear
what I counsel. As well for your own sins, as for the
sins of your father, hasten to the Holy Land ; and before
you embark, call together the noblemen of the kingdom,
and explain to them your intent. And because your
sister is your only heir, charge them to be obedient to
her. Then, turning to me, command that she be placed
under my custody ; and that, as I value my life, she be
securely and happily lodged. I will so provide that her

parturition be kept secret, and every one remain ignorant of her fate—unless, indeed, my wife be made acquainted with it, in order to wait upon her in her necessity." "You counsel well," rejoined the king, "and I will do as you have said."

Immediately the noblemen were summoned, and preparations made for the emperor's departure to the Holy Land. His sister was conveyed to the knight's castle; and when his wife beheld her she inquired whom he had brought. He answered, "The king's sister; but, wife, swear to me by all that thou holdest sacred, on penalty of thy life, never to communicate to a living soul that which I am about to impart." She swore accordingly; and the knight then informed her of the situation of the lady, and his desire that no one might attend her but herself. The obedient spouse promised compliance, and the lady was privately introduced into the hall appointed for her residence. She was splendidly attended, and when the time of her confinement came on, she was safely delivered of a beautiful boy. As soon as the knight understood this, he entreated permission to call in a priest for the purpose of performing the rite of baptism. But she positively refused, declaring that its shameful birth forbade her to interfere, since it would expose her to detection and disgrace. "Your crime indeed is heavy," returned the knight, "but consider, should your child, therefore, perish immortally?" "My vow is registered in heaven," said the lady; "I have sworn, nor will I add perjury to my faults. Moreover, I command you to prepare an empty cask." The knight obeyed; and the lady, placing therein the cradle with the new-born boy, inscribed on small tablets the following words: "Know ye, to whomsoever chance may conduct this infant, that it is not baptized, because it is the unholy offspring of incestuous affection. For the love of God, then, cause it to be baptized. Under the child's head you will discover a quantity of gold, and with this let it be nurtured. At the feet is an equal weight of silver, designed to assist it in the future prosecution of study." This done, she deposited the tablets by the infant's side, the gold at the head, and the silver at its feet; then, enveloping it in silk garments embroidered with gold, she enclosed it in the cask, and directed the knight to cast it forthwith into the sea—trusting that, by the overruling providence of God, it might be carried into a place of safety. The knight faithfully executed the lady's wishes; he threw the cask into the sea, and, standing upon the shore, watched its progress, until it was at length lost to his sight.

As he returned to his castle, a king's messenger met him, whom he thus accosted: "Friend, whence come you?"

"From the Holy Land."

"Indeed! what rumours are abroad?"

"My lord the king is dead; and we have brought his corpse to one of his own castles."

Hearing this, the good knight could not refrain from tears. At that moment, his wife approached, and, learning the unwelcome tidings, joined her tears to his. But the knight, recovering somewhat of the dejection of spirit into which the intelligence had thrown him, said to his wife, "Weep not, I pray thee, lest our mistress should perceive it, and inquire the cause. It were better to keep silence on this unwelcome subject, until she be risen from her child-bed." Saying this, the knight entered the queen's apartment, followed by his wife. But the manifest sorrow on their countenances could not escape the penetration of the lady, and she eagerly asked the occasion. "Dear lady, we are not sad," they said, "but rather joyful at your rapid recovery." "That is not true," replied she; "I conjure you, conceal nothing, be it for good or evil." "A messenger," answered the knight, "has just returned from the Holy Land, conveying intelligence of my lord, your brother."

"What does the messenger say? Let him be called hither."

This was done; and the lady asked after the king. "He is dead," said the messenger, "and we have brought the body to his own kingdom, to be buried according to the rites of his country." The lady, possessed of this fatal intelligence, fell upon the ground; and the knight and his wife, participating in her extreme grief, cast themselves beside her. For a length of time, they all three continued in this attitude; and so intense was their sorrow, that neither sound nor sense appeared remaining. The lady arose first; tore her hair, wounded her face, and exclaimed in a shrill voice, " Woe is me! May that day perish in which I was conceived! May that night be no more remembered in which so great a wretch was born. How vast is my iniquity! In me all things are fulfilled. My hope is broken, and my strength; he was my only brother—the half of my soul. What I shall do hereafter, alas! I know not." The knight arose and said, " Dearest lady, listen to me. If you suffer yourself to be thus concerned, the whole kingdom will perish. You only are left; and you are the lawful heir. Should you destroy yourself, the nation will remain at the mercy of foreign powers. Arise, then, and direct the body to be brought hither, and honourably interred. Afterwards, we will debate concerning the prosperity of the kingdom." Quieted, if not comforted, by the knight's words, she arose, and proceeded with a noble company to the castle, where her brother's body lay. It was placed upon a bier; and no sooner had the queen entered, than she fell upon the corpse and kissed it, from the crown of his head, even to the soles of his feet. Now, the soldiers, perceiving the violent grief of their queen, drew her from the bier, and led her into the hall; and then, with great pomp, carried the body to its sepulchre.

A short period after this, a certain Duke of Burgundy sent messengers to demand the lady in marriage; but she declared her fixed determination never to marry. Irritated at her refusal, the duke observed, " If she had married me, I should indeed have been king of the country; but since it is her pleasure to despise me, she who fills the throne shall enjoy little satisfaction." Whereupon he collected his troops, and devastated every place to which he marched. He perpetrated an immensity of ill, and subdued all opposition. The queen, in this extremity, fled to a strongly fortified city, where there was a castle well appointed and defended; and here she continued many years.

Let us now return to the boy, who was thrown into the sea. The cask in which he was placed floated through many countries, until it reached, at length, a certain monastery, about the sixth festival.* On that day, the abbot of the monastery proceeded to the sea-shore, and said to his fishermen, "My friends, make ready to fish;" and whilst they were preparing their nets, the vessel was tossed by the motion of the waves upon the shore. The abbot observed it, and said to his servants, "See ye that cask? open it, and find out what is within." They did so, and behold, it was a newly born boy covered with very rich clothing. No sooner had the child looked upon the abbot, than it smiled. The sight greatly concerned the worthy monk. "Oh, my God," said he, "how comes it that we find a child in this deplorable situation?" Raising it with his own hands, he perceived the tablets under its side, which the mother had placed there; and when he had read them, he discovered that it was the offspring of an incestuous bed, and not yet baptized—and saw that this sacrament was implored, for the sake of Heaven; and that gold and silver were deposited for his nurture and education. When he had read this, and observed that the cradle was ornamented with rich cloth, he saw that the boy was of noble blood. He immediately baptized and called him after his own name, Gregory. He then intrusted him to a fisherman to nurse, with the gold and silver found upon him. The boy grew up universally beloved. In his seventh year the abbot provided for his studies, which he mastered in a surprising manner; insomuch that the monks were as fond of him as though he had been of their own order. In a short time he acquired more knowledge than them all.

It happened that one day, as he played at ball with the son of the fisherman, his presumed father, by chance he struck him with the ball. The lad wept bitterly, and running home, complained to his mother that he had been struck by his brother Gregory. Instantly the angry mother issued out of doors, and harshly reproved him, exclaiming, "Audacious little vagabond, why hast thou struck my son? Thou!—of whose origin and country we know nothing—how darest thou do this?" "Dear mother," answered Gregory, "am I not your son? Why

* That is, six monkish holy days from the time of its departure.

do you speak to me in this manner?" "My son!" said the woman; "no, in good troth; neither do I know whose thou art. All I know is that thou wert one day discovered in a cask, and that the abbot delivered thee to me to bring up." When the boy heard this he burst into tears, ran hastily to the superior, and said, "Oh, my lord, I have been a long time with you, and I believed that I was the fisherman's son; but I learn that it is not so: consequently, I am ignorant who my parents are. If it please you, my lord, suffer me to become a soldier, for here I will not remain." "My son," said the abbot, "think not of it. The monks all love you, and I doubt not, after my decease, will promote you to the abbacy." "My good lord," answered Gregory, "I know not my parents, and I will not continue longer than I can help in this intolerable suspense." The abbot, finding solicitation useless, entered the treasury and brought to him the tablets which he had found in the cradle. "My son," he said, "read this; and what you are will be clear to you." When he had read, he fell to the earth, and exclaimed, "Alas! are such, then, my parents? I will hasten to the Holy Land, and do battle for the sins of the unhappy authors of my being; and there I will end my life. I entreat you, therefore, my lord, without delay to make me a knight." * The abbot complied, and when his departure was made known, the whole convent and neighbourhood were loud in their lamentation.

Straightway he agreed with certain sailors for his passage to the Holy Land, and embarked. But as they

---

* The power of the superior of a convent to create knights is a well-known fact in chivalry.

Upon a passage in the romance of "Sir Eglamour of Artoys," Mr. Ellis has remarked that "The author in this place certainly appears to quote the *Gesta Romanorum* for this singularly absurd story; but I have not been able to discover it in that collection."— *Early Eng. Rom.*, vol. iii. p. 274. The story which Mr. Ellis could not find is unquestionably the present. In the romance, a child and its mother are deposited in a vessel, and left to float upon the waves. Here some variation occurs, but the infant, as in the *gest*, is conveyed to a place of safety, and received under the protection of a king, who is *hunting*; he educates, and finally confers knighthood upon him. The youth afterwards marries his mother. Farther than this, the tales have nothing in common, but here is enough to prove imitation.

sailed the wind became contrary, and they were suddenly
driven upon the coast of that country in which his
mother's castle stood. What the state was, and who
reigned there, the sailors knew not; but as Gregory
entered the city a citizen met him, and said, "My lord,
whither are you going?" "To seek an inn," was the
reply. On which the hospitable citizen led him to his
own house, and entertained him magnificently. As they
sat at table Gregory inquired of his host what state it
was, and who was the lord of it. "Sir," returned the
other, "awhile ago we had a very powerful emperor, but
he died in the Holy Land, and left his throne to his sister.
The Duke of Burgundy would have married her, but
she was pleased to refuse his offer. Whereupon he has
forcibly made himself master of the whole kingdom, save
a single city in which the queen resides." "May I,"
returned the young knight, "declare with safety the
secret wish of my heart?"

"With the greatest safety."

"I am," continued the other, "a soldier. If it please
you, go to-morrow to the palace and obtain for me a communication with the seneschal, and if he will promise to
remunerate me, I will fight for this year in behalf of the
lady." "I doubt not, my lord," answered the citizen,
"but that he will acquiesce with alacrity. To-morrow I
will do as you desire." He went accordingly, and declared
the occasion of his coming. The seneschal, not a little
exhilarated, immediately sent off a messenger for Gregory;
and, on his arrival, presented him to the queen, who
expressed herself well satisfied with her champion. She
observed him closely, but had not the remotest suspicion
that it was her son, for she thought him long since overwhelmed in the waves. The seneschal therefore, in the
presence of his mistress, covenanted that he should serve
a full year. On the morrow he prepared for war, and
assembled a large host. So judicious were his movements
that Gregory triumphed in every engagement, and penetrated to the very palace of the duke, whom he finally
took and beheaded.

Gregory after this continued the war from day to day
with constant success; and the fame of his great prowess.

was carried to all parts of the realm. Thus, before the
completion of the year which he had covenanted to serve,
he had wrested the whole kingdom from the hands of
their enemies. Then he went to the seneschal, and said,
" Good friend, you know in what state I found your affairs,
and in what a good condition I leave them. I therefore
beg you to give me my hire, for I intend to proceed to
another country." " My lord," said the seneschal, " you
have merited much more than our agreement stipulated;
let us hasten to the queen, and there conclude as to the
recompense." They went accordingly; and the seneschal
thus spoke: " My dear lady, I would say something, which
will be to your advantage. From the absence of a head,
we have sustained many grievous afflictions. It were desirable, therefore, for you to take a husband, who is able
to defend us from a return of the like troubles. Your kingdom is rich enough, so that I would not advise you to
select a spouse for his wealth. And this being allowed,
I know not where you could find one in every respect so
suitable and beneficial to the state as my lord Gregory."
The lady, as we have seen before, rejected a second
marriage; but overcome by the arguments and urgency
of her seneschal, appointed a day on which, after mature
deliberation, she would give an answer. That day came;
and in the presence of all the assembled nobles, she arose
and spoke thus: " Since my lord Gregory has valiantly
and effectually liberated both us and our kingdom from
the thraldom of oppressive foes, I *will* receive him for my
husband." The audience rejoiced; and an early period
was fixed for the celebration of their nuptials. They
were then espoused with the approbation of the whole
country—the son to his own mother: but both were
ignorant of the relationship. They loved each other
tenderly: it happened, however, that the lord Gregory
on one particular occasion went out to hunt; and a handmaid of the queen said to her, " Dear lady, have you not
offended my lord in something?" " Surely not," returned
she. " I believe that there is not in the whole world a
married pair so mutually attached to each other as we
are. But why do you ask?" " Because," said the handmaid, " every day, when the table is laid, my lord enters

his private chamber in great apparent pleasure; but when he returns it is with lamentation and wailing. After that he washes his face; but why all this is done, I do not comprehend."

On hearing this, the lady immediately entered the private chamber before alluded to, and narrowly inspected every closet and crevice. At length, she came to the place wherein the tablets, inscribed with the ignominy of his birth, and which he was wont to read day by day, were deposited; and then she wept most piteously. For they were the same which she had laid in the cradle; and which, when they now started up before her, as it were, by magic, she remembered too well. She opened them, and recognized her own handwriting. "Alas!" she exclaimed, "how has he obtained this dark testimony of my crime, if he be not my son?" And then bursting into a lamentable cry, "Woe is me, that I ever saw the light of heaven—would that I had died ere I was born." The soldiers in the hall, hearing the clamour produced by the anguish and perturbation of her mind, ran into the chamber, and found her stretched upon the earth. They stood around her a considerable time before she was able to ejaculate, and when at length she could speak, she said, "If ye desire me to live, hasten immediately for my lord." The spectators hearing her wish, mounted their horses, and rode to the king. They explained to him the imminent danger of his wife; and he forthwith left the chase, returned to the castle, and entered the chamber where the queen lay. When she saw him, she said, "Oh, my lord, command us to be left alone; what I have to say is for your private ear." The room was accordingly cleared; and the lady eagerly besought him to say of what family he was. "That is a singular question," replied he, "but know that I am a native of a distant country." "Oh," returned the lady, "I solemnly vow to God that, unless you declare to me the whole truth, I am sure I shall quickly die." "I tell you," he said, "I was poor—possessed of nothing but the arms with which I freed you and the kingdom from slavery." "Only tell me," urged the lady, "from what country you came, and who are your parents; and unless you speak truly, I will never more touch food." "You shall be satisfied," said the king. "I was brought up by an abbot from my earliest age; and from him I learnt that I was found cradled in a cask." Here the queen showed him the tablets, and said, "Dost thou remember these?" He looked, and fell prostrate on the earth. "My *son!*" cried she, "for thou art so; my only son, and my husband, and my lord! Thou art the child of my brother and myself. Oh, my son, I deposited in the cask with thee these tablets. Woe is me! why, O God, didst thou permit my birth, since I was born to be guilty of so much wickedness! Would that the eye which looks upon me might reduce me to ashes; would that I had passed from the womb to the grave!" Then striking her head against the wall, she cried, "Oh, thou Almighty Being, behold my son—my husband, and the son of my brother." "I thought," replied Gregory, "to shun this danger, and I have fallen into the snares of the devil. Dismiss me, lady, to bewail my misery: woe! woe! my mother is my mistress—my wife! See how Satan hath encompassed me!" When the mother perceived the agony of her child, she said, "Dear son, for the residue of my life, I will expiate our crimes by hardships and wanderings. Thou shalt govern the kingdom." "Not so," returned he; "do you remain, my mother: you are wanted to rule the realm. I will roam about, until our sins are forgiven."

The same night he arose, broke his lance, and put on the dress of a pilgrim. He bade his mother farewell, and, with naked feet, walked till he reached the uttermost boundaries of the kingdom. Having entered a certain city, he sought out the house of a fisherman, with whom he requested permission to lodge. When the fisherman had considered him attentively, and observed the come-liness of his person and the grace of his form, he said, "Friend, you are no true pilgrim; this is evident from the elegance of your body." "Well," answered the other, "though I be not a true pilgrim, yet, for the love of God, I beseech you to give me harbourage." Now, the fisher-man's wife, looking upon him, was moved with a devout feeling, and entreated that he might be sheltered. He entered therefore; but directed his bed to be made for

him at the gate. Fish, with water and bread, were given to
him. Amongst other things, the fisherman said "Pilgrim,
if you would become holy, go into some remote place."
"Sir," answered Gregory, "I would willingly follow your
advice, but I know of no such place." "On the morrow,"
returned he, "I will myself conduct you." "May God
reward you," said the pilgrim. The next morning the
fisherman bade him rise, and hurried him so much that he
left his tablets behind the gate where he had slept.

The fisherman, with his companion, embarked upon
the sea, and sailing about sixteen miles came to a huge
rock, having chains at its feet, which, without a key,
could not be unloosed. After the fisherman had undone
them, he cast the keys into the sea, and returned home.
The pilgrim remained in that place seventeen years, with
every feeling of the most perfect penitence.

About this period the pope died; and at the moment
of his decease, a voice from heaven cried out," Search
after a man of God, called Gregory, and appoint him my
vicar." The electors, greatly rejoiced at what they heard,
sent messengers into different parts of the world to seek
him. At length, some of them lodged in the house of the
fisherman; and as they sat at supper, one said, "My
friend, we are much harassed by journeys through town
and country, in pursuit of a holy man, called Gregory,
whom, when we find, we are to place in the pontificate."
The fisherman, then recollecting the pilgrim, answered,
"It is now seventeen years since a pilgrim named Gregory
lodged in this house. I conducted him to a certain rock
in the midst of the sea, and there I left him. But it is so
long ago, that he may be dead." It happened that on the
same day, a number of fishes were caught; and as he
gutted one of them, he found the keys which seventeen
years before he had cast into the sea.* Immediately he
shouted, "Oh, my friends, behold these keys! I cast
them into the sea; and I draw from this circumstance

* This incident is purely oriental; and occurs frequently both in
the *Arabian Nights' Entertainments*, and in the *Persian Tales*.
[Though what Mr. Swan says in this note is probably true, it is
worth while to remind the reader of the story of Polycrates of Samos
and the ring. But that story *may* be of Eastern origin.—ED.]

a good omen respecting the success of your labours." The messengers were much pleased with the man's prognostication, and early in the morning desired him to bring them to the rock. He did so; and there finding Gregory, they said, "Man of God, go up with us; by the command of the Omnipotent, go up with us: for it is His will that thou shouldst be appointed His vicar upon earth." To which Gregory replied, "God's will be done;" and then followed them from the rock. As soon as he approached the city, the bells rang of their own accord, which the citizens hearing, said, "Blessed be the Most High, he cometh who shall be Christ's vicar," and hastened to meet him. St. Gregory, thus appointed, conducted himself worthily in every respect; and multitudes from every part of the world came to ask his counsel and assistance. Now, his mother, hearing of the remarkable sanctity of the reigning pope, thought that nowhere could she find help sooner than from so holy a man. But that he was her son and husband she knew not. Hastening, therefore, to Rome, she confessed herself to the vicar of God; nor was it till after confession that the pope recollected his unhappy mother. He then spoke thus: "Dearest mother, and wife, and mistress, the devil dreamt of bringing us to hell; but, by the grace of God, we have evaded his toils." At these words, she fell at his feet; and even for very joy, wept bitterly. But the pope raised her up, and tenderly embraced her. He founded a monastery over which he made her abbess, and a short time afterwards, both yielded up their souls to God.

APPLICATION.

My beloved, the emperor is Christ, who gave His daughter, that is, the human soul, to the charge of the brother, that is, the flesh. They lay in one chamber, that is, in one heart, or in one mind. The son born of these is all mankind. The cask is the Holy Spirit, which floats upon the sea of the world. The Duke of Burgundy is the devil, who invades the soul, exposed by sin, and conquers it; until the Son, that is Christ, who is God and *man*, enfranchises it, and marries the mother, that is the soul. The tablets are the ten commandments. The abbot is God, who saved us by His only-begotten Son. The fisherman-nurse is any prelate; the ship St. Gregory afterwards embarks in is the Church. The seneschal is a confessor. The broken lance is to put away or destroy an evil life. The rock is penitence.

TALE LXXXII.

OF JUDGMENT AGAINST ADULTERERS.[*]

A CERTAIN knight had a very beautiful castle, upon which two storks built their nest. At the foot of this castle was a clear fountain, in which the storks were wont to bathe themselves. It happened that the female stork brought forth young, and the male flew about to procure food. Now, while he was absent, the female admitted a gallant; and before the return of the male went down to the fountain to wash herself, in order that the other might perceive no disorder in her appearance. But the knight, often observing this with wonder, closed up the fountain, that the stork might no longer wash or bathe herself. In this dilemma, after meeting her lover, she was obliged to return to her nest; and when the male came and saw by various signs that she had been unfaithful, he flew away, and brought back with him a great multitude of storks, who put the adulterous bird to death, in presence of the knight.

APPLICATION.

My beloved, the two storks are Christ and the soul, the spouse of Christ. The knight is the devil; and the

[*] "The STORKE wreker of advouterie" [adultery]. CHAUCER, *The Assemblie of Fowles*, fol. 235.

"This bird," says Speght (Gloss. in v.), "breedeth in the chimney-tops of houses, and as it is written of him, if the man or the wife commit adultery, he presently forsaketh the place. And as Aristotle saith, if his female play false, he will, if he can, kill her: or else utterly forsake her. Therefore, Chaucer calleth him the wreker of adultery."

fountain, that of confession and repentance. If Christ at the day of judgment find us unwashed, *i.e.* impenitent, He will come with a multitude of angels and put us to death.

TALE LXXXIII.

OF THE TIMOROUS GUARDIANSHIP OF THE SOUL.

WHEN Trajan reigned he took great. pleasure in gardens. Having constructed one of uncommon beauty, and planted in it trees of every kind, he appointed a keeper with injunctions to defend it faithfully. But by and by a wild boar broke into the garden, overturned the young trees, and rooted up the flowers. The keeper, whose name was Jonathan, perceiving this, cut off the boar's left ear, and the animal with a loud noise departed. But another day, the same boar re-entered the garden and committed great depredations; upon which Jonathan cut off his right ear. But notwithstanding this, he entered a third time; and the keeper, on seeing this, cut off his tail—with which ignominious loss he departed, as formerly, making a tremendous uproar. However, he appeared on a fourth occasion, and committed the like injuries; when Jonathan, more and more incensed, caught up a lance and transfixed him upon the spot. He was then sent to the royal kitchen and prepared for the king's table. Now Trajan, it seems, was especially partial to the heart of any animal; and the cook observing that the boar's heart was particularly fat and delicate, reserved it for his own tooth. When, therefore, the emperor's dinner was served up, the heart was inquired after; and the servants returned to the cook. "Tell my lord," said the fellow, "that it had no heart; and if he disbelieves it, say that I will adduce convincing reasons for the defect." The servants delivered the cook's message, and the astonished emperor exclaimed, "What do I hear? There is no animal without a heart! But since he offers to prove his assertion we will hear him." The cook was sent for, and spoke thus, "My lord, listen to me. All thought proceeds from the heart. It follows, therefore, that if there be no thought, there is no heart. The boar, in the first instance, entered the garden and committed much injury. I * seeing it, cut off his left ear. Now, if he had possessed a heart, he would have recollected the loss of so important a member. But he did not, for he entered a second time. Therefore, he had no heart. Besides, if he had had a heart, when I had cut off his right ear, he would have meditated on the matter; which he did not, for he came again and lost his tail. Moreover, having lost his ears and his tail, had he possessed even a particle of heart, he would have thought; but he did not think, for he entered a fourth time and was killed. For these several reasons I am confident that he had no heart." The emperor, satisfied with what he heard, applauded the man's judgment. And thus he escaped.

APPLICATION.

My beloved, the emperor is Christ, who delights in fair gardens; that is, in religious men, in whom our Lord planted many virtues. The keeper is a prelate; the boar is any worldly-minded man who sins, and is punished for his transgressions. The abscission of the left ear represents the decease of a beloved relation; the right, of a son or daughter; and the tail, of a *wife*. At last Death, that is *Jonathan*, transfixes the sinner himself. The heart here emblems the soul, which never would have transgressed had it retained its reason.

TALE LXXXIV.

OF GOD'S BENEFITS.

IN the reign of Pompey there lived a fair and amiable lady; and near to her residence dwelt a handsome and noble knight. He was in the habit of visiting her fre-

------

* [There is a confusion between the keeper and the cook.—ED.]

quently, and was much beloved by her. The knight coming once to see her, observed a falcon upon her wrist, which he greatly admired. "Dear lady," said he, "if you love me, give me that beautiful bird." "I consent," returned she, "but on one condition : that you do not attach yourself so much to it as to rob me of your society." "Far be such ingratitude from your servant," cried the knight; "I would not forsake you on whatever emergency. And believe me, this generosity binds me more than ever to love you." The lady presented the falcon to him; and bidding her farewell, he returned to his own castle. But he derived so much satisfaction from the bird, that he forgot his promise to the lady, and thought but little of her, while every day he sported with the falcon. She sent messengers to him, but it was of no use; he came not: and at last she wrote a very urgent letter entreating him, without the least delay, to hasten to her and bring the falcon along with him. He acquiesced; and the lady, after salutation, requested him to let her touch the bird. No sooner was it in her possession, than she wrenched its head from the body. "Madam," said the knight, not a little grieved, "what have you done?" To which the lady answered, "Be not offended, but rather rejoice at what I have done. That falcon was the occasion of your absence, and I killed him that I might enjoy your company as I was wont." The knight, satisfied with the reason, became once more a regular visitant.

APPLICATION.

My beloved, the king is our heavenly Father; the lady, our human nature joined to the divinity in Christ. The knight is any Christian, and the falcon temporal prosperity.

TALE LXXXV.

OF PRAYER, WHICH IS AS HARMONY BEFORE GOD.

WHEN Tiberius reigned he was passionately fond of music. It happened that, as he once pursued the chase, he was struck with the sound of a harp, whose sweetness so delighted him, that he turned his horse's head and rode to the place from which it issued. When he arrived there, he perceived a broad sheet of water, and near it a certain poor man seated on the ground, having a harp in his hand. From hence arose the melody; and the emperor was refreshed and exhilarated by the delicious tones the harp gave forth. "My friend," said the king, "inform me how it is that your harp sounds so sweetly." "My lord," answered the other, "for more than thirty years I have sat by this stream, and God has bestowed upon me such grace, that the moment I touch the chords of my harp, the very fishes, enchanted with the harmony, come even into my hand, and afford sustenance to my wife and family. But, unhappily for me, a certain whistler has arrived within these few days from another country; and he whistles so admirably, that the fishes forsake me and go over to him. Therefore, my lord, since you are powerful, and the ruler of this kingdom, give me some aid against this abominable whistler." "My friend," returned the king, "I can help you only in one thing; but I hope this will be enough. I have in my hunting-bag a golden hook, which I will give you: fasten it on the top of a rod, and then strike your harp. The sound will inveigle the fishes, and as soon as they approach, by the means of the hook draw them to land. If you follow my advice, the whistler will depart in great trouble." The poor man did as he was directed; and before the fishes could arrive at the place where the whistler was stationed, the hook brought them to land. The whistler, perceiving himself outdone, retired in much tribulation.*

* There is a fable of a fisherman piping to the fishes in the Latin Æsop; but the story is different.

My beloved, the emperor is Christ; the harmony which delights him is prayer. The water is the world; the fishes are sinners. The poor man is a preacher; and the harp is the Sacred Writings. The whistler is the devil; and the golden hook is divine grace.

TALE LXXXVI.

OF SINNERS, WHO RECEIVE THE DIVINE GRACE ON EARNESTLY SEEKING IT.

A CERTAIN emperor made a law by which, if any woman were taken in adultery, she should be condemned to perpetual imprisonment. It happened that a knight espoused a noble lady, to whom he was greatly attached. The knight having been called by some emergency into foreign parts, his wife fell under the sentence of the law. She was accordingly cast into a dungeon, and there brought forth a remarkably handsome boy. The child grew, and was beloved by all who saw him. But the mother consumed her hours in groans and tears, nor experienced the smallest comfort. The boy, observing the continual lamentation of his mother, said to her, "For what reason, dearest mother, do you afflict yourself in this manner?" "Oh, my son!" returned she, "I have much reason to weep. Above our heads is an intercourse with mankind; and there the sun shines in his splendour. Here we are kept in utter darkness, and light never blesses our sight." "I am ignorant of all this," said the boy, "because I was born in prison. As long as I receive a sufficiency of meat and drink, I shall willingly remain here." As they thus conversed, the emperor and his guards were standing near the door of the prison. One of them solicited his sovereign to liberate the mother and son; and he, compassionating their distress, and in consideration of the entreaties of his attendants, set them at liberty, and absolved them from future punishment.

My beloved, the emperor is our heavenly Father, the wife is the soul, and the husband is Christ. The prison is hell; the child is the powerful and wealthy of the world, who are satisfied with sensual delights. The intercessor is any good prelate.

TALE LXXXVII.

OF CHRIST, WHO GAVE HIMSELF TO DEATH FOR US.

An emperor, engaged in mortal war, was in imminent peril of death. A zealous knight, perceiving his danger, placed himself between the emperor and his enemies, and thus saved him from destruction. But in the attempt the knight was grievously wounded, and not until after a tedious and dangerous illness, healed. The scars, however, remained, and gave occasion to many commendations upon the valour and loyalty which he had exhibited. It happened that the same knight was in danger of being defrauded of his inheritance. He went, therefore, to the emperor, and entreated that he would assist him and give sentence in his favour. "My good friend," replied the emperor, "I cannot attend to you at present; but I will appoint a judge who shall examine into your case, and do you every justice." "My lord," cried the other, "how can you say so?" And immediately tearing open his vesture, he exposed the scars left by his wounds. "See what I have borne for you—yet you will neither vindicate nor assist me! Is it not unjust that, after I have undergone so much, another should be deputed to judge and advocate my cause?" The emperor, hearing this, instantly replied, "My friend, you say true; when I was in peril you, and not another, preserved me." Then, ascending the tribunal, he gave judgment in his favour.*

* We have here the well-known anecdote of Augustus Cæsar, and of the Roman soldier who fought in the battle of Actium.

APPLICATION.

My beloved, the knight is Christ, who received many wounds in our behalf. Let us not depute another to show our gratitude, but exert ourselves in the most earnest manner.

TALE LXXXVIII.

OF THE CUNNING OF THE DEVIL.

It is related of a certain prince that, with all his power, he could not subdue his enemies. At length he made use of the following stratagem. He feigned a flight, and resigned his castles, with the provisions they contained, into the hands of his foes. Now, the castles were furnished with casks of wine empoisoned with the seed of a certain herb; insomuch that whosoever drank of it immediately fell asleep. He knew that his opponents were hunger-starved and gluttonous; and that, overjoyed to find such excellent quarters, they would drink to excess, and fall into a death-like sleep. They did so, and the prince returning put them all to death.

APPLICATION.

My beloved, the prince is the devil: let us beware of what he leaves.

TALE LXXXIX.

OF THE TRIPLE STATE OF THE WORLD.

A CERTAIN knight had three sons, and on his death-bed he bequeathed the inheritance to his first-born; to the second, his treasury; and to the third, a very valuable ring, of more worth indeed than all he had left to the others.

But the two former had also rings; and they were all apparently the same. After their father's death the first son said, "I possess that precious ring of my father." The second said, "You have it not—I have." To this the third son answered, "That is not true. The elder of us hath the estate, the second the treasure, and therefore it is but meet that I should have the most valuable ring." The first son answered, "Let us prove, then, whose claims to it have the pre-eminence." They agreed, and several sick men were made to resort to them for the purpose. The two first rings had no effect, but the last cured all their infirmities.*

APPLICATION.

My beloved, the knight is Christ: the three sons are the Jews, Saracens, and Christians. The most valuable ring is faith, which is the property only of the younger; that is, of the Christians.

* This story is in the *Decameron*, first day, Nov. 3, with some considerable variations.

"There was a very wealthy man who, among other precious jewels of his own, had a goodly ring of great value; the beauty and estimation whereof made him earnestly desirous to leave it as a perpetual memory and honour to his successors. Whereupon, he willed and ordained that he among his male children with whom this ring (being left by the father) should be found in custody after his death, he, and none other, was to be reputed his heir, and to be honoured and reverenced by all the rest, as being the prime and worthiest person."

In process of time the ring fell to one who had three sons, and doubtful who should have it, he caused two other rings to be constructed exactly similar. "Lying upon his death-bed, and his sons then plying him by their best opportunities, he gave to each of them a ring. And they (after his death), presuming severally upon their right to the inheritance and honour, grew to great contradiction and square; each man producing then his ring, which were so truly all alike in resemblance, as no one could know the right ring from the other." "In like manner, my very good lord, concerning those three laws given by God the Father, to three such people as you have propounded" (the Jews, Saracens, and Christians), "each of them do imagine that they have the heritage of God, and his true law, and also duly perform his commandments, but which of them do so, indeed, the question (as of the three rings) is yet remaining."

It also occurs in the *Cento Novelle Antiche*, Nov. 71, and perhaps in Swift's *Tale of a Tub*. Tyrwhitt, however, thinks otherwise.

TALE XC.

OF FREE WILL.

THERE was formerly a king, in whose reign a law was enacted that the elder brother should divide the inheritance, and then that the younger should have the choice; the reason of which was that they considered it a greater proof of discretion to apportion than to select, and the elder ought to be the wiser. There was also another law, which permitted a son by a slave woman to receive an inheritance as well as the lawfully begotten sons. Now, there were two brothers, the one born of a handmaid, and the other of a free woman, between whom an estate was to be divided. The elder, therefore, divided it in this manner. On one side he placed the whole inheritance, and on the other his brother's mother. The latter reflected that he ought to love his parent beyond all else; and consequently chose her, trusting to the kindness and liberality of his brother. But here he was deceived; for he would supply him with nothing. Upon which he hastened to the judge, and complained that his brother had excluded him from his inheritance. The brother made answer that the matter rested not with him, since he who chose, not he who divides, is secure of his portion.

APPLICATION.

My beloved, the two sons are Christ and man; the elder, that is Christ, divided the inheritance; the mother is the earth, which the younger chose, and thereby lost heaven.

TALE XCI.

OF SLOTH.

THE Emperor Pliny had three sons, to whom he was extremely indulgent. He wished to dispose of his kingdom, and calling the three into his presence, spoke thus:

" The most slothful of you shall reign after my decease."
" Then," answered the elder, " the kingdom must be mine;
for I am so lazy, that sitting once by the fire, I burnt my
legs, because I was too indolent to withdraw them." The
second son observed, " The kingdom should properly be
mine, for if I had a rope round my neck, and held a sword
in my hand, my idleness is such, that I should not put
forth my hand to cut the rope." " But I," said the third
son, " ought to be preferred to you both ; for I outdo both
in indolence. While I lay upon my bed, water dropped
from above upon my eyes ; and though, from the nature
of the water, I was in danger of becoming blind, I neither
could nor would turn my head ever so little to the right
hand or to the left." The emperor hearing this, bequeathed
the kingdom to him, thinking him the laziest of the
three.*

APPLICATION.

My beloved, the king is the devil; and the three sons,
different classes of corrupt men.

* There is in the Latin Æsop a story of a *Father and his three
Children*, of which the latter part resembles the present tale.
" And the mill, how was it demised by your father, to be parted
among you three? They answered the judge, he that shall be the
most lyar, most evil, and most slow, ought to have it. Then said the
eldest son, I am most slothful, for many years past I have dwelled in
a great house, and lay under the conduits of the same, where fell upon
me all the foul waters, as dish-water and other filth, that most wonderfully stank, insomuch that all my flesh was rotten therewith, and mine
eyes blind, and the durt under my back was a foot high, and yet by
sloth I had rather abide there than rise up. The second said I
suppose, that the mill shall be mine, for if I came to a table covered
with all manner of delicate meats, wherof I might eat if I would take
of the best; I am so slothful that I may not eat, unless one should
put the meat in my mouth. The third sayd, the mill shall be mine,
for I am yet a greater lyar, and more slothful than any of you both,
for if I had thirst unto the death, and if I found then myselfe within
a fair water up to the neck, I would rather dye, than move myselfe to
drink one drop thereof. Then said the judge, Ye wot not what ye
say; for neither I, nor any other, may well understand you; but the
cause I remit among you."

TALE XCII.

OF CHRIST, WHO DIED THAT WE MIGHT LIVE.

A CERTAIN king had a wife named Cornelia. It happened that, under a wall in one of the king's castles, two serpents were discovered; one male, and the other female. The king, hearing of this, interrogated his learned men as to the signification; and they assured him that they were hidden there to predict the death of a man or woman. They further declared that if the male were killed, a man should die; if the female, a woman and a wife. "If this be so," said the king, " kill the male serpent, and let the female live; for a man ought more willingly to die himself than permit the death of his wife." And he gave this reason for it: " If my wife live, she may bring forth many sons who may succeed to my throne; but if she should die, the kingdom would want an heir."

APPLICATION.

My beloved, the king is Christ; the wife, our human nature, for which He gave himself to death.

TALE XCIII.

OF THE INHERITANCE AND JOY OF A FAITHFUL
SOUL.

A CERTAIN powerful lord sent his two sons to study, that they might, by their own assiduity, obtain a livelihood. After some time he sent letters to them, to command their return to their own country; and they returned accordingly. One of the brothers rejoiced at this, and was received with equal pleasure. He was, moreover, put in possession of a fair inheritance. But the other was much distressed at his recall. When his mother ran out to meet him, she kissed him, and while doing so bit off his lips. His sister, also, following the mother's example, bit off his nose. His brother also put out his eyes; and the father, entering, canght him by the hair of his head and flayed him alive.*

APPLICATION.

My beloved, the rich lord is God, and the two sons are soul and body; the latter of which is unwilling to return to its native earth. The sister and brothers are toads and serpents, who devour the nose, eyes, &c.

TALE XCIV.

OF THE SOUL, WHICH BEING INFECTED WITH THE LEPROSY OF SIN, CANNOT RECOVER ITS ANCIENT BEAUTY, EXCEPT BY PENITENTIAL SIGHS AND TEARS.

A KING being desirous of visiting foreign countries, and possessing an only daughter of great beauty, indeed infinitely brighter than the sun, knew not into whose custody he might fearlessly consign her. At last he put her under the charge of his secretary, for whom he had

---

* I omitted in its proper place to notice a fable somewhat similar in the Latin Æsop. It is as follows:—

"There was a young child which in his youth began to steal, and all that he did steal he brought to his mother, and the mother took it gladly, and would in no wise correct him; and after he had stolen many things, he was taken and condemned to be hanged; and as men led him to the justice, his mother followed him and wept sore: and then the child prayed the justice that he might say somewhat to his mother, and having leave, he approached to her, and making as tho' he would speak to her in her ear, with his teeth he bit off her nose: for which, when the judge blamed him, he answered him in this manner, My lord, she is the cause of my death, for if she had well chastised me, I had not come to this shame."

This fable, it is true, has a different application, and the plot of it (so to speak) likewise varies; but the singular thought of biting off a person's nose can have had but one origin.

the greatest regard. He commanded him to take every precaution, and especially to guard against her drinking of a singular fountain which sprung up in that country. For it had the property, although of a most exquisite flavour, of infecting with leprosy whosoever tasted it. The secretary, therefore, in order to restore her to her father as beautiful as when he departed, reflected much upon his precarious employment; remembering, at the same time, that if she were at all injured he should lose his office, and be unable to meet his master. For a while he watched his charge with extreme vigilance; but the lady having discovered the fountain, went so cunningly to work, that she drank of it, and was consequently infected with a loathsome disease. The secretary perceiving this, was filled with the most poignant grief, and carried her away to a desert region. There he found a hermit; and beating with his hands upon the door of his cell, related to him all that had happened, beseeching him to point out how she might be healed. "Go," said the hermit, "to a mountain which I will show you: in that place you will discover a certain stone and a peculiar kind of rod. Take this rod, and strike the stone sharply, strongly, and boldly, until a moisture exudes from it. Anoint the lady with this liquid, and she will be presently restored to her original beauty." The secretary strictly followed the hermit's injunctions, and the lady became as she was before.

APPLICATION.

My beloved, the king is Christ; the daughter is the soul, originally brighter than the sun. The fountain is the world, which infects it with sin. The recluse is the Church; the rod, penitence; and the moisture, the tears of a contrite heart.

TALE XCV.

OF CHRIST, WHO RESTORED OUR HEAVENLY INHERITANCE.

WE read in the Roman annals of a certain tyrant called Maxentius, who would have deprived the Romans of their paternal estates. Yielding to the cruelty of the tyrant, they fled to Constantine, king of Britain. At length, when many were assembled at his court, the emigrants stirred up the British monarch to revenge them upon the tyrant. Moved by their entreaties, Constantine mounted his horse, overthrew the tyrant, and restored the exiles to their inheritance.*

APPLICATION.

My beloved, the tyrant is the devil; and Constantine represents that God to whom the distressed should flee for succour.

TALE XCVI.

OF THE LIFE PRESENT, WHICH IS A LIFE OF REMISSION AND GRACE.

KING Alexander placed a burning candle in his hall, and sent heralds through the whole kingdom, who made the following proclamation :—" If there be any under forfeiture to the king, and he will come boldly into his presence, while the candle burns, the king will forgive the forfeiture. And whosoever is in this predicament, and comes not before the expiration of the candle, he shall perish by an ignominious death." Many of the populace, hearing the proclamation, came to the king and besought his mercy. The king received them kindly; but there

* " I think there is the romance of Maxence, Constantine's antagonist."—WARTON.

were many who neglected to come; and the very moment in which the candle expired, they were apprehended and put to death.

APPLICATION.

My beloved, Alexander is Christ, the burning candle is the life present, and the heralds are the preachers.

———

TALE XCVII.

OF DEATH.

WE read in the Roman chronicles that, about the twenty-second year from the building of the city, the people erected in the Forum a marble column, and on the top of it placed an image of Julius Cæsar.* Upon the head they inscribed his name, because it was erected in his honour. The same Julius Cæsar received three signs which were to happen at his death, or just before he was to die. On the hundredth day preceding this event, the effigy in the Forum was struck by lightning, and the first letter of his name erased. The very night before his death, the windows of his bed-chamber burst open with such a tremendous noise, that he thought the whole building had been overturned. And on the same day that he died, when about to go into the Capitol, letters were given him, declaring the danger in which he stood. If he had read them he would have been saved.

APPLICATION.

My beloved, God does thus with mankind. We receive many warnings, but not attending to them are eternally destroyed.

* A very singular anachronism; but for what reason (save that of ignorance!) chronology has been so much violated, it is not easy to conceive. There does not appear any necessity for fixing the date.

TALE XCVIII.

OF CONCILIATING GOD WHILST WE HAVE OPPORTUNITY.

THE Romans had an ancient custom, that when they besieged a castle or city, they lighted a single candle of a certain length; and as long as it burnt, they were prepared to receive overtures of peace, however vile the proposer. But after it was consumed they exercised the severest justice upon their enemies, nor could any one then be redeemed even by the sacrifice of all he was worth.*

APPLICATION.

My beloved, God thus treats sinners. For the soul, when beset by vices, has an opportunity of procuring peace as long as the light of life burns.

TALE XCIX.

OF CHRIST'S MANLY CONTEST AND VICTORY.

IN the reign of Cæsar there lived a noble and valiant knight, who once rode by a certain forest, and beheld a serpent engaging with a toad.† The latter obtained the mastery; which when the knight saw, he assisted the serpent; and grievously wounding the toad, reduced it to seek safety in flight. But the conqueror was also affected by the toad's venom. The knight turned homeward, and for a long time lay sick of his wound. At last he made his will and prepared himself for death. Now, as he reclined near the fire, utterly hopeless of life, the

---

* This apologue is very similar to Tale XCVI.

† "The stories, perhaps fabulous, of the serpent fighting with his inveterate enemy, the weasel, who eats rue before the attack begins; and of the serpent fighting with, and being killed by the spider, originate from Pliny, *Nat. Hist.* x. 84, xx. 13."—WARTON.

serpent which he had preserved entered the apartment. When the attendants beheld it, they said, "My lord, my lord, a serpent has entered the room!" When the knight saw it, he recollected that it was the same he had aided in its contest with the toad, and through which he was laid upon his bed incurable. "Do not molest it," said the knight, "I do not believe that it will harm me." The serpent glided towards him, and applying its tongue to the wound, sucked up the poison till its mouth was quite full; and then, hastening to the door, cast it out. It returned twice to the wound, and did as before, until the venom was exhausted. The knight commanded milk to be given to the serpent, which it instantly drank; and no sooner had it done so, than the toad from which the wound had been received, entered, and again attacked the serpent, in revenge for its having healed the knight. The latter seeing this, said to his servants, "Without doubt, my friends, this is the toad which I wounded in defence of that serpent, and from which I derive all my infirmity. If it conquer, it will attack me; therefore, as ye love your master, kill it incontinently." The servants, obedient to the knight's command, slew it with swords and clubs; while the serpent, as if to praise and thank its defender, twined around his feet, and then departed. The knight completely recovered his health.

APPLICATION.

My beloved, the emperor is God; the knight, Christ; the toad is the devil, and the serpent, man.

TALE C.

OF CHRIST, WHO IS LONG-SUFFERING AND MERCIFUL.

WHEN Diocletian reigned, he decreed that whatsoever woman committed adultery should be put to death. It happened that a certain knight married a girl and had a son by her. The child grew, and every one loved him. After a while his father went out to battle, and, fighting manfully, was deprived of his right arm. In the mean time his wife lost her honour; and the husband, on his return, discovering the shame, ought, according to law, to have put her to death. Calling his son, therefore, he said, "My dear boy, your mother has committed adultery, and by law should die by my hand; but I have lost my arm, and am unable to destroy her. I command you to do this." The son answered, "The law enjoins children to honour their parents; and if I were to slay my own mother, I should act contrary to the law, and bring down her curse on myself. Therefore in this I cannot obey you." So the woman was saved from death by her son.

APPLICATION.

My beloved, the emperor is God; the knight, Christ; and the wife, the soul. If the soul err, the law of God commands its death. Christ fights against the devil, and loses an arm; that is, all the austerity which was His previous to his incarnation.

TALE CI.

OF WORLDLY EVIL AND DISTRESS.

WE read of a certain man, named Ganter, who wished that his pleasures might never end. He got up one morning, and walked until he came to a kingdom in which the prince was lately deceased. The noblemen observing that he was a bold man, chose him for their king.* He was, of course, much elevated with the election. But at night, when the servants brought him into his chamber, he perceived at the head of the bed a very fierce lion; a dragon was at the foot; on the right side, a huge bear; and

---

* Perhaps this part of the story may arise in the classical tale of Gordius, who was similarly raised to the throne. See *Justin.* ii. c. 7.

serpents and toads on the left. " What is all this?" asked
Ganter; " am I to sleep in company with all these beasts?"
" Yes, my lord," was the reply; " for all the former kings
have done so, and by these beasts have been devoured."
" That is all very fine," returned Ganter, " but as I feel no
relish for either the bed or the beasts, I will not be your
king." He therefore went his way, and came into another
kingdom, where, in like manner, he was called to the
throne. At night he entered the bed-chamber, and beheld
a very superb couch, full of sharp razors. " What!" exclaimed he, " am I to sleep in this bed?" " Even so, my
lord," replied the attendants; " for in this bed all our
kings have laid, and have perished." " Why," said Ganter,
" everything is excellent, except this bed; but because of
this I will not be your sovereign." In the morning he
again departed, and travelled for three days alone. On
the way he saw an old man sitting above a fountain.
His hand contained a staff, and when our traveller approached, he said, " My dear Ganter, whence come you?"
" I come," he replied, " from foreign countries." " And
where are you going?" " To seek three things which
I cannot find." " What are they?" " The first," said
Ganter, " is unfailing plenty; the second, joy without
sorrow; and the third, light without darkness." " Take
this staff," said the old man, " and go thy way. Before
you is a high mountain, and at its foot a ladder with six
steps. Go up it, and when you have attained the sixth,
you will be at the top of the mountain. There you will
discover a magnificent palace; strike three times at the
gate, and the porter will answer you. Show him the
staff, and say, ' The master of the staff commands you to
admit me.' When you have gained admittance, you will
find the three things which you seek." Ganter did as the
old man desired; and the porter, seeing the staff, permitted him to enter. He found what he had sought, and
much more; and there he continued during the residue of
his life.

APPLICATION.

My beloved, Ganter is any good Christian, who seeks
eternal life. The first bed is human life, with its various

attendant evils: do not rest there. The second is hell,
with its torments—and, oh! avoid that. Take the staff
of penitence, and climb by the ladder of holiness unto a
heavenly place, whose porter is divine goodness.*

TALE CII.

OF THE TRANSGRESSIONS AND WOUNDS OF THE SOUL.

In the reign of Titus there lived a certain noble and
devout knight, who had a beautiful wife; but she dishonoured herself, and persisted in her dishonour. The
knight, therefore, was very sorrowful, and resolved to visit
the Holy Land. In this determination he said to his wife,
"My beloved, I go to the Holy Land, and leave you to
the guidance of your own discretion." No sooner had he
embarked than the lady sent for a certain skilful necromancer, whom she loved; and he dwelt with her. It
happened that, as they lay in bed, the lady observed,
"If you would do one thing for me, I might become your
wife." "What is it," replied he, "that will please you,
and which I can perform for you?"

"My husband is gone to the Holy Land, and loves me
little; now, if by your art you could destroy him, all that
I possess is yours." "I acquiesce," said the clerk, "but
on condition that you marry me." To this the lady
bound herself, and the necromancer fashioned an image
under the similitude and name of the knight, and fixed
it before him on the wall.

In the mean time, while the knight was passing

---

* "In a more confined sense, the first part of this apologue may be
separately interpreted to signify that a king, when he enters on his
important charge, ought not to suppose himself to succeed to the
privilege of an exemption from care, and to be put into the immediate
possession of the highest pleasures, conveniences, and felicities of
life; but to be sensible, that from that moment, he begins to
encounter the greatest dangers and difficulties."—WARTON.

through the main street of Rome, a wise master met him in the way, and observing him narrowly, said, "My friend, I have a secret to communicate."

"Well, master, what would you please to say?"

"This day you are one of death's children, unless you follow my advice: your wife is a harlot, and contrives your death." The knight, hearing what was said of his spouse, put confidence in the speaker, and said, "Good master, save my life, and I will amply recompense you." "Willingly," answered the other, "if you will do as I shall tell you." The knight promised, and the master took him to a bath, undressed him, and desired him to bathe. Then putting into his hand a polished mirror, said, "Look attentively upon this, and you will see wonders." He did so, and the meanwhile the master read to him from a book. "What see you?" he asked. "I see," said the knight, "a certain clerk in my house, with an image of wax which resembles me, and which he has fastened in the wall." "Look again," continued the master; "what do you perceive now?"

"He takes a bow, and places in it a sharp arrow; and now he aims at the effigy."

"As you love your life, the moment you discern the arrow flying to its mark, place yourself in the bath, and remain there until I tell you to come out."

As soon, therefore, as the arrow quitted the string, he plunged his body into the water. This done, the master said, "Raise your head and look into the mirror. What do you perceive now?" "The effigy is not struck, and the arrow is sticking by its side. The clerk appears much concerned." "Look in the mirror once more," said the master, "and observe what he does." "He now goes nearer to the image, and refixes the arrow in the string in order to strike it."

"As you value your life, do as before."

Again the knight plunged his body into the water as soon as he saw by the mirror that the clerk was bending the bow; and then, at the command of the master, resuming his inspection of the mirror, said—

"The clerk makes great lamentation, and says to my wife, 'If the third time I do not strike the effigy, I shall

lose my life.' Now he approaches so near that I think he
cannot miss it."

"Take care," said the master, "as soon as you see him
bend the bow, immerse your body as I before told you."
The knight watched attentively, and as soon as he saw
the clerk draw back the bow to shoot, plunged below the
water. "Rise quickly, and look into the mirror." When
he had done so, he began to laugh. "My friend," said
the master, "why do you laugh?" "I observe," answered
he, "very distinctly, that the clerk has missed the effigy,
and that the arrow, rebounding, has entered his bowels
and destroyed him. My wife makes a hole under my bed,
and there he is buried."

"Rise, then, dress yourself, and pray to God."

The knight returned sincere thanks for his life, and,
having performed his pilgrimage, journeyed toward his
own home. His wife met and received him with much
apparent pleasure. He dissembled for a few days, and
then sending for her parents, said to them, "My dear
friends, hear why I have desired your presence. This
woman, your daughter and my wife, has committed
adultery; and, what is worse, designed to murder me."
The lady denied the accusation with an oath. The knight
then began to relate the whole story of the clerk's actions
and end. "And," he continued, "if you do not credit this,
come and see where the clerk is buried." He then led
them into the bed-chamber, and dragged the body from
its hiding-place. The judge was called, and sentenced
her to be burnt, and her ashes to be scattered in the air.
The knight soon afterwards espoused a beautiful virgin,
by whom he had many children; and with whom he
finished his days in peace.* (8)

APPLICATION.

My beloved, the emperor is Christ; the knight is man;
and the wife, the flesh. To visit the Holy Land is by
good works to attain Heaven. The wise master is a

* [This is one of the best stories of the whole collection, and it is
a pity that it is so poorly worked out.—ED.]

prudent confessor. The clerk is the devil, and the image represents human pride and vanity. The bath is confession; the mirror, the Sacred Writings, which ward off the arrows of sin.

TALE CIII.

OF DOING ALL THINGS WITH CONCORD AND FORETHOUGHT.

DOMITIAN was a very wise and just prince,* and suffered no offender to escape. It happened that as he once sat at table, a certain merchant knocked at the gate. The porter opened it, and asked what he pleased to want. "I have brought some useful things for sale," answered the merchant. The porter introduced him; and he very humbly made obeisance to the emperor. "My friend," said the latter, "what merchandise have you to dispose of?" "Three maxims of especial wisdom and excellence, my lord." "And how much will you take for your maxims?" "A thousand florins." "And so," said the king, "if they are of no use to me, I lose my money?" "My lord," answered the merchant, "if the maxims do not stand you in stead, I will return the money." "Very well," said the emperor; "let us hear your maxims." "The first, my lord, is this—'Whatever you do, do wisely, and think of the consequences.' The second is—'Never leave the *highway* for a *byway.*' And, thirdly, 'Never stay all night as a guest in that house where you find the master an old man, and his wife a young woman.' These three maxims, if you attend to them, will be extremely serviceable." The emperor, being of the same opinion, ordered him to be paid a thousand florins; and so pleased was he with the first, that he commanded it to be inscribed in his court, in his bed-chamber, and in every place where he was accustomed to walk; and even upon the table-cloths of the palace. Now, the rigid justice of the

* A strange contradiction of history.

emperor occasioned a conspiracy among a number of his subjects; and finding the means of accomplishing their purposes somewhat difficult, they engaged a barber, by large promises, to cut his throat as he shaved him. When the emperor, therefore, was to be shaved, the barber lathered his beard, and began to operate upon it; but casting his eyes over the towel which he had fastened round the royal neck,* he perceived woven thereon— "Whatever you do, do wisely, and think of the consequences." The inscription startled the tonsor, and he said to himself, "I am to-day hired to destroy this man; if I do it, my end will be ignominious; I shall be condemned to the most shameful death. Therefore, whatsoever I do, it is good to consider the end, as the writing testifies." These cogitations disturbed the worthy tonsor so much that his hand trembled, and the razor fell to the ground. The emperor seeing this, inquired the cause. "Oh, my lord," said the barber, "have mercy upon me: I was hired this day to destroy you; but accidentally, or rather by the will of God, I read the inscription on the towel, 'Whatever you do, do wisely, and think of the consequences.' Whereby, considering that, of a surety, the consequence would be my own destruction, my hand trembled so much, that I lost all command over it." "Well," thought the emperor, "this first maxim hath assuredly saved my life: in a good hour was it purchased. My friend," said he to the tonsor, "on condition that you be faithful hereafter, I pardon you."

The noblemen, who had conspired against the emperor, finding that their project had failed, consulted with one another what they were to do next. "On such a day," said one, "he journeys to a particular city; we will hide ourselves in a bypath, through which he will pass, and so kill him." The counsel was approved. The king, as had been expected, prepared to set out; and riding on till he came to the bypath, his knights said, "My lord, it will be better for you to go this way, than to pass along the

---

* A curious picture. One sees the whole process—the towel twisted under his jaws, the lather shining round the chin, and the razor elevated for the operation. If he "shaved for twopence," the description would be complete.

broad road; it is considerably nearer." The king pondered the matter within himself. "The second maxim," thought he, "admonishes me never to forsake the highway for a by-way. I will adhere to that maxim." Then turning to his soldiers, "I shall not quit the public road; but you, if it please ye, may proceed by that path, and prepare for my approach." Accordingly a number of them went; and the ambush, imagining that the king rode in their company, fell upon them and put the greater part to the sword. When the news reached the king, he secretly exclaimed, "My second maxim hath also saved my life."

Seeing, therefore, that by this piece of cunning they were unable to slay their lord, the conspirators again took counsel, and said among themselves, "On a certain day he will lodge in a particular house, where all the nobles lodge, because there is no other fit for his reception. Let us then agree with the master of that house and his wife, for a sum of money, and then kill the emperor as he lies in bed." This was agreed to. But when the emperor had come into the city, and had been lodged in the house to which the conspirators referred, he commanded his host to be called into his presence. Observing that he was an old man, the emperor said, "Have you not a wife?" "Yes, my lord." "I wish to see her." The lady came; and when it appeared that she was very young—not eighteen years of age—the king said hastily to his chamberlain, "Away, prepare me a bed in another house. I will remain here no longer." "My lord," replied he, "be it as you please. But they have made everything ready for you: were it not better to lie where you are, for in the whole city there is not so commodious a place." "I tell you," answered the emperor, "I will sleep elsewhere." The chamberlain, therefore, removed; and the king went privately to another residence, saying to the soldiers about him, "Remain here, if you like; but join me early in the morning." Now, while they slept, the old man and his wife arose, being bribed to kill the king in his sleep, and put to death all the soldiers who had remained. In the morning the king arose and found his soldiers slain. "Oh," cried he, "if I had continued here, I should have been destroyed. So the third maxim hath also preserved me." But the old man and his wife, with the whole of their family, were crucified. The emperor retained the three maxims in memory during life, and ended his days in peace. (9)

APPLICATION.

My beloved, the emperor is any good Christian; the porter is free will. The merchant represents our Lord Jesus Christ. The florins are virtues, and the maxims received for them are the grace and favour of God. The highway is the ten commandments; the byway, a bad life; those who lay in ambush are heretics. The old man is the world, and his wife is vanity. The conspirators are devils.

TALE CIV.

OF THE REMEMBRANCE OF BENEFITS.

THERE was a knight who devoted much of his time to hunting. It happened one day, as he was pursuing this diversion, that he was met by a lame lion, who showed him his foot. The knight dismounted, and drew from it a sharp thorn; and then applied an unguent to the wound, which speedily healed it. A while after this, the king of the country hunted in the same wood, and caught that lion, and held him captive for many years. Now, the knight, having offended the king, fled from his anger to the very forest in which he had been accustomed to hunt. There he betook himself to plunder, and spoiled and slew a multitude of travellers. But the king's sufferance was exhausted; he sent out an army, captured, and condemned him to be delivered to a fasting lion. The knight was accordingly thrown into a pit, and remained in terrified expectation of the hour when he should be devoured. But the lion, considering him attentively, and remembering his former friend, fawned upon him; and remained seven days with him destitute of food. When this reached the ears of the king, he was struck with wonder, and directed the knight to be taken from the pit. " Friend," said he, " by what means have you been able to render the lion harmless?" " As I once rode along the forest, my lord, that lion met me lame. I extracted from his foot a large thorn, and afterwards healed the wound, and therefore he has spared me." " Well," returned the king, " since the lion has spared you, I will for this time ratify your pardon. Study to amend your life." The knight gave thanks to the king, and ever afterwards conducted himself with all propriety. He lived to a good old age, and ended his days in peace.*

* " The learned reader must immediately recollect a similar story of one Androclus, who being exposed to fight with wild beasts in the Roman amphitheatre, is recognized, and unattacked by a savage lion, whom he had formerly healed exactly in the same manner. But I believe the whole is nothing more than an oriental apologue on gratitude, written much earlier; and that it here exists in its original state. Androclus's story is related by Aulus Gellius, on the authority of a Greek writer, one Appion, called Plistonices, who flourished under Tiberius. The character of Appion, with which Gellius prefaces this tale, in some measure invalidates his credit; notwithstanding he pretends to have been an eye-witness of this extraordinary fact. ' Ejus libri,' says Gellius, ' non incelebres feruntur; quibus *omnium* ferme quæ *mirifica* in Ægypto visuntur audiunturque, historia comprehenditur. Sed in his quæ audivisse et legisse sese dicit, fortasse a vitio studioque *ostentationis* fit *loquacior*,' &c.[1] Had our compiler of the GESTA taken this story from Gellius, it is probable he would have told it with some of the same circumstances; especially as Gellius is a writer whom he frequently follows, and even quotes; and to whom, on this occasion, he might have been obliged for a few more strokes of the marvellous. But the two writers agree only in the general subject. Our compiler's narrative has much more simplicity than that of Gellius; and contains marks of Eastern manners and life. Let me add that the oriental fabulists are fond of illustrating and enforcing the duty of gratitude, by feigning instances of the gratitude of beasts towards men. And of this the present compilation, *which is strongly tinctured mith orientalism*, affords several other proofs."—WARTON.

Warton is clearly correct in his idea of the oriental origin of this apologue. It also occurs in Æsop's fables, but he has not noticed this.

[1] *Noct. Attic.* lib. v. cap. xiv.

My beloved, the knight is the world; the lame lion is the human race; the thorn, original sin, drawn out by baptism. The pit represents penitence, whence safety is derived.

TALE CV.

OF THE VICISSITUDE OF EVERYTHING GOOD, AND ESPECIALLY OF A RIGHT JUDGMENT.

THE Emperor Theodosius had the misfortune to lose his sight. He put up a bell in his palace; and the law was, that whoever had any suit to make should pull the string with his own hands. When the bell rang, a judge, appointed to this end, descended and administered justice. It chanced that a serpent made her nest immediately under the bell-rope, and in due time brought forth young. When they were old enough, one day she conducted them forth to enjoy the fresh air beyond the city. Now, while the serpent was absent, a toad entered and occupied her nest. When, therefore, the former returned with her young, she found the toad in possession, and instantly began an attack. But the latter baffled her attempts, and obstinately maintained his station. The serpent, perceiving her inability to eject the intruder, coiled her tail around the bell-rope, and forcibly rang the bell; as though she had said, "Descend, judge, and give me justice; for the toad has wrongfully seized my nest." The judge, hearing the bell, descended; but not seeing any one, returned. The serpent, finding her design abortive, once more sounded the alarm. The judge again appeared, and upon this occasion, seeing the serpent attached to the bell-rope, and the toad in possession of her nest, declared the whole circumstance to the emperor. "Go down, my lord," said the latter, "and not only drive away the toad, but kill him; let the serpent possess her right." All which was done. On a subsequent day, as the king lay in his bed, the serpent entered the bed-chamber, carrying a precious stone in her mouth. The servants, perceiving this, informed the emperor, who gave directions that they should not harm it; " for," added he, " it will do me no injury." The serpent, gliding along, ascended the bed, and approaching the emperor's eyes, let the stone fall upon them, and immediately left the room. No sooner, however, had the stone touched the eyes than their sight was completely restored. Infinitely rejoiced at what had happened, the emperor made inquiry after the serpent, but it was not heard of again. He carefully treasured this invaluable stone, and ended his days in peace.*

APPLICATION.

My beloved, the emperor is any worldly-minded man who is blind to spiritual affairs. The bell is the tongue of a preacher; the cord is the Bible. The serpent is a wise confessor, who brings forth young—that is, good works. But prelates and confessors are often timid and negligent, and follow earthly more than heavenly matters; and then the toad, which is the devil, occupies their place. The serpent carries a stone—and the confessor the Sacred Writings, which alone are able to give sight to the blind.

* " This circumstance of the Bell of Justice occurs in the real history of some Eastern monarch, whose name I have forgot.

" In the Arabian philosophy, serpents, either from the brightness of their eyes, or because they inhabit the cavities of the earth, were considered as having a natural, or occult, connection with precious stones. In Alphonsus's CLERICALIS DISCIPLINA, a snake is mentioned, whose eyes were real jacinths. In Alexander's romantic history, he is said to have found serpents in the vale of Jordian, with collars of huge emeralds growing on their necks. The toad, under a vulgar indiscriminating idea, is ranked with the reptile race: and Shakspeare has a beautiful comparison on the traditionary notion that the toad has a rich gem inclosed within its head. Milton gives his serpent eyes of carbuncle (*Paradise Lost*, ix. 500)."—WARTON.

[The " Eastern monarch" of whom Warton was thinking is Jehanjeer.—ED.]

TALE CVI.

OF THE DECEITS OF THE DEVIL.

THERE were once three friends, who agreed to make a pilgrimage together. It happened that their provisions fell short, and having but one loaf between them, they were nearly famished. "Should this loaf," they said to each other, "be divided amongst us, there will not be enough for any one. Let us then take counsel together, and consider how the bread is to be disposed of." "Suppose we sleep upon the way," replied one of them; "and whosoever hath the most wonderful dream shall possess the loaf?" The other two acquiesced, and settled themselves to sleep. But he who gave the advice arose while they were sleeping and eat up the bread, not leaving a single crumb for his companions. When he had finished he awoke them. "Get up quickly," said he, "and tell us your dreams." "My friends," answered the first, "I have had a very marvellous vision. A golden ladder reached up to heaven, by which angels ascended and descended. They took my soul from my body, and conveyed it to that blessed place, where I beheld the Holy Trinity, and where I experienced such an overflow of joy as eye hath not seen nor ear heard. This is my dream." "And I," said the second, "beheld the devils with iron instruments, by which they dragged my soul from the body, and plunging it into hell flames, most grievously tormented me, saying, 'As long as God reigns in heaven this will be your portion.'" "Now then," said the third, who had eaten the bread, "hear my dream. It appeared as if an angel came and addressed me in the following manner:—'My friend, would you see what is become of your companions?' I answered, 'Yes, Lord. We have but one loaf between us, and I fear that they have run off with it.' 'You are mistaken,' he rejoined, 'it lies beside us: follow me.' He immmediately led me to the gate of heaven, and by his command I put in my head and saw you; and I thought that you were snatched up into heaven and sat upon a throne of gold, while rich wines and delicate meats stood around you. Then said the angel, ' Your companion, you see, has an abundance of good things, and dwells in all pleasures. There he ·will remain for ever; for he has entered the celestial kingdom, and cannot return. Come now where your other associate is placed.' I followed, and he led me to hell-gates, where I beheld you in torment, as you just now said. Yet they furnished you, even there, with bread and wine in abundance. I expressed my sorrow at seeing you in misery, and you replied, ' As long as God reigns in heaven here I must remain, for I have merited it. Do you then rise up quickly and eat up all the bread, since you will see neither me nor my companion again.' I complied with your wishes, arose, and eat the bread." *

APPLICATION.

My beloved, the Saracens and Jews, the rich and powerful, and, finally, the perfect among men, are typified by the three companions. The bread represents the kingdom of heaven.

TALE CVII.

OF REMEMBERING DEATH, AND FORGETTING THINGS TEMPORAL.

THERE was an image in the city of Rome standing in an erect posture, with the dexter hand outstretched; and upon the middle finger was written, " STRIKE HERE." The image stood a long time in this manner, and no one understood what the inscription signified. It was much wondered at, and commented on; but this was all, for they invariably departed as wise as they came. At last, a certain subtle clerk, hearing of the image, felt anxious to see it; and when he had done so, he observed the super-

---

* " This apologue is in Alphonsus."—WARTON.

scription, " *Strike here.*" He noticed that when the sun
shone upon the image, the outstretched finger was discernible in the lengthened shadow. After a little consideration he took a spade, and where the shadow ceased,
dug to the depth of about three feet. This brought him
to a number of steps, which led into a subterranean cavity.
Not a little exhilarated with his discovery, the clerk prose-
cuted the adventure. Descending the steps, he entered
the hall of a magnificent palace, in which he perceived a
king and a queen and many nobles seated at table, and
the hall itself filled with men. They were all habited in
costly apparel, and kept the most rigid silence. Looking
about, he beheld in one corner of the place a polished
stone, called a carbuncle, by the single aid of which the
hall was lighted. In the opposite corner stood a man
armed with a bow and arrow, in the act of taking aim
at the precious stone. Upon his brow was inscribed, " I
am what I am : my shaft is inevitable ; least of all can yon
luminous carbuncle escape its stroke." The clerk, amazed
at what he saw, entered the bed-chamber, and found a
multitude of beautiful women arrayed in purple garments,
but not a sound escaped them. From thence he proceeded
to the stables, and observed a number of horses and asses
in their stalls. He touched them, but they were nothing
but stone. He visited all the various buildings of the
palace, and whatsoever his heart desired was to be found
there. Returning to the hall, he thought of making good
his retreat. " I have seen wonders to-day," said he to
himself, " but nobody will credit the relation, unless I
carry back with me some incontrovertible testimony."
Casting his eyes upon the highest table, he beheld a
quantity of golden cups and beautiful knives, which he
approached, and laid his hands upon one of each, designing
to carry them away. But no sooner had he placed them
in his bosom, than the archer struck the carbuncle
with the arrow, and shivered it into a thousand atoms.
Instantly, the whole building was enveloped in thick
darkness, and the clerk, in utter consternation, sought
his way back. But being unable, in consequence of the
darkness, to discover it, he perished in the greatest misery,
amid the mysterious statues of the palace. (10)

My beloved, the image is the devil; the clerk is any covetous man, who sacrifices himself to the cupidity of his desires. The steps by which he descends are the passions. The archer is death, the carbuncle is human life, and the cup and knife are worldly possessions.

TALE CVIII.

OF CONSTANCY IN ADHERING TO PROMISES.

In the reign of a certain emperor, there were two thieves who bound themselves by an oath never to quit one another on any emergency, even though death were the alternative. They afterwards committed many depredations, and were, on some occasions, guilty of murder. It happened that one of them, being caught in some theft, was imprisoned and placed in fetters. His companion, understanding what had chanced, hastened to him, and said, "My friend, by the engagement which we have formed, I adjure you to tell me what I can do to serve you." "It appears," answered the other, "that I must die, having been taken in the fact for which I am sentenced. But I will show you how to oblige me. Obtain permission to remain in my place, while I hasten to arrange my affairs, and provide for my wife and children. Having done this, I will return in due time and liberate you." "My friend," answered the first, "I will readily comply with your wishes." He went therefore to the judge, and spoke thus: "My lord, my friend has been thrown into prison, and condemned to death. It seems that there is no chance for him; let it please you, then, to permit him to return home to arrange the affairs of his family, and I, in the mean time, will become his surety, and remain in prison." "On such a day," replied the judge, "he, with some others, will be executed; if, upon that day, he return not before a certain hour, look you to it: your death is inevitable." "My lord," answered the man, "I am prepared for the worst." "Let him go, then: I consent to your wishes." The judge ordered the substitute to be ironed, and placed in prison in the room of his friend, who immediately set out to his family. So long, however, did he postpone his return, that the day of execution arrived, and his pledge was unredeemed. The latter, therefore, was brought, with many others, to the seat of judgment. "Where is your friend?" said the judge; "he has not arrived to make good his word." "I hope the best, my lord," replied the other; "I do not think he will fail me." Some time passed over, and still he came not; and the prisoner was at length conducted to the cross. "You must attribute your death to yourself," said the judge; "do not charge it upon me. You have rashly trusted to your friend, and he has deceived you." "My lord," replied he, "defer the crucifixion but for a moment, and suffer me to play upon an instrument three times before my death." "Play!" exclaimed the judge; "of what nature is that playing?" "I will shout, my lord." "As you please." Accordingly he began to vociferate. He shouted loudly once, twice, and at the third shout he distinguished, at some distance, a man running toward them with surprising velocity. "My lord! my lord! there is a man coming; stay the execution—perhaps it is my friend, and I shall yet be liberated!" The judge waited, and the person they looked for made his appearance. "I am the man you expect," he exclaimed. "I have arranged my affairs, and meanwhile my friend has been in peril of death for me; let him now freely depart, for I am ready to suffer death for my crimes." The judge regarded him for a few moments with attention, and then said, "My friend, tell me whence it comes that you are so faithful to one another?" "My lord," he replied, "from our youth up we have been friends, and ever pledged ourselves to be faithful. For this reason he put himself in my place till I had settled my affairs." "Well," said the judge, "because of this remarkable instance of fidelity, I pardon you. Remain with me, and I will provide all things necessary for your well-being." They returned thanks to the judge, and promised equal fidelity to him. He then received them to favour; and all praised the judge who showed them this mercy.*

My beloved, the emperor is God; the two thieves, soul and body, which are united in sin. The thief who is taken is the body captured by its lusts. The first shout typifies contrition, the second confession, and the third satisfaction.

TALE CIX.

OF THE AVARICIOUS PURSUIT OF RICHES, WHICH LEADS TO HELL.

A CERTAIN carpenter residing in a city near the sea, very covetous and very wicked, collected a large sum of money, and placed it in the trunk of a tree,† which he placed by his fireside, that no one might have any suspicion that it held money. It happened once that, while all his household slept, the sea overflowed its boundaries, broke down that side of the building where the log was situated, and carried it away. It floated many miles, and reached, at length, a city in which there lived a person who kept open house. Arising early in the morning, he perceived the trunk of a tree in the water, and brought it to land, thinking it was nothing but a bit of timber thrown away by some one. He was a liberal, kind-hearted man, and a great benefactor to the poor. It one day chanced that he entertained some pilgrims in his house; and the weather being extremely cold, he cut up the log for firewood. When he had struck two or three blows with the axe, he heard a rattling sound; and cleaving it in twain, the gold pieces

---

* This appears to be the classical story of Damon and Pythias, with a few inconsiderable variations. From hence, or from similar stories, may probably have arisen the proverbial saying of "Honour among thieves."

† *Truncus.* Warton calls it *a chest.*

rolled out in every direction. Greatly rejoiced at the
discovery, he reposited them in a secure place, until he
should ascertain who was the owner.

Now, the carpenter, bitterly lamenting the loss of his
money, travelled from place to place in pursuit of it. He
came, by accident, to the house of the hospitable man, who
had found the trunk. He failed not to mention the object
of his search ; and the host, understanding that the money
was his, said to himself, " I will prove, if God will, that
the money should be returned to him." Accordingly, he
made three cakes, the first of which he filled with earth;
the second, with the bones of dead men ; and in the third,
he put a quantity of the gold which he had discovered in
the trunk. " Friend," said he, addressing the carpenter,
" we will eat three cakes, composed of the best meat in
the house. Choose which you will have." The carpenter
did as he was directed ; he took the cakes and weighed
them in his hand, one after another, and finding that with
the earth weigh heaviest, he chose it. " And if I want
more, my worthy host," added he, " I will have that,"
laying his hand upon the cake containing the bones.
" You may keep the third cake yourself." " I see clearly,"
murmured the host, " I see very clearly that God does not
will the money to be restored to this wretched man."
Calling, therefore, the poor and infirm, the blind and the
lame, and opening the cake of gold in the presence of the
carpenter, to whom he spoke, " Thou miserable varlet,
this is thine own gold. But thou preferredst the cake of
earth, and dead men's bones. I am persuaded, therefore,
that God wills not that I return thee thy money "—without delay, he distributed the whole amongst the paupers,
and drove the carpenter away in great tribulation. (11)

APPLICATION.

My beloved, the carpenter is any worldly-minded man ;
the trunk of the tree denotes the human heart, filled with
the riches of this life. The host is a wise confessor. The
cake of earth is the world; that of the bones of dead men
is the flesh; and that of gold is the kingdom of heaven.

TALE CX.

OF THE MIRACULOUS RECALL OF SINNERS, AND OF
THE CONSOLATIONS WHICH PIETY OFFERS TO THE
DISTRESSED.

IN the reign of Trajan there lived a knight named Placidus,*
who was commander-in-chief of the emperor's armies. He
was of a very merciful disposition, but a worshipper of
idols. His wife also participated in the same feelings,
and adhered to the same religious rites. They had two
sons, educated in all the magnificence of their age and
station; and from the general kindness and goodness of
their hearts, they merited a revelation of the way of truth.
As he was one day following the chase, he discovered a
herd of deer, amongst which was one remarkable for the
beauty and magnitude of its form. Separating itself from
the rest, it plunged into the thicker part of the brake.
While the hunters, therefore, occupied themselves with
the remainder of the herd, Placidus gave his attention to
the noble animal in question, and followed the course it
had taken with all the celerity in his power. While he
was giving all his strength to the pursuit, the stag at
length scaled a lofty precipice, and Placidus, approaching
as near to it as he could, considered by what means it
might be secured. But as he regarded it with fixed attention, there appeared, impressed upon the centre of the
brow, the form of the cross, which glittered with greater
splendour than a meridian sun. Upon this cross an image
of Jesus Christ was suspended (12); and as formerly hap-
pended to the ass of Balaam, utterance was supplied to
the stag, which thus addressed the hunter: "Why dost
thou persecute me, Placidus? For thy sake have I assumed
the shape of this animal: I am Christ whom thou ignorantly
worshippest. Thine alms have gone up before Me, and
therefore I come, that as thou hast hunted this stag, so
may I hunt thee." Some indeed assert that the image,
hanging between the deer's antlers, said these things.

---

* " Sir Placidas is the name of a knight in the *Faerie Queene*."—
WARTON.

However that may be, Placidus, filled with terror, fell from his horse; and in about an hour returning to himself, arose from the earth and said, "Declare what Thou sayest, that I may believe in Thee." "I am Christ, O Placidus! I created heaven and earth; I caused the light to arise, and divided it from the darkness. I appointed days, and seasons, and years. I formed man out of the dust of the earth; and I became incarnate for the salvation of mankind. I was crucified, and buried; and on the third day I rose again." When Placidus heard this, he fell again upon the earth, and exclaimed, "I believe, O Lord, that Thou art He that made all things; and that Thou art He who bringest back the wanderer." The Lord answered, "If thou believest this, go into the city and be baptized."

"Wouldst Thou, O Lord, that I impart what has befallen me to my wife and children, that they also may believe?"

"Do so; tell them that they also may be cleansed from their iniquities. And do you, on the morrow, return hither, where I will appear again, and show you more fully of the future."

Placidus, therefore, departed to his own home, and communicated all that had passed to his wife. But she, too, had had a revelation; and in like manner had been enjoined to believe in Christ, together with her children. So they hastened at midnight to the bishop of the city of Rome, where they were entertained and baptized with great joy. Placidus was called Eustacius, and his wife, Theosbyta; the two sons, Theosbytus and Agapetus. In the morning Eustacius, according to custom, went out to hunt, and coming with his attendants near the place, he dispersed them, as if for the purpose of discovering the prey. Immediately the vision of yesterday reappeared, and prostrating himself, he said, "I implore Thee, O Lord, to make clear what Thou didst promise to Thy servant."

"Blessed art thou, Eustacius, because thou hast received the laver of My grace, and thereby overcome the devil. Now hast thou trod him to dust who beguiled thee. Now will thy fidelity appear; for the devil, whom thou hast deserted, is arming himself against thee in a variety of ways. Much must thou undergo ere thou

possessest the crown of victory.   Much must thou suffer
that thou mayst be humbled, and abandon the deep-
seated vanity of this world, and once more be raised by
spiritual wealth.   Fail not, therefore, nor look back upon
thy former condition.   Thou must demonstrate thyself
another Job; but from the very depth of thy humiliation,
I will restore thee to the summit of earthly splendour.
Choose, then, whether thou wouldst prefer thy trials now,
or at the conclusion of life."   Eustacius replied, "If it
become me, O Lord, to be exposed to trials, let them presently approach; but do Thou uphold me, and supply me
with patient fortitude."

"Be bold, Eustacius: My grace shall support your
souls."   Saying thus, the Lord ascended into heaven.
After which Eustacius returned home to his wife, and
explained to her what had been decreed.   In a few days
a pestilence carried off the whole of their men-servants
and maid-servants; and before long the sheep, horses,
and cattle also perished.   Robbers plundered their habitation, and despoiled them of every ornament; while he
himself, together with his wife and sons, fled naked and
in the deepest distress.   But devoutly they worshipped
God; and, apprehensive of an Egyptian redness (13),
went secretly away.   Thus were they reduced to
utter poverty.   The king and the senate, greatly afflicted
with their general's calamities, sought for, but found
not the slightest trace of him.   In the mean time this
unhappy family approached the sea; and finding a ship
ready to sail, they embarked in it.   The master of the
vessel observing that the wife of Eustacius was very
beautiful, determined to secure her; and when they
had crossed the sea, demanded their passage money,
which, as he anticipated, they did not possess.   Notwithstanding the vehement and indignant protestations of
Eustacius, he seized upon his wife; and, beckoning to the
mariners, commanded them to cast the unfortunate husband headlong into the sea.   Perceiving, therefore, that
all opposition was useless, he took up his two children,
and departed with much and heavy sorrow.   "Alas for
me and for you!" he exclaimed, as he wept over his
bereaved offspring; "your poor mother is lost, and in a

strange land, in the arms of a strange lord, must lament her fate." Travelling along, he came to a river, the water of which ran so high that it appeared hazardous in an eminent degree to cross with both the children at the same time: one, therefore, he placed carefully upon the bank, and then passed over with the other in his arms. This effected, he laid it upon the ground, and returned immediately for the remaining child. But in the midst of the river, accidentally glancing his eye back, he beheld a wolf hastily snatch up the child, and run with it into an adjoining wood. Despairing of saving it, he hastened to the other; but while he was yet at some distance, a huge lion approached the child he had left, and, seizing it, presently disappeared. (14) To follow was useless, for he was in the middle of the water. Giving himself up, therefore, to his desperate situation, he began to lament and to pluck away his hair; and would have cast himself into the stream had not Divine Providence preserved him.

Certain shepherds, however, observing the lion carrying off the child in his teeth, pursued him with dogs; and by the peculiar dispensation of Heaven it was dropped unhurt. As for the other, some ploughmen witnessing the adventure, shouted lustily after the wolf, and succeeded in liberating the poor victim from its jaws. Now, it happened that both the shepherds and ploughmen resided in the same village, and brought up the children amongst them. But Eustacius knew nothing of this, and his affliction was so poignant that he was unable to control his complaints. "Alas!" he would say, "once I flourished like a luxuriant tree, but now I am stripped of my leaves. Once I was encompassed with military ensigns and bands of armed men; now I am a single being in the universe: I have lost all my children, and everything that I possessed. Remember, O Lord, that thou saidst my trials should resemble Job's; behold, they exceed them. For, although he was destitute, he had a couch, however vile, to repose upon; I, alas! have nothing. He had compassionating friends, while I have savage beasts, who have carried off my sons, for my friends. His wife remained, but mine is forcibly carried off. Assuage my anguish, O Lord! and place a bridle upon my lips, lest I utter foolishness, and be cast away from before Thy face." With such words he gave free course to the fulness of his heart; and after much travel entered a village, where he abode.   In this place he continued for fifteen years, and tended the lambs of the men of that place as their hired servant.

To return to the two boys.   They were educated in the same neighbourhood, but had no knowledge that they were brothers.   And as for the wife of Eustacius, she preserved her purity, and suffered not the infamous usage which circumstances led her to apprehend.   After some time her persecutor died.

In the mean while the Roman emperor was beset by his enemies, and recollecting how valiantly Placidus had behaved himself in similar straits, his grief at the deplorable mutation of fortune was renewed.   He despatched soldiers through various parts of the world in pursuit of them; and promised to the discoverer infinite rewards and honours.   It happened that some of the emissaries, being of those who had attended upon the person of Placidus, came into the country in which he laboured, and one of them he recognized by his gait.   The sight of these men brought back to the exile's mind the situation of wealth and honour which he had once possessed; and being filled with fresh trouble at the recollection—"O Lord!" he exclaimed, " even as beyond expectation I have seen these people again, so let me be restored to my beloved wife. Of my children I speak not; for I know too well that they are devoured by wild beasts."   At that moment a voice whispered, " Be faithful, Eustacius, and thou wilt shortly recover thy lost honours, and again look upon thy wife and offspring."   Now, when the soldiers met Placidus, they knew not who he was; and accosting him, they asked if he were acquainted with any foreigner named Placidus, with his wife and two sons.   He replied in the negative, but requested that they would tarry in his house.   They consented; and he conducted them home, and waited on them.   And here, as before, at the recollection of his former splendour, his tears flowed.   Unable to contain himself, he went out of doors, and when he had washed his face he re-entered, and continued his service.* By and by the appearance of their ancient master underwent a more exact scrutiny; and one said to the other, "Surely this man bears great resemblance to him we inquire after." "Of a truth," answered his companion, "you say well. Let us examine if he possess a scar on his head, which he received in action." They did so, and finding a scar which indicated a similar wound, they leaped up and embraced him, and inquired after his wife and sons. He related his adventures; and the neighbours, coming in, listened with wonder to the account delivered by the soldiers of his military achievements and former magnificence. Then, obeying the command of the emperor, they clothed him in sumptuous apparel. On the fifteenth day they reached the imperial court; and the emperor, apprized of his coming, went out to meet him, and saluted him with great gladness. Eustacius related all that had befallen him; he was then invested with the command of the army, and restored to every office that he had held prior to his departure. When the soldiers were numbered, they were found to be too few to meet the enemy. He therefore drew together from all parts the young men of the country; and it fell in the lot of the village where his own children were educated, to send two to the army; and these very youths were selected by the inhabitants as the best and bravest of their number. They appeared before the general; and their elegant manners, united to a singular propriety of conduct, won his esteem. He placed them in the van of his troops, and began his march against the enemy. After the rout of the foe, he caused his army to halt for three days at a certain place, where, as it happened, his wife was living in poverty. Strange to say, the sons themselves, in the general distribution of the soldiers, were quartered with their own mother, but all the while ignorant with whom they were stationed.

About mid-day the lads, sitting together, related the various mutations to which their infancy had been subject; and the mother, who was at no great distance, became an attentive auditor. "Of what I was, while a child," said

* A curious picture of the olden times!

the elder of the brothers, " I remember nothing, except that my beloved father was a leader of a company of soldiers; and that my mother, who was very beautiful, had two sons, of whom I was the elder. We accompanied our parents from the habitation in which we had constantly resided during the night, and embarking on board a vessel that immediately put to sea, sailed I know not whither. Our mother remained in the ship, but wherefore, I am also ignorant. In the mean time our father carried my brother and myself in his arms, and me he left upon the nearer bank of a river, until he had conveyed the younger of us across. But no sooner had he accomplished his design, and was returning to my assistance, than a wolf darted from a thicket and bore my brother off in his mouth. Before he could hasten back to his succour, a prodigious lion seized upon me, and carried me into a neighbouring wood. Certain shepherds, however, delivered and educated me amongst them, as you know. What has become of my father and my brother, I know not." The younger brother here burst into a flood of tears, and exclaimed, " Surely I have found my brother; for they who brought me up frequently declared that I was emancipated from the jaws of a wolf." Then did they exchange embraces and shed tears. The mother, who listened, it may be well supposed, with intense interest to what was going forward, felt a strong conviction that they were her own children. She was silent, however; and the next day went to the commander of the forces, and entreated permission to go into her own country. " I am a Roman woman," said she, " and a stranger in these parts." As she uttered these words, her eye fixed with an earnest and anxious gaze upon the countenance of him she addressed. It was her husband, whom she now for the first time recollected; and she threw herself at his feet unable to contain her joy. " My lord," cried the enraptured matron, " I entreat you to relate some circumstances of your past life; for, unless I greatly mistake, you are Placidus, the master of the soldiery, since known by the name of Eustacius, whom our blessed Saviour converted, and tried by such and such temptations : I am *his* wife, taken from him at sea by a perfidious wretch, but who accomplished not his atrocious purposes. I had two sons, called Agapetus and Theosbytus." When Eustacius heard this, he looked at her earnestly, and saw that it was his wife. They embraced and wept; giving glory to God, who brings joy to the sorrowful. The wife then observed, "My lord, what has become of our children?" "Alas!" replied he, "they were carried off by wild beasts;" and he repeated the circumstance of their loss. "Give thanks," said his wife, "give manifold thanks to the Lord; for as His Providence hath revealed our existence to each other, so will He give us back our beloved offspring." "Did I not tell you," returned he, "that wild beasts had devoured them?"

"True; but yesternight, as I sat in the garden, I overheard two young men relate the occurrences of their childhood, and whom I believe to be our sons. Interrogate them, and they will tell you."

Messengers were immediately despatched for this purpose, and a few questions convinced Eustacius of the full completion of his happiness. They fell upon each other's necks and wept aloud. It was a joyful occasion; and the whole army rejoiced at their being found, and at the victory over the barbarians. Previous to their return the Emperor Trajan died, and was succeeded by Adrian, more wicked even than his predecessor.* However, he received the conqueror and his family with great magnificence, and sumptuously entertained them at his own table. But the day following the emperor would have proceeded to the temple of his idols to sacrifice, in consequence of the late victory; and desired his guests to accompany him. "My lord," said Eustacius, "I worship the God of the Christians; and Him only do I serve, and propitiate with sacrifice." The emperor, full of rage, placed him, with his whole family, in the arena, and let loose a ferocious lion upon them. But the lion, to the astonishment of all, held down his head before them, as if in reverence, and humbly went from them. On which the emperor ordered a brazen bull to be heated, and into this his victims were cast alive; but with prayer and supplica-

---

* Neither Trajan nor Adrian deserve this character; but the former is vilely slandered.

tion they commended themselves to the mercy of God, and three days after, being taken out of the furnace in the presence of the emperor, so untouched were they by the fire that not a hair of their heads was singed, nor had the fiery vapours in any way affected them. The Christians buried their corpses in the most honourable manner, and over them constructed an oratory. They perished in the first year of Adrian, A.D. 120, in the calends of November; or, as some write, the 12th of the calends of October.*

APPLICATION.

My beloved, the emperor is Christ; Placidus, any worldly-minded man. The stags are the senses. The large and beautiful stag is reason; it ascends a precipice, which is justice or rectitude. The horns are the old and new law. The wife of Placidus is the soul; the two sons are the will and the works of man. The master of the ship is a prelate, who would detain the soul from error; and the ship is the Church. The river is the world; the lion is the devil; and the wolf, the flesh. The shepherds are confessors; and the ploughmen, preachers. The messengers sent in pursuit of Placidus represent the patriarchs and prophets.

TALE CXI.

OF VIGILANCE IN OUR CALLING.

A CERTAIN nobleman had a white cow, to which he was extremely partial. He assigned two reasons for this. First, because she was spotlessly white; and next, because she gave abundance of rich milk. The estimation in

------

* However careless the structure of this tale, it conveys an admirable moral. It teaches that the eye of God is vigilant for the safeguard of mankind; and that in the darkest hour with which humanity can be visited, "all things are working together for good." But the tendency of the whole of these stories is unexceptionable.

which the nobleman regarded his beast increased so much, that he constructed golden horns for her, and thought for a long time how she might be best secured. Now, there lived at that time a man called Argus, who was entirely faithful to his employer, and, moreover, possessed an hundred eyes. The nobleman despatched a messenger to Argus, to request his attendance without delay. On his arrival, he said, "I commit to your custody my cow with golden horns; and if you guard it securely I will liberally remunerate you. But if you permit her horns to be stolen, you shall die the death." Argus accordingly received the cow under his charge; and every day attended her to the pasture, and watched her with unremitting care. At night he drove her home. But there dwelt in these days a certain avaricious knave called Mercury, whose skill in music was surpassing. He had a great desire to possess the animal so narrowly watched; and he went frequently to her keeper, in the hope of prevailing with him, by prayers or promises, to deliver the horns to him. But Argus fixed a shepherd's staff, which he held, firmly in the ground; and addressed it in the person of his master : * "Thou, oh staff, art my master, and at night I shall return to your castle. You will question me about the cow and her horns; I answer, 'My lord, the cow has lost her horns; for a robber, coming while I slept, ran off with them.' Now, you reply, 'Rascal! had you not an hundred

* A similar colloquy to that in this story occurs in the *Turkish Tales* :—

"Let me suppose that I am at court (continued he, taking his cap off his head, and laying it on the floor before him), let me suppose my cap to be Togaltimur, and see if I can have the confidence to insist upon a lie in the face of the king. Entering into his presence, I salute him. Saddyq, says he to me, let my black horse be got ready, I mean to ride him to-day.—Sir, an accident has befallen him; yesterday, in the evening, he would eat nothing whatever that was offered to him, and he died at midnight; nor can I imagine what has killed him.—How! my black horse, that carried me so well but yesterday, is he dead? Why must it be he rather than so many others that are in the same stable? What story is this you tell me? Begone, you are a liar. Thou hast either sold my horse to some foreigner, who went away with him last night into his own country, or killed him yourself in some freak or other. Think not of escaping my vengeance, you shall be punished according to your deserts. One of you stab that villain to the heart this moment; cut him to pieces!"

eyes? How was it that they were all asleep, while the robber stole the horns? This is a lie, and I will put you to death.' And if I say that I have sold it, I shall be equally exposed to the indignation of my lord." "Get thee gone, then," answered Mercury: "thou shalt have nothing." With this threat Mercury departed, and the next day returned with a musical instrument. He then began to tell Argus stories, and to sing to him; until at last two of his eyes dropped asleep; then two more, and finally, the whole head sunk into a deep slumber. Mercury perceiving this, decapitated him, and bore away the cow with her golden horns.*

APPLICATION.

My beloved, the nobleman is Christ; the white cow is the soul. The milk represents prayer and supplication, on account of which he gave her golden horns, that is, eternal life. Argus is any prelate, who ought to be circumspect and watchful. The pastoral staff is the ecclesiastical power communicated to him; the songs are put for singing women. Then, if the prelate fall asleep, the head is cut off, that is, he loses eternal life. Mercury is the devil.

TALE CXII.

OF THE CARE OF THE SOUL.

THE Emperor Gorgonius had a beautiful wife, who was delivered of a son. The boy grew up a universal favourite; but on attaining his tenth year the mother died, and was splendidly interred. By the advice of his counsellors, the emperor took another wife, who conceived a dislike for her son-in-law, and did him many injuries.† When this was

---

* "The classical story of Argus and Mercury, with some romantic additions."—WARTON.

† Warton says, in his analysis of this story, "The son of king Gorgonius is beloved by his stepmother." This is a mistake. The Latin text is, "Rex, aliam uxorem duxit, quæ filium primæ uxoris *non dilexit, sed opprobria multa sibi intulit.*" Nothing can be plainer.

communicated to the king, being desirous of gratifying his new spouse, he banished the young man from the kingdom. Thus driven from his home, he turned his attention to physic, and became in the course of time a great and perfect physician. The emperor, hearing of his celebrity, was much pleased at it; and happening a short time afterwards to fall sick, sent letters to recall him. When the son understood his father's pleasure, he made haste to comply with it, and by his skill in medicine soon restored him to convalescence. The fame of this cure spread through the whole kingdom. Now, it chanced that his stepmother sickened even to death, and physicians from every place were summoned to attend her. They all, however, unanimously declared that death was inevitable, and, full of grief at the intelligence, the emperor desired his son to undertake the cure. " No, my lord," said he, " I cannot comply with your wishes." " If you deny me," returned the father, " I will again banish you the kingdom." " Then," he replied, " you will act with the greatest injustice. You acknowledged yourself my father, yet banished me from you through this very woman's suggestion. My absence occasioned your sickness and sorrow, and my presence produces a like effect upon the queen, my unkind stepmother; therefore I will not cure her, but will immediately depart." " The queen," returned the father, " is afflicted with the same infirmity that I was, and which you so effectually dispelled: let me entreat you to preserve her also." " My beloved father," answered he, " although she has the same infirmity, her complexion is different. When I entered the palace, the joy you felt at my return contributed to your speedy recovery; but the reverse happens to my stepmother. If I speak, she is full of grief; if I touch her, she is carried beyond herself. Now, nothing is more beneficial to the sick than compliance with their wishes. She cannot bear my presence, and why should you wish it?" By these excuses the son evaded the matter, and his stepmother died.

APPLICATION.

My beloved, the emperor is our first parent, Adam; the first wife is the soul; and the son is Christ, who cures our infirmities. The stepmother is the devil.

TALE CXIII.

OF SPIRITUAL CONTESTS.

THE Emperor Adonias was exceedingly rich, and delighted in tournaments and in tilting. He once held a tournament, and caused it to be proclaimed that the conqueror should obtain a magnificent reward. This caused a great assemblage of the princes and peers of the kingdom; and the emperor ordained that the knights should be divided, so many on one side and so many on the other. But they who first entered the field were to dispose their shields and arms in order in a certain place; and further, whosoever of the adverse party would touch the shield of another with his lance, immediately he whose shield was touched, being previously armed by a maiden selected for the purpose, should descend to the contest, and if he proved victorious, should be crowned with a kingly crown, and eat meat at the royal table. Now, a certain knight, having diligently inspected the shields of his antagonists, was wonderfully taken with one bearing three apples *or;* and that shield he touched. Instantly the owner of it armed and met his opponent, and, after a short conflict, cut off the challenger's head, and received the promised recompense.*

* " The most curious anecdote of chivalry, now on record, occurs in the ecclesiastical history of Spain. Alphonsus the Ninth, about the year 1214, having expelled the Moors from Toledo, endeavoured to establish the Roman missal in the place of Saint Isidore's. This alarming innovation was obstinately opposed by the people of Toledo, and the king found that his project would be attended with almost insuperable difficulties. The contest at length between the two missals grew so serious, that it was mutually resolved to decide the controversy, not by a theological disputation, but by single combat;

APPLICATION.

My beloved, the emperor is our Lord Jesus Christ; the tournament is the contest between God and the devils; the shields are some of the attributes of the Almighty; and the field is human nature. The shield bearing three golden apples is the Trinity in Unity, against which the knight—that is, any man—strikes when he commits a mortal sin. The reward of the conqueror is eternal life.

TALE CXIV.

OF DELIVERANCE FROM HELL.

In the reign of a certain king there lived a poor man who was accustomed to go every day to a neighbouring forest to cut wood for sale. On one occasion, as he went with an ass, the thickness of the underwood caused him to lose his footing, and he fell unawares into a pit, from which he was unable to deliver himself. In this pit lay a horrible dragon, whose scaly length completely encompassed it. The higher part was occupied by a number of serpents; as also the bottom; half way down was a round stone, which the serpents daily ascended and licked. After that the dragon licked it. The poor man wondered at what he saw, and deliberated upon the meaning. "I have already remained here many days," thought he, "without sustenance; and unless I can obtain food, with-

in which the champion of the Toletan missal proved victorious."—WARTON.

In illustration of the mode of conducting tournaments, a short quotation from *Froissart* may be adduced:—

"They ordayned in a fayre playne betwene Calays and Saynt Ingilbertes thre fressh grene pauilyons to be pyght up; and at the entre of every pauilion there hanged two sheldes, with the armes of the knightes; one shelde of peace, another of warre; and it was ordayned that suche as shoulde ryn and do dedes of armes shoulde *touch one of the sheldes,* or *cause to be touched* whiche as pleaseth them, and he should be delyuered according to his desire."—BERNER'S *Froissard,* vol. ii. cap. clxviii.

out doubt I must perish. I will do, therefore, as the serpents and dragon do." Accordingly, he went up to the stone and began to lick it, when, to his astonishment, he found that it partook of every delicious flavour that imagination could devise, and was as much invigorated as if he had eaten all the food in the world. A few days after, a dreadful thunderstorm burst overhead; insomuch that the serpents left their retreat one after another: and when they had departed, the dragon which lay at the bottom of the well raised itself above, and would have flown away; but the poor man, observing this, caught hold of it by the tail, and by these means succeeded in escaping from the pit. The dragon carried him a considerable distance, and dropped him in the same wood; but, ignorant of his situation, he was unable to find the way out. A company of merchants, however, happening to travel through that forest, showed him the path he wanted. Very happy at his marvellous deliverance, he returned to his own city, and published what had occurred; but his death followed immediately afterwards.

APPLICATION.

My beloved, the king is our heavenly Father; the poor man is as men are naturally, who enter a wood— that is, the world. The pit is mortal sin. The round stone in the centre is Christ. The thunderstorm typifies confession, which being heard, the serpents—that is, sins and devils—are affrighted, and depart. The dragon is the devil, and the merchants are preachers.

TALE CXV.

OF RECONCILIATION THROUGH CHRIST.

A CERTAIN emperor possessed a forest, in which was an elephant whom no one dare approach. This caused his majesty no little surprise, and calling together his nobles and wise men, he asked them what was the nature of this elephant. They replied that he mightily approved pure

and modest virgins. Thereupon, the emperor wished to
despatch two beautiful and virtuous maids, who were
likewise skilled in music, if any such were to be found in
his kingdom. At last, his emissaries discovered two who
were honest and fair enough, and causing them to be
stripped, one of them was required to carry a basin, and
the other a sword. They entered the forest, and began
to sing ; and the elephant, attracted by the sound, soon
approached. In the mean time the virgins continued
their song, till the elephant fondled them, and by and by
fell asleep in the lap of one of the maids. The other,
perceiving this, slew him with the sword she had carried,
while her companion filled the bowl with blood. Thus
they returned to the king ; and when he heard of their
success, he rejoiced succeedingly, and ordered a very
beautiful purple, and many other curious matters, to be
made of the blood.*

* "In this wild tale, there are circumstances enough of general
analogy, if not of peculiar parallelism, to recall to my memory the
following beautiful description, in the MS. romance of Syr Launfal, of
two damsels, whom the knight unexpectedly meets in a desolate
forest :—

> "As he sat in sorrow sore
> He saw come out of holt-*es* hoar,
>   Gentle maidens two ;
> Their kirtles were of Ind sandal[1]
> Ylaced small, jolyf[2] and well,
>   There might none gayer go.
> Their mantles were of green velvet,
> Y bordered with gold right well y set,
>   Y pelured[3] with gris and gro.[4]
> Their head-*es* were well dight withal,
> Each had on a jolyf coronal
>   With sixty gems and mo.[5]
> Their faces were white as snow on down,
> Their rode[6] was red, their eyen were brown,
>   I saw never none such.
> The one bare of gold a basin,
> That other a towel white and fine,
>   Of silk that was good and rich.
> Their kerchiefs wer well schyre[7]
> Arrayed with a rich gold wire."—WARTON.

[1] Indian silk. *Cendal*, Fr. See Du Fresne.   [2] Pretty.   [3] Furred.
    [4] Gris is *fur* ; *gris and gro* [*gray* ; meaning perhaps gray fur] is a common phrase
in the metrical romances.
        [5] **More.**   [6] Complexion.   [7] Cut.

APPLICATION.

My beloved, the emperor is our heavenly Father; the elephant is Christ; and the two virgins, Mary and Eve, who were both born free from sin,* Mary being sanctified in the womb. She carries a sword, that is, sin, by which Christ died.

TALE CXVI.

OF THE LOVE OF GOD.

King Pepin married a very beautiful girl, by whom he had a son; but the mother died in her confinement. He therefore espoused another, and she also brought forth a son, whom he sent with the elder-born to be educated in another country. Now, they so much resembled one another, that it was impossible to distinguish them; and when, after a length of time, the anxiety of the living mother to behold her son occasioned their return, although the one was younger by perhaps a year, he was as tall as his brother, which indeed frequently happens. But the resemblance to each other was so strong, that the mother knew not her own child. She earnestly entreated the king to determine her doubts, but he refused compliance with her wishes. This occasioned a flood of tears; and the king, feeling distressed at her trouble, said, "Weep not; that is your son," and pointed to him who was born of the first wife. This deception comforted the queen; and without delay she studiously sought to supply all his wants, to the neglect of him who was really her offspring. The king, seeing this, asked, "Why do you deceive yourself? One of these two is your son, but which you have yet to learn." "To what end is this?" answered she; "tell me which is he?" "No," said the king; "certainly not, and for this reason. If I tell you the truth, you will love one and neglect the other. I desire you, therefore,

* We may observe that the Catholics lose no opportunity of honouring the Virgin Mary, at whatever expense.

to attend equally to both, and when they have arrived at man's estate, I will show you which is which; then your happiness will be perfect." The queen complied with her husband's will; she conducted herself with the strictest impartiality, until they had attained to manhood. On discovering her own child, she gave free course to her joy. Thus her days glided on, and ended in peace.*

APPLICATION.

My beloved, the king is Christ; the two sons are the elect and the reprobate. The mother of the last son is the Church. The dead mother represents the old law. The Church distinguishes not between those who are elect and reprobate; but when they come of age—that is, at the day of judgment—the truth will be declared.

TALE CXVII.

OF UNCONVERSION.

THE Emperor Frederic decreed that, if any female were violated, whosoever freed her from the hand of the oppressor should have her for his wife if he wished. Now, it happened that a certain vile wretch caught up a young girl, and dragging her into a forest, there abused her. She shrieked violently; and a noble knight, riding by some chance in the same forest, heard her exclamations, and spurred on his horse to her assistance. He inquired the occasion of the clamour. "Oh, my lord," said the damsel, "for the love of God, succour me. This villain has abused me, and threatened me with destruction." "My lord," answered the fellow, "she is my wife, whom I have taken in adultery, and I therefore menaced her with death." "Do not believe it, my lord," said the girl.

---

* "A favourite old romance is founded on the indistinctible like-ness of two of Charlemagne's knights, Amys and Amelion; originally celebrated by Turpin, and placed by Vincent of Beauvais, under the reign of Pepin."—WARTON.

" I never was his wife, nor have I been other than a maid, until treacherously maltreated by this ruffian. Help me, then, I implore you." " I perceive plainly," said the knight, " that this wretch has oppressed you, and I will therefore free you from his hands." " You will do this at your peril," answered the other; " I will defend my right to the last." Saying which, he prepared himself for a contest. After a desperate struggle, the knight obtained the victory, but was dangerously wounded. He then said to the lady, " Are you pleased to espouse me?" " Willingly," returned she; " I wish it from my heart, and here pledge my faith." This done, the knight said, " You shall reside in my castle for a few days; and in the mean time I will go to my parents, and provide everything requisite for our union. After that, I will return and espouse you with great splendour." " I am ready to obey you in all things," answered the lady; and the knight, having placed her as he had said, bade her farewell. But while he was absent, an oppressive lord of that country went to the castle, where the girl was placed, and knocked at the gate. She denied him admission; and he had then recourse to magnificent promises. He declared himself ready to espouse her honourably; and she, lending too credulous an ear to what was said, at last opened the gate. He went in, and remained with her during the night. In about a month's space, the knight returned to his castle. He knocked, but no one replied to him. Filled with the greatest bitterness of heart, he said, " Oh, dear girl, recall how I saved thy life, and the faith which you solemnly pledged me. Speak, dear girl, and let me behold thy face." The lady, hearing this, opened the window, and said, " Look, you ass! what does it please ye to want?" " I marvel," replied he, " at thy ingratitude. I received several dangerous wounds in defending thee; and if thou art incredulous, I will show them." Saying this, he loosed his robe, and discovered the scars. " Do not," added he, " be ungrateful; open the gate, that I may receive you as my beloved wife." But she made no answer, and turned away. The knight complained to the judge, and alleged the services he had rendered her. He displayed the wounds taken in her behalf, and claimed her in recompence as his wife. The judge, therefore, sent for the seducer, and said, "Hast thou withheld the woman whom the knight's bravery freed from uncourteous usage?"

"I have, my lord."

"And, according to law, she voluntarily became his wife? How, then, darest thou affect the wife of another? First, you entered his castle during his absence; next, you violated his bed; lastly, for a long time you have kept his wife from him: what have you to answer?"

He was silent; and the judge, turning to the woman, said, "Girl! by the law of the land, you are doubly the wife of this knight. First, because he freed you from a violator; and secondly, because you contracted yourself to him. Why hast thou opened the gate of thy husband's castle to another than he?" She, also, was unable to answer; and the judge condemned both to be crucified. This was done accordingly, and much praise was given to the judge for the sentence he had pronounced.

APPLICATION.

My beloved, the emperor is God; the woman is the soul; and the violater, the devil. The knight is Christ; the castle, the human body.

TALE CXVIII.

OF DECEIT.

A CERTAIN knight, who had made a temporary residence in Egypt, was desirous of laying up a sum of money which he possessed in that country. He inquired, therefore, for some person in whom he might repose confidence; and a certain old man being pointed out, he went and delivered to him ten talents. He then prepared for a pilgrimage. His business completed, he returned, and demanded the amount of what he had deposited. But his agent, proving a rogue, asserted that he had never seen him; and, totally regardless of the knight's supplications and conciliatory language, bade him with much contumely trouble him no further. The knight, exceedingly disturbed at such unexpected usage, having accidentally met an old woman equipped in the garb of a devotee, and supported by a staff, removed a number of stones which stood in the way, and which might have cut her feet. Observing the despondency of the knight's demeanour, and at the same time suspecting that he was a foreigner, she entreated him to come near, and questioned him upon the cause of his solicitude. He gave her a full account of it, and the old woman counselled him what he should do. "Bring me," said she, "to a man of your own country whom we may trust." He did so, and she directed him to fabricate ten chests, painted outwardly with curious devices and rich colours, bound with iron, and fastened with silver locks, but filled up with stones. All this was done, and the woman then bade the knight send them by ten porters to the warehouse of the rascally factor. "Let them come one after another, in order ; and as soon as the first man has entered, do you boldly demand your money. I trust you will find it restored to you." Accordingly, they proceeded to the factor's house, and the old woman addressed him as follows :—"My master, this stranger" (pointing to the artificer of the chests) "lodges with me, and wishes to return to his native land. But first he would deposit his wealth, which is contained in ten chests, under the safeguard of some honourable and faithful person. And because I have heard this character of you, I should be unwilling to let any one else have the care of them." As she spoke, a porter entered with the first chest; and at the same instant the knight appeared, to require his money. The knavish factor, fearing that if he disputed the right of the last, he should lose the golden harvest which the custody of ten such apparently valuable chests promised, came up to him in a soothing tone, and said, "My friend, where have you been? Receive, I pray you, the money which you laid up with me." The knight was not slow in complying, and gave great thanks to God, and the old woman, for the sums he had almost despaired of. "Master," said she to the factor, "I and my man will go and make inquiry about the other chests, and hasten back immediately. Expect us; and take care of that which we have brought." Thus, by the assistance of the devotee, the knight recovered his property.

APPLICATION.

My beloved, the knight is any Christian; the ten talents are the ten commandments. The factor is the world. The old devotee is a good conscience; and the iron-bound chest, filled with stones, is a heart full of virtues.

TALE CXIX.

OF INGRATITUDE.

In the reign of a certain king there lived a proud and oppressive seneschal. Now, near the royal palace was a forest well stocked with game; and by the direction of this person various pits were dug there, and covered with leaves, for the purpose of entrapping the beasts. It happened that the seneschal himself went into this forest, and with much exaltation of heart exclaimed internally, "Lives there a being in the empire more powerful than I am?" This braggart thought was scarcely formed, ere he rode upon one of his own pitfalls, and immediately disappeared. The same day had been taken a lion, a monkey, and a serpent. Terrified at the situation into which fate had thrown him, he cried out lustily, and his noise awoke a poor man called Guido, who had come with his ass into that forest to procure firewood, by the sale of which he got his bread. Hastening to the mouth of the pit, he was promised great wealth if he would extricate the seneschal from his perilous situation. "My friend," answered Guido, "I have no means of obtaining a livelihood except by the faggots which I collect: if I neglect this for a single day, I shall

---

* This tale is in Alphonsus; in the *Cente Novelle Antiche,*. Nov. 74; in Boccaccio, Day 8, Nov. 10; and in the *Arabian Nights.*

be thrown into the greatest difficulties." The seneschal
reiterated his promises of enriching him; and Guido went
back to the city, and returned with a long cord, which he
let down into the pit, and bade the seneschal bind it round
his waist. But before he could apply it to the intended
purpose, the lion leaped forward, and seizing upon the
cord, was drawn up in his stead. Immediately, exhibiting
great signs of pleasure, the beast ran off into the wood.
The rope again descended, and the monkey, having noticed
the success of the lion, vaulted above the man's head, and
shaking the cord, was in like manner set at liberty, and
hurried off to his haunts. A third time the cord was let
down, and the serpent, twining around it, was drawn up,
gave signs of gratitude, and escaped. "Oh, my good friend,"
said the seneschal, "the beasts are gone, now draw me
up quickly, I pray you." Guido complied, and afterwards
succeeded in drawing up his horse, which the seneschal
instantly mounted and rode back to the palace. Guido
returned home; and his wife observing that he had come
without wood, was very dejected, and inquired the cause.
He related what had occurred, and the riches he was to
receive for his service. The wife's countenance brightened.
Early in the morning her husband went to the palace.
But the seneschal denied all knowledge of him, and ordered
him to be whipped for his presumption. The porter executed the directions, and beat him so severely that he left
him half dead. As soon as Guido's wife understood this,
she saddled their ass, and brought him home in a very
infirm state. The sickness which ensued consumed the
whole of their little property; but as soon as he had
recovered, he returned to his usual occupation in the wood.
Whilst he was thus employed, he beheld afar off ten asses
laden with packs, and a lion following close on them,
pursuing the path which led towards Guido. On looking
narrowly at this beast, he remembered that it was the same
which he had freed from its imprisonment in the pit.
The lion signified with his foot that he should take the
loaded asses, and go home. This Guido did, and the lion
followed. On arriving at his own door, the noble beast
fawned upon him, and wagging his tail as if in triumph,
ran back to the woods. Guido caused proclamation to be

made in different churches,* that if any asses had been
lost, the owners should come to him; but no one appearing
to demand them, he opened the packages, and, to his great
joy, discovered them full of money. On the second day
Guido returned to the forest, but forgot an iron instrument
to cleave the wood. He looked up, and beheld the monkey
whose liberation he had effected; and the animal, by help
of teeth and nails, accomplished his desires. Guido then
loaded his asses and went home. The next day he renewed
his visit to the forest; and sitting down to prepare his
instrument, discerned the serpent, whose escape he had
aided, carrying a stone in its mouth of three colours; on
one side white, on another black, and on the third red.
It opened its mouth and let the stone fall into Guido's lap.
Having done this, it departed. Guido took the stone to
a skilful lapidary, who had no sooner inspected it than he
knew its virtues, and would willingly have paid him an
hundred florins † for it. But Guido refused; and by
means of that singular stone obtained great wealth, and
was promoted to a military command. The emperor
having heard of the extraordinary qualities which it possessed, desired to see it. Guido went accordingly; and
the emperor was so struck with its uncommon beauty,
that he wished to purchase it at any rate; and threatened,
if Guido refused compliance, to banish him the kingdom.
"My lord," answered he, "I will sell the stone; but let
me say one thing—if the price be not given, it shall be
presently restored to me." He demanded three hundred
florins, and then, taking it from a small coffer, put it into
the emperor's hands. Full of admiration, he exclaimed,
"Tell me where you procured this beautiful stone." This
he did; and narrated from the beginning the seneschal's
accident and subsequent ingratitude. He told how
severely he had been injured by his command; and the

* "Per ecclesias proclamare fecit." This may either mean that a
notice was fastened to the church door, or given out from the pulpit.
The last is most probable.

† "A florin or franc; an ancient coine of gold in France, worth
2s. sterl., not current at this day; (though Languedoc, and the
countries adjoyning, retaine the name still, in a piece that's worth
18d. sterl.)."—COTGRAVE.

benefits he had received from the lion, the monkey, and serpent. Much moved at the recital, the emperor sent for the seneschal and said, "What is this I hear of thee?" He was unable to reply. "O wretch!" continued the emperor—"monster of ingratitude! Guido liberated thee from the most imminent danger, and for this thou hast nearly destroyed him. Dost thou see how even irrational things have rendered him good for the service he performed? but thou hast returned evil for good. Therefore I deprive thee of thy dignity, which I will bestow upon Guido; and I further adjudge you to be suspended on a cross." This decree infinitely rejoiced the noblemen of the empire; and Guido, full of honours and years, ended his days in peace.*

APPLICATION.

My beloved, the emperor is God; the pauper, man. The forest is the world, which is full of pits. The lion

---

* "This story occurs in Symeon Seth's translation of the celebrated Arabian fable-book, called CALILAH U DUMNAH.[1] It is recited by Matthew Paris, under the year 1195, as a parable which king Richard the First, after his return from the East, was often accustomed to repeat, by way of reproving those ungrateful princes who refused to engage in the crusade. It is versified by Gower, who omits the Lion, as Matthew Paris does the ape, in the fifth book of the CONFESSIO AMANTIS."—WARTON.

There is some little difference in Gower.

> "The stone he proffereth to the sale.
> *　　*　　*　　*　　*　　*　　*
> Thus when this stone was bought and sold,
> Homeward with joy many-fold;
> This Bardus goeth, and when he came
> Home to his house, and that he name[2]
> His gold out of his purse within,
> He found his stone also therein.
> *　　*　　*　　*　　*
> "And thus it fell him overall
> Where he it sold in sundry place,
> Such was the fortune, and the grace."
> *Confessio Amantis*, lib. v. fol. 111-12.

[1] "This work was translated into English under the title of 'DONIE'S MORAL PHILOSOPHE, translated from the Indian tongue, 1570.' B.L. with wooden cuts, 4to. But Doni was the Italian translator."—WARTON.

[2] Reckon, count.

is the Son of God, who assumed humanity; the monkey is
conscience; and the serpent is a prelate or confessor. The
cord is Christ's passion; the loaded asses are the divine
precepts.

TALE CXX.

OF FEMININE SUBTLETY.

KING Darius was a circumspect prince, and had three sons,
whom he much loved. On his deathbed he bequeathed
the kingdom to his first-born; to the second, all his own
personal acquisitions; and to the third a golden ring, a
necklace, and a piece of valuable cloth. The ring had
the power to render any one who bore it on his finger
beloved; and, moreover, obtained for him whatsoever he
sought. The necklace enabled the person who wore it
upon his breast to accomplish his heart's desire; and the
cloth had such virtue, that whosoever sat upon it and
thought where he would be carried, there he instantly
found himself. These three gifts the king conferred upon
the younger son, for the purpose of aiding his studies;
but the mother retained them until he was of a proper
age. Soon after the bequests, the old monarch gave up
the ghost, and was magnificently buried. The two elder
sons then took possession of their legacies, and the mother
of the younger delivered to him the ring, with the caution
that he should beware of the artifices of women, or he
would otherwise lose the ring. Jonathan (for that was
his name) took the ring, and went zealously to his studies,
in which he made himself a proficient. But walking
on a certain day through the street, he observed a very
beautiful woman, with whom he was so much struck, that
he took her to him. He continued, however, to use the
ring, and found favour with every one, insomuch that
whatever he desired he had.

Now, the lady was greatly surprised that he lived so
splendidly, having no possessions; and once, when he was
particularly exhilarated, tenderly embraced him, and pro-

tested that there was not a creature under the sun whom she loved so much as she did him. He ought therefore, she thought, to tell her by what means he supported his magnificence. He, suspecting nothing, explained the virtues of the ring; and she begged that he would be careful of so invaluable a treasure. "But," added she, "in your daily intercourse with men you may lose it: place it in my custody, I beseech you." Overcome by her entreaties, he gave up the ring; and when his necessities came upon him, she asserted loudly that thieves had carried it off. He lamented bitterly that now he had not any means of subsistence; and, hastening to his mother, stated how he had lost his ring. "My son," said she, "I forewarned you of what would happen, but you have paid no attention to my advice. Here is the necklace; preserve it more carefully. If it be lost, you will for ever want a thing of the greatest honour and profit." Jonathan took the necklace, and returned to his studies. At the gate of the city his mistress met him, and received him with the appearance of great joy. He remained with her, wearing the necklace upon his breast; and whatever he thought, he possessed. As before, he lived so gloriously that the lady wondered, well knowing that he had neither gold nor silver. She guessed, therefore, that he carried another talisman; and cunningly drew from him the history of the wonder-working necklace. "Why," said the lady, "do you always take it with you? You may think in one moment more than can be made use of in a year. Let me keep it." "No," replied he, "you will lose the necklace, as you lost the ring; and thus I shall receive the greatest possible injury." "O my lord," replied she, "I have learnt, by having had the custody of the ring, how to secure the necklace; and I assure you no one can possibly get it from me." The silly youth confided in her words, and delivered the necklace.

Now, when all he possessed was expended, he sought his talisman; and she, as before, solemnly protested that it had been stolen. This threw Jonathan into the greatest distress, "Am I mad," cried he, "that after the loss of my ring I should give up the necklace?" Immediately hastening to his mother, he related to her the whole circumstance. Not a little afflicted, she said, " Oh, my dear child, why didst thou place confidence in the woman? People will believe thee a fool: but be wise, for I have nothing more for you than the valuable cloth which your father left: and if you lose that, it will be quite useless returning to me." Jonathan received the cloth, and again went to his studies. The harlot seemed very joyful; and he, spreading out the cloth, said, " My dear girl, my father bequeathed me this beautiful cloth; sit down upon it by my side." She complied, and Jonathan secretly wished that they were in a desert place, out of the reach of man. The talisman took effect; they were carried into a forest on the utmost boundary of the world, where there was not a trace of humanity. The lady wept bitterly, but Jonathan paid no regard to her tears. He solemnly vowed to Heaven that he would leave her a prey to the wild beasts, unless she restored his ring and necklace; and this she promised to do. Presently, yielding to her request, the foolish Jonathan discovered the power of the cloth; and, in a little time being weary, placed his head in her lap and slept. In the interim, she contrived to draw away that part of the cloth upon which he reposed, and sitting upon it alone, wished herself where she had been in the morning. The cloth immediately executed her wishes, and left Jonathan slumbering in the forest. When he awoke, and found his cloth and his mistress departed, he burst into an agony of tears. Where to bend his steps he knew not; but arising, and fortifying himself with the sign of the cross, he walked along a certain path, until he reached a deep river, over which he must pass. But he found it so bitter and hot, that it even separated the flesh from the bones. Full of grief, he conveyed away a small quantity of that water, and when he had proceeded a little further, felt hungry. A tree upon which hung the most tempting fruit invited him to partake; he did so, and immediately became a leper. He gathered also a little of the fruit, and conveyed it with him. After travelling for some time, he arrived at another stream, of which the virtue was such, that it restored the flesh to his feet; and eating of a second tree, he was cleansed from his leprosy. Some of that fruit he likewise took along with him.

Walking in this manner day after day, he came at length to a castle, where he was met by two men, who inquired what he was. "I am a physician," answered he. "This is lucky," said the other; "the king of this country is a leper, and if you are able to cure him of his leprosy, vast rewards will be assigned you." He promised to try his skill; and they led him forward to the king. The result was fortunate; he supplied him with the fruit of the second tree, and the leprosy left him; and washing the flesh with the water, it was completely restored. Being rewarded most bountifully, he embarked on board a vessel for his native city. There he circulated a report that a great physician was arrived; and the lady who had cheated him of the talismans, being sick unto death, immediately sent for him. Jonathan was so much disguised that she retained no recollection of him, but he very well remembered her. As soon as he arrived, he declared that medicine would avail nothing, unless she first confessed her sins; and if she had defrauded any one, it must be restored. The lady, reduced to the very verge of the grave, in a low voice acknowledged that she had cheated Jonathan of the ring, necklace, and cloth; and had left him in a desert place to be devoured by wild beasts. When she had said this, the pretended physician exclaimed, "Tell me, lady, where these talismans are?" "In that chest," answered she; and delivered up the keys, by which he obtained possession of his treasures. Jonathan then gave her of the fruit which produced leprosy; and, after she had eaten, of the water which separated the flesh from the bones. The consequence was that she was excruciated with agony, and shortly died. Jonathan hastened to his mother, and the whole kingdom rejoiced at his return. He told by what means God had freed him from such various dangers; and, having lived many years, ended his days in peace. (15)

APPLICATION.

My beloved, the king is Christ; the queen-mother, the Church; and the three sons, men living in the world. The third son is any good Christian: the ring is faith; the necklace is grace or hope; and the cloth, charity. The concubine is the flesh; the bitter water is repentance, and the first fruit is remorse; the second water is confession, and the second fruit is prayer, fasting, and almsgiving. The leprous king is any sinful man; the ship in which Jonathan embarked is the divine command.

TALE CXXI.

OF WORLDLY GLORY AND LUXURY.

THERE formerly lived a king who had two knights resident in one city. One of them was old, the other young. The old knight was rich, and had married a youthful damsel on account of her exquisite beauty. The young knight was poor, and espoused an old woman in consequence of her immense wealth. It happened that the young knight walked by the castle of the elder, and in a window his wife sat, and sang deliciously. The youth was much taken with her, and said in his heart, "It would be ten thousand times better if that sweet girl were united to me, and her old doting husband possessed of my infirm wife." From that hour he conceived a violent affection for her, and made her many valuable presents. The lady entertained a similar feeling, and, whenever she could, permitted him to visit her. She endeavoured also to secure him for her husband in the event of the old man's death. Now, near the window of the castle which the old knight occupied, there grew a fig-tree, on which a nightingale stationed herself every evening, and uttered the most ravishing harmony. This circumstance drew the lady thither; and it became a custom with her to remain at the window a long time, to listen to the song of the nightingale. When her hus-

band, good man! noticed this extreme watchfulness, he
said, "My dear, what is the reason that you get up every
night with so much regularity?" "A nightingale,"
answered she, "sings upon the fig-tree, opposite my
window; and her song is so delightful that I cannot
resist the pleasure of listening to it." The old knight
hearing this, arose early in the morning, and, armed with
bow and arrow, hastened to the fig-tree. He shot the
nightingale, and taking out the heart, presented it to his
wife. The lady wept exceedingly, and said, "Sweet bird,
thou didst but what became thee. I alone am the occasion
of thy death." Immediately she despatched a messenger
to the youthful knight, to inform him of her husband's
cruelty. The intelligence grieved him to the heart's core,
and he exclaimed internally, "If this cruel old wretch only
knew how much his wife and I are attached to each other,
he would treat me even more vilely!" This reflection
determined him; he cased himself in a double coat of
mail, and entering the castle, slew the aged knight. Soon
after this, his old wife dying, he married the relict of the
old knight. They lived many years, and ended their
days in peace.*

APPLICATION.

My beloved, the two knights are Moses and Christ,
The latter, who is the old knight, married a young wife,
that is, the new law. The old wife is the old law. The
fig-tree is the Cross; the nightingale, Christ's humanity,
which the Jews destroyed. The heart of the bird is the
love exhibited by our Saviour. The double arms are the
Jewish ceremonies, &c.

* This is strange justice; but I suppose the monk meant to incul-
cate what Pope, after Chaucer, has since observed, that—

"No greater folly can be seen
Than crooked eighty, coupled with eighteen."

The maxim is indisputable; but I wish the writer of the *Gest* had
otherwise expressed it.

The above story is among the Lays of Marie (a French poetess,
temp. Henry III., resident in England) under the title of LAUSTIC.
Mr. Ellis, in his abstract, has not noticed its occurrence in the *Gesta
Romanorum*.

TALE CXXII.

OF ECCLESIASTICAL BLINDNESS.

A CERTAIN knight went to gather grapes in his vineyard. His wife, imagining that he would be absent for a longer time than he actually was, sent hastily for her gallant. While they were together the knight returned; for it seems, while plucking down a bunch of grapes, he had struck out an eye, and came home in great agony. The lady, hearing his knock at the gate, was much perturbed, and immediately concealed her lover. The knight entering, complained of his wounded eye, and directed a bed to be prepared, that he might lie down. But the wife, fearing lest the gallant, who was hidden in the chamber, should be detected, said, "Why would you go to bed? tell me what has happened." He told her. "My dear lord," cried she, "permit me to strengthen the uninjured eye by medicinal applications,* or the diseased part may communicate with the sound, and thereby both be irremediably injured." The knight made no objection, and his wife spreading a large plaster so as completely to obstruct his sight, beckoned to her gallant, who escaped. Satisfied with her successful stratagem, the lady observed to the husband, "There, dear! now I feel satisfied that your sound eye will take no injury. Go into your bed, and sleep." †

APPLICATION.

My beloved, the knight is a prelate of the Church; the adulterous wife is the soul. The prelate's eye is struck out as often as it is blinded with gifts.

* The ladies, it is well known, were in former days the best, indeed, the only chirurgeons.

† This tale is in Alphonsus, and many of the Italian novelists.

TALE CXXIII.

OF ABSENCE OF PARENTAL RESTRAINT.

A SOLDIER, going into a far country, intrusted his wife to the care of her mother. But some time after her husband's departure the wife fell in love with a young man, and communicated her wishes to the mother. She approved of the connection, and without delay sent for the object of her daughter's criminal attachment. But while they feasted, the soldier unexpectedly returned and beat at his gate. The wife, in great tremor, concealed the lover in her bed, and then opened the door for her husband. Being weary with travel, he commanded his bed to be got ready; and the wife, more and more disturbed, knew not what she should do. The mother observing her daughter's perplexity, said, "Before you go, my child, let us show your husband the fair sheet which we have made." Then standing up, she gave one corner of the sheet to her daughter and held the other herself, extending it before him so as to favour the departure of the lover, who took the hint and escaped. When he had got clearly off, "Now," said the mother, "spread the sheet upon the bed with your own hands—we have done our parts in *weaving* it." *

APPLICATION.

My beloved, the soldier is any man who is a wanderer in this world. The wife is the flesh; the mother is the world; and the sheet, worldly vanities.

TALE CXXIV.

OF CONFIDENCE IN WOMEN.

A CERTAIN noble knight had grievously offended a king whose vassal he was. He sent messengers to the monarch to intercede for him, and they obtained his pardon, but on

* This fable is in Alphonsus. It is very similar to the preceding.

condition that he should enter the senate-house on foot
and on horseback at the same time; that is, half walking,
half riding. Moreover, he was to bring with him his
most attached friend, the best joculator or jester,* and
his most deadly foe. The knight, exceedingly distressed,
reflected how these strange conditions were to be fulfilled.
One night, as he exercised the hospitality of his mansion
towards a pilgrim, he said privately to his wife, "I know
those pilgrims often carry considerable sums of money
along with them. If you think fit, let us kill this fellow,
and get possession of his money." "You say well," returned the lady; and when all were asleep, at an early
hour in the morning, the knight arose, and awaking the
pilgrim, bade him begone. He then slaughtered a calf,
cut it into small pieces, and placed its mutilated body in
a sack. Arousing his wife, he gave her the sack to hide
in a corner of the house, observing, "I have only deposited
the head, legs, and arms in the sack; the body is interred
in our stable." He then showed her a little money, as if
he had taken it from the murdered pilgrim.

Now, when the day approached on which he was
bound to appear before his liege lord, he took upon his
right hand a dog, and on his left his wife and unweaned
child. As they drew near the royal castle he put one leg
over the back of the dog, as if he were riding, while
with the other he walked; and thus, as a pedestrian and
equestrian, he entered the palace. When the king observed his cunning, he was greatly surprised. "But,"
said the judge, "where is your most attached friend?"
Instantly unsheathing his falchion, he severely wounded
the dog, which fled howling away. The knight then

---

* The *Joculators* were licensed jesters. "Latin terms were used
by the Middle Age writers so licentiously, and with such extreme
carelessness, that in many cases it is difficult to obtain a precise idea
of their meaning. Thus the jesters and minstrels were indefinitely
expressed by the words *joculator, scurra, mimus, minstrallus,* &c., a
practice that may admit of justification, when we consider that in
early times the minstrel and buffoon characters were sometimes united
in one person. It must be allowed, however, that in an etymological
point of view, the term *Joculator* is much better adapted to the jester
than the minstrel."—DOUCE, *On the Clowns and Fools of Shakspeare,*
vol. ii. p. 307.

called to him, and the dog returned. "Here," said he, "here is the most faithful of all friends." "True," answered the king; "where is your jester?" "Here also," replied the knight, pointing to his infant: "I never have so much pleasure as in the disportings of this child." "Well," continued the king, "where is your worst enemy?" Turning toward his wife, he struck her a violent blow, and exclaimed, "Impudent harlot, how darest thou look wantonly upon the king?" The wife, furious at the injustice of the attack, shrieked violently. "Cursed homicide," said she, "why dost thou smite me? Dost thou forget that, in thine own house, thou perpetratedst the most atrocious murder, and didst kill a pilgrim for the sake of a little gold?" Again the knight beat her. "Wretch!" said he, "why dost thou not fear to disgrace thy child?" To which she fiercely replied, "Come with me, and I will discover to you where the head and arms of the murdered pilgrim have been deposited in a sack; the body he has buried in the stable." Search was accordingly made; and digging where the wife directed, they were astonished to find manifest tokens of a calf's flesh. The attending nobles, recognizing in this the wit of the man, greatly extolled him; and he was ever after exceedingly valued and honoured by his feudal lord.

APPLICATION.

My beloved, the knight is any sinner who finds favour with the Lord; and who upon certain conditions pardons his offences. The pedestrian and equestrian condition is our nature, partly human and partly celestial; the dog typifies man's good angel, or a priest, who is wounded as often as the soul sins. The joculator, that is, the infant, is conscience; the wife is the flesh.

TALE CXXV.

OF WOMEN, WHO NOT ONLY BETRAY SECRETS, BUT LIE FEARFULLY.

THERE were two brothers, of whom one was a layman and the other a parson. The former had often heard his brother declare that there never was a woman who could keep a secret.* He had a mind to put this maxim to the test in the person of his own wife, and one night he addressed her in the following manner : "My dear wife, I have a secret to communicate to you, if I were certain that you would reveal it to nobody. Should you divulge it, it would cause me the greatest uneasiness and vexation." " My lord," answered his wife, " fear not; we are one body, and your advantage is mine. In like manner, your injury must deeply affect me." " Well, then," said he, " know that, my bowels being oppressed to an extraordinary degree, I fell very sick. My dear wife, what will you think? I actually voided a huge black crow, which instantly took wing, and left me in the greatest trepidation and confusion of mind."† " Is it possible ? " asked the innocent lady; " but, husband, why should this trouble you? You ought rather to rejoice that you are freed from such a pestilent tenant." Here the conversation closed; in the morning, the wife hurried off to the house of a neighbour. " My best friend," said she, " may I tell you a secret ? " " As safely as to your own soul," answered the fair auditor. " Why," replied the other, " a marvellous thing has happened to my poor husband. Being last night extremely sick, he voided two prodigious black crows, feathers and all, which immediately flew away. I am much concerned." The other promised very faithfully—and immediately told her neighbour that *three* black crows had taken this most alarming flight.

---

* In this scandalous story, the monks seem to have introduced the *parson* for the sake of conveying a species of wisdom which accords ill with his situation. But they were great monopolizers.

† "Cum ad privata accessissem ut opus naturæ facerem, corvus ingerrimus a parte posterorii evolabat."

The next edition of the story made it *four ;* and in this way it spread, until it was very credibly reported that *sixty* black crows had been evacuated by one unfortunate varlet. But the joke had gone further than he dreamt of ; he became much disturbed, and assembling his busy neighbours, explained to them that having wished to prove whether or not his wife could keep a secret, he had made such a communication. Soon after this, his wife dying, he ended his days in a cloister, where he learnt three letters ; of which one was black ; the second, red ; and the third, white.* (16)

APPLICATION.

My beloved, the layman is any worldly-minded man who, thinking to do one foolish thing without offence, falls into a thousand errors. But he assembles the people —that is, past and present sins—and by confession expurgates his conscience.

TALE CXXVI.

OF WOMEN ; WHO ARE NOT TO BE TRUSTED.

MACROBIUS (17) states that a Roman youth, named Papirius, was once present with his father in the senate at a time when a very important matter was debated, which, on pain of death, was to be kept secret. When the lad returned home, his mother asked him what it was that was guarded under so heavy a penalty. He replied that it was unlawful to reveal it. The mother, little satisfied with the boy's reply, entreated, promised, threatened, and even scourged him, in the hope of extorting a communication. But he remained inflexible ; and at last, willing to satisfy her, and yet retain his secret, said, " The council

---

* This seems merely introduced to tell us, in the application, that the black letter is recollection of our sins ; the red, Christ's blood ; and the white, the desire of heaven.

met upon this matter : whether it were more beneficial to the state that one man should have many wives, or one woman many husbands." The mother no sooner heard this, than away she posted to divide the important secret with other Roman dames. And on the following day, assembling in a large body, they went without hesitation to the senators, earnestly requesting that one woman might be married to two men, rather than two women to one man. The senators, astonished at the shameless frenzy of a sex naturally modest, deliberated upon the best remedy. The boy Papirius, finding this, related to them the circumstance which had occasioned the uproar ; and they, bestowing great commendation on his ingenuity, passed a decree that he should be present at their consultations whenever he would.*

APPLICATION.

My beloved, the boy is any one whose life is pure ; the father is a prelate ; and the mother is the world.

TALE CXXVII.

OF JUSTICE AND EQUITY.

A CERTAIN tyrannical and cruel knight retained in his service a very faithful servant. One day, when he had been to the market, he returned with this servant through a grove, and by the way lost thirty silver marks. As soon as he discovered the loss, he questioned his servant about it. The man solemnly denied all knowledge of the matter, and he spoke truth. But when the money was not to be found, he amputated the servant's foot, and leaving him in that place, rode home. A hermit, hearing the groans and exclamations of the man, went speedily to his assistance. He confessed him ; and being satisfied of

---

* This story has been modernized ; and occurs in a volume entitled *Beauties of Poetry*, edited by a Mr. Melmoth, and probably in many others.

his innocence, conveyed him upon his shoulders to his hermitage. Then entering the oratory,* he dared to reproach the All-just with want of justice, inasmuch as he had permitted an innocent man to lose his foot. For a length of time he continued in tears, and prayers, and reproaches; until at last an angel of the Lord appeared to him, and said, "Hast thou not read in the Psalms, 'God is a just judge, strong and patient'?" "Often," answered the hermit meekly, "have I read and believed it from my heart; but to-day I have erred. That wretched man, whose foot has been amputated, perhaps under the veil of confession deceived me." "Tax not the Lord with injustice," said the angel; "His way is truth, and His judgments equitable. Recollect how often thou hast read, 'The decrees of God are unfathomable.' Know that he who lost his foot, lost it for a former crime. With the same foot he maliciously spurned his mother, and cast her from a chariot, for which he has never done worthy penance. The knight, his master, was desirous of purchasing a war-horse, to collect more wealth, to the destruction of his soul; and therefore, by the just sentence of God, the money was lost. Now hear; there is a very poor man with his wife and little ones, who daily supplicate Heaven, and perform every religious exercise. He found the money, when otherwise he would have starved, and therewith procured for himself and family the necessaries of life, intrusting a portion to his confessor to distribute to the poor. But first he diligently endeavoured to find out the right owner. Not accomplishing this, the poor man applied it to its proper use. Place, then, a bridle upon thy thoughts; and no more upbraid the righteous Disposer of all things, as thou but lately didst. For he is true, and strong, and patient." †

APPLICATION.

My beloved, the knight is a prelate; the amputation of the servant's foot is the cutting off rebellion from the

---

* "Oratorie; a closet, or private chappell to pray in."—COTGRAVE.
† This story has some resemblance to Tale LXXX., and it contains a beautiful lesson.

Church. The hermit is a prudent confessor. The angel is a pure conscience. The poor man is Christ.

TALE CXXVIII.

OF INJUSTICE.

In the reign of the Emperor Maximian there were two knights, of whom one feared God and loved justice, while the other was covetous and rich, and more studious of pleasing the world than his Maker. Contiguous to this person's lands, the just knight had a piece of ground, which his avaricious neighbour ardently desired to possess. He offered large sums for it; but being denied, he was filled with vexation. It happened, however, that the just knight died; on hearing which, the other forged an instrument purporting to be written by the deceased knight. It stated that the land in question had been sold for a specified sum a short time previous to his death; and three men were hired to attest it. Having, by some means, obtained access to the dead knight, he introduced the witnesses; and finding his signet in the hall where he lay, took it, and, fixing it upon the thumb of the deceased, sealed the paper with the usual formalities. "You are witnesses of this deed?" said he to the men who accompanied him. "We are," answered they; and then making good their retreat, the knight seized upon the land. The son of the deceased complained grievously of this injustice. "Why have you taken possession of my land?" asked he. "It was sold to me by your father." "Impossible," cried the other; "my father many times refused to sell it; and that he afterwards did so, I will never believe." They both went before the judge; and the covetous knight triumphantly produced the forged instrument, bearing the impression of the deceased's signet-ring, and brought forward the false witnesses to the sealing. After examining it, the son said, "I know that this is my father's signet, but I know also that he never disposed of the land. How you obtained the signet and these witnesses, I am ignorant." The judge, after some deliberation, took each of the witnesses aside in turn; and separately examined them, together with the knight. He asked the eldest if he knew the Lord's Prayer, and made him repeat it from beginning to end.* He did this accurately, and was then placed apart. When the second witness appeared, the judge said, "My friend, your companion has told me facts as true as the Lord's Prayer; therefore, unless you inform me what I demand, you shall instantly hang upon a cross." The fellow, imagining that his comrade had revealed the fraud, confessed how they had obtained the seal to the document. When the communication was made, he placed him apart; and sending for the third, spoke to him as to the other, and threatened him with the like penalty, unless he declared the fact. This man, therefore, corroborated his companion's account, and was than stationed by himself. The old knight was then called; and the judge, putting on a stern aspect, spoke thus: "Wretched man! thy avarice hath blinded thee. Tell me how the deceased knight sold you the land." The culprit, not divining that the truth had been discovered, boldly persevered in the account he had before given. "Foolish man!" answered the judge, "thy own witnesses accuse thee. Didst thou not place the signet on the dead man's thumb, and sign the paper?" When the knight found that his forgery was revealed, he fell prostrate upon the earth, and entreated mercy. "Such mercy as thou meritest, thou shalt have," said the judge: "bear them away, and drag them at the tails of horses to the cross, upon which let them be immediately suspended." The noblemen of

* Whether this was the usual mode of administering an oath, or whether it is only of the number of those whimsical and arbitrary circumstances which continually occur in these volumes, I am unable to say.

[The object of making the man repeat the Lord's Prayer is tolerably plain. It was necessary that he should appear to be making some continuous statement to the judge, to induce the other witness to believe that the forgery was being made known. It was of no consequence what he said as long as he appeared to say something. The false witness would be only too ready to show his knowledge of the Prayer, with the view of manifesting his piety to the judge. Why then should this be called a "whimsical and arbitrary circumstance"?—Ed.]

the kingdom applauded the sentence, not less than the ingenuity of the investigation. The property of the unjust knight was conferred upon the son of him whom he had wished to wrong; the young man gave thanks to the king, and possessed his inheritance in peace.*

APPLICATION.

My beloved, the two knights are the devil and our first parent, whose son is the whole human race. The inheritance is Paradise; the forged writing, original sin; and the seal, Adam's consent to partake with Eve of the forbidden tree. The three witnesses are the pride of life, concupiscence of the flesh, and concupiscence of the eyes.

TALE CXXIX.

OF REAL FRIENDSHIP.

A CERTAIN king had an only son, whom he much loved. The young man was desirous of seeing the world and making friends for himself, and obtained his father's permission to this end. After an absence of seven years,† he returned, and his father, overjoyed at his arrival, asked what friends he had acquired. "Three," said the son; "the first of whom I love more than myself; the second, equally with myself; and the third, little or nothing." "You say well," returned the father; "but it is a good thing to prove them before you stand in need of their assistance. Therefore kill a pig, put it into a sack, and go at night to the house of him whom you love best, and say that you have accidentally killed a man, and if the body should be found you will be condemned to an ignominious death. Entreat him, if he ever loved you, to give his assistance in this extremity." The son did

---

* The examination of the false witnesses in this story will remind the reader of the mode by which the wickedness of the elders was discovered in the Apocrypha.

† The moral says twelve; meaning, however, the term of human life.

so; and the friend answered, "Since you have rashly destroyed a man, you must pay the penalty: for if the body were found in my house I should very likely be crucified. Now, because you were my friend, I will go with you to the cross, and bestow upon you three or four ells of cloth, to wrap your body in when you are dead." The youth, hearing this, went in much indignation to the second of his friends, and related the same story. He received him like the first, and said, "Do you believe me mad, that I should expose myself to such peril? But, since I have called you my friend, I will accompany you to the cross, and console you as much as possible upon the way. The prince then went to the third, and said, "I am ashamed to address you, for I have never benefited you in any way: but, alas! I have accidentally slain a man, and must hide the body or perish." "My friend," answered the other, "I will readily do what you wish, and take the crime on myself; and, should it be necessary, I will be crucified for your sake." *This* man, therefore, proved that he was his friend.*

APPLICATION.

My beloved, the king is God; the only son is any Christian. The first friend is the world; and if it gives, in your necessity, two or three ells of cloth, it is much indeed. The second friend is your wife, and sons, and daughters; they will bewail you to your sepulchre, but soon forget you after you are laid there.† The third friend

---

* This story is in Alphonsus. "It is remarkable that Le Grand, as well as Barbazan, seems to have known nothing about Petrus Alphonsus, whom he classes, under his Frenchified name of Pierre Anfors, amongst the Norman fableours."—Douce.

† Massinger has a sentiment so similar, that if the experience of all ages were not alike, one might fancy that the poet had borrowed from the monk.

"When dead, we are
With solemn pomp brought hither, and our heirs,
Masking their joy in false dissembled tears,
Weep o'er the hearse: but earth no sooner covers
The earth brought hither, but they turn away
With inward smiles—the dead no more remembered."
The Maid of Honour, Act ii. Sc. 3.

is Christ, for whom we have done little, who loves us even upon the cross, and joyfully gave away His life for our preservation.

———

TALE CXXX.

OF WISDOM, WHICH EXCELS STRENGTH.

THERE was a king who promoted a poor man to great wealth, and committed to him the custody of one of his castles. Thus elevated, he became proud to an excess, and conspired against the king, and surrendered his castle into the hands of the enemy. This conduct gave the king great concern; and he deliberated upon the best means of regaining what he had lost. But he was told that this could not be done but by the possession of three things, viz. bravery, wisdom, and the love of his subjects. Now, there were at that time in the kingdom three knights, of whom the first was the bravest of all men; the second, the wisest; and the third, the most attached to the king. These knights were severally sent with large armies to besiege the castle. The bravest knight conducted his troops through a forest, in which the king's enemies awaited him; but while he was performing prodigies of valour, an arrow from a cross-bow struck him in the groin, and he died of the wound. In the mean time the wise knight brought up his forces and began to speak of right and law, hoping by these means to draw them to surrender the castle. But while he spoke, an arrow penetrated between the lungs and the stomach, and killed him. The third knight perceiving the death of his comrades, entered the forest, and spoke so eloquently and wittily to the insurgents, that they listened gladly, and at last permitted him to enter the castle. And he so ordered matters that the opposing armies joined with him, and gave him entire possession; so that he planted his standard on the top. When the king understood how prudently he had obtained the disputed fortress, he promoted him to great honours.

APPLICATION.

My beloved, the king is Christ; the poor man who was raised to honour is Adam, appointed the seneschal of a castle, that is, of Paradise. The first and bravest knight is the rich and powerful of the world, whom the arrow of pride spiritually slays. The second knight denotes the wise or prudent of this world, and they are slain by the arrow of avarice. The third knight is any Christian who loves God with all his heart; and who, in his simplicity, is often a match for the more cunning of mankind.

TALE CXXXI.

OF RICHES.

A KING issued a proclamation that whosoever would come to him should obtain all they asked. The noble and the rich desired dukedoms, or counties, or knighthood; and some, treasures of silver and gold. But whatsoever they desired they had. Then came the poor and the simple, and solicited a like boon. "Ye come tardily," said the king; "the noble and the rich have already been, and have carried away all I possess." This reply troubled them exceedingly; and the king, moved with a feeling of pity, said, "My friends, though I have given away all my temporal possessions, I have still the sovereign power; for no one required this. I appoint ye, therefore, to be their judges and masters." When this came to the ears of the rich, they were extremely disturbed, and said to the king, "My lord, we are greatly troubled at your appointing these poor wretches our rulers; it were better for us to die, than admit such servitude." "Sirs," answered the king, "I do you no wrong:* whatever you asked I gave; insomuch that nothing remains to me but the supreme power. Nevertheless, I will give you counsel. Whosoever

* We are here reminded of our Lord's parable of the labourers in the vineyard; in fact, it is clearly the prototype of this tale.

of you has enough to support life, let him bestow the superfluity upon these poor people. They will then live honestly and comfortably, and upon these conditions I will resume the sovereignty and keep it, while you avoid the servitude ye apprehend." And thus it was done.*

APPLICATION.

My beloved, the king is God; the herald is a preacher; the rich, etc., are the men of this world, and the poor are the poor in spirit.

TALE CXXXII.

OF ENVY TOWARD THE GOOD.

THERE once lived in the same city four physicians, well skilled in medicine. The younger of them, however, excelled the other three; insomuch that the sick went only to him. This excited the envy of the rest, and talking together upon this subject, they said, "How shall we get rid of that troublesome fellow? everybody runs to him, and our gains are a mere trifle." "Why," said one, "you know he goes every week on a visit to the duke, about three leagues off, and he will pay a visit there to-morrow. Now, I will go a league beyond the city, and there await his coming. You shall be stationed at the second league, and our fellow here at the third. And when he has advanced the first league, I will meet him and make the sign of the cross before him. Both of

* [It may be doubted whether the author of this remarkable fable had any intention of putting forward a political theory by means of it. Nevertheless a communistic ideal was by no means contrary to the spirit of the Church in the Middle Ages. The Church of Rome being, so to speak, a theocratized Cæsarism, has always had considerable sympathy with the mass of the people. It was until the Reformation a despotism with democratic leanings and republican institutions; for any priest, however poor, might become pope, if an able man. But it certainly sounds strange to find a 14th century monk at one with Dr. Karl Marx.—ED.]

you must do the like. He will then ask the reason of this, and we will answer, 'Because you are a leper;' and his fear will certainly occasion it: 'for,' says Hippocrates, 'he who fears leprosy will through fear become a leper.' Thus diseased, no one will approach him." And so it was done.*

APPLICATION.

My beloved, by the three physicians, who infected the fourth, three vices are signified—the devil, the world, and the flesh. The fourth physician is a good Christian.

TALE CXXXIII.

OF SPIRITUAL FRIENDSHIP.

A KING had two greyhounds, whom he kept alternately chained up. As long as they were thus fastened they mutually loved and fawned upon each other, but no sooner were they unloosed than they exhibited the most deadly signs of mutual hostility. The king was much concerned at this; because when he would have coursed with them, and for that purpose set them at liberty, they fought so fiercely that he was unable to follow his sport. This led him to consult some learned man, who recommended that the first of the dogs should be encountered by a strong and savage wolf; and then the second should be encouraged to the attack when his companion was in danger of being defeated. For when the first saw how the other aided him, they would in future be friends. This was accordingly done; and as the strength of the first dog failed, the second was let loose, who, after a severe struggle, killed the wolf. From this time, bound

---

* [Compare the story in the Hitopadésa, entitled "The Brahman and the Goat" in which three knaves obtain a goat from a Brahmin who was carrying it on his shoulders by successively asking him why he carried a dog (the dog being an unclean animal). See the *Book of Good Counsels*, by Edwin Arnold, p. 130.—ED.]

or unbound, they lived together in the most perfect friendship.

APPLICATION.

My beloved, the king is Christ; the two dogs are the soul and body. If loosed by mortal sin, they are at war. The wolf is the devil, which being overcome, they live together in peace.

TALE CXXXIV.

OF CHRIST, WHO DIED INNOCENT.

SENECA * relates that there was a law in some city, by which a knight was obliged to be buried in armour; and further, that it was ordained if any one deprived the dead man of this armour, he should be put to death. It happened that a certain city was besieged by a tyrannical despot, who, planting ambuscades and pitfalls around the city, destroyed an indefinite number of the inhabitants. Fear made them incapable of longer resistance; and, while thus situated, a noble and valiant knight entered the city, and compassionated the distresses of the despairing citizens. They humbly petitioned him to undertake their defence, and free them from the imminent peril in which they stood. "My friends," replied he, "this cannot be done, except by a strong hand; and you perceive I am unarmed. It is in vain, therefore, to expect that I should go out to fight." "My lord," observed one of the citizens, "but a few days since a knight was buried in this sepulchre, clad in most admirable armour; take it, and save our city." The knight assented, received the arms of the deceased, and, encountering the enemy, put them

---

* Seneca is cited here, but I can give no reference. The story is a very singular one. In the old English *Gesta* [see the Introduction] it forms the "*Seventh Hystory*;" although the termination is somewhat different. The knight's pleading is successful with the judge; but the accusers, taking upon themselves the execution of the law, slay him in opposition to all justice.

to flight. He then restored the arms to their original position. But certain men, envious of the fame which he acquired by the exploit, accused him before the judge of having despoiled the dead of his armour contrary to law. " My lord," answered he, " of two evils, the greater is to be avoided.* Now, I could not defend your city without armour; and having taken that of the deceased, I returned it when the exigence had ceased. A thief would not have acted in this manner; he would have kept the arms, which I did not, and therefore merit rather recompense than charges of such a nature. Besides, if a house be on fire in the midst of a city, would it not be better that that single dwelling should be, without delay, completely destroyed, before other houses catch fire and the whole city is burnt to the ground? Apply this in my case. Was it not more beneficial that I should preserve your town by borrowing the armour than, by not borrowing, endanger all your lives?" " Away with him, away with him," shouted they who were jealous and envious of his fame; " he deserves death; away with him!" The judge could not resist their urgent petition, and condemned him to death. The sentence was accordingly executed, and the whole state lamented him with unfeigned regret.

APPLICATION.

My beloved, the besieged city is the world. The knight without arms is Christ; the armour is His humanity. The envious men are Jews, who put Him to death.

TALE CXXXV.

OF CONSCIENCE.

AUGUSTINE relates, in his work *De Civitate Dei*, that Lucretia, a noble Roman lady, was the wife of Calatinus.† The latter invited to his castle Sextus, the son of the

---

* " De duobus malis majus malum est vitandum." Here is another English proverb, " Of two evils, chuse the least."
† Meaning *Collatinus*.

Emperor Tarquinius, who became violently enamoured of his beautiful wife. Selecting a seasonable opportunity, when both Calatinus and the emperor had departed from Rome, he returned to the above-mentioned castle, and slept there. During the night, not as a friend but foe, he secretly entered the bed-chamber of Lucretia, and putting one hand upon her breast, while he held a drawn sword in the other, said, "Comply with my wishes, or I will kill you." But she resolutely repelled him; and Sextus, enraged, assured her that he would stab a slave and place him in her bed, so that the world should believe her guilty of the most low-lived and flagrant wickedness. At last Sextus, accomplishing his villainy, went away; and the lady, full of the deepest grief, despatched letters to her father and husband, to her brothers, to the emperor, together with the proconsuls; and when they were all present she spoke thus: "Not as a friend, but as a foe, Sextus entered my house. Calatinus, your bed has known the garments of a stranger;* but though my body is violated, my mind is innocent. Acquit me of crime, and I will provide my own punishment." At these words, snatching a sword which she had hidden beneath her robe, she plunged it into her breast. The assembled friends, taking up the weapon, swore by the blood of the injured Lucretia to drive the family of the Tarquins from Rome. And they did so. As for Sextus, the author of this tragedy, he was miserably slaughtered not long after.†

* "Scias tu, O Calatine, *vestimenta viri alieni in lecto tuo fuisse;*" a refined expression, and little according with the usual indelicacy of the age.

[If Mr. Swan had turned to his Livy he would there have found the cause of this unusual "refinement." The passage is nothing but a distorted echo of the well-known "vestigia viri alieni, Collatine, in lecto sunt tuo" (*Liv.* i. 57, 58).—ED.]

† This story is from St. Austin's *City of God.*

"A more classical authority for this story, had it been at hand, would have been slighted for St. Austin's CITY OF GOD, which was the favourite spiritual romance; and which, as the transition from religion to gallantry was anciently very easy, gave rise to the famous old French romance, called the CITY OF LADIES."—WARTON.

My beloved, Lucretia is the soul; Sextus is the devil; and the castle represents the heart, into which he enters. The sword is penitence.

TALE CXXXVI.

OF VIGILANCE IN OUR CALLING.

A THIEF went one night to the house of a rich man, and scaling the roof, peeped through a hole to examine if any part of the family were yet stirring. The master of the house, suspecting something, said secretly to his wife, "Ask me in a loud voice how I acquired the property I possess, and do not desist until I bid you." The woman complied, and began to vociferate, "My dear husband, pray tell me, since you never were a merchant, how you obtained all the wealth which you have now collected." "Foolish woman," answered her husband, "do not ask such questions." But she persisted in her inquiries; and at length, as if overcome by her urgency, he said, "Keep what I am going to tell you a secret, and your curiosity shall be gratified."

"Oh, trust me."

"Well, then, you must know that I was a thief, and obtained what I now enjoy by nightly depredations." "It is strange," said the wife, "that you were never taken." "Why," replied he, "my master, who was a skilful clerk, taught me a particular word, which, when I ascended the tops of people's houses, I pronounced seven times, and then got down into the house by the rays of the moon and took what I wanted, and then in like manner ascended again without danger and departed." "Tell me, I conjure you," returned the lady, "what that powerful word was." "Hear, then; but never mention it again, or we shall lose all our property." "Be sure of that," said the lady; "it shall never be repeated."

" It was—is there no one within hearing ?—the mighty
word was ' SAXLEM.' "

The lady, apparently quite satisfied, fell asleep; and
her husband feigned it. He snored lustily, and the thief
above, who had heard their conversation with much
pleasure, attempting to take hold of a moon-ray and
repeating the charm seven times, relaxed the hold both of
hands and feet, and let himself drop through the skylight.
He fell with a loud thud, and in the fall dislocated his leg
and arm, and lay half dead upon the floor. The owner of
the mansion, hearing the noise, and well knowing the
reason, though he pretended ignorance, asked what was
the matter. " Oh ! " groaned the suffering thief, " the
words of your tale have deceived me." The man captured
him, and had him suspended on a cross in the morning.*

APPLICATION.

My beloved, the thief is the devil; the house is the
human heart. The man is a good prelate, and his wife is
the Church.

———

TALE CXXXVII.

OF CHRIST'S CLEMENCY.

IN the chronicles of Eusebius we read of an emperor who
governed the Roman people with the greatest equity,
sparing none, whether rich or poor; but measuring the
punishment according to the extent of the crime. The
factious senators, however, deposed him, and obliged him
to flee in poverty from the kingdom. Immediately he fled
to Constantine, and, entering into a close compact with
him, on all occasions conducted himself so boldly and prudently, that he succeeded him to the sovereignty of the
empire. Then assembling an army, he besieged the city

* Something like this story is in the *Directorium Humanæ Vitæ*,
i.e. the Latin version from the Hebrew of Pilpay. See also Le Grand,
Fabl. iii. 288.

of Rome; and, when the Romans were unable to escape, but were always captured by him, the people sent out to him their senators, and young men and women, with their feet bare, who prostrated themselves before him, and humbly requested the forgiveness which he refused to grant. At length they despatched his parents, who were resident in the city, alone upon this embassy. His mother wept and entreated; conjuring him by the breasts which he had sucked, to spare the place of his nativity. Unable to resist the force of natural affection, he pardoned on her account their offences. He then marched into the city, and was honourably entertained.*

APPLICATION.

My beloved, the emperor is Christ; the city is the human heart, from which He is expelled; Constantine is God; the senators, etc., are the prophets, and patriarchs, and apostles.

TALE CXXXVIII.

OF SEVERITY, WHICH AVAILS LESS THAN KINDNESS.

A CERTAIN king, named Medrus, had an only son, whom he constituted his heir. The son was ungrateful to his father, who punished him by immediate disinherison. The son, thus circumstanced, fled to the King of the Persians, the rival and enemy of his parent. He stated that he was ready to serve him to the death; and declared himself ready to make war upon the author of his being. War was accordingly declared, and they fought together for some time with equal fortune. It happened that Medrus the king was grievously wounded, and the blood flowed very copiously. No sooner had his son perceived this, and reflected on it, then he straightway hurried to his father's side, and attacking the troops of the Persian monarch,

* We have here a new version of the story of Coriolanus.

put them to flight.　After this, of course, the compact was made void; and the son, returning to his father, meekly sought forgiveness, and obtained it.　Thus, peace being established, he was again constituted his father's heir.

APPLICATION.

My beloved, the two kings are God and the devil.　The son is the human soul, which Christ (who is God), by the effusion of His blood, redeemed.

TALE CXXXIX.

OF THE SOUL'S WOUNDS.

ALEXANDER the Great was lord of the whole world.　He once collected a large army, and besieged a certain city, around which many knights and others were killed without any visible wound.　Much surprised at this, he called together his philosophers, and said, "My masters, how is this?　My soldiers die, and there is no apparent wound!"　"No wonder," replied they; "on the walls of a city is a basilisk, (18) whose look infects your soldiers, and they die of the pestilence it creates."　"And what remedy is there for this?" said the king.

"Place a mirror in an elevated situation between the army and the wall where the basilisk is; and no sooner shall he behold it, than his own look, reflected in the mirror, will return upon himself, and kill him."　And so it was done.*

---

* "Œlian, in his *Various History*, mentions a serpent, which, appearing from the mouth of a cavern, stopped the march of Alexander's army through a spacious desert.　The wild beasts, serpents, and birds, which Alexander encountered in marching through India, were most extravagantly imagined by the oriental fabulists, and form the chief wonders of that monarch's romance."—WARTON.

Amongst the fabulous monsters of old romance, the GRIPPE (distinguished from the Griffin, or Gryphon) seems to be pre-eminent. In an old and very rare French romance there is a curious description

APPLICATION.

My beloved, look into the glass of *reflection*, and, by remembrance of human frailty, destroy the vices which time elicits.

TALE CXL.

OF EQUITY.

THE Emperor Heraclius, amongst many other virtues, was remarkable for his inflexible justice. It happened that a certain man accused a knight of the murder of another knight, in this form :—" They two went out, in company with another, to war; but no battle was fought. He, however, returned without his companion; and, therefore, we believe that he murdered him." The king appeared satisfied with the inference, and commanded the prisoner to be executed. But as they approached the place of execution, they beheld the lost knight advancing towards them, alive

of this creature, which the reader may be pleased to see. " To give you an idea of the nature of this kind of monstrous serpent, know that its body is as strong as an enraged bull. He has a human face ; but instead of a nose he has the beak of an eagle. He possesses a goose's eyes, an ass's ears, and the teeth of a dog. His tongue is long and venomous; with which, when he is chafed, he darts a prodigious number of fire-brands united with a smoke so fetid, that it is enough to infect a whole city. He has the legs, feet, and claws of a lion ; a dragon's tail, which is as long as a lance. His back is armed with a scale so hard, that no steel, however excellently tempered, is able to penetrate. Moreover, the shoulders are ornamented with the strong wings of a *Griffin*, which enable him to cleave the air even more rapidly than was possible to the cunning Dædalus, or to the horse of Pacolet " (fol. x). The full title of the very curious and entertaining work from which the quotation is taken is as follows:—" LE PREMIER LIURE DE L'HISTOIRE ET ANCIENNE CRONIQUE DE GERARD D'EUPHRATE, DVC DE BOURGONGUE : *traitant, pour la plus part, son origine, ieunesse, amors et cheualereux faitz d'armes: auec rencontres, et auantures merueilleuses, de plusieurs Cheualiers, et grans seigneurs de son temps : Mis de nouueau en nostre vulgaire Francoys.*" PARIS, 1549. But the Colophon speaks of twelve books, and we have here the first only. It is in Sion College library.

and well. The judge, enraged at this interruption of the sentence, said to the accused, "I order you to be put to death, because you are already condemned." Then turning to the accuser, "And you also, because you are the cause of his death." "And you, too," addressing the restored knight—"because you were sent to kill a knight, and you did not." *

APPLICATION.

My beloved, the king is God: the first two knights, body and soul. The third is any prelate.

TALE CXLI.

OF GOOD ADVICE.

In the reign of the Emperor Fulgentius, a certain knight, named Zedechias, married a very beautiful but imprudent wife. In a certain chamber of their mansion a serpent dwelt. Now, the knight's vehement inclination for tournaments and jousting brought him to extreme poverty: he grieved immoderately, and, like one who was desperate, walked backward and forward, ignorant of what he should do. The serpent, beholding his misery, like the ass of Balaam, was on that occasion miraculously gifted with a voice, and said to the knight, "Why do you lament? Take my advice, and you shall not repent it. Supply me every day with a certain quantity of sweet milk, and I will enrich you." This promise exhilarated the knight, and he faithfully followed the instructions of his subtle friend. The consequence was that he had a beautiful son, and became exceedingly wealthy. But it happened that his wife one day said to him, "My lord, I am sure

* This is justice with a *vengeance.*
This story is told by Seneca of Cneius Piso, *De Ira.* lib. i. c. 8, and it is found in Chaucer's Sompnour's Tale, who mentions the same authority.

that serpent has great riches hidden in the chamber where he dwells. Let us kill him and get possession of the whole." The advice pleased the knight, and at the request of his wife he took a hammer to destroy the serpent, and a vessel of milk. Allured by the milk, it put its head out of the hole, as it had been accustomed; and the knight lifted the hammer to strike it. The serpent, observing his perfidy, suddenly drew back its head; and the blow fell upon the vessel. No sooner had he done this, than his offspring died, and he lost everything that he formerly possessed. The wife, taught by their common loss, said to him, "Alas! I have ill counselled you; but go now to the hole of the serpent, and humbly acknowledge your offence. Peradventure you may find grace." The knight complied, and standing before the dwelling-place of the serpent, shed many tears, and entreated that he might once more be made rich. "I see," answered the serpent, "I see now that you are a fool, and will always be a fool. For how can I forget that blow of the hammer which you designed me, for which reason I slew your son and took away your wealth? There can be no real peace between us." The knight, full of sorrow, replied thus : "I promise the most unshaken fidelity, and will never meditate the slightest injury, provided I may this once obtain your grace." "My friend," said the serpent, "it is the nature of my species to be subtle and venomous. Let what I have said suffice. The blow offered at my head is fresh upon my recollection; get you gone before you receive an injury." The knight departed in great affliction, saying to his wife, "Fool that I was to take thy counsel!" But ever afterwards they lived in the greatest indigence. (19)

APPLICATION.

My beloved, the king is God; the knight is Adam, who by following his wife's advice lost Paradise. The serpent in the chamber signifies Christ retained in the human heart, by virtue of baptism.

TALE CXLII.

OF THE SNARES OF THE DEVIL.

A CERTAIN powerful king planted a forest, and surrounded it with a wall. He stocked it with various animals, in which he took infinite pleasure. It happened that one being discovered meditating traitorous designs, his property was confiscated, and himself banished the land. This person, therefore, provided various kinds of dogs and nets, and went privately into the royal forest to take and destroy the animals which it contained. The names of his dogs were Richer, Emuleym, Hanegiff, Baudyn, Crismel, Egofyn, Beamis, and Renelen.* By means of these dogs and the nets he destroyed every animal in the forest. The king was greatly enraged at this circumstance, and said to his son, "My dear son, arm yourself; call out the troops, and slay this traitor, or drive him from the kingdom." The youth answered, "I am ready to comply with your wishes; but as I have heard that he is a man of exceeding prowess, it would be advisable to conceal myself for a certain time, in company with a beautiful girl, whose wisdom surpasses that of all others. I will converse with her, and then prepare myself for battle." The father replied, "Go to the castle Varioch; † there you will find a girl of inimitable prudence. By her means, you may send a defiance to our enemy, and I will then promote her to many honours." This heard, the son entered the castle secretly, and was received by the lady with great joy. He remained there some time, and then departed, armed with the power of his father, against the traitorous despoiler of the royal forest. In the end he overthrew him, cut off his head, and returned in triumph to the king's palace.

* This tale seems to be of Saxon origin. Many of the names are derivable from that language, as Richer, Hanegifl, Beamis, Renelen (perhaps from Sax. RENEL, cursor), &c.

[See *Oesterley*, p. 264.—ED.]

† Query if from Sax. ∇æꝥ, septem or bellum, and Ioc, jugam?

[The Cologne edition, printed by Ulric Zell (1490 ?), omits " vade ad castrum Varioch."—ED.]

APPLICATION.

My beloved, the emperor is God; the forest the world, whose wall is the divine precepts. The traitor is any evil Christian; the dogs and nets are vices; the son is Christ; and the castle, the Virgin Mary.

TALE CXLIII.

OF TERROR.

A KING made a law, by which whosoever was suddenly to be put to death in the morning, before sunrise should be saluted with songs and trumpets, and, arrayed in black garments, should receive judgment. This king made a great feast, and convoked all the nobles of his kingdom, who appeared accordingly. The most skilful musicians were assembled, and there was much sweet melody.* But the sovereign was discontented and out of humour; his countenance expressed intense sorrow, and sighs and groans ascended from his heart. The courtiers were all amazed, but none had the hardihood to inquire the cause of his sadness. At last they requested the king's brother to ask the cause of his sorrow; he made known to him the surprise of his guests, and entreated that he might understand the occasion of his grief. " Go home now," answered

---

* " In the days of chivalry, a concert of a variety of instruments of music constantly made a part of the solemnity of a splendid feast. So in an unprinted metrical romance of Emare, MSS., *Cott. Calig.* A 2, fol. 72 a.

> " ' Sir Ladore let make a feast,
> That was fair and honest,
>   With his lord the king;
> There was *much minstrelsy*,
> Tromp-*es*, tabors, and psaltery,
>   Both harp and fiddl-*e*-ing:'

" And in Chaucer's *January and May*, v. 1234 :—

> " ' At every course came the loud minstrelsy.' "

WARTON.

the king; "to-morrow you shall know." This was done.
Early in the morning the king directed the trumpets to
sound before his brother's house, and the guards to bring
him to the court. The brother, greatly alarmed at the
sounding of the trumpets, arose, and put on sable vesture.
When he came before the king, the latter commanded a
deep pit to be dug, and a rotten chair with four decayed
feet to be slightly suspended over it. In this chair he
made his brother sit; above his head he caused a sword
to hang, attached to a single silk thread; * and four men,
each armed with an extremely sharp sword, to stand near
him, one before and one behind, a third on the right hand,
and the fourth on the left. When they were thus placed,
the king said, "The moment I give the word, strike him
to the heart." Trumpets and all other kind of musical
instruments were brought, and a table, covered with
various dishes, was set before him. "My dear brother,"
said the king, "what is the occasion of your sorrow?
Here are the greatest delicacies—the most enrapturing
harmony; why do you not rejoice?" "How can I rejoice?"
answered he. "In the morning trumpets sounded for my
death; and I am now placed upon a fragile chair: if I
move ever so little it will fall to pieces, and I shall fall
into the pit and never come out again. If I raise my
head, the weapon above will penetrate to my brain.
Besides this, the four torturers around stand ready to kill
me at your bidding. These things considered, were I
lord of the universe, I could not rejoice." "Now, then,"
answered the king, "I will reply to your question of
yesterday. I am on my throne, as you on that frail chair.
For my body is its emblem, supported by four decayed
feet, that is, by the four elements. The pit below me is
hell; above my head is the sword of divine justice, ready to
take life from my body. Before me is the sword of death,
which spares none, and comes when it is not expected;
behind, a sword—that is, my sins, ready to accuse me at
the tribunal of God. The weapon on the right hand is

---

* This circumstance seems to appertain to the story of the tyrant
Dionysius and his flatterers.

[For the well-known story of the "Sword of Damocles," referred
to in the above note, see Horace, *Carm.* iii. 1, 17 seq.—Ed.]

the devil; and that on the left is the worms which after death shall gnaw my body. And, considering all these circumstances, how can *I* rejoice? If you to-day feared me, who am mortal, how much more ought I to dread my Creator? Go, dearest brother, and be careful that you do not again ask such questions." The brother rose from his unpleasant seat, and rendering thanks to the king for his life, firmly resolved to amend himself. All who were present commended the ingenuity of the royal answer. (20)

TALE CXLIV.

OF THE ACTUAL STATE OF THE WORLD.

In the reign of a certain king there happened a sudden and remarkable change, as from good to evil, from truth to falsehood, from strength to weakness, from justice to injustice. This mutableness excited the king's wonder; and inquiring the cause of four of the wisest philosophers, they went, after much deliberation, to the four gates of the city, and severally inscribed thereon three causes. The first wrote—" Power is justice; therefore the land is without law. Day is night; therefore there is no pathway through the land. The warrior flees from the battle; therefore the kingdom has no honour." The second wrote—" One is two; therefore the kingdom is without truth. The friend is an enemy; therefore the kingdom is without faith. Evil is good; therefore the kingdom is without devotion." The third wrote—" Reason is united with licentiousness; therefore the kingdom is without name. A thief is set on high; therefore the kingdom is without wealth. The dove would become an eagle; therefore there is no prudence in the land." The fourth wrote— " The will is a counsellor; therefore the kingdom is ill ordered. Money gives sentence; therefore the kingdom is badly governed. God is dead; therefore the whole kingdom is full of sinners." *

* The application is long and uninteresting, and incapable of abridgment; I have therefore thought it best to omit it entirely. It

TALE CXLV.

OF SALVATION.

ALBERTUS * relates that in the time of Philip there was
a pathway lying between two mountains of Armenia,
which had long been unused. For the air of that country
was so pestilential, that whosoever breathed it died. The
king, therefore, was desirous of ascertaining the cause of
the evil, but no one could discover it. At length Socrates
was sent for, who requested him to build a mansion equal
in loftiness with the mountains. This was done; and the
philosopher then constructed a mirror of steel, with a perfectly pure and polished surface, so that from every part
the appearance of the mountains was reflected in it.
Entering the edifice, Socrates beheld two dragons, one
upon the mountain and the other in the valley, which
simultaneously opened their mouths and drew in the air. As
he looked, a youth on horseback, ignorant of the danger,
wished to pass that way: suddenly he fell from his horse
and died incontinently. Socrates went without delay to
the king, and declared what he had seen. The dragons
were afterwards taken by a cunning trick, and instantly
slain. Thus the path over these mountains became safe
and easy to all who passed by.

contains, however, what may lead us to suspect that certain of these
tales (though very few, I believe) are of German derivation. "Corabola," says the original, "vulgariter: *die schnock wil fliegen also hoch
als der adler.* Ideo non est discretio," &c. So one edition; two others
read, "*Der weul wylt vlyegen also hoge als der arnt aquila,* Ideo, &c.;
and two (one of which belonged to Mr. Tyrwhitt, now in the *British
Museum*) have the Latin translation, "Culex cupit tam altè volare,
sicut ipsa aquilla." *Corabola* above, I apprehend, should be *Parabola.*
[Oesterley, who has examined an enormous number of MSS.,
states that the proverb does not appear in one of them, but is an
addition made by the editors of the printed copies: "Das sprichwort
kommt in den handschriften gar nicht vor" (*Oest.* p. 262).—ED.]

* *Albertus* was an abbot of Stade, and author of a chronicle from
Adam to 1256.

APPLICATION.

My beloved, the mountains are the noble and powerful of the world; the dragons are pride and luxury. The mirror is our Saviour Christ; and the edifice, a good life. The young man who perished is a man killed by vanity. Socrates is a good prelate.

TALE CXLVI.

OF REBUKES TO PRINCES.

AUGUSTINE tells us in his book, *De Civitate Dei*, that Diomedes, in a piratical galley, for a long time infested the sea, plundering and sinking many ships. Being captured by command of Alexander, before whom he was brought, the king inquired how he dared to molest the seas. "How darest *thou*," replied he, " molest the earth? Because I am master only of a single galley, I am termed a robber; but you, who oppress the world with huge squadrons, are called a king and a conqueror. Would my fortune change, I might become better; and were you more unlucky, you too would have so much the worse name." "I will change thy fortune," said Alexander, "lest Fortune should be blamed by thy malignity." Thus he became rich; and from a robber was made a prince and a dispenser of justice.*

APPLICATION.

My beloved, the pirate in his galley is a sinner in the world; Alexander is a prelate.

* "St. Austin's CITY OF GOD is quoted for an answer of Diomedes the pirate to king Alexander."—WARTON.

TALE CXLVII.

OF THE POISONOUS NATURE OF SIN.

THE enemies of a certain king wished to slay him, and since he was powerful they resolved to destroy him by poison. Some of them came to the city where he abode, arrayed in humble garments. Now, there was a fountain of water, from which the king frequently drank, and they impregnated it with the poison. The king, ignorant of their treason, drank according to custom, and died.

APPLICATION.

The king is Adam; his enemies are the devils; and the fountain is the human heart.

TALE CXLVIII.

OF THE PUNISHMENT OF SIN.

AULUS GELLIUS says of Amon,* who was extremely rich, that when he wished to pass from one kingdom to another, he hired a ship. The sailors designed to kill him for his wealth; but he obtained from them, that first he should sing in honour of the dolphins, which are said to be much delighted with the songs of men. When, therefore, he was cast overboard, a dolphin caught him up, and carried him to land; and while the sailors believed him drowned, he was accusing them to the king, by whom they were condemned to death.†

* [It is very strange that all the printed editions should read *Amon*, except one which has *Amor*, when the story is that of Arion. The likeness between the three names is so close that we are almost forced to suppose that some of the early MSS. must have had the name correctly. None of those examined by Oesterley have it. The ed. princ. has *Amor*.—ED.]

† Aulus Gellius relates this story (*Noct. Attic.* lib. xvi. cap. xix.)

APPLICATION.

My beloved, the rich man is any virtuous person; the sailors are devils; and the king is God.

TALE CXLIX.

OF VAIN GLORY.

VALERIUS records that a certain nobleman inquired of a philosopher how he might perpetuate his name. He answered that if he should kill an illustrious personage, his name would be eternally remembered. Hearing this, he slew Philip, the father of Alexander the Great. But he afterwards came to a miserable end.*

APPLICATION.

My beloved, the nobleman is any one who seeks a worldly name by bad means.

---

from Herodotus, in whom it is now extant (lib. viii.) This character of the dolphin has been often alluded to.

> "Sweet sir, 'tis nothing;
> Straight comes a *dolphin*, playing near your ship,
> Having his crooked back up, and presents
> A feather bed to waft ye to the shore
> As easily as if you slept i' th' court."
> FORD, *The Lover's Melancholy*, Act i. Sc. 3.

[The reference to Herodotus is erroneously given. It should be Herod. i. 23, 24, τῷ δὴ λέγουσι Κορίνθιοι κ.τ.λ.—ED.]

* This curious anecdote is recorded of Pausanias, in the eighth book of Valerius Maximus, *De Cupiditate Gloriæ*, cap. xiv. Exter. 4.

"Nam dum Hermocles percontatus esset, *quonam modo subito clarus posset evadere*, atque is respondisset, *si illustrem virum aliquem occidisset, futurum ut gloria ejus ad ipsum redundaret :* continuò Philippum interemit. Et quidem quod petierat, assecutus est. Tam enim se parricidio, quam Philippus virtute, notum posteris reddidit."

TALE CL.

OF CELESTIAL DEW.

PLINY says that there is a certain land in which neither dew nor rain falls. Consequently, there is a general aridness; but in this country there is a single fountain, from which, when people would draw water, they are accustomed to approach with all kinds of musical instruments, and so march around it for a length of time. The melody which they thus produce causes the water to rise to the mouth of the spring, and makes it flow forth in great abundance, so that all men are able to obtain as much as they will.*

APPLICATION.

My beloved, the arid land is man; the fountain, God; the musical instruments, devotional exercises.

TALE CLI.

OF A SINFUL AND LEPROUS SOUL.

IN the kingdom of a certain prince there were two knights, one of whom was avaricious, and the other envious. The former had a beautiful wife, whom every one admired and loved. But the spouse of the latter was ugly and disagreeable. Now, the envious knight had a piece of land adjoining the estate of his covetous neighbour, of which the last exceedingly desired possession. He made him many offers, but the envious person invariably refused to sell his inheritance for silver or gold. At last, in the envy of his soul, he meditated how to destroy the beauty of the

---

* I am unable to find this account in Pliny. In the second book, cap. ciii., and in the thirty-first, cap. ii., the reader will find many wonderful properties of fountains, but that of gushing forth to musical sounds appeareth not.

wife of the covetous knight, and offered him the land on
condition of enjoying his wife for one night. The covetous wretch immediately assented; and bade his wife
submit herself to his will. This diabolical contract ad-
justed, the envious knight instantly infected himself with
the leprosy, and communicated the disease to the lady, for
which he assigned the following reason. He said that, being
filled with envy at the beauty and grace which he observed
in his neighbour's wife, while his own was so deformed
and hateful, he had resolved to remove the disparity. The
lady wept exceedingly; and related to her husband what
had happened. This troubled him, but he bethought himself of a remedy. "As yet," said he, "no symptoms of the
disorder are perceptible. At a short distance from hence,
there is a large city, and in it a university. Go there;
stand in the public way, and entice every passenger to
you. By this means, you will free yourself from the distemper." * The lady did as she was directed; and the
emperor's son, passing by, fell violently in love with her.
Afraid to infect a person so near the throne, she resisted
his advances, and informed him that she was a leper. This,
however, altered not the feelings of the young man; and
accordingly the leprosy of the woman adhered to him.
Ashamed of what had befallen, and at the same time
fearful of discovery, he went to his mistress, and abode
with her. This circumstance she stated to her husband,
and he, much troubled, set his bed-chamber in order, and
there the prince dwelt in the strictest seclusion, attended
upon only by the lady. Here he continued seven years.

It chanced in the seventh year that there was an intolerable heat, and the leprous man had a vessel of wine
standing by his side, designed to refresh his exhausted
spirits. At this moment a serpent came out of the
garden, and, after bathing itself in the vessel, lay down
at the bottom. The prince, awaking from sleep, under
the influence of an excessive drought, took up the vessel
and drank; and, without knowing it, swallowed the
serpent. The creature, finding itself thus unexpectedly
imprisoned, began to gnaw his bowels so grievously as to

* For an account of the leprosy see Note 13; the qualities attributed
to it are as whimsical as fabulous.

put the leper to inconceivable anguish. The lady greatly compassionated him; and, indeed, for three days, he was an object of pity. On the fourth, however, an emetic being administered, he vomited, and cast up, together with the inward disease, the serpent which had tormented him. Immediately the pain ceased; and by little and little the leprosy left him. In seven days his flesh was as free from the disorder as the flesh of a child; and the lady, much delighted, clothed him in sumptuous apparel, and presented him a beautiful war-horse, on which he returned to the emperor. He was received with all honour, and after his father's death ascended the throne, and ended his days in peace.

APPLICATION.

My beloved, the two knights are the devil and the first man. The first, envious of human happiness, possesses a deformed wife, that is, pride; the second had a beautiful wife, which is the soul. The leprosy is iniquity, which drove us from Paradise into the university of the world. The son of the emperor is Christ, who took upon Himself our nature, but by His sufferings freed us from the consequence of sin. As the leper thirsted, so did Christ thirst upon the cross; but not for *wine*: it was for the salvation of our souls. The serpent is His crucifixion; the war-horse, the divine and human nature, with which He ascended into heaven.

TALE CLII.

OF ETERNAL DESTRUCTION.

A PRINCE, named Cleonitus, wishing to give instructions to certain of his subjects who were beleaguered by an enemy, ordered a soldier to go to the place attacked. In order to insult the beleaguerers, he directed an inscription, skilfully fastened upon some arrows, to be prepared, and shot amongst the hostile armies. It ran thus: "Have hope in the Lord, and be faithful; Cleonitus comes in person to raise the siege."

APPLICATION.

My beloved, the prince is Christ; the people besieged are sinners; and the beleaguerers, the devils. The messenger is a preacher.

TALE CLIII.

OF TEMPORAL TRIBULATION.

ANTIOCHUS, the king of Antioch (from whom the city takes its name), had a daughter of such uncommon beauty, that when she came of marriageable years, she was sought after with the greatest eagerness. But on whom to bestow her was a source of much anxiety to the king; and, from frequently contemplating the exquisite loveliness of her face, the delicacy of her form, and the excellence of her disposition, he began to love her with more than a father's love. He burned with an unhallowed flame, and would have excited a simultaneous feeling in his daughter.* She, however, courageously persevered in the path of duty, until at length violence accomplished what persuasion had in vain struggled to effect. Thus situated, she gave a loose to her tears, and wept in an agony of the bitterest sorrow. At this moment her nurse entered, and asked the occasion of her uneasiness; she replied, "Alas, my beloved nurse, two noble names have just perished." "Dear lady," returned the other, "why do you say so?" She told her. "And what accursed demon has been busy?" asked the nurse. "Where," replied the lady, "where is my father? I have no father; in me that sacred name has perished. But death is a remedy for all, and I will die." The nurse, alarmed at what she heard, soothed her into a less desperate mood, and engaged her word not to seek so fearful a relief.

* "This king unto him took a pheere,
  Who died and left a female heir,
  So buxom, blithe, and full of face,
  As Heaven had lent her all His grace."
      SHAKESPEARE, *Pericles.*

In the mean time the impious parent, assuming the specious garb of hypocrisy, exhibited to the citizens the fair example of an honest life. In secret he exulted at the success of his iniquity, and reflected upon the best means of freeing his unhappy daughter from the numerous suitors who honourably desired her hand. To effect this, he devised a new scheme of wickedness. He proposed certain questions, and annexed to them a condition, by which whosoever furnished an appropriate answer should espouse the lady; but failing, should be instantly decapitated. A multitude of crowned heads from every quarter, attracted by her unmatchable beauty, presented themselves: but they were all put to death. For, if any one chanced to develop the horrid secret, he was slain equally with him who failed, in order to prevent its being divulged. Then the head of the victim blackened upon the gate. The suitors, therefore, naturally grew less; for, perceiving so many ghastly countenances peering above them, their courage quailed, and they returned hastily to their several homes.

Now, all this was done that he who had produced this scene of wickedness might continue in uninterrupted possession. After a short time, the young prince of Tyre, named Apollonius, well-lettered and rich, sailing along the coast, disembarked and entered Antioch. Approaching the royal presence, he said, "Hail, oh king! I seek thy daughter in marriage." The king unwillingly heard him communicate his wishes, and fixing an earnest look upon the young man, said, "Dost thou know the conditions?" "I do," answered he boldly, "and find ample confirmation at your gates."* The king, enraged at his firmness, returned, "Hear, then, the question—'I am transported with wickedness; I live upon my mother's flesh. I seek my brother, and find him not in the offspring of my

---

* "He made a law
(To keep her still, and men in awe),
That whoso asked her for his wife,
His riddle told not, lost his life:
So for her many a wight did die,
As yon grim looks do testify."

SHAKESPEARE, *Pericles.*

mother.'" * The youth received the question, and went from the presence of the king; and after duly considering the matter, by the good providence of God, discovered a solution. He immediately returned, and addressing the incestuous wretch, said, " Thou hast proposed a question, oh king! attend my answer. Thou hast said, ' *I am transported with wickedness,*' and thou hast not lied: look into thy heart. ' *I live upon my mother's flesh,*'— look upon thy daughter." The king, hearing this explication of the riddle, and fearing the discovery of his enormities, regarded him with a wrathful eye. " Young man," said he, " thou art far from the truth, and deservest death; but I will yet allow thee the space of thirty days. Recollect thyself. In the mean while, return to thy own country: if thou findest a solution to the enigma, thou shalt marry my daughter; if not, thou shalt die." † The youth, much disturbed, called his company together, and hastening on board his own vessel, immediately set sail.

No sooner had he departed, than the king sent for his steward, whose name was Taliarchus, and spoke to him in this manner: " Taliarchus, you are the most faithful repository of my secrets; you know, therefore, that the Apollonius of Tyre has found out my riddle. Pursue

---

* " [*Pericles reads the riddle.*]
I am no viper, yet I feed
On mother's flesh which did me breed;
I sought a husband, in which labour,
I found that kindness in a father.
He's father, son, and husband mild,
I mother, wife, and yet his child.
How they may be, and yet in two,
As you will live, resolve it you."
SHAKESPEARE, *Pericles.*

† " *Ant.* Young prince of Tyre,
Though by the tenour of our strict edict,
Your exposition misinterpreting,
We might proceed to cancel of your days;
Yet hope, succeeding from so fair a tree
As your fair self, doth tune us otherwise:
Forty days longer we do respite you;
If by which time our secret be undone,
This mercy shows, we'll joy in such a son:
And, until then, your entertain shall be,
As doth befit our honour and your worth." *Ibid.*

him instantly to Tyre, and destroy him either with the
sword or with poison. When you return, you shall receive
a liberal recompense." Taliarchus, arming himself, and
providing a sum of money, sailed into the country of the
young man.*

When Apollonius reached his own home, he opened his
coffers, and searched a variety of books upon the subject
in question, but he still adhered to the same idea. "Unless I am much deceived," said he to himself, "king
Antiochus entertains an impious love for his daughter."
And continuing his reflections, he went on, "What art
thou about, Apollonius? thou hast resolved his problem,
and still he has not given thee his daughter. Therefore,
God will not have thee die." Commanding his ships to
be got ready, and laden with a hundred thousand measures
of corn, and a great weight of gold and silver, with many
changes of garments, he hastily embarked during the night,
in company with a few faithful followers. They put to
sea immediately; and much wonder and regret arose the
next day among the citizens respecting him. For he was
greatly beloved amongst them; and such was their sorrow,
that the barbers, for a length of time, lost all their occupation; public spectacles were forbidden; the baths were
closed, and no one entered either the temples or taber-
nacles.

While these things were going on, Taliarchus, who had
been despatched by Antiochus to destroy the prince, observing every house shut up, and the signs of mourning
general, asked a boy the occasion of it. "Sir," replied he,
"are you ignorant of this matter, that you ask me?
Understand, then, that Apollonius, prince of this country,
having returned from a visit to King Antiochus, is nowhere to be found." Much rejoiced at what he heard,
Taliarchus returned to his vessel, and sailed back again to

* " *Enter* THALIARD.

    Thal. Doth your highness call?
    Ant. Thaliard, you're of our chamber, and our mind
  Partakes her private actions to your secresy;
  And for your faithfulness we will advance you.
  Thaliard, behold, here's poison and here's gold;
  We hate the prince of Tyre, and thou must kill him."
                    SHAKESPEARE, *Pericles.*

his own country.* Presenting himself to the king, he exclaimed, " Be happy, my lord; Apollonius, through dread of you, is not to be found anywhere." He has fled," returned the king; "but long he shall not escape me." And he immediately put forth an edict to this effect: " Whosoever brings before me the traitor Apollonius shall receive fifty talents of gold ; but whosoever presents me with his head shall be rewarded with a hundred." This tempting proposal stimulated not only his enemies, but his pretended friends, to follow him, and many dedicated their time and activity to the pursuit. They traversed sea and land, near and remote countries, but he fortunately escaped their search. The malicious king fitted out a navy for the same purpose, and commanded them to proceed with the utmost diligence in their employment.

Apollonius, however, arrived safely at Tharsus, and walking along the shore, he was distinguished by a certain slave of his own household, called Elinatus, † who happened that very hour to have reached it. Approaching, he made obeisance to the prince, and Apollonius, recognizing him, returned his salute as great men are wont to do ; for he thought him contemptible. The old man, indignant at his reception, again saluted him, " Hail, King Apollonius ! Return my salute, and despise not poverty, if it be ornamented by honest deeds. Did you know what I know, you would be cautious." " May it please you to tell me what you know ? " answered the prince. " You are proscribed," returned the other.

---

* " *Thal.* Well, I perceive   (*Aside*).
I shall not be hang'd now, although I would;
But since he's gone, the king it sure must please,
He 'scaped the land, to perish on the seas.—
But I'll present me.—Peace to the lords of Tyre !
   Hel. Lord Thaliard from Antiochus is welcome.
   Thal. From him I come
With message unto princely Pericles;
But since my landing, as I have understood
Your lord has took himself to unknown travels,
My message must return from whence it came."
               SHAKESPEARE, *Pericles.*

† Called Hellanicus in the Latin copy of 1595.

"And who shall dare proscribe a prince in his own land?"

"Antiochus has done it."

"Antiochus! For what cause?"

"Because you sought to be what the father of his daughter is."

"And what is the price of my proscription?"

"He who shall take you alive is to receive fifty talents of gold; but for your head he will have a hundred. And therefore I caution you to be upon your guard."

Saying this, Elinatus went his way. Apollonius recalled him, and proffered the hundred talents of gold which had been set upon his head. "Take," said he, "so much of my poverty; thou hast merited it: cut off my head, and gratify the malicious king. You possess the sum, and still you are innocent. I engage you, therefore, of my own free will, to do so great a pleasure to him who seeks my destruction." "My lord," answered the old man, "far be it from me to take away your life for hire; the friendship of good men is of more value, and cannot be bought." Then, returning thanks to the prince for his munificence, he departed. But as Apollonius tarried on the shore, he perceived a person named Stranguilio approaching him with a sorrowful aspect, and every now and then uttering a deep lament. "Hail, Stranguilio!" said the prince. "Hail, my lord the king!" was his reply. "You appear concerned; tell me what occasions it?"

"To say truth," returned Apollonius, "it is because I have required the daughter of a king in marriage. Can I conceal myself in your country?" "My lord," answered Stranguilio, "our city is extremely poor, and cannot sustain your attendants, in consequence of a grievous famine which has wasted the land. Our citizens are hopeless and helpless; and death, with all its accompanying horrors, is before our eyes." "Give thanks to God," replied Apollonius, "who hath driven me a fugitive to your shores. If you will conceal my flight, I will present to you a hundred thousand measures of corn." Full of joy, Stranguilio prostrated himself at the feet of the prince, and exclaimed, "My lord, if you will assist our starving city we will not only conceal your flight, but, if necessary, unsheath our

swòrds in your defence." Apollonius, therefore, hastened
into the forum, and ascending the tribunal, spoke thus to
the assembled population: " Men of Tharsus, understanding that an afflicting dearth of provisions troubles you, I,
Apollonius, proffer aid. I believe that you will not forget
the benefit I render you, but conceal my flight from those
who unjustly pursue me. Ye know what the malice of
Antiochus aims at, and by what providence I am brought
hither to relieve you in this terrible emergency. I present
to you a hundred thousand measures of corn at the price
I gave for it in my own country—that is, at eight pieces
for each measure." The citizens, delighted at what they
heard, gave thanks to God, and immediately prepared the
corn for use. (21)

But Apollonius, not forgetting the dignity of a king
in the traffic of a merchant, returned the purchase-money
to the state; and the people, struck with wonder at this
unexpected instance of generosity, erected in the forum
a chariot drawn by four horses, running side by side.
In the car was a statue, representing Apollonius with his
right hand rubbing the corn from the ear. His left foot
trampled upon it; and on the pediment they placed the
following inscription:—" APOLLONIUS, PRINCE OF TYRE, BY
A GIFT TO THE CITY OF THARSUS, PRESERVED ITS INHABITANTS
FROM A CRUEL DEATH." * A few days afterwards, by the
advice of Stranguilio and his wife Dionysias,† the prince
determined to sail for Pentapolis,‡ a city of the Tyrrheni,

* " And to remember what he does,
        Gild his statue glorious."—SHAKESPEARE.

Gower says,
        " It was of *latten* over-gilt."—*Conf. Aman.*

† DIONYZA in Shakespeare.

‡ Pentapolis was properly a *country* of Africa, and so called from
its five cities, Berenice, Arsinoe, Ptolemaïs, Cyrene, and Apollonia; it
was also a country of Palestine. But I suppose a city of Tuscany
is meant here, which was called by the name of Pentapolis. Mr.
Stevens, however, says that it is an imaginary city, and its name
probably borrowed from some romance. " That the reader may know
through how many regions the scene of this drama is dispersed, it is
necessary to observe that *Antioch* was the metropolis of Syria; *Tyre*,
a city of Phœnicia in Asia; *Tarsus*, the metropolis of Cilicia, a country
of Asia Minor; *Mitylene*, the capital of Lesbos, an island in the Ægean
Sea; and *Ephesus*, the capital of Ionia, a country of Lesser Asia."—
STEVENS.

where he might remain in greater tranquillity and
opulence.* They brought him, therefore, with much
ceremony to the sea-shore; and then bidding his hosts
farewell, he embarked. For three days and nights he
sailed with favourable winds; but after losing sight of
the Tharsian coast, they veered round, and blew from the
north with great violence. The rain fell in heavy showers,
mixed with hail; and the ship was carried away by the
fury of the storm. Dark clouds brooded over them; and
the blast, still increasing, threatened them with immediate
death. The crew, imagining all was lost, caught hold of
planks, and committed themselves to the mercy of the
waves. In the extreme darkness that followed, all
perished. But Apollonius, riding on a plank, was cast
upon the Pentapolitan shore; on which, after quitting the
water, he stood thoughtfully, and fixing his eyes upon
the ocean, now in a calm, exclaimed, "Oh, ye faithless
waves! better had I fallen into the hands of that savage
king!—to whom shall I now go? What country shall
I seek? Who will afford succour to an unknown and
helpless stranger?" As he spoke this, he beheld a young
man coming towards him. He was a robust, hard-
favoured fisherman, clad in a coarse frock. Apollonius,
driven by his distresses, humbly besought this man's
assistance, even with tears starting from his eyes. "Pity

---

* "(*Dumb show.*)

Enter at one door PERICLES, *talking with* CLEON; *all the train with*
them. Enter at another door a Gentleman, with a letter to PERICLES;
PERICLES *shows the letter to* CLEON; *then gives the Messenger a reward,*
and knights him. Exeunt Pericles, Cleon, &c., severally.

> Gow. Good Helicane hath stay'd at home,
> Not to eat honey, like a drone,
> From others' labours; for tho' he strive
> To killen bad, keep good alive;
> And, to fulfil his prince' desire,
> Sends word of all that haps in Tyre:
> How Thaliard came full bent with sin,
> And hid intent to murder him;
> And that in Tharsus was not best
> Longer for him to make his rest:
> He, knowing so, put forth to seas,
> Where when men been, there's seldom ease."

SHAKESPEARE, *Pericles.*

me," said he, "whosoever thou art; pity a man stripped of all by shipwreck—one to whom better days have been familiar, and who is descended from no ignoble family. But that you may know whom you succour, understand that I am a prince of Tyre, and that my name is Apollonius. Save, then, my life, I entreat you." The fisherman, compassionating his sufferings, brought him to his own roof, and placed such as he had before him. And that there might be no deficiency in the charitable part he was acting, he divided his cloak, and gave one-half to the stranger; "Take," said the benevolent man, "take what I can give, and go into the city; there, perhaps, you will find one with more power to serve you than I am. If you are unsuccessful in your search, return hither to me. What poverty can provide you shall share. Yet, should you hereafter be restored to your throne, do not forget or despise the coarse, threadbare cloak of the poor fisherman."* "Fear not," said Apollonius; "should I prove ungrateful may I be shipwrecked again, nor find in my extremity a man like yourself." As he spoke, the fisherman pointed out the way to the city gates, which Apollonius shortly entered.

Whilst he reflected upon the path he should pursue, he beheld a naked boy running along the street, having his head anointed with oil, and bound with a napkin.† The youth lustily vociferated, "Hear, hear, pilgrims or slaves; whosoever would be washed, let him haste to the gymnasium." Apollonius, according to the proclamation, entered the bath, and pulling off his cloak, made use of the water. Whilst he was doing this, he cast his eyes around to discover some one of an equality with himself; and at last Altistrates,‡ king of all that country, entered with a troop of his attendants. The king played with

* "2 *Fish*. Ay, but hark you, my friend; 'twas we that made up this garment through the rough seams of the waters : there are certain condolements, certain vails. I hope, sir, if you thrive, you'll remember from whence you had it."—SHAKESPEARE, *Pericles*.

† The custom of anointing the body after bathing is a well-known Eastern practice ; but the *nudity* of the boy running through the streets with a proclamation, I do not exactly understand.

† Called by Shakespeare *Simonides*; but the incident following is omitted, and another used instead.

them at tennis ; * and Apollonius running forward, caught
up the ball, and, striking it with inconceivable skill and
rapidity, returned it to the royal player. The king,
motioning to his servants, said, " Give up your sport,
give up your sport; for I suspect this youth is as good
a player as I am." † Apollonius, flattered by this praise,
approached the king, and catching up an unguent,‡ with
a dexterous hand anointed the king's body. Then, having
gratefully administered a bath, he departed. After he
was gone, " I swear to you," said his majesty to his
surrounding friends, " that I have never bathed so agree-
ably as I have done to-day by the kindness of a youth
whom I do not know. " Go," added he, to one of the

* " *Ludum Spheræ.*"

† An extract from Gower here, may throw some light upon the
game alluded to :—

> " And as it should then befall
> That day was set of such assise,
> That they should in the land-*es* guise,
> (As was heard of the people say)
> Their common game then play.
> And cried was, that they should come
> Unto the gam-*e* all and some ;
> Of them that ben deliver and wite,
> To do such mastery as they might.
> They made them *naked* (as they should)
> For so that ilke gam-*e* would ;
> And it was the custom-*e* and use,
> Among-*es* them was no refuse.
> The flower of all the town was there,
> And of the court also there were ;
> And that was in a larg-*e* place,
> Right even before the king-*es* face,
> Which Arthescates then hight.
> The play was played right in his sight,
> And who most worthy was of deed,
> Receive he should a certain meed,
> And in the city bear a price.
> Apollonius, which was ware and wise,
> Of every game could an end
> He thought assay, how so it went."
>
> *Confessio Amantis*, lib. **viii.** fol. 178.

‡ " *Cyramaco* accepto," in the text of the *Gesta Romanorum ;* but
in the " *Narratio*," &c., " *accepto ceromata*," a compound of oil and
wax.

attendants, " go, and inquire who he is." He followed
accordingly, and beheld him equipped in the mean cloak
received from the fisherman. Returning to the king, he
said, "The youth is one who has suffered shipwreck."
"How do you know!" replied he. "The man said
nothing," answered the servant, "but his dress pointed
out his circumstances." "Go quickly," returned the
king, "and say that I entreat him to sup with me."
Apollonius was content, and accompanied the servant
back. The latter, approaching the sovereign, stated the
return of the shipwrecked person, but that, ashamed of
his mean habit, he was unwilling to enter. The king
instantly gave command that he should be clothed in
honourable apparel, and introduced to the supper-room.

Apollonius therefore entered the royal drawing-room,
and was placed opposite to the king. Dinner was brought,
and then supper. He feasted not, however, with the
feasters, but continually cast his eye upon the gold and
silver ornaments of the table, and wept. One of the
guests observing this, said to the king, "He envies your
regal magnificence, unless I am much deceived." "You
suspect unhappily," answered he; "he does not envy me,
but laments somewhat that he has lost." * Then, turning
to Apollonius, with a smiling countenance he said, "Young
man, feast with us to-day, and hope that God has better
things in store for you." As he thus endeavoured to raise
the drooping spirits of the youth, his daughter, a beautiful
girl, entered, and first kissed her father, and then those
who were his guests.† When she had gone through this
ceremony, she returned to the king, and said, "My dear
father, who is that young man reclining opposite to you
in the place of honour, and whose grief appears so ex-

---

* " *Sim.* Yet pause a while;
Yon knight, methinks, doth sit too melancholy,
As if the entertainment in our court
Had not a show might countervail his worth."
SHAKESPEARE, *Pericles.*

† This presents us a *family* picture, rather than the delineation of
a court: but they were primitive times, and, more forcibly than any
other circumstance, these touches denote the high antiquity of the
stories.

cessive?" "Sweet daughter," answered he, "that is a shipwrecked youth, who pleased me to-day in the gymnasium; therefore I invited him to supper; but who he is I know not. If you wish to ascertain this, ask him —it becomes you to know all things; and perhaps, when you are made acquainted with his sorrows, you may compassionate and relieve them." The girl, happy in the permission, approached the young man, and said, "Good friend, kindness proves nobility: if it be not troublesome, tell me your name and fortunes." "Would you inquire my name?" replied he: "I lost it in the sea; or my nobility? I left it in Tyre." "Speak intelligibly," said the girl; and Apollonius then related his name and adventures.* When he had made an end he wept, and the king, perceiving his tears, said to his daughter, "My dear child, you did ill to inquire the name and occurrences of the young man's life. You have renewed his past griefs.† But since he has revealed the truth, it is right that you should show the liberty you enjoy as queen." The lady complied with the wishes of her father, and looking upon the youth, exclaimed, "You are our knight,

---

* "*Sim.* Tell him, we desire to know,
Of whence he is, his name and parentage.
  Thai. The king my father, sir, has drunk to you.
  Per. I thank him.
  Thai. Wishing it so much blood unto your life.
  Per. I thank both him and you, and pledge him freely.
  Thai. And further he desires to know of you,
Of whence you are, your name and parentage.
  Per. A gentleman of Tyre—(my name, Pericles;
My education being in arts and arms;)
Who, looking for adventures in the world,
Was by the rough sea reft of ships and men,
And, after shipwreck, driven upon this shore.
  Thai. He thanks your grace; names himself Pericles,
A gentleman of Tyre, who only by
Misfortune of the sea has been bereft
Of ships and men, and cast upon this shore.
  Sim. Now, by the gods, I pity his misfortune,
And will awake him from his melancholy."

SHAKESPEARE, Pericles.

† "Veteres ejus dolores renovasti."—One does not expect to meet Virgil's "Regina jubes renovare dolorem," in a writer of monastic romances, who certainly never went to the fountain-head.

Apollonius!* Put away your afflictions, and my father will make you rich." Apollonius thanked her with modesty and lamentation. Then said the king, "Bring hither your lyre, and add song to the banquet." She commanded the instrument to be brought, and began to touch it with infinite sweetness. Applause followed the performance. "There never was," said the courtiers, "a better or a sweeter song." Apollonius alone was silent, and his want of politeness drew from the king a remark. "You do an unhandsome thing. Everybody else extols my daughter's musical skill; why then do you only discommend it?" "Most gracious king," replied he, "permit me to say what I think. Your daughter comes near to musical pre-eminence, but has not yet attained it. Command, therefore, a lyre to be given me, and you shall then know what you are now ignorant of." "I perceive," observed the king, "that you are universally learned," and directed a lyre to be presented to him. Apollonius retired for a few moments, and decorated his head; then, re-entering the dining-room, he took the instrument, and struck it so gracefully and delightfully that they unanimously agreed that it was the harmony not of APOLLONIUS, but of APOLLO.†

The guests positively asserted that they never heard or saw anything better; and the daughter, regarding the youth with fixed attention, grew suddenly and violently enamoured. "Oh, my father," cried she, "let me reward him as I think fit." The king assented; and she, looking

* " *Thai.* But you, my knight and guest;
To whom this wreath of victory I give,
And crown you king of this day's happiness.
Per. 'Tis more by fortune, lady, than my merit."
SHAKESPEARE, *Pericles.*

† " *Enter* PERICLES.
Per. All fortune to the good Simonides!
Sim. To you as much! Sir, I am beholden to you
For your sweet music this last night: my ears,
I do protest, were never better fed
With such delightful pleasing harmony.
Per. It is your grace's pleasure to commend;
Not my desert.
Sim. Sir, you are music's master.
Per. The worst of all her scholars, my good lord." *Ibid.*

tenderly upon the youth, said, "Sir Apollonius, receive out of my royal father's munificence two hundred talents of gold and four hundred pounds of silver, a rich garment, twenty men-servants, and ten handmaids;" then, turning to the attendants present, she continued, "Bring what I have promised." Her commands were obeyed; and the guests then rising, received permission to depart.

When they were gone, Apollonius also arose, and said, "Excellent king, pitier of the distressed! and you, O queen, lover of study and friend of philosophy, fare ye well." Then addressing the servants bestowed upon him, he commanded them to bear away the presents he had received to an hostelry; but the girl, who became apprehensive of losing her lover, looked sorrowfully at her parent, and said, "Best king and father, does it please you that Apollonius, whom we have so lately enriched, should leave us? The goods we have given him will be purloined by wicked men." The king admitted this, and assigned him apartments in the palace, where he lived in great honour.

But the lady's affection so much increased, that it deprived her of all rest; and in the morning she hastened to the bedside of her father. Surprised at the early visit, he inquired what had roused her at so unusual an hour. "I have been unable to sleep," answered the lady; "and I wish you to permit me to receive instructions in music from the young stranger." The king, pleased with his daughter's zeal for improvement, cheerfully assented, and commanded the youth to be brought into his presence. "Apollonius," said he, "my daughter is extremely desirous of learning your science; if you will instruct her, I will reward you abundantly."* "My lord," he answered, "I am ready to comply with your wishes;" and, accordingly, the girl was placed under his tuition. But her love preyed upon her health, and she visibly declined. Physicians were called in, and they had recourse to the usual ex-

---

* "*Sim.* My daughter, sir, thinks very well of you;
Ay, so well, sir, that you must be her master,
And she'll your scholar be; therefore look to it.
   Per. Unworthy I to be her schoolmaster.
   Sim. She thinks not so."

SHAKESPEARE, Pericles.

pedients;* but the diagnostics led them to no certain conclusion.

In a few days three young noblemen, who had long desired to espouse the lady, presented themselves before the king, and besought his favour. " You have often promised us," said they, " that one or the other should marry your daughter. We are rich, and of noble lineage: choose, then, which of us shall be your son-in-law." " You come," replied the king, " at an unseasonable time. My daughter is unable to follow her usual pursuits, and for this reason languishes on her bed. But that I may not appear to you unnecessarily to protract your uncertainty, write each of you your names, and the settlement you will make her. She shall examine them, and chuse between ye." The suitors complied, and gave the writings to the king, who read, and sealed, and then despatched Apollonius with them to the lady. As soon as she beheld him whom she loved, she exclaimed, " Sir, how is it that you enter my chamber alone?" He presented the writings which her father had sent, and, having opened them, she read the names and proposals of the three suitors. Casting them aside, she said to Apollonius, " Sir, are you not sorry that I must be married?" " No," returned he; " whatever is for your honour is pleasant to me." " Ah! master, master," continued the girl; " but if you loved me, you would grieve." She wrote back her answer, sealed, and delivered it to Apollonius to carry to the king. It ran in these words: " Royal sir and father, since you have permitted me to write my wishes, I do write them. I will espouse him who was shipwrecked." The king read, but not knowing which of them had been in this predicament, he said to the contending parties, " Which of you has been shipwrecked?" One, whose name was Ardonius, replied, "I have, my lord." " What!" cried another, " diseases confound thee; mayst thou be neither safe nor sound. I know perfectly well that thou hast never been beyond the gates of the city; where, then, wert thou shipwrecked?" When the king could not discover the shipwrecked suitor, he turned to

* " Venas et singulas partes corporis tangebant." We may gather from notices like these some idea of the state of physic at the period in which these tales were fabricated.

Apollonius, and said, " Take thou the tablets and read ;
perhaps they will be more intelligible to you than they
are to me." He took them, and running his eye over the
contents, perceived that he was the person designed, and
that the lady loved him. He blushed. " Dost thou discover this shipwrecked person, Apollonius ? " asked the
king. He blushed still deeper, and made a brief reply.
Now, in this the wisdom of Apollonius may be perceived,
since, as it is in *Eccles.*, "There is no wisdom in many
words." And in 1 *Peter* ii.: " Christ hath left you an
example to be diligently followed, who never sinned,
neither was deceit found in His mouth." The same, also,
the Psalmist declares : " As He said, so it was done ; "
wherefore He was to be called a true Israelite, in whom
there was no guile. And *John* i.: " Therefore let us
imitate Him in not cursing, nor rendering malediction for
malediction, but reserve the tongue for blessing." Thus
shall it become the pen of a ready writer—that is, of the
Holy Spirit, suddenly pouring forth its gifts; according
as it is said, " Suddenly a noise was heard in heaven."
So 1 *Peter* iii. " He who would see happy days, let him refrain his tongue from evil, and his lips that they speak no
guile : " that is, man ought not to murmur within himself,
nor act outward evil ; so shall he enjoy quietness in this
life, and in the future, eternal rest. For the first prevents
the outbreaking of reproachful words to the injury of his
neighbours; and it is the beginning of eternal peace. So
the Psalmist : " I will sleep and repose in peace." For as
the tongue of a good and quiet man is directed by the
power of God ; so the tongue of a malicious person is
ministered unto by evil spirits. As it is written, " In our
garden grows a whitethorn, upon which the birds rest."
By this garden we should understand the mouth, surrounded by a double hedge—to wit, the teeth and the lips
—for no other cause than that we may place a guard upon
the mouth, and speak nothing but what is in praise of
God. The thorn in the garden is the tongue itself, so
called from its likeness ; because, as the material thorn
pricks (*St. Matt.* xxviii.: " Twining a crown of thorns,
they placed it upon His head, and the blood flowed down
His blessed body in consequence of the puncture of the

thorns "), thus the thorn, that is the tongue, pierces a man
—one while by taking away his good sense ; at another, by
falsehood; and then, again, by discovering the evil that
there is in any person : all which ought carefully to be
shunned. But the birds resting upon the thorn are the
devils, who incline man to vice, so that he becomes their
servant. Therefore they will exclaim, in the last day,
" Cast this man to us, O righteous judge ! for since he
would not be thine in all virtue, he is ours in all malice."
Let every one of us keep in his tongue, which Cato declares
to be the first virtue.

But to return to our story. When the king became
aware of his daughter's inclination, he said to the three
lovers, " In due time I will communicate with you."
They bade him farewell and departed. But the king hastened to his daughter. " Whom," said he, " wouldst
thou chuse for thy husband?" She prostrated herself
before him with tears, and answered, " Dear father, I
desire to marry the shipwrecked Apollonius." His child's
tears softened the parent's heart; he raised her up, and
said, " My sweet child, think only of thy happiness; since
he is thy choice, he shall be mine. I will appoint the
day of your nuptials immediately." The following morning, he sent messengers to the neighbouring cities to
invite the nobles. When they arrived, he said, " My
lords, my daughter would marry her master. I desire
you, therefore, to be merry, for my child will be united to
a wise man." Saying this, he fixed the period of their
spousals.

Now, it happened, after she became pregnant, that she
walked with her husband, prince Apollonius, by the sea-
shore, and a fine ship riding at anchor in the distance, the
latter perceived that it was of his own country. Turning
to the master of the vessel, he said, " Whence are you?"
" From Tyre," replied the man.

" You speak of my own land, my friend."

" Indeed ! and are you a Tyrian?"

" As you have said."

" Do you know," continued the master, " a prince of
that country, called Apollonius? I seek him; and whenever you happen to see him, bid him exult. King Antio-

chus and his daughter, at the very same instant, were
blasted with lightning.* The kingdom has fallen to
Apollonius." Full of pleasure at the unexpected intelligence he had received, the prince said to his wife, "Will
you acquiesce in my setting out to obtain the throne?"
The lady instantly burst into tears. "Oh, my lord," said
she, "the journey is long, and yet you would leave me!
If, however, it is necessary that you should go, we will
go together." † Instantly hastening to her father, she
communicated the happy news which had just been heard,
that Antiochus and his daughter, by the just judgment of

* "*Helicanus.* No, no, my Escanes; know this of me,—
Antiochus from incest lived not free;
For which the most high gods not minding longer
To withhold the vengeance that they had in store,
Due to this heinous capital offence;
Even in the height and pride of all his glory,
When he was seated, and his daughter with him,
In a chariot of inestimable value,
A fire from heaven came, and shrivell'd up
Their bodies, even to loathing; for they so stunk,
That all those eyes adored them, ere their fall,
Scorn now their hand should give their burial."
SHAKESPEARE, Pericles.

† "*Gow.* At last from Tyre
(Fame answering the most strong inquire)
To the court of king Simonides
Are letters brought, the tenour these:
Antiochus and his daughter's dead;
The men of Tyrus on the head
Of Helicanus would set on
The crown of Tyre, but he will none:
The mutiny there he hastes t' appease;
Says to them, if king Pericles
Come not, in twice six moons, home,
He, obedient to their doom,
Will take the crown. The sum of this,
Brought hither to Pentapolis,
Y-ravished the regions round,
And every one with claps 'gan sound,
Our heir apparent is a king:
Who dream'd, who thought of such a thing?
Brief, he must hence depart to Tyre:
His queen with child makes her desire
(Which who shall cross?) along to go;
(Omit we all their dole and woe)." *Ibid.*

an offended God, had been struck with lightning, and his wealth and diadem reserved for her husband. And lastly, she entreated his permission to accompany him. The old king, much exhilarated with the intelligence, was easily prevailed upon to assent; and ships were accordingly prepared for their conveyance. They were laden with everything necessary for the voyage; and a nurse, called Ligoridis,* was embarked, and a midwife, in anticipation of the young queen's parturition. Her father accompanied them to the shore, and with an affectionate kiss of each, took his leave.

When they had been at sea some days, there arose a fearful tempest; and the lady, brought by this circumstance into premature labour, to all appearance perished. The moaning and tears of her family almost equalled the storm; and Apollonius, alarmed at the outcry, ran into the apartment, and beheld his lovely wife like an inhabitant of the grave. He tore his garments from his breast, and cast himself with tears and groans upon her inanimate body. "Dear wife!" he exclaimed, "daughter of the great Altistrates, how shall I console thy unhappy parent?"† Here the pilot, interrupting him, observed, "Sir, it will prejudice the ship to retain the dead body on board; command that it be cast into the sea." "Wretch that you are," returned Apollonius, "would you wish me to hurl this form into the waves, that succoured me shipwrecked and in poverty?" Then calling his attendants, he directed them to prepare a coffin, and smear the lid with bitumen. He also commanded that a leaden scroll should be placed in it, and the body, arrayed in regal habiliments, and crowned, was then deposited in the coffin. He kissed her cold lips, and wept bitterly. Afterwards giving strict charge respecting the new-born infant, he committed all that remained of his wife to the sea. (22) On the third day the chest was driven by the waves to the shores of Ephesus, not far from the residence of a physician, called Cerimon, who happened at that hour to

---

* In Shakspeare, *Lychorida.*
† "*Lych.* Patience, good sir; do not assist the storm.
Here's all that is left living of your queen,—
A little daughter." SHAKESPEARE, *Pericles.*

be walking with certain of his pupils upon the sands. Observing the chest deserted by the waters, he commanded his servants to secure it with all speed, and convey it to his house: this done, he opened it, and discovered a beautiful girl, attired in royal apparel. (23) Her uncommon loveliness struck all the spectators with astonishment; for she was as a sunbeam of beauty, in which nature had created everything pure and perfect, and failed in nothing but in denying her the attribute of immortality.* Her hair glittered like the snow, beneath which a brow of milky whiteness, smooth and unwrinkled as a plain, peacefully rested. Her eyes resembled the changeableness, not the prodigality,† of two luminous orbs; for their gaze was directed by an unshaken modesty, which indicated a constant and enduring mind. Her eyebrows were naturally and excellently placed; and her shapely nose, describing a straight line, rose centrically upon the face. It possessed neither too much length nor too little. Her neck was whiter than the solar rays, and ornamented with precious stones; while her countenance, full of unspeakable joy, communicated happiness to all who looked on her. She was exquisitely formed; and the most critical investigation could not discover more or less than there ought to be. Her beautiful arms, like the branches of some fair tree, descended from her well-turned breast; to which, delicately chiselled fingers, not outshone by the lightning, were attached. In short, she was outwardly a perfect model,—flashing through which, the divine spark of soul her Creator had implanted might be gloriously distinguished. (24) Works of power ought to

---

* " Quoniam verus erat pulchritudinis radius: in quo natura nihil viciosum constituit; nisi quòd eam immortalem non formaverat." This is far beyond the common strain of a monkish imagination; and, in truth, the whole passage forms a brilliant description of female beauty. See Note 24.

† Prodigality (in the original, *prodigus*) seems to imply an impudent stare; an eye prodigal of its favours, as may be said of a star. The changeableness of the eye is a great beauty. Pope says of his Belinda—

> " Her lovely looks a sprightly mind disclose,
> Quick as her eyes, and as *unfixed* as those."
> *Rape of the Lock.*

accord with each other: and hence all corporal beauty originates in the soul's loveliness. It has even been said, that mental excellence, however various, adapts the mass of matter to itself.*

Be this as it may, the most perfect adaptation of soul and body existed in this lady, now discovered by Cerimon. "Fair girl," said he, "how camest thou so utterly forsaken?" The money, which had been placed beneath her head, now attracted his attention, and then the scroll of lead presented itself.

"Let us examine what it contains."

He opened it accordingly, and read as follows :—

"Whomsoever thou art that findest this chest, I entreat thy acceptance of ten pieces of gold ; the other ten expend, I pray thee, on a funeral. For the corse it shrouds hath left tears and sorrows enough to the authors of her being. If thou dost neglect my request, I imprecate upon thee curses against the day of judgment, and devote thy body to death, unhonoured and uninhumed." †

When the physician had read, he directed his servants to comply with the mourner's injunction. "And I solemnly vow," added he, "to expend more than his sorrow requires." Immediately he bade them prepare a funeral pile. When this was done, and everything laid in order, a pupil of the physician, a young man, but possessing the wisdom of old age, came to look upon the lady. As he considered her fair form attentively, already laid upon the pile, his preceptor said to him, "You come opportunely ; I have expected you this hour. Get a vial of precious ointment, and, in honour of this bright creature, pour it upon the funeral pile." The youth obeyed, approached the body, and drawing the garments from her breast, poured out the ointment. But accidentally passing his hand over her heart,

---

* These are Platonic fancies.

† " Here I give to understand,
  (If e'er this coffin drive a-land,)
  I, king Pericles, have lost
  This queen, worth all our mundane cost.
  Who finds her, give her burying,
  She was the daughter of a king:
  Besides this treasure for a fee,
  The gods require his charity!" SHAKESPEARE, *Pericles.*

he fancied that it beat. The youth was electrified. He touched the veins, and searched if any breath issued from the nostrils. He pressed his lips to hers; and he thought he felt life struggling with death. Calling hastily to the servants, he bade them place torches at each corner of the bier. When they had done this, the blood, which had been coagulated, presently liquefied; and the young man, attentive to the change, exclaimed to his master, "She lives! she lives! You scarcely credit me; come and see." As he spoke, he bore the lady to his own chamber. Then heating oil upon his breast, he steeped in it a piece of wool, and laid it upon her body. By these means, the congealed blood being dissolved, the spirit again penetrated to the marrows.* Thus, the veins being cleared, her eyes opened, and respiration returned.† "What are you?" said she. "Touch me not otherwise than I ought to be touched; for I am the daughter and the wife of a king." Full of rapture at the sound of her voice, the young man hurried into his master's room, and related what had occurred. "I approve your skill," returned he, "I magnify your art, and wonder at your prudence. Mark the results of learning, and be not ungrateful to science. Receive now thy reward; for the lady brought much wealth with her." Cerimon then directed food and clothes to be conveyed to her, and administered the best restoratives. A few days after her recovery, she declared her birth and misfortunes; and the good physician, commiserating her situation, adopted her as his daughter. With tears she solicited

---

* The modern disciple of Galen may learn something, peradventure, from this same wise youth, but I question much if his gratitude be commensurate.

> † "*Enter a Servant, with boxes, napkins, and fire.*
> *Cer.* Well said, well said; the fire and the cloths.—
> The rough and woeful music that we have,
> Cause it to sound, 'beseech you.
> The viol once more;—How thou stirr'st, thou block!—
> The music there.—I pray you, give her air:—
> Gentlemen,
> This queen will live: nature awakes; a warmth
> Breathes out of her: she hath not been entranced
> Above fire hours. See, how she 'gins to blow
> Into life's flower again!" SHAKESPEARE, *Pericles.*

permission to reside among the vestals of Diana; and he placed her with certain female attendants in the magnificent temple of the goddess.

In the mean while Apollonius, guided by the good providence of God, arrived at Tharsus, and disembarking, sought the mansion of Stranguilio and Dionysias. After mutual greetings, he narrated his adventures. "Wretched as I am in the death of a beloved wife, I have yet cause for joy in the existence of this infant. To you I will intrust her; for never, since his offspring has perished, will I again revisit the old Altistrates. But educate my girl with your own daughter Philomatia;* and call her after your city, by the name of Tharsia.† I would, moreover, pray you to take charge of her nurse, Ligoridis." With such words, he gave the child up to them, accompanied by large presents of gold and silver, and valuable raiment. He then took an oath that he would neither cut his beard, or hair, or nails, until his daughter were bestowed in marriage.‡ Grieving at the rashness of the vow, Stranguilio took the infant, and promised to educate it with the utmost care; and Apollonius, satisfied with the assurance, went on board his vessel, and sailed to other countries.

While these things were transacting, Tharsia attained her fifth year, and commenced a course of liberal studies with the young Philomatia, her companion. When she was fourteen, returning from school, she found her nurse, Ligoridis, taken with a sudden indisposition, and seating herself near the old woman, kindly inquired the cause. "My dear daughter," replied she, "hear my words, and treasure them in your heart. Whom do you believe to be your father and mother; and which is your native country?" "Tharsus," returned she, "is the place of my nativity; my father, Stranguilio, and my mother,

---

* In Shakespeare, *Philoten.*

† Called *Marina* in Shakespeare.

‡ "*Per.* Till she be married, madam,
By bright Diana, whom we honour all,
Unscissored shall this hair of mine remain,
Tho' I show will [1] in't." SHAKESPEARE, *Pericles.*

[1] Obstinacy.

Dionysias." The nurse groaned, and said, "My daughter, listen to me; I will tell you to whom you owe your birth, in order that, when I am dead, you may have some guide for your future actions. Your father is called Apollonius; and your mother's name is Lucina, the daughter of King Altistrates. She died the moment you were born; and Apollonius, adorning her with regal vesture, cast the chest which contained her into the sea. Twenty sestertia of gold were placed beneath her head, and whosoever discovered it was entreated to give her burial. The ship in which your unhappy father sailed, tossed to and fro by the winds which formed your cradle, at last put into this port, where we were hospitably received by Stranguilio and Dionysias, to whom your sire also recommended me. He then made a vow never to clip his beard, or hair, or nails, until you were married. Now, I advise that if, after my death, your present friends would do you an injury, hasten into the forum, and there you will find a statue of your father. Cling to it, and state yourself the daughter of him whose statue that is. The citizens, mindful of the benefits received from him, will avenge your wrong." "My dear nurse," answered Tharsia, "you tell me strange things, of which, till now, I was ignorant." After some future discourse, Ligoridis gave up the ghost. Tharsia attended her obsequies, and lamented her a full year.

After this, she returned to her studies in the schools. Her custom was, on returning, never to eat until she had been to the monument erected in honour of her nurse. She carried with her a flask of wine, and there tarried, invoking the name of her beloved and lamented parents. Whilst she was thus employed, Dionysias, with her daughter Philomatia, passed through the forum; and the citizens, who had caught a glimpse of Tharsia's form, exclaimed, "Happy father of the lovely Tharsia; but as for her companion, she is a shame and a disgrace." The mother, hearing her daughter vilified, while the stranger was commended, turned away in a madness of fury. She retired to solitary communication with herself. "For fourteen years," muttered she, "the father has neglected his daughter; he has sent no letters, and certainly he is dead. The nurse is also dead, and there is no one to oppose me. I will kill her, and deck my own girl with her ornaments." As she thus thought, her steward, named Theophilus,* entered. She called him, and promising a vast reward, desired him to put Tharsia to death. "What hath the maid done?" asked he. "She hath done the very worst things; you ought not therefore to deny me. Do what I command you; if you do it not, you will bring evil on yourself." "Tell me, lady, how is it to be done?"

"Her custom is," replied Dionysias, "on coming from the schools, not to take food until she has entered her nurse's monument; arm yourself with a dagger, seize her by the hair of the head, and there stab her. Then throw her body into the sea, and come to me; I will give you your liberty, with a large reward." † The steward, taking the weapon, went with much sorrow to the monument. "Alas!" said he, "shall I not deserve liberty except by the sacrifice of a virgin's life?" He entered the monument, where Tharsia, after her occupation in the schools, had as usual retired; the flask of wine was in her hand. The steward attacked the poor girl, and, seizing her by the hair, threw her upon the ground. But as he was on the point of striking, Tharsia cried out, "Oh, Theophilus! what crime have I committed against you, or against any other, that I should die?" "You are innocent," answered he, "of everything, save possessing a sum of money and certain royal ornaments left you by your father." "Oh, sir!" said the forsaken orphan, "if I have no hope, yet suffer me to supplicate my Maker before I die." "Do so," answered the steward, "and God knows that it is upon

---

* In Shakespeare, *Leonine.*

† "*Dion.* Thy oath remember; thou hast sworn to do it;
'Tis but a blow, which never shall be known.
Thou canst not do a thing i' the world so soon,
To yield thee so much profit. Let not conscience,
Which is but cold, inflame love in thy bosom,
Inflame too nicely; nor let pity, which
Even women have cast off, melt thee, but be
A soldier to thy purpose.
    Leon. I'll do't; but yet she is a goodly creature.
    Dion. The fitter then the gods should have her. Here
Weeping she comes for her old nurse's death.
Thou art resolv'd?
    Leon. I am resolv'd."   SHAKESPEARE, *Pericles.*

compulsion that I slay thee." Now, while the girl was engaged in prayer, certain pirates rushed into the monument, expecting to carry off a booty; and observing a young maid prostrated, and a man standing over her in the act to destroy her, they shouted out, "Stop, barbarian! that is our prey, not your victory." Theophilus, full of terror, fled hastily from the monument and hid himself by the shore. (25)

The pirates carried off the maid to sea; and the steward, returning to his mistress, assured her that he had obeyed her commands. "I advise you," said he, "to put on a mourning garment, which I also will do, and shed tears for her death. This will deceive the citizens, to whom we will say that she was taken off by a sickness." When Stranguilio heard what had been done, his grief was sincere and violent. "I will clothe myself in deep mourning," cried he, "for I too am involved in this fearful enormity. Alas! what can I do? Her father freed our city from a lingering death. Through our means he suffered shipwreck; he lost his property, and underwent the extreme of poverty. Yet we return him evil for good! He intrusted his daughter to our care, and a savage lioness hath devoured her! Blind wretch that I was! Innocent, I grieve. I am bound to a base and venomous serpent." Lifting up his eyes to heaven, he continued, "O God, thou knowest that I am free from the blood of this girl—require her of Dionysias." Then fixing a stern look upon his wife, "Enemy of God, and disgrace of man, thou hast destroyed the daughter of a king."

Dionysias made much apparent lamentation: she put her household into mourning, and wept bitterly before the citizens. "My good friends," said she, "the hope of our eyes, the beloved Tharsia, is gone—she is dead. Our tears shall bedew the marble which we have raised to her memory." The people then hastened to the place where her form, moulded in brass, had been erected, in gratitude for the benefits conferred upon that city by her father.*

* " *Dion.* Her monument
Is almost finished, and her epitaphs
In glittering golden characters express
A general praise to her." SHAKESPEARE, *Pericles.*

The pirates transported the maid to Machilenta,* where she was placed among other slaves for sale. A most wretched and debauched pimp, hearing of her perfections, endeavoured to buy her. But Athanagoras, prince of that city, observing her lofty port, her beautiful countenance, and wise conduct, offered ten golden sestertia.

P. I will give twenty.

Athanag. And I, thirty.

P. Forty.

Athanag. Fifty.

P. Eighty.

Athanag. Ninety.

P. I will give a hundred sestertia in ready money; if any one offer more, I will give ten gold sestertia above.

" Why should I contend any farther with this pimp," thought Athanagoras. " I may purchase a dozen for the price she will cost him. Let him have her; and by and by I will enter covertly his dwelling and solicit her love."

Tharsia was conducted by the pimp to a house of ill fame, in an apartment of which there was a golden Priapus, richly ornamented with gems.

" Girl! worship that image," said the wretch.

Tharsia. I may not worship any such thing. Oh, my lord! are you not a Lapsatenarian.†

P. Why?

Tharsia. Because the Lapsateni worship Priapus.

P. Know you not, wretched girl, that you have entered the house of a greedy pimp?

Casting herself at his feet, she exclaimed, " Oh, sir! do not dishonour me; be not guilty of such a flagrant outrage."

P. Are you ignorant that, with a pimp and the torturer, neither prayers nor tears are available?

He sent for the overseer of the women, and desired him

---

* *Mitylene* in Shakspeare.

† Of the Lapsateni, I am unable to give any account, unless they are meant for the *Lampsaceni*, the people of Lampsacus, a city in Asia, upon the Hellespont. *They* were worshippers of Priapus, in which place this divinity is said to have had his birth.

On referring to the romance of Apollonius (i.e. the *Narratio*, &c.), I find my supposition confirmed. It is there written *Lampsaceni*.

to array Tharsia in the most splendid apparel, and proclaim around the city the price of her dishonour.* The
overseer did as he was ordered; and on the third day a
crowd of people arrived, preceded by the pimp with music.
But Athanagoras came first in a mask, and Tharsia, looking despairingly upon him, threw herself at his feet.
"Pity me, my lord; pity me, for the love of Heaven. By
that Heaven I adjure you to save me from dishonour.
Hear my story; and knowing from whom I sprung, respect
my descent and defend my innocence." She then detailed
the whole fortunes of her life; and Athanagoras, confused
and penitent, exclaimed, "Alas! and I too have a daughter,
whom fate may in like manner afflict. In your misfortunes I may apprehend hers. Here are twenty gold
pieces; it is more than your barbarous master exacts from
you. Relate your narrative to the next comers, and it
will insure your freedom." Full of gratitude for the
generous treatment she experienced, Tharsia returned him
thanks, but entreated that her story might not be communicated to others. "To none but my own daughter,"
said he, "for it will be replete with moral advantage."
So saying, and shedding some tears over her fallen estate,
he departed. As he went out he met a friend, who stopped
him and asked how the girl had behaved. "None better,"
returned the prince; "but she is very sorrowful." The
youth entered, and she closed the door as on the former
occasion. "How much has the prince given you?" asked
he. "Forty pieces," answered the girl.

"Here, then; take the whole pound of gold."† Tharsia
took the present, but falling at his feet, explained her
situation. Aporiatus (for that was the young man's name)
answered, "Rise, lady; we are men. All of us are subject
to misfortunes." He went out, and observing Athanagoras
laughing, said to him, "You are a fine fellow! Have you
nobody to pledge in tears but me?" Afraid that these
words should betray the matter, they gave another turn

---

* "Quicunque Tharsiam violaverit, mediam libram dabit; postea
ad singulos solidos parebit populo."

† "Princeps audiens ait—Quanto plus dabis tanto plus plorabit."
This sentence is quite irrelevant. The prince could not be within
hearing, for she had closed the door.

to the discourse,* and awaited the coming of some other person. Great numbers appeared, but they all returned in tears, having given her sums of money. Tharsia having obtained the sum which the pimp had fixed as the price of her dishonour, presented it to him. "Take care," said the monster, "that you bring me whatever money is presented to you." But the next day, understanding that she yet preserved her honour, his rage knew no bounds; and he immediately commissioned the overseer of the women to complete the iniquity. When he appeared, the poor girl's tears flowed in profusion. "Pity me, sir," she said, falling at his feet; "my misfortunes have created the compassion of others, and surely you will not alone spurn my request. I am the daughter of a king; do not dishonour me." "This pimp," replied he, "is avaricious: I know not what I can do." "Sir," answered Tharsia, "I have been educated in liberal pursuits. I understand music; if, therefore, you will lead me to the forum, you shall hear my performance.† Propose questions to the people, and I will expound them; I have no doubt but I shall receive money enough." "Well," said the fellow, "I will do as you would have me."

Proclamation being made, the people crowded to the forum; and her eloquence and beauty impressed them all. Whatever question they proposed, she lucidly answered; and by these means drew much wealth from the curious citizens.‡ Athanagoras, also, watched over her with much

---

* The original text is, "*Jurabant* ne hæc verba cuique proderent," which means, I suppose, that they *conspired* to render the words unintelligible to others.

† "*Marina.* If that thy master would gain aught by me
Proclaim that I can sing, weave, sew, and dance,
With other virtues, which I'll keep from boast;
And I will undertake all these to teach." SHAKESPEARE, *Pericles.*

‡ "*Gow.* Marina thus the brothel scapes, and chances
Into an honest house, our story says.
She sings like one immortal, and she dances
As goddess-like to her admired lays:
Deep clerk she dumbs; and with her neeld composes
Nature's own shape, of bud, bird, branch, or berry;
That even her art sisters the natural roses;
Her inkle, silk, twin with the rubied cherry:
That pupils lacks she none of noble race,
Who pour their bounty on her." *Ibid.*

anxiety—with little less, indeed, than he showed to his only child. He recommended her to the care of the over-seer, and bought him to his interest by valuable presents.

Let us now return to Apollonius. After a lapse of fourteen years, he again made his appearance at the house of Stranguilio and Dionysias, in the city of Tharsus : no sooner had the former beheld him, than he strode about like a madman. "Woman," said he, addressing his wife, "what wilt thou do now? Thou hast said that Apollonius was shipwrecked and dead. Behold, he seeks his daughter; what answer shall we make?" "Foolish man," returned she, "let us resume our mourning, and have recourse to tears. He will believe that his child died a natural death." As she said this, Apollonius entered. Observing their funeral habiliments, he asked, "Do you grieve at my return? Those tears, I fear, are not for yourselves, but for me." "Alas!" replied the woman, "I would to Heaven that another, and not me or my husband, had to detail to you what I must say. Your daughter Tharsia is suddenly dead!" Apollonius trembled through every limb, and then stood fixed as a statue.

"Oh, woman, if my daughter be really as you describe, have her money and clothes also perished?" "Some part of both," replied Dionysius, "is of course expended; but that you may not hesitate to give faith to our assurances, we will produce testimony in our behalf. The citizens, mindful of your munificence, have raised a brazen monument to her memory, which your own eyes may see." Apollonius, thus imposed upon, said to his servants, "Go ye to the ship; I will visit the grave of my unhappy child." There he read the inscription, as we have detailed above, and then, as if imprecating a curse upon his own eyes, he exclaimed in a paroxysm of mental agony, "Hateful, cruel sources of perception, do ye now refuse tears to the memory of my lamented girl." With expressions like these, he hastened to his ship, and entreated his servants to cast him into the sea.*

They set sail for Tyre, and for a time the breezes blew prosperously; but changing, they were driven considerably

* The whole of the above is expressed by Shakspeare (or, at least, by the writer of *Pericles, Prince of Tyre*) in dumb show.

out of their course. Guided by the good providence of God, they entered the port of Machilena,* where his daughter still abode. The pilot and the rest of the crew shouted loudly on their approach to land, and Apollonius sent to inquire the cause. "My lord," answered the pilot, "the people of Machilena are engaged in celebrating a birthday." Apollonius groaned, "All can keep their birthdays except me. But it is enough that I am miserable; I give my attendants ten pieces of gold, and let them enjoy the festival. And whosoever presumes to utter my name, or rejoice in my hearing, command that his legs be immediately broken." † The steward took the necessary sums, and having purchased supplies, returned to the ship. Now, the bark which contained Apollonius being more honourable than the rest, the feast was celebrated there more sumptuously. It happened that Athanagoras, who was enamoured of the fair Tharsia, walked upon the sea-shore near the king's ship. "Friends," said he to those who accompanied him, "that vessel pleases me." The sailors with which she was manned, hearing him applaud their vessel, invited him on board. He went accordingly; and laying down ten gold pieces upon the table, observed, "You have not invited me for nothing." They thanked him; and, in answer to certain questions he had put, informed the prince that their lord was in great affliction, and wished to die: they added, that he had lost a wife and daughter in a foreign country. "I will give you two pieces of gold," said Athanagoras to Ardalius, one of the servants, "if you will go and say to him that the prince of this city desires a conference." "Two gold pieces," answered the person he spoke to, "will not repair my broken legs. I pray you send another; for he has determined thus to punish any one who approaches him." "He made this law for you," returned the prince, "but not, I think, for me: I will descend myself; tell me his name." They told him—Apollonius. "Apollonius?" said he to himself; "so Tharsia calls her father."

* _Mitylene_ is evidently meant; both here, and in the former mention of _Machilenta._
† Another testimony of Eastern origin.

He hastened into his presence, and beheld a forlorn and desolate person. His beard was of great length, and his head in the wildest disorder. In a low, subdued tone of voice, he said, " Hail, Apollonius ! " Apollonius, supposing it to be one of his own people, fixed on him a furious look, but, seeing an honourable and handsome man, remained silent. " You are doubtless surprised," said the prince, " at my intrusion. I am called Athanagoras, and am prince of this city. Observing your fleet riding at anchor from the shore, I was attracted by it ; and amongst other things, being struck with the superior structure of this vessel, your sailors invited me on board. I inquired for their lord, and they answered that he was overwhelmed with grief. I have therefore ventured hither, in the hope of administering comfort to you, and drawing you once more into the light of joy. I pray God that it may prove so." Apollonius raised his head. " Whomsoever you are, go in peace. I am unworthy to appear at the banquet ; and I do not desire to live." Perplexed, yet anxious to console the unhappy king, Athanagoras returned upon deck ; and despatched a messenger to the pimp, to require the immediate presence of Tharsia, whose musical skill and eloquence, he thought, could not but produce some effect.* She came, and received instructions from the prince. " If you succeed," said he, " in softening this royal person's affliction, I will present to you thirty gold sestertia, and as many of silver ; moreover, for thirty days,

---

* " *Lys.* Sir king, all hail ! the gods preserve you ! Hail, Hail, royal sir !
Hel. It is in vain ; he will not speak to you.
1 *Lord.* Sir, we have a maid in Mitylene, I durst wager, Would win some words of him.
Lys. 'Tis well bethought.
She, questionless, with her sweet harmony
And other choice attractions, would allure,
And make a battery through his deafen'd parts,
Which now are midway stopp'd :
She, all as happy as of all the fairest,
Is, with her fellow maidens, now within
The leafy shelter, that abuts against
The island's side."

SHAKESPEARE, *Pericles.*

redeem you from the power of your master." * The girl
accordingly prepared herself for the task. Approaching
the mourner, "Heaven keep you," said she, in a low plain-
tive voice, "and make you happy; a virgin that hath
preserved her honour amid her misfortunes salutes you."
She then sang to an instrument, with such a sweet and
ravishing melody, that Apollonius was enchanted. Her
song† related to the fortunes she had experienced, and was
to the following effect :—That she fell into the hands of
dishonest people, who sought to traffic with her virtue;
but that she passed innocent through all her trials.
"Thus," continued she, "the rose is protected by its
thorns. They who bore me off beat down the sword of
the smiter. I preserved my virtue when attacked by my
brutal owner. The wounds of the mind linger, and tears
fail. In me behold the only offspring of a royal house.
Contain your tears, and limit your anxiety. Look up to
heaven, and raise your thoughts above. The Creator and
Supporter of mankind is God; nor will He permit the

* "*Lys.* Fair one, all goodness that consists in bounty
Expect even here, where is a kingly patient;
If that thy prosperous-artificial feat
Can draw him but to answer thee in aught,
Thy sacred physic shall receive such pay
As thy desires can wish."   SHAKESPEARE, *Pericles.*

† In a rare Latin copy of this story, entitled "Narratio eorum
quæ contigerunt Apollonio Tyrio. Ex Membranis vetustis. Anno
M.D.XCV." the reading of these verses (else hardly distinguishable)
is as follows:

"Per sordes gradior, sed sordium conscia non sum,
Sic rosa de spinis nescit violarier ullis.
Corripit et raptor gladii ferientis ab ictu:
Tradita Lenoni non sum violata pudore.
Vulnera cessassent animi, lacrymæque deessent,
Nulla etenim melior, si nossem certa parentes,
Unica regalis generis sum stirpe creata:
Ipsa jubente deo lætari credo aliquando.
Fige modo lacrymas, curam dissolve molestam,
Redde polo faciem, mentemque ad sydera tolle.
Nam deus et hominum plasmator, rector et auctor,
Non sinet has lacrymas casso finire labore."

I have collated this copy with the text from which the translation
is made, but the material variations are inconsiderable. The Latin,
however, is very much better.

tears of His virtuous servants to be shed in vain." As she concluded, Apollonius fixed his eyes upon the girl, and groaned deeply. "Wretched man that I am," said he, "how long shall I struggle with my sorrows? But I am grateful for your attentions; and if again permitted to re-joice in the zenith of my power, your memory will support me. You say you are royally descended?—who are your parents? But begone; here are a hundred gold pieces; take them, and speak to me no more. I am consumed with new afflictions." The girl received his donation, and would have left the ship; but Athanagoras stopped her. "Whither are you going?" said he; "you have as yet done no good: is your heart so pitiless that you can suffer a man to destroy himself, without striving to prevent it?" "I have done everything that I could," answered Tharsia: "he gave me a hundred gold pieces, and desired me to depart."

"I will give you two hundred pieces if you will return the money to him, and say, 'My lord, I seek your safety, not your money.'"

Tharsia complied, and seating herself near to the king, said, "If you are determined to continue in the squalid state to which you have accustomed yourself, give me leave to reason with you. I will propose a question: if you can answer it, I will depart; if not, I will return your present and go."

"Keep what I have given; I will not deny your request. For though my evils admit of no cure, yet I determine to hearken to you. Put your question, then, and depart."

"Hear me; there is a house in a certain part of the world which bounds and rebounds, but it is closed against mankind. This house loudly echoes, but its inhabitant is ever silent; and both—the house and inhabitant—move forward together.* Now, if you are a king, as you aver, you should be wiser than I am. Resolve the riddle."

---

* In the Latin "*Narratio eorum quæ contigerunt Apollonio Tyrio*," this riddle is in Latin hexameter verse.

> "Est domus in terris quæ nobis clausa resultat
> Ipsa domus resonat, tacitus sed non sonat hospes;
> Ambo tamen currunt, hospes simul et domus una."

" To prove to you that I am no impostor," said Apollonius, " I will reply. The house which bounds and rebounds and echoes is the wave; the mute inhabitant is a fish, which glides along with its residence." * Tharsia continued, " I am borne rapidly along by the tall daughter of the grove, which equally encloses an innumerable company. I glide over various paths, and leave no footstep."†
" When I have answered your questions," said Apollonius, " I will show you much that you know not. Yet I am astonished that one so young should be endowed with wit so keen and penetrating. The tree enclosing a host, and passing through various ways without a trace, is a ship."

" A person passes through circumferences and temples without injury. There is a great heat in the centre which no one removes. The house is not uncovered, but it suits a naked inhabitant. If you would allay pain, you must enter into fire."

" I would enter, then, into a bath, where fire is introduced by means of round tables.‡ The covered house suits a naked inhabitant; and he who is naked in this situation will perspire." §

When she had said these and similar things, the girl threw herself before Apollonius, and drawing aside his

---

* This ingenious apologue, with the following, is omitted in the drama of Shakspeare.

> † " Longa feror velox formosæ filia silvæ,
> Innumerâ pariter comitum stipante catervâ;
> Curro per vias multas, vestigia nulla reliquo."

‡ " Intrarem balneum ubi hincinde flammæ *per tabulas* surgunt."

§ There is an obscurity here which I am afraid I have not removed. " Per rotas et ædes innoxius ille pertransit: Est calor in medio magnus quem nemo removit. Non est nuda domus: nudus sed convenit hospes. Si luctum poneres innocuus intraris in ignes." This mysterious affair is thus enunciated in the Latin " *Narratio*," &c. :—

> " Per *totas ædes* innoxius *introit ignis*,
> Est calor in medio magnus, quem nemo removit;
> Non est nuda domus, nudus sed convenit hospes,
> Si luctum *ponas*, insons *intrabis* in ignes."

To this Apollonius answers, " Intrarem balneum, ubi hincinde flammæ per tabulas surgunt, nuda domus in qua nihil intus est, nudus hospes convenit, nudus sudabit."—The reader must make what he can of it.

hands, embraced him. "Hear," said she, "the voice of your supplicant: regard a virgin's prayers. It is wicked in men of so much wisdom to destroy themselves. If you lament your lost wife, the mercy of God can restore her to you; if your deceased child, you may yet find her. You ought to live and be glad." Apollonius, irritated at the girl's pertinacity, arose and pushed her from him with his foot. She fell and cut her cheek, from which the blood copiously flowed. Terrified at the wound she had received, she burst into tears, and exclaimed, "O thou eternal Architect of the heavens! look upon my afflictions. Born amid the waves and storms of the ocean, my mother perished in giving life to her daughter. Denied rest even in the grave, she was deposited in a chest, with twenty gold sestertia, and thrown into the sea. But I, unhappy, was delivered by my remaining parent to Stranguilio and Dionysius, with the ornaments befitting a royal extraction. I was by them devoted to death; but whilst I invoked the assistance of God, a number of pirates rushed in and the murderer fled. I was brought hither; and in His own good time God will restore me to my father Apollonius." (26) Here she concluded, and the royal mourner, struck with her relation, shouted with a loud voice, "Merciful God! Thou who lookest over heaven and earth, and revealest that which is hidden, blessed be Thy holy name." Saying this, he fell into the arms of his daughter. Tenderly he embraced her, and wept aloud for joy. "My best and only child," said he; "half of my own soul! I shall not die for thy loss. I have found thee, and I wish to live." Exalting his voice yet more, "Run hither, my servants, my friends! all of ye; my misery is at an end. I have found what I had lost—my child, my only daughter!" Hearing his exclamations, the attendants ran in, and with them the prince Athanagoras. They discovered the enraptured king weeping upon his daughter's neck. "See, see," said he, "this is she whom I lamented. Half of my soul! now will I live." Participating in their master's happiness, they all wept.

Apollonius now divested himself of his mourning dress, and attired himself in regal habiliments. "Oh, my lord," said his followers, "how much your daughter resembles you! Were there no other guide, that would indicate her birth." * The delighted girl overwhelmed her recovered parent with kisses. "Blessed be God," cried she, "who has been so gracious to me, and given me to see, and live, and die with you." Then, entering into a more detailed account of her adventures, she related what she had endured from the wretched pimp, and how the Almighty had protected her.

Athanagoras, fearing lest another might demand her in marriage, threw himself at the king's feet, and modestly intimating how instrumental he had been in promoting their happy reunion, besought him to bestow his child upon him. "I cannot deny you," returned Apollonius, "for you have alleviated her sorrows, and been the means of my present and future happiness. Take her. But deeply shall that rascal feel my vengeance." Athanagoras immediately returned to the city, and convoked an assembly of the people. "Let not our city perish," said he, addressing them, "for the crimes of one impious wretch. Know that King Apollonius, the father of the beautiful Tharsia, has arrived. Behold where his navy rides. He threatens us with instant destruction, unless the scoundrel who would have prostituted his daughter be given up to him." Scarcely had he spoken when the whole population, men and women, hurried off to implore the king's clemency. "I advise you," said Athanagoras, "to take the wretch with you." Seizing the execrable man, they tied his hands to his back, and carried him along to the presence of offended majesty. Apollonius, clad in royal robes, his hair shorn, and crowned, ascended the tribunal with his daughter. The citizens stood round, in expectation of his address. "Men of Machylena," said he, "to-day I have recovered my daughter, whom that villainous pimp would have corrupted. Neither pity, nor prayers, nor gold could prevail with him to desist from his atrocious purposes. Do ye, therefore, avenge my daughter." The people, with one voice, answered, "Let him be burnt alive, and his wealth given to the lady." Instantly the wretch was brought forward and burnt. "I give you

---

* Yet these wise men did not perceive this striking resemblance *before!* The observation, however, is natural—at least to *courtiers.*

your liberty," said Tharsia to the overseer, "because, by your kindness and the kindness of the citizens, I remained unsullied. I also present to you two hundred gold sestertia." Turning to the other girls, she added, "Be free, and forget your past habits."

Apollonius, again addressing the people, returned them thanks for their kindness to him and his daughter, and bestowed on them a donation of five hundredweight of gold. Shouts and applause followed; and they immediately set about erecting a statue to their benefactor in the midst of the city. Upon the base was the following inscription:—

TO APOLLONIUS, OF TYRE,

THE PRESERVER OF OUR STATE;

AND TO THE MOST HOLY THARSIA,

HIS VIRGIN DAUGHTER.

A few days after the lady was espoused to Athanagoras, amid the universal joy of the city.

Intending to sail with his daughter, and son-in-law, and followers to his own country by way of Tharsus, an angel admonished him in a dream to make for Ephesus,* and there, entering the temple with his daughter and her husband, relate in a loud voice all the varied turns of fortune to which he had been subject from his earliest youth. Accordingly, he sailed for Ephesus. Leaving his ship, he sought out the temple to which his long-lost wife had retired. When his wife heard that a certain king had come to the temple with his daughter, she arrayed herself in regal ornaments, and entered with an honourable

---

* "PERICLES *on the deck asleep;* DIANA *appearing to him as in a vision.*

"*Dia.* My temple stands in Ephesus: hie thee thither,
And do upon mine altar sacrifice.
There, when my maiden priests are met together,
Before the people all,
Reveal how thou at sea didst lose thy wife:
To mourn thy crosses, with thy daughter's, call,
And give them repetition to the life.
Perform my bidding or thou livest in woe:
Do't and be happy, by my silver bow
Awake, and tell thy dream. [*Diana disappears.*"

SHAKESPEARE, *Pericles.*

escort. The surrounding multitude was much struck with her beauty and modesty, and said there never was so lovely a virgin. Apollonius, however, knew her not; but such was her splendour that he and his companions fell at her feet, almost fancying her to be Diana, the goddess. He placed on the shrine precious gifts, and then, as the angel had ordained, he commenced his history. "I was born," said he, "a king. I am of Tyre, and my name is Apollonius. I solved the riddle of the impious Antiochus, who sought to slay me as the detector of his wickedness. I fled, and, by the kindness of King Altistrates, was espoused to his daughter. On the death of Antiochus, I hastened with my wife to ascend his throne; but she died on the passage, after giving birth to this my daughter. I deposited her in a chest, with twenty gold sestertia, and committed her to the waves. I placed my daughter under the care of those whose subsequent conduct was base and villainous, and I departed to the higher parts of Egypt. After fourteen years I returned to see my daughter. They told me she was dead; and crediting it, I endured the deepest anguish of mind. But my child was at length restored to me." (27)

As he ended, the daughter of Altistrates sprung towards him, and would have clasped him in her arms. He repelled her with indignation, not supposing that it was his wife. "Oh, my lord!" cried she, weeping, "better half of my soul! why do you use me thus? I am thy wife, the daughter of King Altistrates; and thou art of Tyre; thou art Apollonius, my husband and lord. Thou wert the beloved one who instructed me. Thou wert the ship-wrecked man whom I loved with pure and fond regard." Apollonius awakening at the mention of these well-known circumstances, recollected his long-lost lady. He fell upon her neck, and wept for joy. "Blessed be the Most High, who hath restored me my wife and daughter." "But where," said she, "is our daughter?" Presenting Tharsia, he replied, "Behold her." They kissed each other tenderly; and the news of this happy meeting was soon noised abroad through the whole city. (28)

Apollonius again embarked for his own country. Arriving at Antioch, he was crowned, and then hastening to Tyre, he appointed Athanagoras and his daughter to the rule of this place. Afterwards assembling a large army, he sat down before Tharsus, and commanded Stranguilio and Dionysias to be seized and brought before him. Addressing the Tharsians, he inquired, " Did I ever do an injury to any one of you ? " " No, my lord," answered they ; " we are ready to die for you. This statue bears record how you preserved us from death." " Citizens," returned Apollonius, " I intrusted my daughter to Stranguilio and his wife : they would not restore her." " Oh, my lord," cried the unhappy woman, " thou hast read her fate inscribed on the monument." The king directed his daughter to come forward ; and Tharsia, reproaching her, said, " Hail, woman ! Tharsia greets thee ; Tharsia returned from the grave." Dionysias trembled ; and the citizens wondered and rejoiced. Tharsia then called the steward. " Theophilus, dost thou know me ? Answer distinctly, who employed thee to murder me ? "

" My lady Dionysias."

The citizens, hearing this, dragged both the husband and wife out of the city and stoned them. They would have killed Theophilus also, but Tharsia, interposing, freed him from death. " Unless he had given me time to pray," she said, " I should not now have been defending him."

Apollonius tarried here three months, and gave large gifts to the city. Thence sailing to Pentapolis, the old King Altistrates received them with delight. He lived with his son, and daughter, and grandchild a whole year in happiness. After that he died, full of years, bequeathing the kingdom to his son and daughter.

As Apollonius walked one day upon the sea-shore, he recollected the kind-hearted fisherman who succoured him after his shipwreck, and he ordered him to be seized and brought to the palace. The poor fisherman, perceiving himself under the escort of a guard of soldiers, expected nothing less than death. He was conducted into the presence of the king, who said, " This is my friend, who helped me after my shipwreck, and showed me the way to the city ; " and he gave him to understand that he was Apollonius of Tyre. He then commanded his attendants to carry him two hundred sestertia, with men-servants and maid-servants. Nor did his kindness stop here—he made him one of his personal attendants, and retained him as long as he lived. Elamitus, who declared to him the intentions of Antiochus, fell at his feet, and said, " My lord, remember thy servant Elamitus." Apollonius, extending his hand, raised him up, and enriched him. Soon after this a son was born, whom he appointed king in the room of his grandfather, Altistrates.

Apollonius lived with his wife eighty-four years; and ruled the kingdoms of Antioch and Tyre in peace and happiness. He wrote two volumes of his adventures, one of which he laid up in the temple of the Ephesians, and the other in his own library. After death, he went into everlasting life. To which may God, of His infinite mercy, lead us all. (29)

TALE CLIV.

OF A CELESTIAL COUNTRY.

GERVASE * relates that in the city of Edessa, in consequence of the presence of Christ's holy image, no heretic could reside—no pagan, no worshipper of idols, no Jew. Neither could the barbarians invade that place ; but if an hostile army appeared, any innocent child, standing before the gates of the city, read an epistle; and the same day on which the epistle was read, the barbarians were either appeased, or, becoming womanish,† fled.

APPLICATION.

My beloved, that city is the city of the Apocalypse, namely, HEAVEN : or it may signify our body, in which, if

* Gervase of Tilbury (county of Essex), a monkish historian. He flourished about the year 1200.

† ["Effeminati." It seems very probable that this legend is a distorted reproduction of a story in *Herodotus* (i. 105), in which a band of Scythians, who plundered the temple of Aphrodite Urania at Ascalon, is said to have been rendered subject to θήλεαν νοῦσον, i.e. became ἀνδρόγυνοι, which to all appearance = effeminati. See Liddell and Scott, sub voc., and sub voc. 'Eνάρεες.—ED.]

Christ dwelt—that is, if our soul be full of His love—
nothing repugnant to Him will inhabit it. The boy is a
clear conscience, and the epistle is confession and repentance.

———

TALE CLV.

OF THE DISCOMFITURE OF THE DEVIL.

THERE is in England, as Gervase tells us, on the borders
of the episcopal see of Ely, a castle called CATHUBICA; a
little below which is a place distinguished by the appellation of Wandlesbury,* because, as they say, the Vandals,
having laid waste the country, and cruelly slaughtered
the Christians, here pitched their camp. Around a small
hillock, where their tents were pitched, was a circular
space of level ground, enclosed by ramparts, to which but
one entrance presented itself. Upon this plain, as it is
commonly reported, on the authority of remote traditions,
during the hush of night, while the moon shone, if any
knight called aloud, " Let my adversary appear," he was
immediately met by another, who started up from the
opposite quarter, ready armed and mounted for combat.
The encounter invariably ended in the overthrow of one
party. Concerning this tradition, I have an actual occurrence to tell, which was well known to many, and which
I have heard both from the inhabitants of the place and
others.†

There was once in Great Britain a knight, whose name
was Albert, strong in arms, and adorned with every virtue.
It was his fortune to enter the above-mentioned castle,
where he was hospitably received. At night, after supper,
as is usual in great families during the winter, the household assembled round the hearth, and occupied the hour in
relating divers tales.‡ At last, they discoursed of the

* Near Cambridge. There is no account of this place in Camden's
Britannia.

† This exordium does not greatly favour Mr. Douce's hypothesis.
See the Introduction.

‡ We have here an interesting picture of the olden times; and it
is such pictures that give an invaluable character to these stories.

wonderful occurrence before alluded to; and our knight, not satisfied with the report, determined to prove the truth of what he had heard, before he implicitly trusted it. Accompanied, therefore, by a squire of noble blood, he hastened to the spot, armed in a coat of mail. He ascended the mount, and then, dismissing his attendant, entered the plain. He shouted, and an antagonist, accoutred at all points, met him in an instant. What followed? Extending their shields, and directing their lances at each other, the steeds were driven to the attaint, and both the knights shaken by the career. Their lances brake, but from the slipperiness of the armour, the blow did not take effect.* Albert, however, so resolutely pressed his adversary, that he fell; and rising immediately, beheld Albert making a prize of his horse. On which, seizing the broken lance, he cast it in the manner of a missile weapon, and cruelly wounded Albert in the thigh. Our knight, overjoyed at his victory, either felt not the blow, or dissembled it; and his adversary suddenly disappeared. He, therefore led away the captured horse, and consigned him to the charge of his squire. He was prodigiously large, light of step, and of a beautiful shape. When Albert returned, the household crowded around him, struck with the greatest wonder at the event, and rejoicing at the overthrow of the hostile knight, while they lauded the bravery of the magnanimous victor. When, however, he put off his cuishes, one of them was filled with clotted blood. The family were alarmed at the appearance of the wound; and the servants were aroused and despatched here and there. Such of them as had been asleep, admiration now induced to watch. As a testimony of conquest, the horse, held by the bridle, was exposed to public inspection. His eyes were fierce, and he arched his neck proudly; his hair was of a lustrous jet, and he bore a war-saddle on his back. The cock had already begun to crow, when the animal, foaming, curveting, snorting, and furiously striking the ground with his feet, broke the bonds that held him and escaped. He was immediately pursued, but disappeared in an instant. The knight retained a perpetual memento of that severe wound; for every year,

* "Ictuque evanescenti per lubricum."

upon the night of that encounter, it broke out afresh.
Some time after, he crossed the seas and fell, valiantly
fighting against the pagans. (30)

APPLICATION.

My beloved, the knight is Christ; his antagonist is the
devil, who is armed with pride; the castle is the world.

TALE CLVI.

OF THE SUBVERSION OF TROY.

OVID, speaking of the Trojan war, relates that when
Helen was carried off by Paris, it was predicted that the
city of Troy could not be captured without the death of
Achilles. His mother, hearing this, placed him, in the
dress of a female, amongst the ladies of the court of a
certain king. Ulixes,* suspecting the stratagem, loaded
a ship with a variety of wares; and besides the trinkets
of women, took with him a splendid suit of armour.
Arriving at the castle in which Achilles dwelt among the
girls, he exposed his goods for sale. The disguised hero,
delighted with the warlike implements upon which he
gazed, seized a lance, and gallantly brandished it. The
secret was thus manifested,† and Ulixes conducted him to

---

* Meaning thereby ULYSSES.

† How far this stratagem would be successful is very doubtful;
and probability is opposed to it. Habit is too mighty to be conquered
in an instant; and man, who is the creature of habit, may as soon
discard his nature as the confirmed prejudices of youth. In fact,
they become his nature, and Achilles, like Lucio, in " Love's Cure,"
delineated by Beaumont and Fletcher, under similar circumstances,
would much more reasonably be expected to say:

> " Go, fetch my work. This ruff was not well starched,
> So tell the maid; 't has too much blue in it:
> And look you, that the partridge and the pullen
> Have clean meat and fresh water, or my mother
> Is like to hear on't,"

than suddenly to assume sword and spear, and change his *petticoat* for
a *coat* of mail.

Troy. The Greeks prevailed; and after his decease, and the capture of the city, the hostages of the adverse side were set at liberty.

APPLICATION.

My beloved, Paris represents the devil; Helen, the human soul, or all mankind. Troy is hell. Ulixes is Christ; and Achilles, the Holy Ghost. The arms signify the cross, keys, lance, crown, etc.

TALE CLVII.

OF THE PUNISHMENT OF OFFENDERS.

THERE was an emperor whose porter was remarkably sagacious. He earnestly besought his master that he might have the custody of a city for a single month, and receive, by way of tax, one penny from every crook-backed, one-eyed, scabby, leprous, or ruptured person. The emperor admitted his request, and confirmed the gift under his own seal. Accordingly, the porter was installed in his office; and as the people entered the city, he took note of their defects, and charged them a penny, in conformity with the grant. It happened that a hunchbacked fellow one day entered, and the porter made his demand. Hunchback protested that he would pay nothing. The porter immediately laid hands upon him, and accidentally raising his cap, discovered that he was *one-eyed* also. He demanded two pennies forthwith. The other still more vehemently opposed, and would have fled; but the porter catching hold of his head, the cap came off, and disclosed a bald *scabby* surface. Whereupon he required three pennies. Hunchback, very much enraged, persisted in his refusal, and began to struggle with the determined

---

* "Gower has this history more at large in the CONFESSIO AMANTIS; but he refers to a *Cronike*, which seems to be the BOKE OF TROIE, mentioned at the end of the chapter (lib. v. fol. 99. See fol. 101)."—WARTON.

porter. This produced an exposure of his arms, by which it became manifest that he was *leprous*. The fourth penny was therefore laid claim to; and the scuffle continuing, revealed a *rupture*, which entitled him to a fifth. Thus, a fellow unjustly refusing to pay a rightful demand of *one* penny was necessitated, much against his inclination, to pay *five*.*

APPLICATION.

My beloved, the emperor is Christ. The porter is any prelate, or discreet confessor; the city is the world. The diseased man is a sinner.

TALE CLVIII.

OF THE SOUL'S IMMORTALITY.

THERE was once discovered at Rome an uncorrupted body, taller than the wall of the city, on which the following words were inscribed:—"Pallas, the son of Evander, whom the lance of a crooked soldier slew, is interred here." A candle burned at his head, which neither water nor wind could extinguish, until air was admitted through a hole made with the point of a needle beneath the flame. The wound of which this giant had died was four feet and a half long. Having been killed after the overthrow of Troy, he had remained in his tomb two thousand two hundred and forty years.

APPLICATION.

My beloved, the giant is Adam, who was formed free from all corruption. The wound of which he died is transgression of the divine command. The burning candle is eternal punishment, extinguished by means of a needle —that is, by the passion of Christ.

* This tale is in Alphonsus, and the *Cento Novelle Antiche*, Nov. 50.

TALE CLIX.

OF THE INVENTION OF VINEYARDS.

JOSEPHUS, in his work on "The Causes of Natural Things," says that Noah discovered the wild vine,* and because it was bitter, he took the blood of four animals, namely, of a lion, of a lamb, a pig, and a monkey. This mixture he united with earth, and made a kind of manure, which he deposited at the roots of the trees.† Thus the blood sweetened the fruit, with which he afterwards intoxicated himself, and, lying naked, was derided by his younger son. Assembling his children, he declared to them by what means he had produced this effect.‡

APPLICATION.

My beloved, the vine manured with the blood of animals indicates its effects. The blood of the lion pro-

---

* " Id est labruscam [vitem]; à *labris terræ et viarum* dictam." *That* is, I suppose, the hedges and outskirts of woods. Strange etymology !

† Perhaps it was alluding to this fancy that Webster, in his *White Devil*, observes,

> " As in cold countries *husbandmen plant vines,*
> And with *warm blood manure them*, even so," &c.

‡ " I know not of any book of Josephus on this subject. The first editor of the Latin Josephus was Ludovicus Cendrata, of Verona, who was ignorant that he was publishing a modern translation."—" The substance of this chapter is founded on a rabbinical tradition related by Fabricius.[1] When Noah planted the vine, Satan attended, and sacrificed a sheep, a lion, an ape, and a sow. These animals were to symbolize the gradations of ebriety. When a man begins to drink, he is meek and ignorant as the lamb, then becomes bold as the lion; his courage is soon transformed into the foolishness of the ape, and at last he wallows in the mire like a sow. Chaucer hence says, in the MANCIPLES PROLOGUE, as the passage is justly corrected by Mr. Tyrwhitt—

> 'I trowe that ye have dronken *wine of ape*,
> And that is when men plaien at a strawe.'

In the old KALENDRIER DES BERGERS, as Mr. Tyrwhitt has remarked, *Vin de singe, vin de mouton, vin de lyon*, and *vin de porceau*, are mentioned in their respective operations on the four temperaments of the human body."—WARTON.

¹ COD. PSEUDEPIGR. VET. TESTAM. vol. i. p. 275.

X

duces anger ; that of the lamb, shame ; of the pig, filthiness ; of the monkey, idle curiosity and foolish joy.

TALE CLX.

OF THE SEDUCTIONS OF THE DEVIL.

It often happens that the devils transform themselves into angels of light, in order to foster in human hearts whatever is fiendish. In proof of which, a most remarkable instance is subjoined.

When Valentine filled the episcopal see of Arles,* there stood on the outskirts of the diocese a castle, the lady of which invariably quitted church before the celebration of mass, for she could not bear to look on the consecration of our Lord's body. This peculiarity gave her husband much uneasiness, and he determined to ascertain the reason of so singular a proceeding. On a certain day, the gospel being ended, she was about to retire, when, after much violent struggling, she was forcibly detained by her husband and his attendants. The priest then continued the service, and at the instant that he proceeded to consecration, the lady, borne along by a diabolical spirit, flew away, carrying along with her a portion of the chapel, and was seen no more in those regions; and part of the very tower is yet standing, in testimony of the truth of the above relation.† (31)

APPLICATION.

My beloved, the castle is the world; and the lord of it, a discreet confessor.

* A town in France.

† [This is as good a proof of veracity as that offered by Smith the weaver for the validity of Jack Cade's claims to be the grandson of Edmund Mortimer. Cade having asserted that his father was stolen by a beggar-woman when young, and brought up as a bricklayer, ignorant of his noble birth, Smith adds : " Sir, he made a chimney in my father's house, and *the bricks are alive at this day to testify it;* therefore, deny it not" (*Second Part of Henry VI.*, Act iv. Sc. 2).— Ed.]

TALE CLXI.

OF GRATITUDE TO GOD.

In the kingdom of England there is a hillock in the midst of a thick wood, about the height of a man. Thither knights and other followers of the chase were accustomed to ascend, when they suffered much from heat and thirst, and sought eagerly for relief. From the nature of the place, and the circumstances of their occupation, each ascended the hill alone; and each, as if addressing some other, would say, " I thirst." Immediately, beyond expectation, there started from the side one with a cheerful countenance and an outstretched hand, bearing a large horn ornamented with gold and precious stones, such as we are still in the habit of using instead of a cup, and full of the most exquisite, but unknown, beverage. This he presented to the thirsty person; and no sooner had he drank, than the heat and lassitude abated. One would not then have thought that he had been engaged in labour, but that he was desirous of commencing an arduous employment. After the liquor had been taken, the attendant presented a clean napkin to wipe the mouth. His ministry completed, he disappeared, without awaiting recompense, or permitting inquiry. He did this daily, and, aged as he seemed to be, his pace was singularly rapid. At last, a certain knight went to these parts for the purpose of hunting; and a draught being demanded, and the horn brought, instead of restoring it to the industrious *skinker* * as custom and urbanity required, he retained it for his own use. But the knight's feudal lord, ascertaining the truth of this matter, condemned the plunderer; and presented the horn to Henry the Elder,† king of England, lest he himself should be held a partaker in the crime.‡

* [See Shakespeare, *First Part of Henry IV.*, Act ii. Sc. 4.—Ed.]
† Henry I. according to Warton.
‡ " This story, which seems imperfect, I suppose, is from Gervase of Tilbury."—Warton.

" The drinking vessels of the northern nations were the horns of animals, of their natural length, only tipt with silver, &c. In York Minster is preserved one of these ancient drinking-vessels, composed of a large elephant's tooth, of its natural dimensions, ornamented with sculpture, &c. See Drake's *Hist*."—Bishop Percy.

APPLICATION.

My beloved, the mountain is the kingdom of heaven; the forest is the world. The hunter is any worldly-minded man. The thirst and heat are divine love; the horn, mercy, which is filled at the fountain of benevolence. ·He who bore it is Christ; and the napkin is confession.

TALE CLXII.

OF AVOIDING IMPRECATIONS.

GERVASE of Tilbury * relates to Otto,† the Roman emperor, a very remarkable occurrence, but at the same time full of excellent advice, and affording a reason for caution to the reckless.

There was in the bishopric of Girona, in Catalonia, a very high mountain, whose ascent was extremely arduous, and, except in one place, inaccessible. On the summit was an unfathomable lake of black water. Here also stood, as it is reported, a palace of demons, with a large gate continually closed; but the palace itself, as well as its inhabitants, existed in invisibility. If any one cast a stone or other hard substance into this lake, the demons exhibited their anger by furious storms. In one part of the mountain was perpetual snow and ice; here there was abundance of crystal, and the sun never was seen. At its foot flowed a river, whose sands were of gold; and the precious metal thus obtained was denominated by the vulgar its *cloak*. The mountain itself, and the parts adjacent, furnished silver; and its unexhaustible fertility was not the least surprising of its peculiarities.

---

* " Whenever our compiler quotes Gervase of Tilbury the reference is to his OTIA IMPERIALIA: which is addressed to the Emperor Otho the Fourth, and contains his *Commentarius de regnis Imperatorum Romanorum*, his *Mundi Descriptio*, and his *Tractatus de Mirabilibus Mundi*. All these four have been improperly supposed to be separate works."—WARTON.

† *i.e.* OTHO.

Not far from hence lived a certain farmer, who one day being much occupied with domestic matters, and troubled exceedingly by the incessant squalling of his little girl, at length, after the manner of people when angry, wished his infant at the devil. This incautious desire was scarcely uttered, ere the girl was seized by an invisible hand, and carried off. Seven years afterwards, a person journeying at the foot of the mountain near the farmer's dwelling, distinguished a man hurrying along at a prodigious rate, and uttering in the most doleful tones, " Alas! for me, wretched man! what shall I do to get rid of this huge load?" The traveller stopped to inquire the occasion; and was told that, for the space of seven years last past, he had been committed to the custody of the demons upon that mountain, who daily made use of him as a chariot, in consequence of an unwary exclamation to that effect. The traveller, startled at an assertion so extraordinary, and a little incredulous, was informed that his neighbour had suffered in a similar degree; for that, having hastily committed his daughter to their power, they had instantly borne her off. He added that the demons, weary of instructing the girl, would willingly restore her, provided the father presented himself on the mountain and there received her.

The auditor, thunder-struck at this communication, doubted whether he should conceal things so incredible, or relate what he had heard. He determined, at last, to declare the girl's situation to her father; and hastening, accordingly, found him still bewailing the lengthened absence of his daughter. Ascertaining the cause, he went on to state what he had heard from the man whom the devils used as a chariot: "Therefore," said he, "I recommend you, attesting the Divine name, to demand of these devils the restitution of your daughter." Amazed at what was imparted to him, the father deliberated upon the best method of proceeding and finally pursued the counsel of the traveller. Ascending the mountain, he passed forward to the lake, and adjured the demons to restore the girl whom his folly had committed to them. Suddenly a violent blast swept by him, and a girl of lofty stature stood in his presence. Her eyes were wild and wandering, and her bones and sinews were scarcely covered with skin. Her horrible countenance discovered no sign of sensibility; and, ignorant of all language, she scarcely could be acknowledged for a human being. The father, wondering at her strange appearance, and doubtful whether she should be taken to his own home or not, posted to the bishop of Girona, and, with a sorrowful aspect, detailed what had befallen him; at the same time requesting his advice. The bishop, as a religious man, and one intrusted with a charge of so much importance, narrated every circumstance respecting the girl to his diocese. He warned them against rashly committing their fortunes to the power of demons, and showed that our adversary the devil, as a raging lion, goeth about seeking whom he may devour; that he will slay those who are given to him, and hold them in eternal bonds, and torment and afflict those devoted to him for a time.

The man who was used by the devils as a chariot, remained a long time in this miserable situation; but his subsequent faith and discretion emancipated him. He stated that near the above-mentioned place there was an extensive subterranean palace, whose entrance was by a single gate, enveloped in the thickest darkness. Through this portal the devils, who had been on embassies to various parts of the world, returned, and communicated to their fellows what they had done. No one could tell of what the palace was constructed, save themselves, and those who passed under their yoke to eternal damnation. From all which, my beloved, we may gather the dangers we are exposed to, and how cautious we should be of invoking the devil to our assistance, as well as of committing our family to his power. Let us guard our hearts, and beware that he catch not up the sinful soul, and plunge it into the lake of everlasting misery; where there is snow and ice unthawed—crystal, that reflects the awakened and agonized conscience, perpetually burning with immortal fire.

TALE CLXIII.

OF EXTREME FEAR.

ALEXANDER had an only son, called Celestinus, whom he loved with the utmost tenderness. He desired to have him well instructed, and sending for a certain philosopher, said, " Sir, instruct my son, and I will bountifully remunerate you." The philosopher acquiesced, and took the boy home with him. He diligently performed his duty; and it happened that one day, entering a meadow with his pupil, they perceived a horse lying on the ground, grievously affected with the mange. Near the animal two sheep were tied together, which busily cropped the grass that grew in abundance around them. It so chanced that the sheep were on each side of the horse, and the cord with which they were bound passed over his back and, chafing the sores, galled him exceedingly. Disturbed by this circumstance, he got up; but the cord, then loaded with the weight of the sheep, afflicted him more and more; and, filled with fury, he began to run off at a great speed, dragging along the unfortunate sheep. And in equal proportion to their resistance was the augmentation of the horse's suffering. For the cord, having worn itself into a hollow, sunk, at every struggle, yet deeper into the wound.

Adjoining the meadow was the house of a miller, toward which the horse, impelled by the anguish of his wound, galloped, and entered, with the sheep hanging as we have said. The house was then unoccupied; but there was a fire burning upon the hearth, and the quadruped, plunging and striking with his hoofs, so scattered the fire that the flame caught hold of the building, and reduced it to ashes, together with the horse and the sheep. "Young man," said the preceptor to his pupil, " you have perceived the beginning, the middle, and the completion of this incident: make me some correct verses upon it, and show me who is responsible for the burning of the house. Unless you do this, I assure you I will punish you severely." Celestinus, during the absence of his master, applied himself diligently to study, but he was unable to execute his task. This much troubled him; and the devil met him in the likeness of a man, and said, "My son, what has made you so sorrowful?"

Celest. Never mind; it is no use telling you.

Devil. You know not that; tell me, and I will help you.

Celest. I am charged, under a heavy punishment, to make some verses about a scabby horse and two sheep, and I don't know how.

Devil. Young man, I am the devil in a human form, and the best poet that ever lived: care nothing about your master, but promise to serve me faithfully, and I will compose such delectable verses for you that they shall excel those of your pedagogue himself.

Celestinus gave his word to serve him faithfully if he fulfilled his engagement. The devil then produced the following verses :—

> Bound by a thong, that passed along
>   A horse's mangy hide,
> Two sheep there lay, as I you say,*
>   One upon either side.
>
> The steed uprose, and upward goes
>   Each sheep with dangling breech;
> Borne by the horse's rapid course,
>   The miller's hut they reach.
>
> Scattering the fire with reckless ire,
>   The rafters caught the flame;
> And bleating breed and scabby steed
>   Were roasted in the same.
>
> Now had that wight, that miller hight,
>   Vouchsafed his house to keep:
> Ere he returned it had not burned,
>   Nor burned his horse and sheep.†

---

* i.e. *As I tell you;* or, *say to you.*

"He said, 'Madam, have good day !
    Sekerly, *as I you say.'* "—*Romance of Sir Isumbras.*

† As these are probably the only verses on record of the devil's composition (at least, so well authenticated), I cannot do less than transcribe them for the edification of the curious:—

> "Nexus ovem binam, per spinam traxit equinam;
>   Læsus surgit equus, pendet utrumque pecus.
> Ad molendinum, pondus portabat equinum,
>   Dispergendo focum, se cremat atque locum.
> Custodes aberant singula damna ferant."

The boy, made happy by the present, returned home.

Master. My child, have you stolen your verses, or made them?

Celest. I made them, sir.

He then read what we have given above; and the master, struck with the greatest astonishment at their uncommon beauty, exclaimed, "My dear boy, tell me if any one made these verses for you?"

Celest. No, sir; no one did.

Master. Unless you tell me the truth, I will flog you till the blood run.

The lad, fearful of what might follow, declared all that had occurred, and how he had bound himself to the devil. The preceptor, grieved at the communication, induced the youth to confess himself and renounce this fearful confederacy. When this was done he became a holy man, and, after a well-spent life, gave up his soul to God.

APPLICATION.

My beloved, the king is Christ; the philosopher, any prelate; the mangy horse, a sinner covered with sins. The two sheep are two preachers bound by the cord of charity; the miller's house is the world; and the fire, detraction.

TALE CLXIV.

OF THE PERVERSITY OF THE WORLD.

WE read in a certain book of a conversation between Jesus Christ and St. Peter. "I saw," said the latter, "five men whom I thought madmen. The first ate the sand of the sea so greedily, that it slipped through his jaws on either side of the mouth. Another I observed standing upon a pit full of sulphur and pitch, of which the smell was intolerable; yet he strove earnestly to inhale it. The third lay upon a burning furnace, whose heat was not enough; he endeavoured to catch the sparks emitted from the furnace that he might eat them. A fourth sat upon a pinnacle of the temple, in order to catch the wind. For this purpose he held his mouth open. The fifth devoured whatsoever of his own members he could get into his mouth, and laughed incessantly at every other man. Many beheld these five men, and much wondered why they did these things."

APPLICATION.

My beloved, the first of these men represents the covetous; the second, the gluttonous and luxurious; the third, the rich and honourable; the fourth, the hypocrites; and the fifth are the calumniators of the good.

TALE CLXV.

OF THE SAME SUBJECT.

WE read in the Lives of the Fathers, that an angel showed to a certain holy man three men labouring under a triple fatuity. The first made a faggot of wood, and because it was too heavy for him to carry he added to it more wood, hoping by such means to make it light. The second drew water with great labour from a very deep well with a sieve, which he incessantly filled. The third carried a beam in his chariot; and wishing to enter his house, whereof the gate was so narrow and low that it would not admit him, he violently whipped his horse, until they both fell together into a deep well. Having shown this to the holy man, the angel said, "What think you of these three men?" "That they are three fools," answered he. "Understand, however," returned the angel, "that they represent the sinners of this world. The first describes that kind of men who, from day to day, add new sins to the old, because they cannot bear the weight of those which they already have. The second man represents those who do good, but do it sinfully, and therefore it is of no benefit. And the third person is he who would enter the kingdom of heaven with all his worldly vanities, but is cast down into hell.

TALE CLXVI.

OF THE GAME OF SCHACI. (32)

Schacarium * has sixty-four points, divided by eight, as husband and wife, bridegroom and bride, clergy and lay, rich and poor. Six men are used at this game. The first is Rochus,† and it is of two kinds, white and black. The white is placed on the right hand, and the black upon the left. The reason of which is, that when all the Schaci are fixed in their places, the noble, as well as the vulgar pieces, have certain goals towards which they must proceed. The Rochi alone, when they are enclosed, have no power of proceeding, unless a way shall be cleared for them either by the higher or lower men. The Rochus moves directly across, and never to the corners, whether in going or returning; and if he move laterally from the other side, and take some piece, he becomes a thief.

The second piece is Alphinus,‡ which passes over three points. For in its proper place, that which is black is fixed to the right of the king, with the white on his left; and they are not called white and black with respect to their colour, but to their situation. Because the black piece, proceeding toward the right, that is, into the black and void space, is stationed before the Husbandman. But the left, by its own power, moves two points, the one towards the white space on the right; and the other, towards the white and void space on the left. Thus also of the third piece to the third square, by preserving its proper situation on the board; § so that if it be black, *to*

* *Schacarium* is the table or board on which the game is played, being distinguished by alternate black and white squares.

† *Rochus, Roccus, Rocus, Hrocus*, from the German word Roch, signifying an upper garment. Whether this etymology can be admitted is very doubtful. It moves to the right, in Pseud.-Ovid.
[This piece is the Castle or *Rook.*—Ed.]

‡ This piece is called, by the French, Le Fol, and by the Italians, Alfino (*Du Fresne* in *v*). According to Pseudo-Ovidius, it moves in an oblique direction.
[The Bishop; which formerly could only move two squares at a time, but could leap over an intervening man.—Ed.]

§ [This sentence is very obscure, and must be corrupt, I think; but this description of the game (chess) is confused all through.—Ed.]

black, and the contrary—proceeding in an angular direction.

The third kind is of Knights, of whom the right is white, and the left black. The white, when on his own square, has three moves—one towards the right in the black place before the HUSBANDMAN; the other in the black and void space before the WOOL-CARDER; the third, towards the left, in the place of a MERCHANT. When this piece is fixed near the king, it may move six squares, and when in the middle, eight. It is the same with the left. When the black is opposite to the king, and the white also opposite, they move together; one is placed before the queen, as the left; the other, before the king, as the right.

The fourth kind is of the inferior pieces, which have one and the same move. For from the square on which they are placed they may proceed to the third, and there, as in security, remain within reach of the king. But when they go out of the king's move, they are content with one square, and proceed in a direct line. Yet they never return in this manner, but secure by their progress those honours which belong by their position to the nobles. If they should be assisted by the knights and other noble pieces, and arrive at the line of squares where the adversary's nobles are posted, they acquire, by their valour, a power conferred by grace on the queen. But it should be observed that if the inferior pieces, going on the right, find any noble or vulgar adversary, and this in an angle, they may take or kill him on the right or the left; but the inferior piece never moves out of the straight line, to the right or left, unless he has obtained power of the queen.*

The fifth piece in the play of the SCHACI is called the Queen. Her move is from white to black, and she is placed near the king: if she quit his side, she is captured. When

* I have thought it useless to translate the very strained application of this game, introduced between each description, but the following illustration perhaps ought not to be discarded:—" Virgil, descended from a low Longobard [i.e. German] family, but a native of Mantua, was most renowned for his wisdom, and the excellence of his poetical talent. When somebody accused him of inserting certain of Homer's verses in his work, he answered, ' That they were strong men who could brandish the club of Hercules.' "

she has moved from the black square in which she was first placed, she can go only from square to square, and this angularly, whether she go forward or return; whether she take, or is taken. But if it be asked why the queen is exposed to war, when the condition of a female is frail and unwarlike, we reply, when husbands go out to battle, it is customary for their women and wives, and the rest of their family, to live in the camp. And though they do not use a bow, and encumber men more by their whims than they destroy the foe by their valour, yet the queen is intended for the king's help. Therefore, that she may evince her affection, she accompanies him to battle.*

The sixth kind of pieces used in this game are the Kings. The king shows above all the rest what is the nature of motion and progression. For since he may reside in the fourth square with the white, though he himself be black, he hath the Knight on the right hand in a white space, but the ALPHINUS and the ROCHUS in the black. In the left he holds opposite places. But though the king has more power and dignity than all the other pieces, it does not become him to move far from his throne; and therefore he begins his move from his own white square, like the ROCHI, from right and left. Yet he cannot be placed on the left in the black space, near the situation of the ROCHUS on the white; but he may go into the white space near the aforesaid ROCHUS in the corner square, where the guards of the city are fixed; and there he hath in such

---

* Among many other matters in dispraise of the fair sex, which are found in this application (and which I should blush to translate!), the writer observes after Seneca, "Quòd mulieres quæ malam faciem habent, leves et impudicæ sunt." But this is a Platonic tenet. Again, "QUIDIUS" (or OVIDIUS) very learnedly remarks, "Casta est quam nemo rogavit." This is no doubt the original of a song in Congreve's *Love for Love.*

> "A nymph and a swain to Apollo once prayed;
> The swain had been jilted, the nymph been betrayed:
> Their intent was to try if his oracle knew
> E'er a nymph that was chaste, or a swain that was true.

> "Apollo was mute, and had like to've been posed,
> But sagely at length he this secret disclosed:
> He alone won't betray in whom none will confide;
> And the nymph may be chaste, that has never been tried."

move the nature of the knight. But he takes these two moves in place of the queen.*

TALE CLXVII.

OF HEARING GOOD COUNSEL.

AN archer, catching a little bird called a nightingale, was about to put her to death. But, being gifted with language, she said to him, "What will it advantage you to kill me? I cannot satisfy your appetite. Let me go, and I will give you three rules, from which you will derive great benefit, if you follow them accurately." Astonished at hearing the bird speak, he promised her liberty on the conditions she had stated. "Hear, then," said she: "never attempt impossibilities; secondly, do not lament an irrecoverable loss; thirdly, do not credit things that are incredible. If you keep these three maxims with wisdom, they will infinitely profit you." The man, faithful to his promise, let the bird escape. Winging her flight through the air, she commenced a most exquisite song; and having finished, said to the archer, "Thou art a silly fellow, and hast to-day lost a great treasure. There is in my bowels a pearl bigger than the egg of an ostrich." Full of vexation at her escape, he immediately spread his nets and endeavoured to take her a second time; but she eluded his art. "Come into my house, sweet bird!" said he, "and I will show thee every kindness. I will feed thee with my own hands, and permit thee to fly abroad at pleasure." The nightingale answered, "Now I am certain thou art a fool, and payest no regard to the counsel I gave thee: 'Regret not what is irrecoverable.' Thou canst not take me again, yet thou hast spread thy snares for that purpose. Moreover, thou believest that my bowels contain a pearl larger than the egg of an ostrich, when I myself am nothing near that

---

* I cannot hope that I have translated this account of an obscure game quite intelligibly; but I was unwilling to omit it.

[As remarked in our Note 32, this "obscure game" is Chess.—ED.]

size! Thou art a fool; and a fool thou wilt always remain." With this consolatory assurance she flew away. The man returned sorrowfully to his own house, but never again obtained a sight of the nightingale. (33)

APPLICATION.

My beloved, the archer is any Christian: the nightingale is Christ; and man attempts to kill Him as often as he sins.

TALE CLXVIII.

OF ETERNAL CONDEMNATION.

BARLAAM says that a sinner is like a man who, being afraid of a unicorn, stepped backward into a deep pit. But when he had fallen he laid hold of the branch of a tree, and drew himself up. Looking below, he espied at the foot of the tree by which he had ascended a very black well, and a horrible dragon encompassing it. The dragon appeared to expect his fall with extended jaws. Now, the tree was constantly being gnawed by two mice, of which one was white and the other black, and the man felt it shake. There were also four white vipers at its foot, which filled the whole pit with their pestilential breath. Lifting up his eyes, the man beheld honey dropping from a bough of the tree; and, wholly forgetful of his danger, he gave himself up to the fatal sweetness. A friend, stretching out to him a ladder, would have raised him entirely out; but, overcome by the allurement, he clung to the tree, which fell, and cast him into the jaws of the dragon. The monster immediately descending to the lowest pit, there devoured him. He thus died a miserable death.*

* "This is another of Barlaam's Apologues in Damascenus's romance of BARLAAM AND JOSAPHAT: and which has been adopted into the Lives of the Saints, by Surius and others. A MORALIZATION is subjoined, exactly agreeing with that in the GESTA."—WARTON.

My beloved, man is that sinner; and the unicorn is death. The pit is the world; the tree is life, which is ever being consumed, as it were, by the white mouse and the black, every hour of the day and night. The post which the vipers occupied is the human frame; the dragon is the devil; and the lower pit is hell. The honeyed bough is the pleasures of sin; the friend, any Christian preacher; and the ladder is penitence.

TALE CLXIX.

OF MANNER OF LIFE.

TROGUS POMPEIUS * relates of Ligurius, a noble knight, that he induced the inhabitants of the state to make oath that they would faithfully preserve certain just and wholesome, though rather severe laws, until he returned with an answer from the oracle of Apollo, whom he feigned to have made them. He then went to Crete, and there abode in voluntary exile. But when he was dead, the citizens brought back his bones, imagining that they were then freed from the obligation of their oath. These laws were twelve in number. The first insisted on obedience to their princes, and enjoined princes to watch over the well-being of their subjects, and to repress wickedness. The second law commanded economy, and considered war better provided for by sobriety than drunkenness. The third law ordained rewards to be proportioned to merit. The fourth laid down that silver and gold were the vilest of all things. The fifth divided the administration of government; empowering kings to make war, magistrates to give judgment, and the senate to try offenders. It also conferred upon the people permission to elect their rulers.

* "Our compiler here means Justin's Abridgment of Trogus; which, to the irreparable injury of literature, soon destroyed its original. An early epitome of Livy would have been attended with the same unhappy consequences."—WARTON.

The sixth law apportioned lands, and settled disputed claims respecting patrimony, so that no one could become more powerful than another. The seventh enjoined all feasts to be held in public, lest one person should be the cause of luxury to another; the eighth, that young men should have but one habit during the year; the ninth, that poor lads should be employed in the fields, and not in the forum, by which their first years should be spent in hard labour, not in idleness. The tenth law exacted that virgins be married without dowry; the eleventh, that wives be not chosen for money; and the twelfth, that the greatest honour should not be assigned to the greatest wealth, but to priority in years. And whatever law Ligurius established, he himself observed beyond all others.*

APPLICATION.

My beloved, the knight is Christ; and the laws, those moral ordinances which He established.

TALE CLXX.

OF REPENTANCE.

A CERTAIN gambler met St. Bernard on horseback. "Father," said he, "I will play with you, and stake my soul against your horse." Immediately St. Bernard dismounted, and said, "If you throw more points than I, you shall have my horse; but if not, I will take possession of your soul." The gambler acceded; and taking up the dice, threw seventeen points. Thinking himself sure of the victory, he laid hold of the bridle of St. Bernard's steed. "My son," said the holy man, "there are more points than that in three dice." Accordingly, he threw eighteen points, one more than the gambler; who forthwith put himself under the guidance of the saint. After

---

* [The lawgiver who acted as stated in this story was Solon.—ED.]

a life of great sanctity, he came to a happy end, and passed into the joy of his Lord.* (34)

APPLICATION.

My beloved, the gambler is any worldly-minded man, and Bernard is a discreet confessor. His horse typifies his heart; and the three dice are the Holy Trinity.

———

TALE CLXXI.

OF TOO MUCH LOVE, AND OF THE FORCE OF TRUTH.

PETRUS ALPHONSUS † relates a story of two knights, of whom one dwelt in Egypt and the other in Baldac.‡ Messengers often passed between them; and whatever there was curious in the land of Egypt, the knight of that country sent to his friend, and he, in like manner, sent back an equivalent. Thus much kindness was manifested on both sides. But neither had ever seen the other.

As the knight of Baldac once lay upon his bed, he held the following soliloquy :—" My correspondent in Egypt has discovered much friendship for me ; but I have never yet seen him : I will go and pay him a visit." Accordingly, he hired a ship and went into Egypt ; and his friend, hearing of his arrival, met him by the way, and received him with much pleasure. Now, the knight had a very beautiful girl in his house, with whom the knight of Baldac was so smitten, that he fell sick and pined away. " My friend," said the other, " what is the matter with you ? " " My heart,"

* From Caxton's *Golden Legend.* See the Note.
 † " This is the story of Boccace's popular novel of TITO AND GISIPPO, and of Lydgate's *Tale of two Marchants of Egypt and of Baldad,* a manuscript poem in the British Museum, and lately in the library of Dr. Askew.[1] Peter Alphonsus is quoted for this story ; and it makes the second fable of his CLERICALIS DISCIPLINA."—WARTON.
 [Compare Tale CVIII.—ED.]
 ‡ Bagdad.

 [1] R. Edwards has a play on this story.

returned his comrade, "has fixed itself upon one of the women of your household, and unless I may espouse her I shall die." Upon this, all the household, save the individual in question, were summoned before him; and having surveyed them, he exclaimed, "I care little or nothing for these. But there is one other whom I have not seen; and her my soul loveth." At last this girl was shown to him. He protested that it was to her alone that he must owe his life. "Sir," said his friend, "I brought this girl up with the intention of making her my wife; and I shall obtain much wealth with her. Nevertheless, so strong is my affection for you, that I give her to you with all the riches which should have fallen to my share." The sick knight, overjoyed at his good fortune, received the lady and the money, and returned with her to Baldac.

After a while the knight of Egypt became so extremely indigent that he possessed no habitation. "I had better," thought he, "go to my friend of Baldac, to him whom I enriched, and inform him of my wants." He did so; and reached Baldac a while after sunset. "It is night," said he to himself; "if I go now to my friend's house, he will not know me, for I am so poorly dressed. I, who once used to have a large household about me, am now desolate and destitute. To-night, therefore, I will rest, and on the morrow will go to his mansion." Happening to look toward a burial-ground, he observed the gates of a church thrown open, and here he determined to remain for the night. But while he was endeavouring to compose himself to sleep in a court of that place, there entered two men, who engaged in battle; and one was slain. The murderer instantly fled to the burial-ground, and escaped on the other side. By and by an extraordinary clamour penetrated through the whole city. "Where is the murderer? Where is the traitor?" was the general cry. "I am he," said our knight; "take me to crucifixion." They laid hands on him and led him away to prison. Early the next morning the city bell rang, and the judge sentenced him to be crucified. Amongst those who followed to witness his execution was the knight whom he had befriended; and the former, seeing him led towards the cross, knew him at once. "What!" cried he, "shall he be crucified, and I alive?" Shouting, therefore, with a loud voice, he said, " My friends! destroy not an innocent man. I am the murderer, and not he." Satisfied with his declaration, they immediately seized him and brought both to the cross. When they were near the place of execution, the real murderer, who happened to be present, thought thus, " I will not permit innocent blood to be shed : the vengeance of God will sooner or later overtake me, and it is better to suffer a short pain in this world than subject myself to everlasting torments in the next." Then lifting up his voice, " My friends! for God's sake, slay not the guiltless. The dead man was killed without premeditation, and without the knowledge of either of these men. I only am the murderer; let these men go." The crowd, hearing what he said, instantly apprehended and brought him with no little amazement to the judge. The judge, seeing the reputed criminals along with them, asked with surprise why they had returned. They related what had occurred ; and the judge, addressing the first knight, said, " Friend, why did you confess yourself the murderer?" "My lord," answered he, " I will tell you without deceit. In my own land I was rich ; and everything that I desired I had. But I lost all this ; and possessing neither house nor home, I was ashamed, and sought in this confession to obtain a remedy. I am willing to die ; and for Heaven's love command me to be put to death." The judge then turning to the knight of Baldac—" And you, my friend! why did you avow yourself the murderer?" " My lord," replied he, " this knight bestowed upon me a wife, whom he had previously educated for himself, with an infinite store of wealth. When, therefore, I perceived my old and valued friend reduced to such an extremity, and saw him led rudely to the cross, I proclaimed myself the murderer. For his love I would willingly perish." " Now then," said the judge to the real homicide, " what have you to say for yourself!" " I have told the truth," answered he. " It would have been a heavy crime, indeed, had I permitted two innocent men to perish by my fault, and I therefore prefer to undergo the penalty here, than to be punished at some other time, or perhaps in hell." " Well," returned the judge, " since you have declared the truth and saved the lives of the innocent, study to amend your future life; for this time I pardon you—go in peace."

The people unanimously applauded the decision of the judge in acquitting the guilty person, whose magnanimity had rescued two innocent persons from death.

APPLICATION.

My beloved, the emperor is God;* the two knights, Christ and our first parent.† The beautiful girl is the soul. The dead man is the spirit destroyed by the flesh.

TALE CLXXII.

OF MENTAL CONSTANCY.

IN the reign of a certain King of England, there were two knights, one of whom was called Guido, and the other Tyrius. The former engaged in many wars, and always triumphed. He was enamoured of a beautiful girl of noble family, but whom he could not prevail upon to marry him, until he had encountered many enemies for her sake. At last, at the conclusion of a particular exploit, he gained her consent, and married her with great splendour. On the third night succeeding their nuptials, about cock-crowing, he arose from his bed to look upon the sky; and amongst the most lustrous stars he clearly distinguished our Lord Jesus Christ, who said, "Guido, Guido! you have fought much and valiantly for the love of a woman; it is now time that you should encounter my enemies with equal resolution." Having so said, our Lord vanished. Guido, therefore, perceiving that it was His pleasure to send him

---

* There is no EMPEROR in the story; but that is of little consequence. The reader must *suppose* one. Long use had so habituated the author or authors of the *Gesta Romanorum* to the anomalous introduction of an emperor, that the omission must have been held a flagrant breach of court etiquette.

† "In *agro Damasceno* plasmatus est" in the original.

to the Holy Land, to avenge Him upon the infidels, returned to his wife. "I go to the Holy Land; should Providence bless us with a child, attend carefully to its education until my return." The lady, startled at these words, sprung up from the bed as one distracted, and catching a dagger, which was placed at the head of the couch, cried out, "Oh, my lord, I have always loved you, and looked forward with anxiety to our marriage, even when you were in battle, and spreading your fame over all the world; and will you now leave me? First will I stab myself with this dagger." Guido arose, and took away the weapon. "My beloved," said he, "your words alarm me. I have vowed to God that I will visit the Holy Land. The best opportunity is the present, before old age come upon me. Be not disturbed; I will soon return." Somewhat comforted with this assurance, she presented to him a ring. "Take this ring, and as often as you look upon it in your pilgrimage, think of me. I will await with patience your return." The knight bade her farewell, and departed in company with Tyrius. As for the lady, she gave herself up to her sorrows for many days, and would not be consoled. In due time she brought forth a son of extreme beauty, and tenderly watched over his infant years.

Guido and Tyrius, in the mean while, passed through many countries, and heard at last that the kingdom of Dacia * had been subdued by the infidels. "My friend," said Guido to his associate, "do you enter this kingdom; and since the king of it is a Christian, assist him with all your power. I will proceed to the Holy Land; and when I have combated against the foes of Christ, I will return to you, and we will joyfully retrace our steps to England." "Whatever pleases you," replied his friend, "shall please me. I will enter this kingdom; and if you live, come to me. We will return together to our country." Guido promised; and exchanging kisses, they separated with much regret. The one proceeded to the Holy Land, and the other to Dacia. Guido fought many battles against the Saracens, and was victorious in all; so that his fame

---

* A country of Scythia beyond Hungary; divided into Transylvania, Wallachia, and Moldavia.

flew to the ends of the earth. Tyrius, in like manner, proved fortunate in war, and drove the infidels from the Dacian territory. The king loved and honoured him above all others, and conferred on him great riches. But there was at that time a savage nobleman, called Plebeus, in whose heart the prosperity of Tyrius excited an inordinate degree of hate and envy. He accused him to the king of treason, and malevolently insinuated that he designed to make himself master of the kingdom. The king credited the assertion, and ungratefully robbed Tyrius of all the honours which his bounty had conferred. Tyrius, therefore, was reduced to extreme want, and had scarcely the common sustenance of life. Thus desolate, he gave free course to his griefs; and exclaimed in great tribulation, " Wretch that I am! what will become of me?" While he was taking a solitary walk in sorrow, Guido, journeying alone in the habit of a pilgrim, met him by the way, and knew him, but was not recognized by his friend. He, however, presently remembered Tyrius, and retaining his disguise, approached him, and said, " My friend, from whence are you?" " From foreign parts," answered Tyrius, " but I have now been many years in this country. I had once a companion in arms, who proceeded to the Holy Land; but if he be alive or dead I know not, nor what have been his fortunes." " For the love of thy companion, then," said Guido, " suffer me to rest my head upon your lap, and sleep a little, for I am very weary." He assented, and Guido fell asleep.

Now, while he slept, his mouth stood open; and as Tyrius looked, he discovered a white weasel pass out of it, and run toward a neighbouring mountain, which it entered. After remaining there a short space, it returned, and again ran down the sleeper's throat. Guido straightway awoke, and said, " My friend, I have had a wonderful dream! I thought a weasel went out of my mouth, and entered yon mountain, and after that returned." " Sir," answered Tyrius, " what you have seen in a dream I beheld with my own eyes. But what that weasel did in the mountain, I am altogether ignorant." " Let us go and look," observed the other; " perhaps we may find something useful." Accordingly, they entered the place

which the weasel had been seen to enter, and found there
a dead dragon filled with gold. There was a sword also,
of peculiar polish, and inscribed as follows: " BY MEANS
OF THIS SWORD, GUIDO SHALL OVERCOME THE ADVERSARY OF
TYRIUS." Rejoiced at the discovery, the disguised pilgrim
said, " My friend, the treasure is thine, but the sword I
will take into my own possession." " My lord," he
answered, " I do not deserve so much gold; why should
you bestow it upon me ? " " Raise your eyes," said Guido.
" I am your friend! " Hearing this, he looked at him
more narrowly; and when he recollected his heroic associate, he fell upon the earth for joy, and wept exceedingly.
" It is enough; I have lived enough, now that I have seen
you." " Rise," returned Guido, " rise quickly; you ought
to rejoice rather than weep at my coming. I will combat
your enemy, and we will proceed honourably to England.
But tell no one who I am." Tyrius arose, fell upon his
neck, and kissed him. He then collected the gold, and
hastened to his home; but Guido knocked at the gate of
the king's palace. The porter inquired the cause, and he
informed him that he was a pilgrim newly arrived from
the Holy Land. He was immediately admitted, and
presented to the king, at whose side sat the invidious
nobleman who had deprived Tyrius of his honours and
wealth. " Is the Holy Land at peace? " inquired the
monarch. " Peace is now firmly established," replied
Guido, " and many have been converted to Christianity."

King. Did you see an English knight there, called
Guido, who has fought so many battles ?

Guido. I have seen him often, my lord, and have eaten
with him.

King. Is any mention made of the Christian kings ?

Guido. Yes, my lord; and of you also. It is said that
the Saracens and other infidels had taken possession of
your kingdom, and that from their thraldom you were
delivered by the valour of a noble knight, named Tyrius,
afterwards promoted to great honour and riches. It is
likewise said that you unjustly deprived this same Tyrius
of what you had conferred, at the malevolent instigation
of a knight called Plebeus.

Plebeus. False pilgrim ! since thou presumest to utter

these lies, hast thou courage enough to defend them? If
so, I offer thee battle. That very Tyrius would have de-
throned the king. He was a traitor, and therefore lost
his honours.

Guido (to the king). My lord, since he has been pleased
to say that I am a false pilgrim, and that Tyrius is a
traitor, I demand the combat. I will prove upon his
body that he lies.

King. I am well pleased with your determination:
nay, I entreat you not to desist.

Guido. Furnish me with arms, then, my lord.

King. Whatever you want shall be got ready for you.

The king then appointed a day of battle; and fearing
lest the pilgrim Guido should in the mean time fall by
treachery, he called to him his daughter, a virgin, and
said, "As you love the life of that pilgrim, watch over
him, and let him want for nothing." In compliance,
therefore, with her father's wish, she brought him into
her own chamber, bathed him,* and supplied him with
every requisite. On the day of battle Plebeus armed
himself, and standing at the gate, exclaimed, "Where is
that false pilgrim? why does he tarry?" Guido, hearing
what was said, put on his armour, and hastened to the
lists. They fought so fiercely, that Plebeus would have
died had he not drank. Addressing his antagonist, he
said, "Good pilgrim, let me have one draught of water."
"I consent," answered Guido, "provided you faithfully
promise to use the same courtesy to me, should I require
it." "I promise," replied the other. Having quenched
his thirst, he rushed on Guido, and they continued the
battle with redoubled animosity. By and by, however,
Guido himself thirsted, and required the same courtesy
to be shown him as he had exhibited. "I vow to
Heaven," answered his enemy, "that you shall taste

---

* "This was a common practice in the time of chivalry, and many
examples of it may be found in ancient romances. The ladies not only
assisted in bathing the knights after the fatigues of battle, but administered proper medicines to heal their wounds. Similar instances
occur in the writings of Homer. In the *Odyssey*, Polycaste, one of
the daughters of Nestor, bathes Telemachus; and it appears that
Helen herself had performed the like office for Ulysses."—Douce,
Illust. of Shakespeare, vol. ii. p. 401.

nothing, except by the strong hand." At this ungrateful return, Guido, defending himself as well as he could, approached the water, leaped in, and drank as much as he wished. Then springing out, he rushed upon the treacherous Plebeus like a raging lion, who at last sought refuge in flight. The king, observing what passed, caused them to be separated, and to rest for that night, that in the morning they might be ready to renew the contest. The pilgrim then re-entered his chamber, and received from the king's daughter all the kindness it was in her power to display. She bound up his wounds, prepared supper, and placed him upon a strong wooden pallet. Wearied with the exertions of the day, he fell asleep.

Now, Plebeus had seven sons, all strong men. He sent for them, and spoke thus: "My dear children, I give you to understand that, unless this pilgrim be destroyed to-night, I may reckon myself among the dead to-morrow. I never looked upon a braver man." "My dear father," said one, "we will presently get rid of him." About midnight, therefore, they entered the girl's chamber, where the pilgrim slept, and beneath which the sea flowed. They said to one another, "If we destroy him in bed, we are no better than dead men: let us toss him, bed and all, into the sea. It will be thought that he has fled." This scheme was approved; and accordingly they took up the sleeping warrior, and hurled him into the waves.* He slept on, however, without perceiving what had happened. The same night a fisherman, following his occupation, heard the fall of the bed, and by the light of the moon saw him floating upon the water. Much surprised, he called out, "In the name of God, who are you? Speak, that I may render assistance, before the waves swallow you up." Guido, awoke by the clamour, arose, and perceiving the sky and stars above, and the ocean beneath, wondered where he was. "Good friend," said he to the fisherman, "assist me, and I will amply reward you. I am the pilgrim who fought in the lists;

---

* This incident might have furnished Lord Byron with the mysterious disappearance of Sir Ezzelin, in his "Lara." But I should scarcely think it.

but how I got hither, I have no conception." The man, hearing this, took him into his vessel, and conveyed him to his house, where he rested till the morning.

The sons of Plebeus, in the mean while, related what they thought the end of the pilgrim, and bade their parent discard his fear. The latter, much exhilarated, arose, and armed himself; and going to the gate of the palace, called out, "Bring forth that pilgrim, that I may complete my revenge." The king commanded his daughter to awake and prepare him for battle. Accordingly, she went into his room, but he was not to be found. She wept bitterly, exclaiming that some one had conveyed away her treasure; and the surprise occasioned by the intelligence was not less, when it became known that his bed was also missing. Some said that he had fled; others, that he was murdered. Plebeus, however, continued his clamour at the gate. "Bring out your pilgrim; to-day I will present his head to the king." Now, while all was bustle and inquiry in the palace, the fisherman made his way to the royal seat, and said, "Grieve not, my lord, for the loss of the pilgrim. Fishing last night in the sea, I observed him floating upon a bed. I took him on board my vessel, and he is now asleep at my house." This news greatly cheered the king, and he immediately sent to him to prepare for a renewal of the contest. But Plebeus, terrified, and apprehensive of the consequence, besought a truce. This was denied, even for a single hour. Both, therefore, re-entered the lists, and each struck twice; but at the third blow Guido cut off his opponent's arm, and afterwards his head. He presented it to the king, who evinced himself well satisfied with the event; and hearing that the sons of Plebeus were instruments in the meditated treachery, he caused them to be crucified. The pilgrim was loaded with honours, and offered immense wealth if he would remain with the king, which he resolutely declined. Through him Tyrius was reinstated in his former dignity, and recompensed for his past suffering. He then bade the king farewell. "Good friend," returned the monarch, "for the love of Heaven, leave me not ignorant of your name." "My lord," answered he, "I am that Guido of

whom you have often heard." Overjoyed at this happy
discovery, the king fell upon his neck, and promised him
a large part of his dominions if he would remain. But he
could not prevail; and the warrior, after returning his
friendly salutation, departed.

Guido embarked for England, and hastened to his own
castle. He found a great number of paupers standing
about his gate; and amongst them, habited as a pilgrim,
sat the countess, his wife. Every day did she thus minister to the poor, bestowing a penny upon each, with a
request that he would pray for the safety of her husband
Guido, that once more, before death, she might rejoice in
his presence. It happened, on the very day of his return,
that his son, now seven years of age, sat with his mother
among the mendicants, sumptuously apparelled. When
he heard his mother address the person who experienced
her bounty in the manner mentioned above, "Mother,"
said he, " is it not my father whom you recommend to the
prayers of these poor people ? " "It is, my son," replied
she; " the third night following our marriage he left me,
and I have never seen him since." Now, as the lady
walked among her dependents, who were ranged in order,
she approached her own husband Guido, and gave him
alms—but she knew not who he was. He bowed his head
in acknowledgment, fearful lest his voice should discover
him. As the countess walked, her son followed; and
Guido raising his eyes and seeing his offspring, whom he
had not before seen, he could not contain himself. He
caught him in his arms, and kissed him. "My darling
child," said he, "may the Lord give thee grace to do that
which is pleasing in His eyes." The damsels of the lady,
observing the emotion and action of the pilgrim, called to
him and bade him stand there no longer. He approached
his wife's presence, and without making himself known,
entreated of her permission to occupy some retired place
in the neighbouring forest; and she, supposing that he
was the pilgrim he appeared to be, for the love of God
and of her husband built him a hermitage, and there
he remained a long time. But being on the point of
death, he called his attendant, and said, "Go quickly to
the countess; give her that ring, and say that if she

wishes to see me, she must come hither with all speed."
The messenger went accordingly, and delivered the ring.
As soon as she had seen it, she exclaimed, "It is my lord's
ring!" and with a fleet foot hurried into the forest. But
Guido was dead. She fell upon the corpse, and with a
loud voice cried, "Woe is me! my hope is extinct!" and
then with sighs and lamentations continued, "Where are
now the alms I distributed in behalf of my lord? I beheld
my husband receive my gifts with his own hands, and
knew him not. And as for thee" (apostrophizing the dead
body), "thou sawest thy child, and touchedst him. Thou
didst kiss him, and yet revealedst not thyself to me! What
hast thou done? Oh, Guido! Guido! never shall I see
thee more!" She sumptuously interred his body; and
bewailed his decease for many days. (35)

APPLICATION.

My beloved, the knight represents Christ; the wife is
the soul, and Tyrius is man in general. The weasel typifies John and the other prophets, who predicted the coming
of Christ. The mountain is the world. The dead dragon
is the old law, and the treasure within it is the ten commandments. The sword is authority; the king's daughter,
the Virgin Mary. The seven sons of Plebeus are seven
mortal sins; the fisherman is the Holy Ghost.

TALE CLXXIII.

OF THE BURDENS OF THIS LIFE.

A CERTAIN king once went to a fair,* and took with him a
preceptor and his scholar. Standing in the market-place,
they perceived eight packages exposed for sale. The

---

* "Among the revenues accruing to the crown of England from
the fair of Saint Botolph, at Boston in Lincolnshire, within the
HONOUR OF RICHMOND, mention is made of the royal pavilion, or booth,
which stood in the fair, about the year 1280. This fair was regularly
frequented by merchants from the most capital trading towns of Nor-
mandy, Germany, Flanders, and other countries."—WARTON.

scholar questioned his teacher respecting the first of them. "Pray," said he, "what is the price of poverty—that is, of tribulation for the love of God?"

Preceptor. The kingdom of heaven.

Scholar. It is a great price indeed. Open the second package, and let us see what it contains.

Preceptor. It contains meekness: blessed are the meek.

Scholar. Meekness, indeed, is a very illustrious thing, and worthy of divine majesty. What is its price?

Preceptor. Gold shall not be given for it; nor shall silver be weighed against it. I demand *earth* for it; and nothing but earth will I receive.

Scholar. There is a spacious tract of uninhabited country between India and Britain. Take as much of it as you please.

Preceptor. No; this land is the land of the dying, the land which devours its inhabitants. Men die there. I demand the land of the living.

Scholar. I muse at what you say. All die, and would you alone be exempt? Would you live for ever? Behold, blessed are the meek, for they shall inherit the EARTH. What is there in the third package?

Preceptor. Hunger and thirst.

Scholar. For how much may these be purchased?

Preceptor. For righteousness. Blessed are they who hunger and thirst after righteousness, for they shall be filled.

Scholar. Therefore you shall possess righteousness, provided there be no neglect. What does the fourth contain?

Preceptor. Tears, wailings, and woe;
Moisture above, and moisture below.*

Scholar. It is not customary to buy tears and wailings, yet I will buy it; because the saints desire it at this price. Blessed are they who mourn, for they shall be comforted. What is the fifth package?

Preceptor. It is a precious thing, and contains *mercy*, which I will weigh to please you. At a word, I will take mercy for mercy, eternity for time.

Scholar. You were a bad umpire to ask this, unless mercy should plead for you. Nevertheless, she shall

---

* "*Magister.* Lacrymas, fletus et ploratus; irriguum superius, et irriguum inferius." This is a curious package!

become your surety. And blessed are the merciful, for they shall obtain mercy. In this life we abound in poverty and wretchedness and hardship. Undo the sixth package; perhaps it may contain something better.

Preceptor. It is clearly full; but it loves not, like a purple robe, to be exposed before the common eye; you shall see it in private, and there we will agree about the price.

Scholar. Very well; what is it?

Preceptor. Purity; which is extremely valuable. There are gold and silver vases, namely, piety, goodness, charity, and spiritual joy. Now, then, let us open these precious garments. Here are lectures, meditations, prayers, and contemplations. The judgments of the Lord are justified in themselves, and more to be desired than gold and precious stones.

Scholar. There is a great reward in the possession. Ask, therefore, what ye will.

Preceptor. To see God.

Scholar. Therefore, blessed are the pure in heart, for they shall see God. Open the seventh package.

Preceptor. It contains *peace.*

Scholar. What! are you going to *sell* me your peace?

Preceptor. It does not accord with my poverty, nor would it with your justice and great wealth, to take anything of me for nothing. But your liberality will make me rich. What then? I am a mean country fellow, and made of clay; formed of the very dust of the earth. My want of nobility oppresses me, and I would no longer bear the reproach which says, " You are earth, and to earth you shall go." I would rather have it said to me, " You are heaven, and to heaven you shall go." I eagerly desire to fulfil the destiny of the sons of God; I would become a son of God.

Scholar. I have done : I confess the truth, and distrust you no longer. Blessed are the peace-makers, for they shall be called the sons of God. If, therefore, you preserve the love of a son, you shall receive the paternal inheritance. Now, what is contained in the last package? Explain it.

Preceptor. It contains only tribulation and persecution for the sake of righteousness.

Scholar. And what do you want for it ?

Preceptor. The kingdom of heaven.

Scholar. I gave you that as the price of poverty!

Preceptor. True; but month after month, week after week, man wanders in his wishes. You are mistaken: I ask this for the present week or month; as to the future I wait humbly.

Scholar. I marvel at your sagacity in making a bargain. Now hear, good and faithful servant! because thou hast been faithful over a few things, I will appoint thee lord over many : enter thou into the joy of thy lord.*

TALE CLXXIV.

OF NATURE AND THE RETURNS OF INGRATITUDE.

An emperor rode out in the afternoon to hunt. Happening to pass a certain wood, he heard a serpent, which some shepherds had caught and bound firmly to a tree, making a most horrible clamour. Moved by pity, he loosed it, and warmed its frozen body in his own bosom. No sooner, however, did the animal find itself recovered, than it began to bite its benefactor, and shot a flood of poison into the wound. " What hast thou done ? " said the emperor. " Wherefore have you rendered evil for good ? " The serpent, like the ass of Balaam, being suddenly endowed with voice, replied, " The propensities which nature has implanted no one can destroy. You have done what you could; and I have only acted according to my nature. You exhibited towards me all the kindness in your power, and I have recompensed you as well as I might. I offered poison, because, except poison, I had nothing to offer. Moreover, I am an enemy to man; for through him I became punished with a curse." As they thus contended, they entreated a philosopher to judge between them, and

---

* This is a curious instance of the once fashionable practice of forcing everything into allegory. Not many would have hit upon so odd an invention. It may be thought that the preceptor and his disciple should change places in the dialogue.

to state which was in the wrong. "I know these matters," answered the umpire, "only by your relation ; but I should like to see the thing itself upon which I am to pronounce judgment. Let the serpent, therefore, be bound to the tree, as he was in the first instance, and let my lord the emperor' remain unbound ; I shall then determine the matter between you." This was done accordingly. "Now you are bound," said the philosopher, addressing the serpent, "loose yourself if you can." "I cannot," said the serpent ; "I am bound so fast that I can scarcely move." "Then die," rejoined the philosopher, "by a just sentence. You were always ungrateful to man, and you always will be. My lord, you are now free ; shake the venom from your bosom, and go your way : do not repeat your folly. Remember that the serpent is only influenced by his natural propensities." The emperor thanked the philosopher for his assistance and advice, and departed.* (36)

APPLICATION.

My beloved, the emperor is any good ecclesiastic, the wood is the world, and the serpent is the devil. The shepherds are the prophets, patriarchs, Christian preachers, &c. The philosopher is a discreet confessor.

TALE CLXXV.

OF THE WORLD'S WONDERS.

PLINY says that there are certain men who have the heads of dogs ; who bark when they converse, and clothe themselves in the skins of animals. (37) These represent preachers, who ought to be coarsely clad, as an example to others.—Also in India there are men who possess a single eye, which is placed in the forehead.† They live upon the flesh of animals. These are they who have the eye of reason.

* This fable is in Alphonsus, *De Clericali Disciplina.*

† "And in one of these isles are men that have but one eye, and that is in the middest of their front, and they eat their flesh and fish all raw."—MANDEVILE ; and PLINY, lib. vii. c. 2.

In Africa there are women without heads, having eyes
and mouth in their breasts.* Such are like humble men.
—In the East, over against the terrestrial Paradise, are
people who never eat, and whose mouth is so small that
what they drink is conveyed into the stomach by means
of a reed. They live upon the odour of apples and flowers;
and a bad smell instantly destroys them.† These designate abstemious men; and to die of an ill odour is to die
of sin.—There are men without a nose, but otherwise with
complete faces; and whatsoever they see they think good.‡
Such are the foolish of the world.—And there are some
whose nose and lower lip is so long, that it covers all the
face, while they sleep.§ These are just men.—In Scythia
are men with ears that completely envelop their whole
body.‖ These represent such as listen to the word of God.
—Some men there are who walk like cattle,¶ and these

* "And in another isle are men that have no heads, and their
eyes are in their shoulders, and their mouth is in their breast."—
MANDEVILE: see also PLINY, and *Turkish Tales*, vol. ii. page 303.

† In the utmost marshes of India, eastward, about the source and
head of the river Ganges, there is a nation called the Astomes, for
they have no mouths: all hairie over the whole bodie, yet clothed
with the soft cotton and downe that come from the leaves of trees;
they live only by the aire, and smelling to sweet odours, which they
draw in at their nose thrills. No meat nor drink they take, onely
pleasant savours from divers and sundrie roots, flowers, and wild
fruits, growing in the woods they entertaine; and those they use to
carry about with them when they take any farre journey, because
they would not misse their smelling. And yet if the scent be any
thing strong and stinking, they are soone therewith overcome, and
die withal."—P. Holland's Transl. of Pliny's *Nat. Hist.*
To this account Sir John Mandevile adds, that "they are not reasonable, but as wild as beasts," p. 124. He calls the place of their
residence PITAN.

‡ "And in another isle are men that have flat faces without noses,
and without eyes—but they have two small round holes instead of
eyes, and they have flat mouths without lips."—MAND.

§ "And in another isle are foul men, that have their lips about
their mouth so great, that when they sleep in the sun, they cover all
their face with their lips."—MAND.

‖ "And in another isle are wild men with hanging ears, who
have feet like a horse," &c.—MAND. "And some again that with
their ears cover their whole bodie."—PLINY, lib. vii. c. 2.

¶ "And in another isle are men that go upon their hands and feet
like beasts, and are all rough, and will leap upon a tree like cats or
apes."—MAND.

are they who honour neither God nor His saints.—There are likewise people who are horned, having short noses and the feet of a goat.* These are the proud.—In Æthiopia are men with but one leg, whose velocity nevertheless is such, that they run down the swiftest animal.† These are the charitable.—In India are pygmies two cubits long; they ride upon goats, and make war against the cranes.‡ These are they who begin well, but cease before they are perfect.—In India there are also men who possess six hands. They are without clothes, but are extremely hairy, and dwell in rivers. These are the zealous workers who labour and obtain eternal life.—There, too, are men who have six fingers on each hand, and six toes on each foot; § during the week they keep themselves

* " And there is in that wilderness many wild men with horns on their heads, very hideous, and they speak not."—MAND.

† " In Ethiope such men as have but one foot, and they go so fast that it is a great marvel; and that is a large foot, for the shadow thereof covereth the body from sun, or rain, when they lie upon their backs; and when their children are first born, they look like russet, but when they wax old, they be all black."—MAND.

Pliny calls these people SCIOPODES.

‡ " Higher in the countrey, and above these, even in the edge and skirts of the mountaines, the *Pygmæi Spythamei* are reported to bee: called they are so, for that they are but a cubite or three shaftments (or spannes) high, that is to say, three times nine inches. The clime wherin they dwell is very wholesome, the aire healthie, and ever like to the temperature of the spring; by reason that the mountaines are on the north side of them, and beare off all cold blasts. And these pretie people, Homer also hath reported to be much troubled and annoied by cranes. The speech goeth, that in the spring time they set out all of them in battel array, mounted upon the back of rammes and goats, armed with bowes and arrowes, and so downe to the seaside they march, where they make foul worke amonge the egges and young cranelings newly hatched, which they destroy without all pitie. Thus for three moneths this their journey and expedilion continueth, and then they make an end of their valiant service; or otherwise if they should continue any longer, they were never able to withstand the new flights of this foule, growne to some strength and bignesse. As for their houses and cottages, made they are of clay or mud, fouls feathers, and birds egge shells. Howbeit Aristotle writeth, that these Pygmæans live in hollow caves and holes under the ground."— *Holland's Pliny.*

Addison has written a Latin poem upon this subject, and Dr. Beattie has translated it into very elegant English verse.

§ " And in another isle are men that go ever on their hands marvellously, and they have on every foot eight toes."—MAND.

pure, and on the seventh day sanctify themselves.—Certain women there are bearded to the breast; but their heads are totally bare.* These represent men who obey the Church, and are turned from that course neither by love nor by hatred.—In Ethiopia there are men with four eyes each.† These are they who fear God, the world, the devil, and the flesh. They turn one eye to God, to live well; another to the world, to flee from it; a third to the devil, to resist him; and the last to the flesh, to chastise it.—In Europe are very *beautiful* men; but they have a crane's head, and neck, and beak.‡ These designate judges, who ought to have long necks and beaks, in order that what the *heart thinks may be long before it reach the mouth.*§ If all judges were thus we should have fewer injudicious awards.

TALE CLXXVI.

OF SPIRITUAL MEDICINE.

THERE was a male child born, divided from the navel upward. Thus he had two heads and breasts, and a proper number of sensitive faculties to each. While one slept or eat, the other did neither. After two years, one part of the boy died, and the other survived about three days.‖

* "In this country . . . . women shave their heads, and not men."
—MAND.

† "The region above Sirbithim, where the mountaines doe end, is reported to have upon the sea-coast certaine Æthiopians called Nisicastes and Nisites, that is to say, men with three or four eies apeece; not for that they are so eied indeed, but because they are excellent archers."—PLINY, *Nat. Hist.* lib. vi. c. 30.

‡ "He and his subjects are not like us, men without heads: they have heads like those of *birds;* and their voice so exactly resembles the voice of birds, that, when any one of them arrives in our island, we take him for a water-fowl and eat him, ... with all the several sauces with which men are wont to eat wild-fowl."—*Turkish Tales,* vol. ii. p. 364.

§ Excellent doctrine!

‖ Bracciolinus, or Brandiolinus Poggius, a Florentine, who flourished in the 15th century, has given an account of the monster here alluded to. I quote the translation of his fables, of 1658 :—

"Also within a little while after it befell out about the marches

Also, as Pliny records, there was a tree in India whose flowers had a sweet smell, and its fruit a delightful flavour. A serpent, called Jacorlus, which dwelt near, had a great aversion to the odour, and that he might destroy its productiveness envenomed the root of the tree. The gardener, observing what was done, took an antidote of that country, and inserted it in a branch at the top of the tree, which presently drove the poison from the root. The tree, before barren, was now loaded with fruit.

APPLICATION.

My beloved, the child represents the soul and body of man. The tree is also man; the fruit, good works. The serpent is the devil; and the gardener is God. The branch is the blessed Virgin Mary:—so Isaiah, " A branch shall spring from the root of Jesse." And thus also VIRGIL, in the second of his Bucolics.*

> " Jam redit et virgo redeunt saturnia regna :
> Jam nova progenies coelo dimittitur alto.
> *Tu modo nascendi* † puero, quo ferrea primum,
> Desinet, *et* ‡ toto surget gens aurea mundo."

In this branch was placed the antidote, that is, Christ.

of Italy, that there was a child born which had two heads, and two visages, beholding one another, and the arms of each other embraced the body; the which body from the navel upward was joined, save the two heads; and from the navel downward, the limbs were all separated one from another. Of the which child tidings came unto the person of Poge at Rome."

* The reader will be surprised to meet with a quotation from Virgil in this place. It is most probable, from its corruptness, that the passage was not drawn immediately from the poet.

† The true reading is—

> " Tu modò nascenti puero, &c.
>
> *　　*　　*　　*　　*
>
> *Casta fave Lucina.*"—Ecl. iv. line 10.

It is nonsense as it stands above; but the edition of 1521, 18mo, has " *tu modo* NASCENTI."

‡ It should be AC.

TALE CLXXVII.

OF PERSECUTION.*

KING ASUERUS made a great feast to all the princes of his kingdom. He commanded the queen, Vasti, to appear at the festival, that his people might behold the splendour of that beauty which he had raised to the throne. When she refused to come in, the king deprived her of her royalty, and raised Hester to the rank of queen in her stead. After this the king promoted a certain Aman, and made all the princes of his empire pay him homage. They complied; but Mardocheus, the king's uncle, would not honour him. Enraged at this disregard of his authority, Aman delivered him to death, with all his family, and made an ordinance under the royal seal to exterminate every Jew in the kingdom; and constructing a high gibbet,† he resolved that Mardocheus should be fastened upon it. But, in the mean time, it was the fortune of the latter to discover two traitors who had conspired to kill the king; and immediately giving such information as led to their apprehension, he was clothed in a purple robe and crowned, and rode on a royal steed through the city, while Aman, with all his knights, were reduced to the necessity of extolling him.‡ When this was done, Mardocheus related to the queen that Aman intended to put all their nation to death; wherefore she proclaimed a fast, and afflicted

---

* There is a metrical romance on this subject; and Thomas of Elmham, a chronicler, calls the coronation feast of King Henry the Sixth a second feast of Ahasuerus. "Hence also Chaucer's allusion at the marriage of January and May, while they are at the solemnity of the wedding dinner, which is very splendid:—

'Queen Esther looked ne'er with such an eye
On Assuere, so meek a look hath she' (*March. Tale*, v. 1260)."

WARTON.

† ["Altum erexit *eculeum*." Swan translated *eculeum* "rack," which would represent fairly, though by no means accurately, the meaning of the term in classical Latin. But in the Middle Ages it meant a *gibbet*. "Equuleus, patibulum, furca cui decollatorum martyrum cadavera affigebant" (DU CANGE).—ED.]

‡ This is decidedly an Eastern custom. See the Arabian Tales, &c., *passim*.

herself with fasting and prayer. She then made a great feast, to which she invited the king and Aman. First imploring the life of her people, she explained how the latter had condemned all to death. Full of indignation, the king ordered him to be fixed upon the same gibbet which he had prepared for Mardocheus, who succeeded to all his honours. Thus, by the disposing hand of Providence, the innocent people were freed, and the generation of the wicked utterly exterminated.*

APPLICATION.

My beloved, the king is Christ; and the queen is the soul. Aman represents the Jewish people, who seek to destroy the Church. The two traitors are the Jew and the Gentile.

TALE CLXXVIII.

OF FORETHOUGHT.

A CERTAIN king was desirous of ascertaining the best mode of governing himself and his empire. He therefore called to him one more excellent in wisdom than the rest, and required of him to impart some rule by which he might attain his wishes. "Willingly, my lord," replied he; and immediately upon a wall he depicted the king, crowned, sitting on a throne and habited in a purple robe. His left hand supported a globe, while his right held a sceptre; above his head was a light burning. On the left was the queen, crowned also, and clad in golden vesture. The other side was occupied by counsellors seated in chairs, and before them an open book. In front of these was an armed knight on horseback, having a helmet on his head, and a lance in his right hand. The shield covered him on

* One would imagine that the story of Mordecai could never have been actually read by the author of this tale; it seems as if a floating tradition had been caught up and worked into the apologue of *Mardocheus*. The latter name is Greek, and occurs in the apocryphal continuation of the Book of Esther.

the left, and a sword hung by his side.* His body was
cased in mail, having clasps† upon the breast. Iron
greaves protected his legs; spurs were upon his heels, and
iron gauntlets on his hands. His horse, practised in war,
was gorgeously trapped. Beneath the king were his
deputies; one, as an equestrian knight, in cloak and cap
of parti-coloured skins, bearing an extended rod in his
right hand. The people stood before the deputies in the
form following:—One man carried a spade in his right
hand, wherewith he was digging, and in his left a rod,
with which he directed the motions of a herd. In his
girdle hung a sickle, with which corn is cut and vines
and other trees pruned. To the right of the king a carpenter was painted before a knight; one hand bore a
mallet, and the other an adze; in his girdle was a trowel.
Also, before the people stood a man having a pair of
pincers in one hand, and in the other a huge sword; with
a note-book and a bottle of ink in his girdle, a pen stuck
in his right ear. Moreover, in the same part of the painting was a man bearing a balance and weights in his right
hand, and an ell-wand in his left; a purse containing
various kinds of money hung at his girdle.

Before the queen were physicians and colourmen under
this form. A man was placed in a master's chair with a
book in his right hand, and an urn and box in his left;
an instrument for probing sores and wounds was in his
girdle. Near him stood another, with his right hand
elevated to invite the passengers to his inn; his left was
full of exceedingly fair bread; and above stood a vessel
full of wine : his girdle held a bunch of keys. Also on the
left side, before a knight, was a man with large keys in
his right hand, and an ell-wand in his left; at his girdle
was a purse filled with pennies. Before the king, also,
was a man with rugged and disorderly hair; in his right
hand was a little money, and three dice were in his left;
his girdle held a box full of letters. When the king had
attentively considered this picture, he found it replete with
wisdom.

* "Ensem in *dextera*," says the original; but he could not hold
both *lance* and *sword* in the same hand at once.

† "*Fibulas* in pectore,"—meaning *knobs* perhaps.

APPLICATION.

My beloved, the king is any good Christian, or rather prelate ; and he is clothed in purple to figure the beauty of virtue. The globe and sceptre are symbols of power. The burning light signifies a threat. The queen is charity. The counsellors or judges are prelates and preachers, and the books before them the Sacred Writings. The armed knight is a good Christian armed with virtues. The other knight rides the horse of Justice, wearing the cloak of Mercy, and the cap of Faith. The extended rod is an equal distribution of right—*et sic de cœteris.*

TALE CLXXIX.

OF GLUTTONY AND DRUNKENNESS.

CESARIUS,* speaking of the detestable vices of gluttony and drunkenness, says that the throat is the most intemperate and seductive part of the whole body. Its daughters are uncleanness, buffoonery, foolish joy, loquaciousness, and dulness. It has five grades of sin. The first is, to inquire for high-seasoned and delicate food ; the second, to dress it curiously ; the third, to take it before there is occasion ; the fourth, to take it too greedily ; and the fifth, in too large a quantity. The first man, Adam, was conquered by gluttony ; and for this Esau gave away his birth-right. This excited the people of Sodom to sin, and overthrew the children of Israel in the wilderness. So the Psalmist, " While the meat was yet in their mouths, the anger of God came upon them." The iniquity of Sodom arose in its superabundance ; and the man of God, who was sent

* " Cesarius, I suppose, is a Cistercian monk of the thirteenth century ; who besides voluminous lives, chronicles, and homilies, wrote twelve books on the miracles, visions, and examples of his own age. But there is another and an older monkish writer of the same name. In the British Museum, there is a narrative taken from Cesarius, in old northern English, of a lady deceived by fiends, or the devil, thro' the pride of rich clothing."—WARTON.

to Bethel, was slain by a lion in consequence of indulging his appetite. Dives, of whom it is said in the Gospel that he feasted sumptuously every day, was buried in hell. Nabusardan,* the prince of cooks, destroyed Jerusalem. How great the danger of gluttony is, let the Scriptures testify. "Woe to the land," says Solomon, "whose princes eat in the morning." Again, "All the labour of man in the mouth will not fill his soul." The daughter of gluttony is drunkenness; for that vice is the author of luxury —the worst of all plagues. What is there fouler than this? What more hurtful? What sooner wears away virtue? Glory laid asleep is converted to madness; and the strength of the mind, equally with the strength of the body, is destroyed. Basilius says, "When we serve the belly and throat, we are cattle; and study to resemble brutes which are prone to this, and made by nature to look upon the earth and obey the belly." † Boethius also, *De Consolatione*, 51, iv.: "He who forsakes virtue ceases to be a man; and since he cannot pass to the divine nature, it remains that he must become a brute." And our Lord, in the Gospel: "Take heed lest your hearts be hardened with surfeiting and drunkenness." Oh, how great had been the counsels of wisdom, if the heats of wine and greediness interposed not. Dangerous is it when the father of a family, or the governor of a state, is warm with wine, and inflamed with anger. Discretion is dimmed, luxury is excited, and lust, mixing itself with all kinds of wickedness, lulls prudence asleep. Wherefore, said Ovidius, "Wine produces lust if taken too copiously." Oh, odious vice of drunkenness! by which virginity—the possession of all good things—the security of happiness—is lost for ever and ever. Noah, heated with wine, exposed himself to his children. The most chaste Lot, thrown by wine

---

* Nabusardan was a general of Nabuchodonosor II., who besieged and took Jerusalem, A.M. 3446; but how he became PRINCE OF COOKS, and what part his culinary skill had in the downfall of the "rebellious city," the writer of the GEST must explain.

† "This is the sentiment of the historian Sallust, in the opening of the Jugurthine war.

"Omnes homines, qui sese student præstare cæteris animalibus, summâ ope niti decet, nè vitam silentio transeant, veluti pecora; *quæ natura prona atque ventri obedientia finxit.*"

into sleep, did that which was evil in the sight of the Lord. We read of men, who were such firm friends that each would expose his life for the other, becoming so inflamed with wine that they slew one another. Herod Antipas had not decapitated the holy John, if he had kept from the feast of surfeiting and drunkenness. Balthasar, king of Babylon, had not been deprived of his life and throne, if he had been sober on the night in which Cyrus and Darius slew him, overpowered with wine.* On which account the Apostle advises us to be "sober and watch." Let us then pray to the Lord to preserve us in all sobriety, that we may hereafter be invited to a feast in heaven.

TALE CLXXX.

OF FIDELITY.

PAULUS, the historian of the Longobards, mentions a certain Onulphus, surnamed Papien, a knight who gave signal proofs of fidelity to his master, King Portaticus; insomuch that he exposed himself to death for his safety. For when Grimmoaldus, duke of Beneventum, forcibly entered the pavilion of Godobert, king of the Longobards, who had been treacherously slain by Geribaldus,† duke of Ravenna, the first betrayer of a royal crown, Portaticus, the brother of the aforesaid king Godobert, flying to the Hungarians, was reconciled to Grimmoaldus by the knight Onulphus, so that without fear he might quit Hungary and solicit pardon at the king's feet. Thus his life was secure, although he obtained not the regal dignity which was his due. But a few days after this reconciliation, some malicious tongues disposed Grimmoaldus to put to death Portaticus. To get rid of him the more easily, and prevent his seeking safety in flight, he commanded that

---

* Darius, the son of Hystaspes, conquered Babylon. But the son and grandson of this monarch are here meant.

† He is called GENEBALDUS here, and afterwards GERIBALDUS, in all the five different editions I have inspected.

wine should be served to him, that he might become intoxicated. Onulphus hearing this, went, with his squire, to the house of Portaticus; and leaving his attendant in bed, concealed with the coverture, he led out Portaticus, disguised as his squire, threatening, and even striking him, the better to cover the deceit. Thus they passed through the watch, or guard, placed before the house of Portaticus, till they reached the abode of the knight, which was built upon the city walls. He then hastened to let him down by a rope; and catching certain horses from the pasture, Portaticus fled to the city of Astensis, and from thence to the king of France. In the morning Onulphus and his squire were brought before the king, and examined as to the escape of their master. They answered exactly as the case was; and Grimmoaldus, turning to his counsellors, said, "What punishment do they deserve who have done this, contrary to our royal pleasure?" All agreed that it should be capital. Some protested that they should be flayed alive; and others, that they should be crucified. "By Him that made me," replied the king, "they are deserving of honour, not death, for their unshaken fidelity." Acting up to this feeling, Grimmoaldus loaded them with favours; but Geribaldus the traitor was miserable, though justly slain by the hand of Godobert's squire, the follower of him whom he had treacherously deprived of life and kingdom. This happened on the solemn festival of St. John the Baptist.

APPLICATION.

My beloved, the knight Onulphus is any good Christian; Portaticus is the soul. Grimmoaldus typifies Christ, and Hungary the world. The horses taken from the pasture are the merits of martyrs and saints; Astensis is the city in the Apocalypse. France signifies heaven.

TALE CLXXXI.

OF ADULTERY.

A CERTAIN king had a lion, a lioness, and a leopard, whom he much delighted in. During the absence of the lion, the lioness was unfaithful, and colleagued with the leopard; and that she might prevent her mate's discovery of the crime, she used to wash herself in a fountain adjoining the king's castle. Now, the king, having often perceived what was going forward, commanded the fountain to be closed. This done, the lioness was unable to cleanse herself; and the lion returning, and ascertaining the injury that had been done him, assumed the place of a judge—sentenced her to death, and immediately executed the sentence.

APPLICATION.

My beloved, the king is our heavenly Father; the lion is Christ; and the lioness, the soul. The leopard is the devil, and the fountain is confession, which being closed, death presently follows.

Remarkable Histories, from the

Gesta Romanorum,

combined with numerous moral and mystical
applications, treating of vices and virtues.
Printed and diligently revised, at
the expence of that provident
and circumspect man,
John Rynman,
of Orin-
gaw;
at the workshop of Henry Gran, citizen of the
imperial town of Hagenaw.   Concluded
happily, in the year of our
safety, one thousand
five hundred
and eight:
March
the
20th.

NOTES.

NOTE 1. Page 16.

THIS fable is very well told by Gower, but with some variations.
[The letters printed in Italics are to be pronounced as separate
syllables; the acute mark denotes the emphasis.]

Ere Rom-*e* came to the creánce [1]
Of Christ-*es* faith, it fell perchance
Cæsar, which then was emperour,
Him list-*e* for to do honóur
Untó the temple Apollinis;
And made an image upon this,
The which was cleped [2] Apolló,
Was none so rich in Rom-*e* tho. [3]
   Of plate of gold, a beard he had,
The which his breast all over spradde. [4]
   Of gold also, withouten fail,
His mantle was of large entayle, [5]
Be-set with perrey [6] all about.
Forth right he stretched his finger out,
Upon the which he had a ring—
To see it, was a rich-*e* thing,
A fine carbuncle for the nones, [7]
Most precious of all stones.
   And fell that time in Rom-*e* thus,
There was a clerk, one Lucius,
A courtier, a famous man;
Of every wit [8] somewhat he can,
Out-take [9] that him lacketh rule,
His own estate to guide and rule;
How so it stood of his speakíng,
He was not wise in his doíng;
But every riot-*e* at last
Must need-*es* fall, and may not last.
After the need of his desert,
So fell this clerk-*e* in povérte,

---

[1] Belief.   [2] Called.   [3] Then.   [4] Spread.
[5] Cut; from the French *entailler*.   [6] Pearls.   [7] Purpose.
[8] Knowledge.   [9] Except.

And wist not how for to rise
Whereof in many a sundry wise
He cast his wit-*es* here and there,
He looketh nigh, he looketh far.
Fell on a tim-*e* that he come
Into the temple, and heed nome [1]
Where that the god Apollo stood;
He saw the riches, and the good; [2]
And thought he wold-*e* by some way,
The treasure pick and steal away.
And thereupon so slily wrought,
That his purpóse about he brought.
And went away unaperceived:
Thus hath the man his god deceived—
His ring, his mantle, and his beard,
As he which nothing was afeard,
All privily with him he bare;
And when the wardens were aware
Of that, their god despoiled was,
They thought it was a wondrous case,
How that a man for any weal,
Durst in so holy plac-*e* steal,
And nam-*e*-ly, so great a thing!—
This tale cam-*e* unto the king,
And was through spoken over-all.
But for to know in special,
What manner man hath done the deed,
They soughten help upon the need,
And maden calculatìon,
Whereof by demonstratión
The man was found-*e* with the good.
In judgment, and when he stood,
The king hath asked of him thus—
"Say, thou unsely [3] Lucius,
Why hast thou done this sacrilege?"
"My lord, if I the cause allege,"
(Quoth he again,) "me-thinketh this,
That I have done nothíng amiss.
Three points there be, which I have do,
Whereof the first-*e* point stands so,
That I the ring have ta'en away—
Unto this point this will I say.
When I the god beheld about,
I saw how he his hand stretched out,
And proffered me the ring to yeve; [4]
And I, which wold-*e* gladly live
Out of povérte thro' his largéss,
It underfang, [5] so that I guess;

[1] Took.   [2] Goods.   [3] Foolish.
[4] Give.   [5] Accepted.

And therefore, am I nought to wite.[1]
   And overmore, I will me 'quit,[2]
Of gold that I the mantle took :
Gold in his kind, as saith the book,
Is heavy both, and cold also ;
And fór that it was heavy so,
Methought it was no garn-*e*-ment [3]
Unto the god convenient,
To clothen him the summer tide : [4]
I thought upon that other side,
How gold is cold, and such a cloth
By reason ought-*e* to be lothe [5]
In winter tim-*e* for the chiel.
And thus thinking thought-*es* fele [6]
As I mine eye about-*e* cast,
His larg-*e* beard-*e* then at last
I saw ; and thought anon therefore
How that his father him before,
Which stood upon the sam-*e* place,
Was beardless, with a youngly face.
And in such wise, as ye have heard
I took away the son-*nes* beard,
For that his father had-*e* none,
To make him like ; and hereupon
I ask for to be excused."
   Lo, thus where sacrilege is used,
A man can feign his consciénce;
And right upon such evidénce
In lov-*es* cause if I shall treat,
There be of such-*e* small and great,
If they no leisure find-*e* else,
They will not wend-*e* for the bells;
Not tho' they see the priest at mass—
That will they letten over-pass :
If that they find their lov-*e* there
They stand, and tellen in her ear;
And ask of God none other grace,
Whil-*e* they be in that holy place.
But ere they go, some advantáge
There will they have; and some pilláge
Of goodly word, or of behest;
Or else they taken at the least
Out of her hand a ring or glove,
So nigh, the weder [7] they will hove [8]—
As who saith, " She shall not forget
Now I this token of her have get."
   Thus hallow they the high-*e* feast,
Such theft-*e* may no church arrest,[9]

---

[1] Blame.   [2] Acquit.   [3] Garment.   [4] Time.   [5] **Warm.**   [6] Many.
[7] Madder. Sax. ⱱⱸⱦⱥn, insanire.   [8] Heave or go.   [9] Stop.

For all is lawful that them liketh,
To whom that els-*e* it misliketh,
And eké right in the self kind [1]
In great cities men may find.
Thus lusty folk, that make them gay,
And wait upon the holy-day,
In churches, and in minsters eke,
They go the women for to seek,
And where that such one goeth about,
Before the fairest of the rout;
Where as they sitten all a row.
There will he most his body show;
His crooked kempt [2] and thereon set
An ouch-*e* [3] with a chap-*e*-let,
Or else one of green leaves,
Which late come out-*e* of the greves. [4]
All for [5] he should seem fresh:
And thus he looketh on his flesh,
Right as a hawk which hath a sight
Upon the fowl, there he shall light:
And as he were a faëry,
He sheweth him before her eye,
In holy plac-*e* where they sit,
All for to make their heart-*es* flytte. [6]

   His eye no where will abide,
But look and pry on every side,
On her and her, as him best liketh,
And other while, among he siketh; [7]
Thinketh " One of them that was for me,"
And so there thinketh two or three;
And yet he loveth none at all,
But where as ever his chanc-*e* fall.

   And nath-*e*-less to say a sooth
The cause why that he so doth,
Is for to steal a heart or two,
Out of the church ere that he go.
And as I said it here above,
All is that sacrilege of love,
For well may be that he stealeth away,
That he never after yield may. [8]

   " Tell me for this, my son, anon,
Hast thou done sacrilege, or none, [9]
As I have said in this mannér ? "

   " My father, as of this mattér,
I will you tellen readily
What I have done; but tru-*e*-ly
I may excus-*e* mine intent
That I never yet to church went

---

[1] Selfsame kind.   [2] *i.e.* His crooked or disorderly hair, combed.
[3] Brooch.   [4] Wᵒods.   [5] In order that.   [6] Beat, palpitate.
[7] Sigheth.   [8] Restore again.   [9] Not.

In such mannér as ye me shrive,[1]
For no woman that is alive.
The cause why I have it laft,[2]
May be, for[3] I unto that craft,
Am nothing able for to steal,
Though there be women not so fele.[4]
But yet will I not say-*e* this,
When I am where my lady is,
In whom lieth wholly my quarrél,
And she to church or to chapél
Will go to matins or to mess,[5]
That time I wait-*e* well and guess.
To church I come, and there I stand,
And tho'[6] I take a book in hand,
My countenance is on the book,
But toward her is all my look;
And if so fallen[7] that I pray
Unto my God, and somewhat say
Of Pater Noster, or of creed,
All is for that I wold-*e* speed,
So that my bead in holy church,
There might-*e* some mirácle wirche,[8]
My lady's heart-*e* for to change,
Which ever hath been to me so strange.
So that all my devotión,
And all my contemplatión,
With all mine heart, and my couráge,
I only set on her imáge,
And ever I wait-*e* upon the tide,
If she look any thing aside,
That I me may of her advise:
Anon I am with covetise[9]
So smit, that me were lefe[10]
To be in holy church a thief.
But not to steal, a vest-*e*-ment,
For that is nothing my talént;
But I would steal, if that I might,
Á glad word, or a goodly sight.
And ever my servíce I proffer,
And namely, when she will go, offer;
For then I had her, if I may:
For somewhat would I steal away
When I beclip her on the waist;
Yet at least, I steal a taste.
And other while ' grant mercy,'[11]
She saith.   And so were I thereby
A lusty touch, a good word eke,
But all the rem-*e*-nant to seek,

[1] Confess to me.   [2] Left.   [3] Because.
[4] Never so many.   [5] Mass.   [6] If.   [7] Befallen.   [8] Work.
[9] Desire.   [10] Fain.   [11] Great thanks.

Is from my purpose wonder far.
So may I say, as I said ere,[1]
In holy church if that I vow,
My con-*sci*-énce I would allow
Be so, that on amend-*e*-ment,
I might-*e* get assign-*e*-ment;[2]
Where, for to speed in other place,
Such sacrilege I hold a grace.

   "And thus, my father, sooth to say,
In church-*e* right as in the way,
If I might ought of lov-*e* take
Such hansel[3] have I nought forsake.
But finally, I me confess,
There is in me no holinéss,
While her I see in holy stead;
And yet for aught that ever I did,
No sacrilege of her I took,
But[4] it were of word or look,
Or els-*e* if that I her freed,[5]
When I towárd offeríng[6] her lead,
Take thereof what I take may,
For els-*e* bear I nought away.
For tho' I wold-*e* ought else have,
All other thing-*es* be so safe,
And kept with such a privilege,
That I may do no sacrilege.
God wote[7] my will nath-*e*-less,
Though I must need-*es* keep-*e* peace,
And maugre mine so let it pass,
My will thereto is not the lass,[8]
If I might otherwise away.

   "For this, my father, I you pray
Tell what you thinketh thereupon,
If I thereof have guilt or none."

   "Thy will, my son, is for to blame,
The rem-*e*-nant is but a game
That I have thee told as yet.
But take this lore into thy wit,
That all things have time and stead.
The church serveth for the bead,[9]
The chamber is of an other speech:
But if thou wistest of the wreche,[10]
How sacrilege it hath abought,
Thou woldest better be bethought."

      Confessio Amantis, lib. v. fol. 122, ed. 1532.

---

[1] Before.   [2] Assignation.
[3] "Estreiné; *handselled*; that hath the handsell *or first use of*."—COTGRAVE. The word is still extant.
[4] Except.   [5] This perhaps signifies *made free with*.   [6] Altar; *place* of offering.
    [7] Knows.   [8] Less.   [9] Prayer.   [10] Work.

I have transcribed the whole of this tale (though the latter part of it is but the *moral*) because of the truth and nature with which it is replete. Our churches are filled in this day with too many of the characters described so admirably by Gower.

Ibid. "For two especial reasons took away the beard. The first was, that she *should look more like her author, and not grow too proud of her golden beard*" (p. 31).

This idea seems to have arisen from a witticism of Dionysius, the tyrant of Syracuse, recorded by Valerius Maximus, lib. i. cap. 1, ex. 37 :

"Idem Epidauri Æsculapio barbam auream demi jussit: quod affirmaret, *non convenire patrem Apollinem imberbem, ipsum barbatum.*"

Note 2. Page 38.

"Allexius, or Alexis, was canonized. This story is taken from his legend. In the metrical *Lives of the Saints*, his life is told in a sort of measure different from that of the rest, and not very common in the earlier stages of our poetry. It begins thus :—

> "Listeneth all, and hearkeneth me,
> Young and old-*e*, bond and free,
> And I you tellen soon,
> How a stout man, gent and free,
> Began this world-*es* weal to flee,
> Yborn he was in Rome.

> "In Rom-*e* was a doughty man,
> That was y-cleped Eufemian,
> Man of much might ;
> Gold and silver he had enows,
> Hall and bowers, oxen and plows,
> And very well it dight.

"When Alexius returns home in disguise, and asks his father about his son, the father's feelings are thus described :—

> "So soon as he spake of his son,
> The good man, as was his wone,[1]
> Gan to sigh sore ;
> His heart fell as cold as stone,
> The tears fellen to his ton,[2]
> On his beard hoar.

"At his burial, many miracles are wrought on the sick.

> "With mochel[3] sighs, and mochel song,
> That holy corse, them all among
> Bishops to church-*e* bare.

---

[1] Wont.   [2] Toes.   [3] Many.

" Amidst right the high street,
So much folk him gone meet,
That they rest a stonde,[1]
All they sighed that to him come,
And healed were very soon,
Of feet, and eke of honde.

" The history of Saint Alexius is told entirely in the same words in the GESTA ROMANORUM, and in the LEGENDA AUREA of Jacobus de Voraigne,[2] translated through a French medium, by Caxton. This work of Jacobus does not consist solely of the legends of the saints, but is interspersed *multis aliis pulcherrimis et peregrinis historiis*, with many other most beautiful and strange histories." [3]—WARTON.

As it may be amusing to the reader to compare the translation in the text with that executed by the venerable patriarch of the press, William Caxton, in the fifteenth century, I am tempted to transcribe it. There are many little additional touches of manners which the antiquary will value; and while the general reader smiles at the primitive simplicity with which the story is narrated, he will, it is presumed, derive some pleasure from the strong contrast afforded by the past and the present era—from the elevated situation on which he may seem to stand: a being, as it were, of another sphere; asserting the pre-eminence of civilization over uncultivated life—the polite refinement of modern manners over the rude character of remote and barbarous times.

𝕳𝕖𝕣𝖊 𝖋𝖔𝖑𝖔𝖜𝖊𝖙𝖍 𝖙𝖍𝖊 𝖑𝖞𝖋𝖊 𝖔𝖋 𝖘𝖆𝖞𝖓𝖙 𝕬𝖑𝖊𝖝𝖎𝖘.

And fyrst of his name.

Alexis is as moche as to saye as goynge out of the lawe of maryage for to keep virginite for goddes sake, and to renounce all the pomp and rychesses of the worlde for to lyue in pouerte.

In the tyme that Archadius and Honorius were emperours of Rome, there was in Rome a ryght noble lord named Eufemyen, which was chefe and aboue all other lordes aboute the emperours, and had under his power a thousande knyghtes. He was a moche iust man to all men, and also he was pyteous and mercyfull unto ye poore. For he had dayly thre tables set and couered for to fede ye orphans, poor wydowes, and pylgryms. And he ete at the houre of none with good and religyous persones. His wyfe yt was named Aglaes ledde a religyous lyfe. But bycause they had no childe, they prayed to god to send them a sone yt myght be theyr heyre after them, of theyr honour and goodes. It was so that god herde theyre prayers, and beheld theyre bounte and good lyvynge, and gave unto them a sone

---

[1] A moment.

[2] "Hystor. lxxxix. fol. clviii. edit. 1479, fol., and in Vincent of Beauvais, who quotes GESTA ALEXII SPECUL. HIST., lib. xviii. cap. 43, seq. f. 241-6."—WARTON.

[3] Warton seems to be in error respecting this work, which he confounds with "THE LIVES OF THE FATHERS, translated out of Frensshe into Englisshe by William Caxton of Westminster, late deed, and fynisshed it at the last day of hys lyff." The GOLDEN LEGEND (properly so called) consists *wholly* of the legends of the Saints; but the LIVES OF THE FATHERS *is* interspersed with stories of the character given above.

which was named Alexis, whome they dyd to be taught and enfourmed in all scyences and honours. After this, they maryed hym unto a fayre damoysel, which was of ye lygnage of ye emperour of Rome. Whan the daye of ye weddynge was comen to even, Alexis beynge in the chambre w^h his wyfe alone, began to enfourme and enduce her to drede god and serue hym, and were all that night togyder in right good doctryne, and fynally he gave to his wyfe his rynge and the buckle of golde of hys gyrdle, bothe bounden in a lytel cloth of purple, and sayd to her. Fayre sister, haue this, and kepe it as longe as it shall please our lord god, and it shall be a token bytweene us, and he gyue you grace to kepe truly your virgynitie. After this he toke of golde and syluer a grete somme, and departed alone fro Rome, and founde a shyppe in which he sayled in to Greece. And fro thens went in to Surrye,[1] and came to a city called Edessia, and gaue there all his money for the loue of God, and clad hym in a cote, and demaunded almes for goddes sake lyke a poore man tofore the chirche of our lady, and what he lefte of the almesses aboue his necessity, he gaue it to other for goddes sake, and euery sondaye he was houseled and receyved the sacrament, suche a lyfe he ladde longe. Some of ye messengers y^t his father had sent to seche hym through all the partyes of the world came to seek hym in the sayd cyte of Edyssia and gaue unto hym theyr almes, he syttynge tofore the chirche with other poore people, but they knew hym not, and he knewe well them, and thanked our Lord, sayenge, I thank the fayre lorde Jesu Chryst y^t thou vouchest safe to call me, and to take almes in thy name of my seruants, I praye the to perfourm in me that which thou hast begon. Whan the messengers were returned to Rome, and Eufemyen his fader sawe they had not founden his sone, he layd hym down upon a matres stratchynge on the erth, waylynge and sayd thus, I shal holde me here and abyde tyll y^t I have tydynges of my sone. And ye wyfe of his sone Alexis sayd wepynge to Eufemyen, I shal not departe out of your hous, but shal make me semblable and lyke to the turtle, whiche after y^t she hath lost her felowe wyl take none other, but all her lyfe after lyveth chaste. In lyke wyse, I shall refuse all felowshyp unto ye time y^t I shall knowe where my ryghte swete frende is becomen. After that Alexis had done his penaunce by right grete poverte in ye sayd cyte, and ledde a ryght holy lyfe by ye space of xvij yere, there was a voyce herde y^t came fro god unto the chirche of our lady and said to the porter, Make the man of god to entre in, for he is worthy to haue the kingdome of heven, and the spiryte of god resteth on hym. Whan the clerke coude not fynde ne knowe hym amonge the other poor men, he prayed unto god to shewe to hym who it was. And a voyce came from heven and sayd, he sytteth without tofore the entre of the chirche. And so the clerke founde hym, and prayed hym humbly that he wolde come into ye chirche. Whan this myracle came to the knowledge of the people, and Alexis sawe that men dyd to hym honour and worshyp, anone for to eschewe vaynglory he departed fro thens and came into Grece when he toke shyppe, and entred for to go to Cecyle,[2] but as god wold there arose

---

[1] Syria.   [2] Sicily.

a grete wynde which made the shyppe to arryue at the porte of Rome. When Alexis sawe this, anone he sayd to hymselfe, By the grace of god I wyl charge no man of Rome, I wyl go to my faders hous in suche wyse as I shal not be beknowen of ony person. And when he was within Rome he mette Eufemyen his fader which came fro y⁰ palays of y⁰ emperours wʰ a grete meyny ¹ followynge hym. And Alexis hys sone a poore man ranne cryenge and sayd. Sergeaunt of god haue pyte on me that am a poor pylgrym, and receyve me into thy hous for to haue my sustenaunce of y⁰ relefe yᵗ shall come fro thy borde, that god [may] blysse the, and haue pyte on thy sone, which is also a pylgrym. Whan Eufemyen herde speke of his sone, anone his herte began to melt and sayd to hys servauntes, Whiche of you wyl haue pyte on this man, and take y⁰ cure and charge of hym. I shall deliver hym from hys servage and make him free, and shall gyve hym of myn herytage. And anone he commysed ² hym to one of his servauntes, and commaunded yᵗ his bedde sholde be made in a corner of y⁰ hall, whereas comers and goers myght se hym. And the servaunt to whom Alexis was commaunded to kepe made anone his bedde under the stayr and steppes of the hall. And there he lay right like a poore wretche, and suffred many vylanyes and despytes of the servauntes of his fader, which oft tymes cast and threwe on hym y⁰ wasshynge of disshes and other fylth, and dyd to hym many euill turnes, and mocked hym, but he neuer complayned, but suffered all pacyently for the loue of god. Finally whan he had ledde this right holy lyfe wᵗin his faders hous in fastynge, in prayenge, and in penaunce by the space of vij yere, and knewe that he sholde soon dye, he prayed the servaunt yᵗ kepte hym to gyve hym a pece of parchement and ynke. And therein he wrote by ordre all hys lyfe and how he was maryed by the commaundement of his fader, and what he had sayd to hys wife, and of the tokens of hys rynge and bocle of hys gyrdell, that he had gyuen to her at his departynge, and what he had suffered for goddes sake. And all this dyd he for to make his fader to understande that he was his sone. After this whan it pleased god for to shewe and manyfest the vyctory of our lorde Jesu Christ in his servaunt Alexis. On a tyme on a sondaye after masse herynge all the people in the chirche, there was a voyce herde from god cryenge and sayenge as is sayd Mathei undecimo capitulo. Come unto me ye that labour and be trauayled, I shall comfort you. Of which voyce all the people were abasshed, whiche anone fell downe unto the erth. And the voyce sayd agayne. Seche ye the servaunt of god, for he prayeth for all Rome. And they sought hym, but he was not founden.

¶ Alexis in a mornynge on a good frydaye gaue his soul to god, and departed out of this worlde. And y⁰ same daye all the people assembled at Saynt Peters churche and prayed god yᵗ he wolde shewe to them where the man of god myght be founden yᵗ prayed for Rome. And a voyce was herde that came fro god that sayd. Ye shall fynde him in the hous of Eufemyen. And the people said unto Eufemyen, Why hast thou hydde fro us, thou hast suche grace in thy hous. And Eufemyen answered. God knoweth that I knowe no thynge therof.

¹ Many; Norm. Fr. Commonly a *household*. ² Committed.

¶ Archadius and Honorious y^t were emperours at Rome, and also ye pope Innocent commaunded y^t men shold go unto Eufemyens hous for to enquyre diligently tydynges of the man of god. Eufemyen went tofore with his servauntes for to make redy his hous agaynst the comynge of the Pope and emperours. And whan Alexis wyfe understode the cause, and how a voyce was herde that came fro god, sayenge. Seche ye ye man of god in Eufemyens hous, anon she sayd to Eufemyen. Syr se yf this poore man that ye have so long kepte and herberowed be the same man of god, I have well marked that he hath lyued a right fayre and holy lyfe. He hath euery sondaye receyved the sacrament of the awter. He hath ben ryght religyous in fastynge, in wakynge, and in prayer, and hath suffred pacyently and debonayrly of our servauntes many vylanyes. And when Eufemyen had herde all this, he ran toward Alexis and founde hym deed. He dyscouered his visage, whiche shone and was bryght as ye face of an aungell. And anone he returned towarde ye emperours and sayd. We have founden the man of god that we sought. And tolde unto them how he had herberowed hym, and how the holy man had lyued, and also how he was deed, and that he helde a byll or lettre in his hande which they might not drawe out. Anone the emperours with the pope went to Eufemyens hous, and came tofore the bedde where Alexis lay deed and sayd. How well that we be synners, yet neuertheless we governe ye worlde, and loo here is ye pope the generall fader of all the chirche, and gyve us the lettre y^t thou holdest in thyn hande, for to knowe what is the wrytyng of it. And the pope wente tofore and toke the lettre, and toke it to his notary for to rede. And ye notary redde tofore the pope, the emperours and all the people. And whan he came to the poynt that made mencyon of his fader and of his moder, and also of his wyfe, and that by the enseygnes[1] that he had gyuen to his wyfe at his departynge, his rynge and bocle of his gyrdle wrapped in a lytell purple clothe at his departynge. Anone Eufemyen fell downe in a swoone, and whan he came agayne to hymselfe he began to draw his heres and bette his brest and fell downe on the corps of Alexis his sone, and kyssed it, wepyng and cryenge in ryght grete sorrowe of herte, sayenge. Alas ryght swete son wherefore hast thou made me to suffre suche sorowe, thou sawest what sorowe and heuynes we had for the, alas why haddest thou no pite on us in so long tyme, how myghtest thou suffre thy moder and thy father wepe so moche for the, and thou sawest it well without takyng pyte on us. I supposed to have herd some tydynges of the, and now I se the lye deed, whiche sholdest be my solace in myne age, alas what solace may I haue that se my right dere son deed, me were better dye than lyve. Whan the moder of Alexis sawe and herd this, she came rennynge lyke a lyonesse and cryed, Alas! alas! drawing her heere in grete sorrowe, scratchynge her pappes with her nayles sayenge. These pappes haue gyven the souke, and whan she myght not come to the corps for the foyson of people y^t was come thyder, she cried and said. Make rome and waye to me sorrowfull moder y^t I may se my desyre and my dere son that

[1] Signs, tokens.

I have engendered and nourisshed. And as soon as she came to the body of her sone, she fell downe on it pyteously and kyssed it, sayenge thus. Alas for sorowe my dere son, y⁰ lyght of myn age, why hast thou made us suffre so moche sorow, thou sawest thy fader, and me thy sorowefull moder so ofte wepe for the, and woldest neuer make to us semblaunt of sone.[1] O all ye y^t haue y⁰ hert of a moder, wepe ye with me upon my dere sone, whome I haue had in my hous vij. yere as a poore man, to whome my servauntes have done moche vylany. A! fayre sone thou hast suffred them right swetely and debonayrly. Alas, thou that were my trust, my comforte, and my solace in myn olde age, how mightest thou hyde y⁰ from me, that am thy sorowfull moder, who shall gyve to myn eyen from hens forth a fountayn of teres for to make payne unto y⁰ sorowe of my herte. And after this came the wyfe of Alexis in wepyng throwynge herselfe upon the body, and with grete syghes and heuyness sayd, Right swete frende and spouse whome longe I haue desyred to se, and chastely I haue to y⁰ kept myselfe lyke a turtle y^t alone without make[2] wayleth and wepeth, and loo here is my ryght swete husbonde, whome I have desyred to se alyue, and now I se hym deed, fro hens forth I wote not in whome I shall haue fyaunce ne hope. Certes my solace is deed, and in sorowe I shall be unto y⁰ deth. For now fortho[3] I am y⁰ most unhappy amonge all women, and rekened amonge the sorowfull wydowes. And after these pyteous complayntes y⁰ people wepte for the deth of Alexis. The pope made the body to be taken up and to be put into a shryne, and borne unto y⁰ chirche. And whan it was borne through y⁰ cyte ryght grete foyson[4] of people came agaynst it and sayd. The man of god is founden y^t the cyte sought. Whatsomever sike body myght touch the shryne, he was anone heled of his malady.

There was a blynde man y^t recouered hys syght, and lame and other he heled. The emperour made grete foyson of golde and syluer to be throwen amonge y⁰ people for to make waye y^t the shryne myght passe. And thus, by grete labour and reuerence, was borne the body of Saint Alexis unto the churche of Saynt Bonyface, y⁰ glorious martyr. And there was the body put in a shryne moche honourably made of golde and syluer, y⁰ seuenth daye of Juyll.[5] And al the people rendred thankynges and laudes to our lorde God for his grete myracles, unto whome be gyuen honour, laude and glory in secula seculorum. Amen.[6]

From the preceding narratives, the reader may discover some of the most prominent features of Roman Catholic worship. Let us glance at the story. Here is a young man connected by the closest of all ties to a deserving female, whom he marries to read a theological lecture, and then leave a prey to irremediable regret. He associates with a number of squalid wretches, and exists on the pre-

---

[1] That is—*Show that thou wert our son.*   [2] Partner, companion.
[3] Henceforward.   [4] Plenty, number.   [5] July.
[6] From the *Golden Legend*, ed. 1526. Printed by Wynkyn de Worde, "*at the sygne of the Sonne*," in Fleet Street.

carious bounty of strangers in the most unprofitable, not to say knavish, indolence. In the mean time his broken-hearted parents are devoured by an intense anxiety, of which he is totally regardless. I pass the miraculous part of this veritable history; if Prince Hohenlohe's marvels deserve credit, it would be incongruous and inconsistent to refuse it here. Our "pious Æneas," disguised in the accumulated filth of seventeen years, returns to his father's house. Here he breeds a race of vermin; and luxuriously battens upon the garbage, which the servants, aware of his peculiar taste, plentifully, and one might think, properly, communicated. All this while he is an eye-witness, and an ear-witness, of the misery his absence occasions; and, as if to complete the perfection of such a character, he leaves behind him a scroll, of which the only effect must necessarily be to arouse a keener agony, and to quicken a dying despair. And this is the monstrous compound, which a voice from heaven proclaims holy, and which miracles are called in to sanction! This is to be emphatically, a "MAN OF GOD!" He who neglects every relative duty; he who is a cruel and ungrateful son, a bad husband, and careless master; he whose whole life is to consume time, not to employ it—to vegetate, but not to exist—to dream away life, with every sense locked up, every capability destroyed, every good principle uncultivated—and that too in the most loathsome and degraded condition—THIS, is to be a *Man of God!*

That the story before us contains a faithful picture of the times, and of many succeeding times; that it describes the prevailing tenets of popery, will be generally admitted. Some, indeed, whose charity "hopeth the best," will be ready to believe that the colours of an imaginative mind have been scattered along it; and that, however correspondent the outline may be, the sketch has been filled up by aid of exaggeration, while embellishment has stepped into the place of truth. But we have unfortunately too many prototypes in nature; history is too copious in examples to oblige us to have recourse to fiction for an illustrative comment. The life of Ignatius Loyola, the founder of the order of Jesus, presents a very singular and apposite confirmation of the remark: and I am happy to have received a most obliging permission to extract an able article on this subject from a late number of the *Retrospective Review*—a work which I have no hesitation in commending, whether for the soundness of its principles, the depth and accuracy of its researches, or the high intellectual superiority with which it has hitherto been conducted.[1]

"We must commence our history in the year 1491, which was

---

[1] This production deserves every share of public favour; and, large as the present sale is said to be, I have no doubt of its increase. The nature of the publication, confined as it is to past ages of literature, will probably preclude that circulation to which its merits justly entitle it; but no man who takes an interest fn the progress of the human mind, and who would know something of works formerly so popular, though now subjected to the mutabilities of human caprice, "to time and chance, which happeneth to all," will neglect an occasion of acquiring as much as investigation can achieve, or ability communicate. In support of these remarks I refer to an article on CHAUCER contained in the Seventeenth Number—not perhaps as the *best*, but as one among many good.

rendered important by the birth of Ignatius, who first saw the light
in Spain, in the district called Guipuscoa. Being descended from an
ancient family, the lords of Ognez and Loyola, and moreover well-
shaped and of a lively temper, his father destined him for the court,
where he was sent at an early age as page to king Ferdinand. In-
cited, however, by the example of his brothers, who had distinguished
themselves in the army, and his own love of glory, he soon grew
weary of the inactivity of a court life, and determined to seek renown
in war. He applied himself with great assiduity and success to his
military exercises, and soon qualified himself for the service of his
prince. It is said that on all occasions he displayed great bravery
and conduct; but the writers of his life being more interested in the
detail of his theological warfare,. have passed his military achievements with a slight notice, except the affair which was the more
immediate cause of what is called his conversion. This was the siege
of Pampeluna by the French; on which occasion Don Ignatius, then
about thirty years of age, displayed great gallantry, and was wounded
by a splinter in his left leg, and his right was almost at the same
moment broken by a cannon shot. The wounds were for a time considered dangerous; and the physicians declared that, unless a change
took place before the middle of the night, they would prove fatal: it
was therefore thought advisable that the sacrament should be administered to him. This fortunately happened to be the eve of St.
Peter, for whom Ignatius had a special veneration, and in whose
praise he had formerly indited certain Spanish verses. This early
piety, says Maffei, produced no small fruit, for before the critical
time of the night arrived, the apostle appeared to him in a vision,
bringing 'healing on his wings.'

"Another of his biographers conjectures that the prince of the
apostles effected his restoration to health, because he had a special
interest in the cure of a man destined by heaven to maintain the
authority of the Holy See against heresy. However this may be,
Ignatius assuredly recovered, although a slight deformity remained
on his leg, caused by the protrusion of a bone under the knee.
Grievously afflicted.that the symmetry of his person should be thus
spoiled, he determined to have the obnoxious bone cut off, and the
operation was performed almost without producing a change of
countenance in the hardy soldier. Notwithstanding all his care, however, his right leg always remained somewhat shorter than the left. Re-
strained from walking, and confined to his bed, he requested, in order
to amuse himself, to be furnished with some books of chivalry, the
sort of reading which chiefly occupied the attention of people of
quality at that time; but instead of *Palmerin of England,* or *Amadis
of Gaul,* they brought him *The Lives of the Saints.* At first he read
them without any other view than that of beguiling the time: but by
degrees he began to relish them, and at length became so absorbed
in the study of asceticism, that he passed whole days in studying
The Lives of the Saints, and finally made a resolution to imitate men
who had so distinguished themselves by warring against their own
flesh and blood. These aspirations were succeeded by his former
desire for military glory; but after various mental conflicts, and a

great deal of reflection, the charms of penance at length completely triumphed.

"For the purpose of gratifying this passion, he determined to go barefoot to the Holy Land, to clothe himself in sackcloth, to live upon bread and water, to sleep on the bare ground, and to choose a desert for his abode; but in the mean time, as his leg was not sufficiently well to allow him to carry his wishes into effect, in order in a slight degree to satisfy the longings of his soul, he spent part of the night in weeping for his sins; and one night, prostrating himself before an image of the blessed Virgin, he consecrated himself to the service of her and her Son. Immediately he heard a terrible noise. The house shook, the windows were broken, and a rent made in the wall, which was long after, and probably may at this day be seen. These extraordinary signs are not noticed by Maffei; but his less cautious brother, Riba-deneira, relates the fact, although he is in some doubt whether it was a sign of the approbation of the Deity, or of the rage of the devils, at seeing their prey ravished from them.

"Another night the Virgin appeared to him, holding her Son in her arms; a sight which so replenished him with spiritual unction, that from that time forward his soul became purified, and all images of sensual delight were for ever razed from his mind. He felt himself re-created, and spent all his time in reading, writing, and meditating on performing something extraordinary. At length he sallied forth from Loyola, where he had been conveyed after the siege of Pampeluna, and took the road to Montserrat, a monastery of Benedictines, at that time famous for the devotions of pilgrims, making by the way a vow of perpetual chastity, one of the instruments with which he proposed to arm himself in his contemplated combats. He had not ridden far before he fell in with a Moor, with whom he entered into conversation, and amongst other topics engaged in an argument about the immaculate purity of the blessed Virgin. The Moor agreed that, until the birth of Christ, Mary preserved her virginity; but he maintained that when she became a mother she ceased to be a virgin. The knight heard this treason against his Lady with the greatest horror; and the Moor, perceiving the discussion was tending to a disagreeable point, set spurs to his horse and made off. The champion of the honour of the blessed Virgin was for a while in doubt whether it was required of him to revenge the blasphemies of the Moor. He, however, followed him, until he arrived at a place where the road parted, one branch of it leading to Montserrat, and the other to a village whither the Moor was going; and being mindful of the expedient which errant knights of old frequently adopted to solve a doubt, he very wisely determined to be guided by his horse, and if the animal took the same road as the Moor, to take vengeance on him: if not, then to pursue his way in peace to Montserrat. The horse being of a peaceable disposition, took the road to Montserrat; and having arrived at a village, at the foot of the mountain on which the monastery stands, his rider purchased the equipage of a pilgrim, and proceeding to the monastery, sought out an able spiritual director, and confessed his sins, which he did in so full and ample a manner, and interrupted it with such torrents of tears, that his confession lasted three days. The next step which Ignatius took was to seek out a poor man, to whom, stripping himself to his shirt, he privately gave all his clothes; then, putting on his pilgrim's weeds, he returned to the church of the monastery.[1] Here, remembering that it was customary for persons to watch a whole night in their arms, previously to their being knighted, he determined in like manner to keep his vigil before the altar of his Lady; and suspending his sword upon a pillar, in token of his renouncing secular warfare, he continued in prayer the whole night, devoting himself to the Saviour and the blessed Virgin, as their true knight, according to the practice of chivalry.

"Early in the morning he departed from Montserrat, leaving his horse to the monastery, and receiving in exchange certain penitential instruments from his ghostly father. With his staff in his hand, his scrip by his side, bare-headed, one foot unshod (the other being still weak from his wound), he walked briskly to Manreza, a small town, about three leagues from Montserrat. Resolved to make Manreza illustrious by his exemplary penance, he took up his abode at the hospital for pilgrims and sick persons; he girded his loins with an iron chain, put on a hair shirt, disciplined himself three times a day, laid upon the bare ground, and lived upon bread and water for a week. Not content with these mortifications, he sometimes added to his hair shirt a girdle of certain herbs full of thorns and prickles. He spent seven hours every day in prayer, and frequently continued a length of time without motion. Considering, however, that this maceration of his body would advance him but a little way to heaven, he next resolved to stifle in himself all emotions of pride and self-love, and for this end, he studiously rendered himself disgusting, neglecting his person, and, to hide his quality, assuming a clownish carriage. With his face covered with dirt, his hair matted, and his beard and nails of a fearful length, but his soul filled with inward satisfaction, he begged his bread from door to door, a spectacle of scorn and ridicule to all the inhabitants and children of Manreza.[2] He persevered in this course, notwithstanding the suggestions of the wily enemy of mankind, who wished to tempt him to the world again, until a report was circulated that he was a person of quality, and the feelings of the people were converted from scorn and ridicule to admiration and reverence, whereupon he retreated to a cave in the neighbourhood.[3] The gloom of his new abode excited in him a lively, vigorous spirit of penance, in which he revelled with the utmost fervour, and without the least restraint. He chastised his body four or five times a day with his iron chain, abstained from food until exhausted nature compelled him to refresh himself with a few roots, and instead of praying seven hours a day, he did nothing but pray from morning until night, and again, from night until morning, lamenting his transgressions, and praising the mercies of God. These excessive indulgences mightily impaired his health, and brought on a disease of the stomach, which at intervals afflicted him, until the time of his death:

[1] Let the reader here turn to the "Life of Alexius," and particularly to page 33 of this volume.

[2] Compare with this account what is said of Alexius in page 34, *et seq.*

[3] Vide page 37.

the spiritual joys which they had formerly brought suddenly disappeared, he became melancholy, had thoughts of destroying himself, and then recollecting to have read of a hermit who, having fruitlessly petitioned for a favour from God, determined to eat nothing until his prayers were heard, he also resolved to do the same; he persevered for a week, and then at the command of his spiritual director left off fasting. His troubles ceased, and he now began to wax into a saint. He had a vision of the mystery of the Holy Trinity, of which he spoke, although he could only just read and write, with so much light, and with such sublime expressions, that the most ignorant were instructed and the most learned delighted. Nay, he wrote down his conceptions of this mystery, but we lament to say that his manuscript was unfortunately lost. His visions began to multiply, the most remarkable of which was an extacy, which lasted eight days, neither more nor less. These illuminations were so convincing, that he was heard to say that had the revelations never been recorded in Scripture, he would still have maintained them to the last drop of his blood. The heavenly favours he thus received he opened in part to his ghostly directors, but with this exception, he shut them up in his own heart. His efforts to conceal himself from the eyes of men were vain; his austerities and extacies, aided by the belief of his being a man of quality in disguise, attracted crowds of people to see and hear him, and he was pronounced—A SAINT.

*　　*　　*　　*　　*　　*　　*　　*　　*

"Notwithstanding that the necessary consequence of actions like these was to attract the attention of the world, he is described as being desirous of withdrawing himself from the notice and esteem of men, and he resolved to carry into execution a design, which he had long nourished, of visiting the Holy Land. He accordingly proceeded to Barcelona, where he embarked on board a ship about to sail for Italy, landed at Gayeta in 1523, and proceeded on foot to Rome, where he received the Pope's benediction, and obtained permission to make a pilgrimage to Jerusalem. From Rome he went to Venice, where he embarked, and arrived at Jerusalem on the 4th of September in that year.

"Here his heart was touched with the most tender devotion, and he began to deliberate whether he should fix his residence on the illustrious soil of Judæa, and apply himself to the conversion of the infidels. For his greater satisfaction, he consulted the superior of the Franciscans, who had the care of the Holy Sepulchre; the superior remitted him to the Father Provincial, who counselled him to return to Europe: but Ignatius, having some scruples about abandoning his design, answered the Provincial, that nothing but the fear of displeasing God should make him leave the Holy Land. 'Why then,' said the Provincial, 'you shall be gone to-morrow; I have power from the holy see to send back what pilgrims I please, and you cannot resist me without offending God.' Ignatius submitted without another word, left Jerusalem on the following day, and arrived at Venice about the end of January, 1524. A Spanish merchant at this place forced him to take fifteen or sixteen reals, but on his coming to Ferrara he gave a real to the first beggar that held out his hand; a second came, and he gave him another. These liberalities drew all the beggars to him, and he refused none so long as his money lasted, and when he had done he began to beg himself, whereupon they cried out, *A saint, a saint!*[1] He needed no more to make him leave the place; he continued his journey through Lombardy to Genoa, where he embarked for Barcelona. During his voyage from the Holy Land, he had reflected a good deal on the subject of converting the infidels, and considering that without the aid of human learning his efforts would be comparatively inefficacious, he determined to put himself under the care of Ardebalo, the master of the grammar school at Barcelona. He was now thirty-three years of age. On his arrival at Barcelona, he fell to the study of the rudiments of the Latin language, and went every day to school with the little children; but whilst his master was explaining the rules of grammar, he was deeply engaged with the mysteries of faith. This distraction of attention he ascribed to the powers of darkness, and made a vow to continue his studies with greater application; nay, he requested of Ardebalo to require the same task from him as the rest of the boys, and if he did not perform . it, to punish him as he punished them, by reprimands and stripes. We do not learn whether the master was necessitated to quicken his scholar's diligence in the way suggested, but it is certain that he now proceeded in his studies with much greater facility. About this time he read the *Enchiridion Militis Christiani* of Erasmus, which had been recommended to him, but finding that it wanted fervour, and, in fact, diminished his devotion and exercises of piety (and was probably reducing him to a reasonable Christian), he threw away the book, and conceived such a horror of it, that he would never read it more, and when he became General of the Jesuits, ordered that the society should not read the works of Erasmus. Being re-established in his health, he renewed his austerities, but, for the sake of study, retrenched a part of his seven hours of prayer. John Pascal, a devout youth, the son of the woman with whom he lodged, would frequently rise in the night to observe what Ignatius was doing in his chamber, and sometimes he saw him on his knees, at others prostrate on the ground, and once he *thought* he saw him elevated from the earth, and surrounded with light, or as Butler expresses it in his *Hudibras*—

> "'Hang like Mahomet in th' air,
>   Or Saint Ignatius at his prayer.'

"But whilst Ignatius was labouring after his own perfection, he did not neglect that of his neighbour, employing those hours which were not devoted to study, in withdrawing souls from vice, by striking examples and edifying discourses. Remarkable instances of his success are related, and on one occasion his interference cost him, to his inward delight, a sound external bastinado, which occasioned fifty days of sickness and pain. Having continued nearly two years at Barcelona, he was advised to pursue a course of philosophy at the University of Alcala, to which place he went accompanied by three young men, whom he had brought into the way of virtue, and who

[1] See page 33.

had desired to accompany him: to them he added a fourth on his arrival at Alcala. He had no sooner arrived than he began to study with such extreme eagerness, applying himself to so many sciences at once, that his understanding became confused, and his labour produced no fruits. Disheartened with his little progress, he employed his time in prayer, in catechising children, and attending the sick in the hospital. The marvellous changes effected by Ignatius in Alcala through his preaching and remonstrances, at length gave rise to a rumour that he was either a magician or a heretic, which coming to the ears of the inquisitors at Toledo, they were induced to believe that he was an Illuminato or Lutheran, and in order to investigate the matter, they came to Alcala to take his examination upon the spot. After an exact inquiry, Ignatius was pronounced innocent, but was admonished by the Grand Vicar that he and his companions, not belonging to any religious order, must not dress in uniform habits, and he forbid him to go barefoot, with both which commands he complied, and ever after wore shoes.

* * * * * * * * * *

"About this time, Ignatius being afflicted with indisposition, partly from his austerities, and partly from the climate of Paris, was advised by his physicians to try the benefit of his native air; an advice which he the more readily adopted, partly because three of his companions had some business to transact in Spain before they could absolutely renounce all their worldly goods, and partly that he might repair the scandal of his youth by his present virtuous demeanour. Having committed the care of the society to Faber, he departed for his native country; making use, however, of a horse, on account of the weakness of his foot. He went to Azpetia, a town near the castle of Loyola, where the clergy, hearing of his approach, assembled to receive him. He refused, however, to take up his abode with his brother at the castle of Loyola; and instead of making use of the bed and provisions which he sent to him at the hospital, he chose to lie on the bed of a poor man, taking care, however, every morning to disarrange the other, as if he had slept in it; and distributed the provisions he received from Loyola amongst the poor, and begged his bread about the town. Once only he went, 'upon compulsion,' to visit the inmates of Loyola, the sight of which renewed the memory of his former life, and inspired him with an ardent love of mortification. In consequence, he forthwith put on a sharp hair shirt, girded himself with a great chain of iron, and disciplined himself every night. He catechised the children, he preached every Sunday, and two or three times in the week besides; until, the churches not being able to contain the great crowds who came to hear him, he was obliged to hold forth in the open fields, 'et auditores arbores complere cogerentur.' The first time he preached, he told the assembly that he had been, for a long time, grievously afflicted by a sin of his youth:—he had, he said, with other boys, broken into a garden, and carried off a quantity of fruit; an offence for which an innocent person was sent to prison, and condemned to pay damages. 'I, therefore,' he proceeded, 'am the offender; he is the innocent person: I have sinned—I have erred!' and he called before him the man, who by chance was present, and gave him, before the public, two farms, which belonged to him. We shall pass over the particular circumstances of success which attended his preaching : it will be sufficient to apprize our readers, that as soon as he preached against the immodest attire of the women, it disappeared ; that the same day he denounced gaming, the gamesters threw their dice into the river ; that the courtezans made holy pilgrimages on foot, and the blasphemers ceased to curse.

* * * * * * * * *

" Although this sketch of the life of Ignatius Loyola bears no proportion to the details which have been given of it by about twenty biographers, it is, we conceive, sufficiently ample to enable the reader to form a correct judgment of his character. It has been thought that the society of Jesuits owed its origin to the enthusiasm, rather than the policy, of its founder.[1] Let the reader trace him from his conversion to his death, follow him through his rigorous infliction of self-punishment, his fastings until exhausted nature was ready to sink under his severe austerities, his voluntary beggary, his growing reputation for sanctity, his flight from public notice and reverence whilst he pursued the very means to obtain them, his being stamped a saint, his application to human learning, the unfolding of his views, the alteration in his austerities, in his habits of life and mode of dress, and he will probably be of a different opinion. Enthusiasm was doubtless the inspiring fountain at which he first drank ; not so much, however, the enthusiasm of an ardent and noble mind, as a preternatural excitement caused by the sort of reading to which accident invited him, working on a debilitated and feverish frame. His enthusiasm, after the first ebullition, seems to have had a method in it ; it led him to just so much voluntary suffering as was necessary to gain him the reputation of a saint, and it was probably at that species of fame that he at first aimed : his affected humility was ostentation ; his pretended seclusion, notoriety ; he did not conceal from his left hand what his right hand did, he distributed the alms he had acquired to beggars, and as soon as he had done began to beg himself, to the admiration of the professors of mendicity ; and it was no wonder they should cry out, A SAINT, A SAINT ! He did not retire into trackless deserts like the 'eremites' of old, but, like a retiring beauty, suffered his flight from the world to be seen, and was shocked when he was followed. Whilst rendering himself an object of loathing and disgust, and attenuating his body to the proper point of sanctity, it was swelling with holy pride and inward gratulation ; but as soon as this part of his object was once accomplished, he threw off his tattered robes and iron chain, he diminished his hours of prayer, and grander prospects and mightier power began to open before him. Not that he would have hesitated to continue them for the purpose of preserving his reputation or securing an important object ; but what is to be remarked, is, that those things which he had formerly considered indispensable were now no longer thought so, and that without any change of the circumstances which

[1] Robertson's *Charles V.*, vol. iii. b. 6. Bayle, Art. LOYOLA.

originally made them necessary, and it is not sufficient to resort to visions to account for the change. For, although an enthusiastic imagination might see such things 'in dim perspective,' the whole of the conduct of Ignatius marks him to be a cool, persevering, and calculating politician,[1] and the visions themselves ceased, when no longer required to spread his name and consolidate his power. Though influenced by motives of ambition, they were not those of wealth or rank, but of real, substantial power; and, although some obscure thoughts of framing a religious Order might have obtruded npon his meditations at Manreza, it is probable that the precise nature of it was only gradually unfolded, and not completed until he was about to leave Paris." [2]

The latter part of the life of Ignatius Loyola bears no proportion to its outset. Enthusiasm had abated, and policy was the cynosure of his subsequent career. In this he differs from Alexius; as he became more active, he became less a SAINT; and as his mind opened, and reason assumed her proper station, he gradually lost the fanatic in the designing founder of a sect. What he retained of fanaticism was chiefly external and artificial; but the leading features of his life accord surprisingly with the legendary character of the text. Had Loyola remained always ignorant, he had been always a bigot; and, judging by the commencement of the life, would have died as useless and as burdensome to society as the son of the senator Eufemian.

NOTE 3. Page 48.

" This story is told in Caxton's GOLDEN LEGENDE, and in the Metrical Lives of the Saints. Hence Julian, or Saint Julian, was called *hospitator*, or the *gode herberjour;* and the Pater Noster became famous, which he used to say for the souls of his father and mother, whom he had thus unfortunately killed. The peculiar excellencies of this prayer are displayed by Boccace. Chaucer, speaking of the hospitable disposition of his Frankelein, says—

<blockquote>" 'Saint Julian he was in his own countre.' [3]</blockquote>

"This history is, like the last, related by our compilers in the words of Julian's Legend, as it stands in Jacobus de Voragine. Bollandus has inserted Antoninus's account of this saint, which appears also to be literally the same. It is told, yet not exactly in the same words, by Vincent of Beauvais."—WARTON.

The passage in Boccacio, above alluded to, is as follows:—

" Falling from one discourse to another, they began to talk of such prayers as men (in journey) use to salute God with all: and one of the thieves (they being three in number) spake thus to Rinaldo:

[1] Though his biographers considered him of an ardent temperament, his physicians thought him of a phlegmatic constitution.

[2] *Retrospective Review*, No. XVII.   [3] Prol. v. 342.

Sir, let it be no offence that I desire to know, what prayer you most use when you travel on the way? Whereto Rinaldo replied in this manner: To tell you true, sir, I am a man gross enough in such divine matters, as meddling more with merchandize, than I do with books. Nevertheless, at all times, when I am thus in journey, in the morning before I depart my chamber, I say a *Pater Noster* and an *Ave Maria* for the souls of the father and mother of St. Julian; and after that, I pray God and St. Julian to send me a good lodging at night. And let me tell you, sir, that very oftentimes heretofore, I have met with many great dangers upon the way, from all which I escaped, and evermore (when night drew on) I came to an exceeding good lodging. Which makes me believe that Saint Julian (in honour of whom I speak it) hath begged of God such great grace for me: and methinks, that if any day I should fail of this prayer in the morning, I cannot travel securely, nor come to a good lodging. No doubt then, sir, (quoth the other) but you have said that prayer this morning? I would be sorry else, said Rinaldo; such an especial matter is not to be neglected."—*Second Day, Novel II.* 1684.

Note 4. Page 55.

" Certaine trochisks [1] there be made of a viper, called by the Greeks *theriaci*: for which purpose they cut away at both ends as toward the head as the taile, the breadth of foure fingers, they rip her bellie also, and take out the garbage within: but especially they rid away the blew string or veine that sticketh close to the ridge-bone. Which done, the rest of the bodie they seeth in a pan with water and dill seed, until such time as all the flesh is gone from the chine: which being taken away, and all the prickie bones thereto belonging, the flesh remaining they incorporate with fine flower, and reduce into troches, which being dried in the shade, are reserved for diverse uses, and enter into many soveraigne antidots and confections. But here it is to bee noted, that although these troches bee called theriaci,[2] yet are they made of *viper*'s flesh onely. Some there be, who after a viper is cleansed, as is above said, take out the fat, and seeth it with a sextar of oile untill the one halfe bee consumed: which serveth to drive away all venomous beasts, if three drops of this ointment be put into oile, and therewith the bodie be anointed all over."—*Pliny's Nat. Hist.* b. 29, c. iv. trans. by Philemon Holland. Ed. 1601.

Note 5. Page 56.

This figment is clearly Eastern. There is a similar story in the veritable *Voyages and Travels of Sir John Mandevile* :—

[1] A trochisk [Latin, *trociscus*] is a kind of medicinal pill or pastille.
[2] Derived from θήρ or θηρίον, a wild beast.

"There was a man that was called Catolonapes, he was ful rich, and had a fair castle on a hill, and strong, and he made a wal all about ye hill right strong and fayre, within he had a fair gardeine wherin were many trees bearing all maner of fruits y^t he might fynd, and he had planted therin al maner of herbs of good smel and that bare flowers, and ther wer many faire wels, and by them wer made many hals and chambers wel dight w^t gold and asure, and he had made there dyverse stories of beastes and birds y^t song and turned by engin and orbage as they had been quick, and he had in his gardeine al thing that might be to man solace and comfort, he had also in that gardeine maydens within ye age of xv yeare, the fairest y^t he myght find, and men children of the same age, and they were clothed with cloth of gold, and he said that they were aungels, and he caused to be made certain hils and enclosed them about w^t precious stones of jasper and christal, and set in gold and pearls, and other maner of stones, and he had made a condute [1] under ye earth, so that whan he wold ye wals ran sometime with milke, sometime with wine, sometime with honey, and this place is called Paradise, and when any yong bachelor of the countrey, knight or sqyer, cometh to him for solace and disport, he ledeth them into his paradise, and sheweth them these things as the songs of birds, and his damosels, and wels; and he did strike diuerse instruments of musyke, in a high tower that might be heard, and sayd they were aungels of god, and that place was paradise, that god hath graunted to those that beleued, when he sayd thus: *Dabo vobis terram fluentem lacte et melle;* that is to say, I shall give you land flowing with mylk and hony. And than this rych man dyd these men drinke a maner of drinke, of which they were dronken, and he sayd to them, if they wold dye for his sake, when they were dead, they shold come to his paradise, and they shold be of the age of those maydens, and shold dwell alway with them, and he shold put them in a fayrer paradise where they shold se god in joy, and in his maiesty: and then they graunted to do that he wold, and he bade them go and sleay such a lord, or a man of the countrey that he was wroth with, and that they shold haue no dread of no man. And if they were slaine themselfe for his sake, he shold put them in his paradise when they were dead. And so went these bachelors to sleay great lords of the countrey, and were slain themselfe in hope to have that paradise, and thus he was avenged of his enemies thro his desert, and when rich men of the countrey perceived this cautell and malice, and the will of this Catolonapes, they gathered them together and assayled the castel and slew hym and destroyed all his goods and his faire places and riches that were in his paradise; and the place of the walls is there yet, and some other things, but the riches are not, and it is not long ago since it was destroyed."—CHAP. XC.

The latter part of this fable is the story of the Assassins, whose Iman or leader was known by the appellation of the " Old Man of the Mountains."

From Mandevile (or rather from Purchas's *Pilgrim*, where similar accounts are met with), Mr. Southey, in his splendid poem of

---

[1] Conduit.

" THALABA," has borrowed the idea of Aloadin's enchanted garden.
See Book VII.

NOTE 6.   Page 106.

" On this there is an ancient French MORALITE, entitled, '*L'Orgueil
et Presomption de l'Empereur* JOVINIAN.' This is also the story of
ROBERT king of Sicily, an old English poem or romance."—WARTON.

An entertaining abstract of this old romance is here added, from
Mr. Ellis's *Specimens.*

"ROBERT OF CYSILLE.

" Robert king of Sicily, brother to Pope Urban and to Valemond
emperor of Germany, was among the most powerful and valorous
princes of Europe; but his arrogance was still more conspicuous than
his power or his valour. Constantly occupied by the survey of his
present greatness, or by projects for its future extension, he considered
the performance of his religious duties as insufferably tedious; and
never paid his adorations to the Supreme Being without evident
reluctance and disgust. His guilt was great; and his punishment
was speedy and exemplary.

" Once upon a time, being present during vespers on the eve of
St. John, his attention was excited by the following passage in the
Magnificat; 'deposuit potentes de sede, et exaltavit humiles.' He
inquired of a *clerk* the meaning of these words; and, having heard
the explanation, replied that such expressions were very foolish, since
he, being the very flower of chivalry, was too mighty to be thrown
down from his seat, and had no apprehension of seeing others exalted
at his expense. The clerk did not presume to attempt any remon-
strance; the service continued; Robert thought it longer and more
tedious than ever; and at last fell fast asleep.

" His slumber was not interrupted, nor indeed noticed by any of
the congregation, because an angel having in the mean time assumed
his features, together with the royal robes, had been attended by the
usual officers to the palace, where supper was immediately served.
Robert, however, awaked at the close of day; was much astonished
by the darkness of the church, and not less so by the solitude which
surrounded him. He began to call loudly for his attendants, and at
length attracted the notice of the sexton, who, conceiving him to be a
thief secreted in the church for the purpose of stealing the sacred
ornaments, approached the door with some precaution, and transmitted
his suspicions through the key-hole. Robert indignantly repelled
this accusation, affirming that he was the king; upon which the
sexton, persuaded that he had lost his senses, and not at all desirous
of having a madman under his care, opened the door, and was glad
to see the supposed maniac run with all speed to the palace. But the
palace gates were shut; and Robert, whose temper was never very
enduring, and was now exasperated by rage and hunger, vainly attempted by threats of imprisonment, and even of death, to subdue the

contumacy of the porter. While the metamorphosed monarch was venting his rage at the gate, this officer hastened to the hall, and falling on his knees, requested his sovereign's orders concerning a madman, who loudly asserted his right to the throne. The angel directed that he should be immediately admitted; and Robert at length appeared, covered with mud, in consequence of an affray in which he had flattened the porter's nose, and had been himself rolled in a puddle by the porter's assistants.

"Without paying the least attention to the accidental circumstances, or the clamours of the wounded man, who loudly demanded justice, he rushed up to the throne; and though a good deal startled at finding not only that, and all the attributes of royalty, but even his complete set of features, in the possession of another, he boldly proceeded to treat the angel as an impostor, threatening him with the vengeance of the pope and of the emperor, who, he thought, could not fail of distinguishing the true from the fictitious sovereign of Sicily.

> " 'Thou art my fool!' said the angel;
> 'Thou shalt be shorn, every deal
> Like a fool, a fool to be;
> For thou hast now no dignity.
> Thine counsellor shall be an ape;
> And o [1] clothing you shall be shape.—
> He shall ben thine own fere:
> Some wit of him thou might lere,
> Hounds, how so it befalle,
> Shall eat with thee in the hall.
> Thou shalt eaten on the ground;
> Thy 'sayer shall ben an hound,
> To assay thy meat before thee;
> For thou hast lore thy dignity.'

> " He cleped a barber him before,
> That, as a fool, he should be shore,
> All around like a frere,
> An *hande-brede* [2] above the ear;
> And on his crown maken a cross. [3]
> He gan cry and make noise;
> And said they should all abye,
> That did him swich villainy, etc.

" Thus was Robert reduced to the lowest state of human degradation; an object of contempt and derision to those whom he had been accustomed to despise; often suffering from hunger and thirst; and seeing his sufferings inspire no more compassion than those of the animals with whom he shared his precarious and disgusting repast. Yet his pride and petulance were not subdued. To the frequent

---

[1] One; i.e. *in one*. [2] "A hand's breadth."
[3] "The custom of shaving fools, so as to give them in some measure the appearance of friars, is frequently noticed in our oldest romances."

inquiries of the angel, whether he still thought himself a king, he continued to answer by haughty denunciations of vengeance, and was incensed almost to madness, when this reply excited, as it constantly did, a general burst of laughter.

" In the mean time, Robert's dominions were admirably governed by his angelic substitute. The country, always fruitful, became a paragon of fertility ; abuses were checked by a severe administration of equal justice ; and, for a time, all evil propensities seemed to be eradicated from the hearts of the happy Sicilians—

> " Every man loved well other ;
> Better love was never with brother.
> In his time was never no strife
> Between man and his wife :
> Then was this a joyful thing
> In land to have swich a king.

" At the end of about three years arrived a solemn embassy from Sir Valemond the emperor, requesting that Robert would join him on holy Thursday, at Rome, whither he proposed to go on a visit to his brother Urban. The angel welcomed the ambassadors ; bestowed on them garments lined with ermine and embroidered with jewels, so exquisitely wrought as to excite universal astonishment ; and departed in their company to Rome.

> " The fool Robert also went,
> Clothed in loathly garnement,
> With fox-tails riven all about :
> Men might him knowen in the rout.
> An ape rode of his clothing ;
> So foul rode never king.

" These strange figures, contrasted with the unparalleled magnificence of the angel and his attendants, produced infinite merriment among the spectators, whose shouts of admiration were enlivened by frequent peals of laughter.

" Robert witnessed, in sullen silence, the demonstrations of affectionate regard with which the pope and the emperor welcomed their supposed brother ; but at length, rushing forward, bitterly reproached them for thus joining in an unnatural conspiracy with the usurper of his throne. This violent sally, however, was received by his brothers, and by the whole papal court, as an undoubted proof of his madness ; and he now learnt for the first time the real extent of his misfortune. His stubbornness and pride gave way, and were succeeded by sentiments of remorse and penitence.

" We have already seen, that he was not very profoundly versed in Scripture history, but he now fortunately recollected two examples which he considered as nearly similar to his own ; those of Nebuchadnezzar and Holofernes. Recalling to his mind their greatness and degradation, he observed that God alone had bestowed on them that power which he afterwards annihilated.

     " ' So hath he mine, for my gult;
       Now am I full lowe pult;
       And that is right that I so be:
       Lord, on thy fool have thou pitè

     " ' That error hath made me to smart
       That I had in my heart;
       Lord, I 'leved not on thee:
       Lord, on thy fool have thou pitè.

     " ' Holy writ I had in despite;
       Therefore reaved is my right;
       Therefore is right a fool that I be:
       Lord, on thy fool have thou pitè,' etc.

" The sincerity of his contrition is evinced, in the original, by a long series of such stanzas, with little variation of thought or expression; but the foregoing specimen will, perhaps, suffice for the satisfaction of the reader.

" After five weeks spent in Rome, the emperor, and the supposed king of Sicily, returned to their respective dominions, Robert being still accoutred in his fox-tails, and accompanied by his ape, whom he now ceased to consider as his inferior. When returned to the palace, the angel, before the whole court, repeated his usual question; but the penitent, far from persevering in his former insolence, humbly replied, ' that he was indeed a fool, or worse than a fool; but that he had at least acquired a perfect indifference for all worldly dignities.' The attendants were now ordered to retire: and the angel, being left alone with Robert, informed him that his sins were forgiven; gave him a few salutary admonitions, and added—

     " ' I am an angel of renown
       Sent to keep thy regioun.
       More joy me shall fall
       In heaven, among mine feren all,
       In an hour of a day,
       Than here, I thee say,
       In an hundred thousand year;
       Though all the world, far and near,
       Were mine at my liking:
       I am an angel; thou art king!'

" With these words he disappeared; and Robert, returning to the hall, received, not without some surprise and confusion, the usual salutations of the courtiers.

" From this period he continued, during three years, to reign with so much justice and wisdom that his subjects had no cause to regret the change of their sovereign; after which, being warned by the angel of his approaching dissolution, he dictated to his secretaries a full account of his former perverseness, and of its strange punishment; and, having sealed it with the royal signet, ordered it to be sent, for the edification of his brothers, to Rome and Vienna. Both received, with due respect, the important lesson : the emperor often recollected with tenderness and compassion the degraded situation of the valiant Robert; and the pope, besides availing himself of the story in a number of sermons addressed to the faithful, caused it to be carefully preserved in the archives of the Vatican, as a constant warning against pride, and an incitement to the performance of our religious duties."

The story of "The King of Thibet and the Princess of the Naimans" in the *Persian* and *Turkish Tales*, presents an incident somewhat similar. But the assumption of another's likeness is a common Eastern figment.

Note 7.   Page 141.

"This is the fable of Parnell's HERMIT, which that elegant and original writer has heightened with many masterly touches of poetical colouring, and a happier arrangement of circumstances. Among other proofs which might be mentioned of Parnell's genius and address in treating this subject, by reserving the discovery of the angel to a critical period at the close of the fable, he has found means to introduce a beautiful description, and an interesting surprise."— WARTON.

That the reader may compare the two stories the more readily, it is inserted here :—

THE HERMIT.

" FAR in a wild, unknown to public view,
From youth to age a reverend hermit grew,
The moss his bed, the cave his humble cell,
His food the fruits, his drink the crystal well :
Remote from men, with God he pass'd his days,
Pray'r all his business, all his pleasure praise.
    A life so sacred, such serene repose,
Seem'd heaven itself, till one suggestion rose ;
That vice should triumph, virtue vice obey,—
This sprung some doubt of Providence's sway :
His hopes no more a certain prospect boast,
Aud all the tenour of his soul was lost :
So when a smooth expanse receives imprest
Calm nature's image on its wat'ry breast,
Down bend the banks, the trees depending grow,
And skies beneath with answering colours glow :
But if a stone the gentle sea divide,
Swift ruffling circles curl on every side,
And glimmering fragments of a broken sun,
Banks, trees, and skies in thick disorder run.
    To clear this doubt, to know the world by sight,
To find if books, or swains, report it right,
(For yet by swains alone the world he knew,
Whose feet came wand'ring o'er the nightly dew)

He quits his cell; the pilgrim's staff he bore,
And fix'd the scallop in his hat before;
Then with the sun a rising journey went,
Sedate to think, and watching each event.
  The morn was wasted in the pathless grass,
And long and lonesome was the wild to pass;
But when the southern sun had warm'd the day,
A youth came posting o'er the crossing way!
His raiment decent, his complexion fair,
And soft in graceful ringlets wav'd his hair.
Then near approaching, 'Father, hail!' he cried,
And 'Hail, my son,' the rev'rend sire replied;
Words follow'd words, from question answer flow'd
And talk of various kind deceiv'd the road,
'Till each with other pleas'd, and loth to part,
While in their age they differ, join in heart.
Thus stands an aged elm in ivy bound,
Thus youthful ivy clasps an elm around.
  Now sunk the sun; the closing hour of day,
Came onward, mantled o'er with sober grey:
Nature in silence bid the world repose;
When near the road a stately palace rose;
There by the moon thro' ranks of trees they pass,
Whose verdure crown'd their sloping sides with grass.
It chanc'd the noble master of the dome
Still made his house the wand'ring stranger's home:
Yet still the kindness, from a thirst of praise,
Prov'd the vain flourish of expensive ease.
The pair arrive; the liv'ried servants wait;
Their lord receives them at the pompous gate.
The table groans with costly piles of food,
And all is more than hospitably good.
Then led to rest, the day's long toil they drown,
Deep sunk in sleep, and silk, and heaps of down.
  At length, 'tis morn, and, at the dawn of day,
Along the wide canals the zephyrs play:
Fresh o'er the gay parterres the breezes creep,
And shake the neighb'ring wood to banish sleep.
Up rise the guests, obedient to the call;
An early banquet deck'd the splendid hall;
Rich luscious wine a golden goblet grac'd,
Which the kind master forc'd his guests to taste.
Then pleas'd and thankful, from the porch they go;
And, but the landlord, none had cause for woe;
His cup was vanish'd; for in secret guise,
The younger guest purloin'd the glittering prize.
  As one who spies a serpent in his way,
Glist'ning and basking in the sunny ray,
Disorder'd stops to shun the danger near,
Then walks with faintness on, and looks with fear;

So seem'd the sire ; when, far upon the road,
The shining spoil his wily partner shew'd :
He stopp'd with silence, walk'd with trembling heart,
And much he wish'd, but durst not ask, to part ;
Murm'ring he lifts his eyes, and thinks it hard
That gen'rous actions meet a base reward.

While thus they pass, the sun his glory shrouds,
The changing skies hang out their sable clouds ;
A sound in air presag'd approaching rain,
And beasts to covert scud across the plain.
Warn'd by the signs, the wand'ring pair retreat,
To seek for shelter at a neighb'ring seat.
'Twas built with turrets on a rising ground,
And strong, and large, and unimprov'd around ;
Its owner's temper, tim'rous and severe,
Unkind and griping, caus'd a desert there.

As near the miser's heavy doors they drew,
Fierce rising gusts with sudden fury blew ;
The nimble light'ning mix'd with show'rs began,
And o'er their heads loud rolling thunders ran.
Here long they knock, but knock or call in vain,
Driv'n by the wind, and batter'd by the rain.
At length some pity warm'd the master's breast,
('Twas then his threshold first receiv'd a guest,)
Slow creaking turns the door with jealous care,
And half he welcomes in the shiv'ring pair ;
One frugal faggot lights the naked walls,
And nature's fervour thro' their limbs recalls :
Bread of the coarsest sort, with eager [1] wine,
(Each hardly granted) served them both to dine
And when the tempest first appear'd to cease,
A ready warning bade them part in peace.

With still remark the pond'ring hermit view'd,
In one so rich, a life so poor and rude :
' And why should such,' within himself he cried,
' Lock the lost wealth a thousand want beside ? '
But what new marks of wonder soon took place,
In every settling feature of his face ;
When from his vest the young companion bore
That cup the gen'rous landlord own'd before,
And paid profusely with the precious bowl
The stinted kindness of the churlish soul.

But now the clouds in airy tumult fly ;
The sun emerging opes an azure sky ;
A fresher green the smelling leaves display,
And, glitt'ring as they tremble, cheer the day ;
The weather tempts them from the poor retreat,
And the glad master bolts the wary gate.

[1] Sour.

While hence they walk, the pilgrim's bosom wrought
With all the travel of uncertain thought;
His partner's acts without their cause appear,
'Twas there a vice and seem'd a madness here,
Detesting that, and pitying this, he goes,
Lost and confounded with the various shows.

Now night's dim shades again involve the sky, ⎫
Again the wand'rers want a place to lie; ⎬
Again they search, and find a lodging nigh. ⎭
The soil improv'd around, the mansion neat,
And neither poorly low, nor idly great:
It seem'd to speak its master's turn of mind,
Content,—and not for praise, but virtue kind.

Hither the walkers turn with weary feet,
Then bless the mansion, and the master greet:
Their greeting fair, bestow'd with modest guise,
The modest master hears, and thus replies:
'Without a vain, without a grudging heart,
To him, who gives us all, I yield a part;
From him you come, for him accept it here,
A frank and sober, more than costly cheer.'
He spoke, and bid the welcome table spread,
Then talk'd of virtue till the time of bed,
When the grave household round his hall repair,
Warn'd by a bell, and close the hours with pray'r.
At length the world, renew'd by calm repose,
Was strong for toil, the dappled morn arose;
Before the pilgrims part, the younger crept
Near the clos'd cradle, where an infant slept,
And writh'd his neck: the landlord's little pride,
O strange return! grew black, and gasp'd, and died.
Horrors of horrors! what! his only son!
How look'd the hermit when the fact was done;
Not hell, tho' hell's black jaws in sunder part,
And breathe blue fire, could more assault his heart.

Confus'd, and struck with silence at the deed,
He flies, but trembling fails to fly with speed.
His steps the youth pursues: the country lay
Perplex'd with roads, a servant show'd the way:
A river cross'd the path; the passage o'er
Was nice to find; the servant trod before;
Long arms of oak an open bridge supplied,
And deep the waves beneath the bending branches glide.
The youth, who seem'd to watch a time for sin,
Approach'd the careless guide, and thrust him in:
Plunging he falls, and rising lifts his head,
Then flashing turns, and sinks amongst the dead.

Wild, sparkling rage inflames the father's eyes,
He bursts the bands of fear, and madly cries,
'Detested wretch '—but scarce his speech began,
When the strange partner seem'd no longer man.

His youthful face grew more serenely sweet;
His robe turn'd white and flow'd upon his feet;
Fair rounds of radiant points invest his hair;
Celestial odours breathe thro' purple air;
And wings, whose colours glitter'd on the day,
Wide at his back their gradual plumes display.
The form etherial bursts upon his sight,
And moves in all the majesty of light.

Tho' loud at first the pilgrim's passion grew,
Sudden he gaz'd, and wist not what to do;
Surprise in secret chains his words suspends,
And in a calm his settling temper ends.
But silence here the beauteous angel broke,
(The voice of Music ravish'd as he spoke):
'Thy pray'r, thy praise, thy life to vice unknown,
In sweet memorial rise before the throne:
These charms success in our bright region find,
And force an angel down to calm thy mind;
For this commission'd, I forsook the sky:—
Nay, cease to kneel—thy fellow-servant I.
'Then know the truth of government divine,
And let these scruples be no longer thine.
The Maker justly claims the world he made,
In this the right of Providence is laid;
Its sacred majesty thro' all depends,
On using second means to work his ends;
'Tis thus, withdrawn in state from human eye,
The Power exerts his attributes on high,
Your action uses, nor controls your will,
And bids the doubting sons of men be still.
'What strange events can strike with more surprise,
Than those which lately struck thy wond'ring eyes?
Yet, taught by these, confess the Almighty just,
And, where you can't unriddle, learn to trust!
'The great vain man, who far'd on costly food,
Whose life was too luxurious to be good;
Who made his iv'ry stands with goblets shine,
And forc'd his guests to morning draughts of wine,
Has, with the cup, the graceless custom lost,
And still he welcomes, but with less of cost.
'The mean, suspicious wretch, whose bolted door
Ne'er mov'd in pity to the wand'ring poor;
With him I left the cup, to teach his mind
That Heav'n can bless, if mortals will be kind.
Conscious of wanting worth, he views the bowl,
And feels compassion touch his grateful soul.
Thus artists melt the sullen ore of lead,
With heaping coals of fire upon his head;
In the kind warmth the metal learns to glow,
And loose from dross the silver runs below.

'Long had our pious friend in virtue trod,
But now the child half-wean'd his heart from God ;
(Child of his age) for him he liv'd in pain,
And measur'd back his steps to earth again.
To what excesses had his dotage run ?
But God, to save the father, took the son.
To all, but thee, in fits he seem'd to go,
(And 'twas my ministry to deal the blow,)
The poor fond parent, humbled in the dust,
Now owns in tears the punishment was just.
   ' But how had all his fortunes felt a wrack,
Had that false servant sped in safety back ;
This night his treasur'd heaps he meant to steal,
And what a fund of charity would fail !
Thus Heav'n instructs thy mind : this trial o'er,
Depart in peace, resign and sin no more.'
   On sounding pinions here the youth withdrew,
The sage stood wond'ring as the seraph flew.
Thus look'd Elisha, when to mount on high,
His Master took the chariot of the sky ;
The fiery pomp ascending left the view ;
The prophet gaz'd, and wish'd to follow too.
   The bending hermit here a pray'r begun,
' LORD, AS IN HEAV'N, ON EARTH THY WILL BE DONE.'
Then, gladly turning, sought his ancient place,
And pass'd a life of piety and peace."

"The same apologue occurs, with some slight additions and variations for the worse, in Howell's LETTERS; who professes to have taken it from the *speculative* Sir Philip Herbert's CONCEPTIONS to his Son, a book which I have never seen. These Letters were published about the year 1650. It is also found in the DIVINE DIALOGUES of Doctor Henry More, who has illustrated its important moral with the following fine reflections :—

"'The affairs of this world are like a curious, but intricately contrived comedy; and we cannot judge of the tendency of what is past, or acting at present, before the entrance of the last act, which shall bring in righteousness in triumph: who, though she hath abided many a brunt, and has been very cruelly and despitefully used hitherto in the world, yet at last, according to our desires, we shall see the knight overcome the giant. For what is the reason we are so much pleased with the reading romances and the fictions of the poets, but that here, as Aristotle says, things are set down as they should be; but in the true history hitherto of the world, things are recorded indeed as they are, but it is but a testimony, that they have not been as they should be? Wherefore, in the upshot of all, when we shall see that come to pass that so mightily pleases us in the reading the most ingenious plays and heroic poems, that long afflicted virtue at last comes to the crown, the mouth of all unbelievers must be for ever stopped. And for my own part, I doubt not but that it will so come to pass in the close of the world. But impatiently to

call for vengeance upon every enormity before that time, is rudely to
overturn the stage before the entrance into the fifth act, out of
ignorance of the plot of the comedy; and to prevent the solemnity of
the general judgment by more paltry and particular executions.'

"Parnell seems to have chiefly followed the story as it is told by
this Platonic theologist, who had not less imagination than learning.
Pope used to say that it was originally written in Spanish. This I
do not believe: but from the early connection between the Spaniards
and Arabians, this assertion tends to confirm the suspicion that it
was an oriental tale." [1]—WARTON.

NOTE 8. Page 176.

"In Adam Davie's GEST, or romance of ALEXANDER Nectabanus,
a king and magician, discovers the machinations of his enemies by
embattling them in figures of wax. This is the most extensive
necromantic operation of the kind that I remember, and must have
formed a puppet-show equal to the most splendid pantomime.

> " Barons were whilome wise and good,
> That this art well understood :
> And one there was Nectabanus
> Wise in this art, and malicious :
> When king or earl came on him to war,
> Quick he looked in the star ;
> Of wax made him puppéts,
> And made them fight with bats : [2]
> And so he learned, *je vous dis,*
> Ay to quell his enemy,
> With charms and with conjurisons : [3]
> Thus he essayed the regiouns,
> That him came for to assail,
> In very manner of battaile ;
> By clear candle in the night,
> He made each one with other fight,
> Of all manner of nations
> That comen by ship or dromouns, [4]
> At the last, of many londe
> Kings thereof had great onde, [5]
> Well thirty [6] y-gathered beoth,
> And bespeaketh all his death,
> King Philip of great thede, [7]
> Master was of that fede. [8]

[1] "I must not forget that it occurs, as told in our GESTA, among a collection of
Latin apologues, quoted above, MSS. HARL, 463, fol. 8a. The rubric is, *De Angelo
qui duxit Heremitam ad diversa Hospitia.*"—WARTON.
    [2] Clubs.   [3] Conjurations.
    [4] Swift-sailing vessels. Gr. δρόμος, or from δρομάς, a DROMEDARY.
    [5] "Jealousy or anger."—WARTON.   [6] Near thirty; i.e. *kings.*
    [7] Might.   [8] Feud.

He was a man of mighty hand,
And with him brought, of divers land,
Nine and twenty rich kings
To make on him bataylings : [1]
Nectabanus it understood ;
Y-changed was all his mood ;
He was afraid sore of harm :
Anon he did cast his charm,
His image he made anon,
And of his barons every one,
And afterward of his fone [2]
He made them together gone [3]
In a basin all by charm :
He saw on him fall the harm ;
He saw fly of his baróns
Of all his land distinctions, [4]
He looked, and knew in the star,
Of all these kings the great war.

" Afterwards he frames an image of the queen Olympias, or Olympia, while sleeping, whom he violates in the shape of a dragon.

" The lady lay upon her bed,
Covered well with silken web
In a chaysel [5] smock she lay,
And in a mantle of douay ; [6]
Of the brightness of her face
All about shone the place,—
Herbs he took in an herber, [7]
And stamped them in a mortar,
And wrung it in a box :
After, he took virgin wox, [8]
And made a puppet of the queen,
His art-table he 'gan unwene ; [9]
The queen's name in the wax he wrote,
While it was some deal hot :
In a bed he it dight,
All about with candle-light,
And spread thereon of the herbis :
Thus charmed Nectanabus.
The lady in her bed lay
About midnight, ere the day,
Whiles he made conjuring ;
She saw fly in her metyng [10]
She thought a dragon light ;
To her chamber he made his flight,
In he came to her bower
And crept under her coverture."

[1] Battles.   [2] Foes.   [3] Go.   [4] Most distinguished.
Qu. *Choisel ?* i.e. choice.   [6] A kind of cloth.   [7] A receptacle for herbs.   [8] Wax.
[9] His table or *book* of art he began to unclose.   [10] " *Dream.*"—WARTON.

"Theocritus, Virgil, and Horace have left instances of incantations conducted by figures in wax. In the beginning of the last century, many witches were executed for attempting the lives of persons, by fabricating representations of them in wax and clay. King James the First, in his DÆMONOLOGIE, speaks of the practice as very common; the efficacy of which he peremptorily ascribes to the power of the devil.[1] His majesty's arguments, intended to prove how the magician's image operated on the person represented, are drawn from the depths of moral, theological, physical, and metaphysical knowledge. The Arabian magic abounded with these infatuations, which were partly founded on the doctrine of sympathy.

"But to return to the GESTA ROMANORUM. In this story one of the magicians is styled *magister peritus*, and sometimes simply *magister*. That is, a *cunning man*. The title *magister* in our universities has its origin from the use of this word in the Middle Ages. With what propriety it is now continued I will not say. *Mystery*, anciently used for a particular art,[2] or skill in general, is a specious and easy corruption of *maistery* or *mastery*, the English of the Latin MAGISTERIUM, or *artificium*; in French *maistrise, mestier, mestrie*, and in Italian *magisterio*, with the same sense." [3]—WARTON.

"Niderus," says Heywood (*Hierarchie of the Blessed Angels*, p. 475), "speaketh of one Œniponte, a most notorious witch, who, by making a picture of wax, and pricking it with needles in divers parts, and then burying it under the threshold of her neighbour's house, whom she much hated, she was tormented by such grievous and insufferable prickings in her flesh, as if so many needles had been then sticking at once in her body. But the image being found and burned, she was instantly restored to her former health and strength."

These kinds of tales are innumerable, and appear to have been most implicitly believed.

NOTE 9.   Page 180.

This is an Eastern fiction, and is thus told in the *Turkish Tales* :—

"STORY OF A KING, A SOFI, AND A SURGEON.

"An ancient king of Tartary went abroad one day to take a walk with his beys. He met on the road an abdal, who cried out aloud, 'Whoever will give me a hundred dinaras, I will give him some good advice.' The king stopped to look on him, and said, 'Abdal, what is this good advice thou offerest for a hundred dinaras?' 'Sir (answered the abdal), order that sum to be given me, and I will tell

---

[1] Edit. 1603, 4to. b. ii. ch. iv. p. 44, et seq.
[2] For instance, "the art and *mystery* of printing."
[3] Chaucer calls his monk

——"fayre for the *maistre*,
    An out-rider that loved Venerie."—Prol. v. 165 ;

and from many other instances which I could produce, I will only add, that the search of the Philosopher's Stone is called in the Latin Geber INVESTIGATIO MAGISTERII.

it you immediately.' The king did so; and expected to have heard something extraordinary for his money; when the dervise said to him, ' Sir, my advice is this: Never begin any thing till you have reflected what will be the end of it.'

" At these words all the beys, and other persons that attended the king, burst out into laughter. 'It must be confessed·(said one of them), that this abdal knows some maxims that are very new.' ' He was not in the wrong (said another) to get paid beforehand.' The king, seeing that they all laughed at the dervise, said, ' You have no reason to laugh at the good advice this abdal has given me : though no man is ignorant, that, when we form any enterprise, we ought to meditate well upon it, and consider maturely what event it may produce. Nevertheless, for want of observing this rule, we engage every day in affairs of ill consequence. For my part, I value very much the dervise's advice. I will always bear it in my mind, and command it to be written in letters of gold on every door of my palace, on the walls, and on the goods; and that it be engraved on all my plate;' which was done accordingly.

" In a short time after this, a great lord of the court, urged on by ambition rather than any cause he had to complain of that prince, resolved to deprive him both of his crown and life. To this end, he found means to get a poisoned lancet, and applying himself to the king's surgeon, said to him, ' If thou wilt bleed the king with this lancet, here are ten thousand crowns in gold, which I give thee as a present. As soon as thou hast done the business, the throne is mine. I have already projected the means to mount it; and I promise thee, that, when I am king, I will make thee my grand vizier, and that thou shalt partake with me in the sovereign power.' The surgeon, blinded with the advantage of the proposal the great man had made him, accepted of it without the least hesitation. He received the ten thousand crowns in hand, and put the lancet in his turban, to use it when there should be an opportunity.

" An opportunity soon offered itself. The king wanted to be bled, and the surgeon was sent for. He came, and began to bind up the king's arm, while they placed a bason to receive the blood. The surgeon took the fatal lancet out of his turban, and was just going to open the vein, when accidentally casting his eye on the bason, he read these words that were engraved upon it : *Never begin any thing till you have first reflected what will be the end of it.* He instantly fell into a deep study, and said within himself, ' If I bleed the king with this lancet, he is a dead man. If he die, I shall certainly be seized, and put to death amidst dreadful torments. When I am dead, what will the crowns of gold that I have received avail me ?' Struck with these reflections, he put the poisoned lancet into his turban, and took another out of his pocket. The king, perceiving it, asked him why he changed his lancet. ' Sir (answered the surgeon), because the point of the first was not good.' ' Show it me (said the prince); I will see it.' Then the surgeon was almost struck dumb with fear, and seemed in great confusion. The king cried out, ' What means this concern thou art in? It conceals some mystery; tell me the reason of it, or thou diest this moment.' The surgeon, intimidated by these threats, threw himself at the king's feet, and said, 'Sir, if your majesty will grant me your pardon, I will confess the truth.' 'I do pardon thee (replied the king), provided thou hidest nothing from me.' Then the surgeon told him all that had passed between the great lord and himself, and confessed that the king owed his life to the words that were engraved on the bason.

"The king gave orders instantly to his guards to go and seize the great lord; and then, turning towards his beys, said to them, 'Are you still of opinion that you had reason to laugh at the dervise? Let him be found, and brought to me. An advice that saves the life of kings, whatever it costs, cannot be bought too dear.'"

NOTE 10.   Page 186.

"Spencer, in the 'FAERIE QUEENE,' seems to have distantly remembered this fable, where a fiend, expecting Sir Guyon will be tempted to snatch some of the treasures of the subterraneous HOUSE of RICHESSE, which are displayed in his view, is prepared to fasten upon him.

> "Thereat the fiend his gnashing teeth did grate,
> And grieved so long to lack his greedy prey;
> For well he weened that so glorious bait
> Would tempt his guest to take thereof assay:
> Had he so done, he had him snatched away
> More light than culver in the falcon's fist.

B. ii. C. viii. 34.

"This story was originally invented of Pope Gerbert, or Sylvester the Second, who died in the year 1003.   He was eminently learned in the mathematical sciences, and on that account was styled a magician. William of Malmesbury is, I believe, the first writer now extant by whom it is recorded; and he produces it partly to show that Gerbert was not always successful in those attempts which he so frequently practised to discover treasures hid in the earth, by the application of romantic arts.   I will translate Malmesbury's narration of this fable, as it varies in some of the circumstances, and has some heightenings of the fiction.

"'At Rome there was a brazen statue, extending the forefingers of the right hand; and on its forehead was written, *Strike here*. Being suspected to conceal a treasure, it had received many bruises from the credulous and ignorant in their endeavours to open it.   At length Gerbert unriddled the mystery.   At noonday, observing the reflection of the forefinger on the ground, he marked the spot.   At night he came to the place, with a page carrying a lamp.   There, by a magical operation, he opened a wide passage in the earth; through which they both descended, and came to a vast palace.   The walls, the beams, and the whole structure, were of gold: they saw golden images of knights playing at chess, with a king and queen of gold at a banquet, with numerous attendants in gold, and cups of immense size and value. In a recess was a carbuncle, whose lustre illuminated the whole palace; opposite to which stood a figure with a bended bow. As they attempted to touch some of the rich furniture, all the golden images seemed to rush upon them. Gerbert was too wise to attempt this a second time : but the page was bold enough to snatch from the table a golden knife of exquisite workmanship. At that moment all the golden images rose up with a dreadful noise; the figure with the bow shot at the carbuncle ; and a total darkness ensued. The page then replaced the knife, otherwise they both would have suffered a cruel death.'

"Malmesbury afterwards mentions a brazen bridge, framed by the enchantments of Gerbert, beyond which were golden horses of gigantic size, with riders of gold, richly illuminated by the most serene meridian sun. A large company attempt to pass the bridge, with a design of stealing some pieces of the gold. Immediately the bridge rose from its foundations, and stood perpendicular on one end : a brazen man appeared from beneath it, who struck the water with a mace of brass, and the sky was overspread with the most horrible gloom. Gerbert, like some other necromancers of the Gothic ages, was supposed to have fabricated a brazen head under the influence of certain planets, which answered questions. But I forbear to suggest any more hints for a future collection of Arabian tales. I shall only add Malmesbury's account of the education of Gerbert, which is a curious illustration of what has often been inculcated in these volumes, concerning the introduction of romantic fiction into Europe.

" ' Gerbert, a native of France, went into Spain for the purpose of learning astrology, and other sciences of that cast, of the Saracens ; who, to this day, occupy the upper regions of Spain. They are seated in the metropolis of Seville; where, according to the customary practice of their country, they study the arts of divination and enchantment. Here Gerbert soon exceeded Ptolemy in the astrolabe, Alchind in astronomy, and Tulius Firmicus in fatality. Here he learned the meaning of the flight and language of birds, and was taught how to raise spectres from hell. Here he acquired whatever human curiosity has discovered, for the destruction or convenience of mankind. I say nothing of his knowledge in arithmetic, music, and geometry, which he so fully understood, as to think them beneath his genius, and which he yet, with great industry, introduced into France, where they had been long forgotten. He certainly was the first who brought the algorithm from the Saracens, and who illustrated it with such rules as the most studious in that science cannot explain. He lodged with a philosopher of that sect.' "—WARTON.

NOTE 11. Page 190.

A similar story is in the *Decameron.* "The king conducted him then into the great hall, where (as he had before given order) stood two great chests fast locked, and in the presence of all his lords, the king thus spake: 'Signior Rogiero, in one of these chests is mine imperial crown, the sceptre royal, the mound, and many more of my richest girdles, rings, plate, and jewels, even the very best that are mine: the other is full of earth only. Chuse one of these two, and which thou makest election of, upon my royal word thou shalt enjoy it.'"—Tenth Day, Novel I.

In Gower's *Confessio Amantis* it again occurs, fol. 96:—

> " Anon he let two coffers make,
>   Of one semblance, of one make;
>   *   *   *   *   *   *
>   His own hands that one chest
>   Of fine gold, and of fine perie,[1]
>   The which out of his treasury
>   Was take, anon he filled full:
>   That other coffer of straw and mull,[2]
>   With stones mened [3] he filled also,
>   Thus be they full both two."

As in the other stories, the courtiers chuse the wrong casket; and

> " Thus was the wise king excused,
>   And they left off their evil speech,
>   And mercy of the king beseech."

It may also be found in the LXV. Nov. of the *Cento Novelle Antiche*.

"The story, however, as it stands in Gower, seems to be copied from one which is told by the hermit Barlaam to King Avenamore, in the spiritual romance, written originally in Greek, about the year 800, by Joannes Damascenus, a Greek monk, and entitled, BARLAAM AND JOSAPHAT. But Gower's immediate author, if not Boccace,[4] was perhaps Vincent of Beauvais, who wrote about the year 1290, and who has incorporated Damascenus's history of Barlaam and Josaphat, who were canonised, into his SPECULUM HISTORIALE. As Barlaam's fable is probably the remote, but original source, of Shakspeare's CASKETS, in the MERCHANT OF VENICE,[5] I will give the reader a translation of the passage in which it occurs, from the Greek original, never yet printed:—

"'The king commanded four chests to be made: two of which were covered with gold, and secured by golden locks, but filled with rotten bones of human carcasses. The other two were overlaid with pitch, and bound with rough cords; but replenished with the most precious stones and exquisite gems, and with ointments of the richest odour. He called his nobles together, and placing these chests before them, asked which they thought the most valuable. They pronounced those with the golden coverings to be the most precious, supposing they were made to contain the crowns and girdles of the king. The

---

[1] Pearls.   [2] Rubbish.   [3] Accompanied.
[4] This is most probable.
[5] The immediate source of Shakspeare's " Merchant of Venice " will be found in the INTRODUCTION.

two chests covered with pitch they viewed with contempt. Then said
the king, I presumed what would be your determination: for ye look
with the eyes of sense. But to discern baseness or value which are
hid within, we must look with the eyes of the mind. He then ordered
the golden chests to be opened, which exhaled an intolerable stench,
and filled the beholders with horror.'[1]

" In the METRICAL LIVES OF THE SAINTS, written about the year
1300, these chests are called *four fates,* that is, four *vats* or vessels."—
WARTON.

The historian goes on to observe that the romantic legend of
Barlaam and Josaphat contains strong traces of oriental composition;
and that it possibly originated with the monk whose name it bears,
or, at least, with " some devout and learned ascetic of the Greek Church,
and probably before the tenth century."

NOTE 12. Page 191.

There is a surprising similarity in the marvellous conversion here
spoken of, to that which is on record relative to Colonel Gardiner:—

" This memorable event happened towards the middle of July,
1719; but I cannot be exact as to the day. The major had spent the
evening (and, if I mistake not, it was the Sabbath) in some gay company, and had an unhappy assignation with a married woman, of what
rank or quality I did not particularly inquire, whom he was to attend
exactly at twelve. The company broke up about eleven; and
not judging it convenient to anticipate the time appointed, he
went into his chamber to kill the tedious hour, perhaps with some
amusing book, or some other way. But it very accidentally happened
that he took up a religious book, which his good mother or aunt had,
without his knowledge, slipped into his portmanteau. It was called,
if I remember the title exactly, *The Christian Soldier, or Heaven taken
by Storm;* and was written by Mr. Thomas Watson. Guessing by the
title of it that he should find some phrases of his own profession
spiritualized in a manner which he thought might afford him some
diversion, he resolved to dip into it; but he took no serious notice of
anything he read in it: and yet, while this book was in his hand, an
impression was made upon his mind (perhaps God only knows how),
which drew after it a train of the most important and happy consequences.

" There is indeed a possibility that, while he was sitting in this
attitude, and reading in this careless and profane manner, he might
suddenly fall asleep, and only dream of what he apprehended he saw.
But nothing can be more certain than that, when he gave me this
relation, he judged himself to have been as broad awake during the
whole time as he ever was in any part of his life; and he mentioned
it to me several times afterwards as what undoubtedly passed, not only
in his imagination, but before his eyes.

[1] MSS. Laud. c. 72. Bibl. Bodl. Compare Caxton's GOLDEN LEGENDE, fol. 393b,
and Su rius VITA SANCTORUM.

" He thought he saw an unusual blaze of light fall on the book while he was reading, which he at first imagined might happen by some accident in the candle. But lifting up his eyes, he apprehended, to his extreme amazement, that there was before him, as it were, suspended in the air, a visible representation of the Lord Jesus Christ upon the cross, surrounded on all sides with a glory; and was impressed as if a voice, or something equivalent to a voice, had come to him, to this effect (for he was not confident as to the very words), ' Oh, sinner! did I suffer this for thee, and are these the returns?' But whether this were an audible voice, or only a strong impression on his mind equally striking, he did not seem very confident; though, to the best of my remembrance, he rather judged it to be the former. Struck with so amazing a phenomenon as this, there remained hardly any life in him; so that he sunk down in the armchair in which he sat, and continued, he knew not exactly how long, insensible (which was one circumstance that made me several times take the liberty to suggest that he might possibly be all this while asleep). But however that were, he quickly after opened his eyes, and saw nothing more than usual.

" It may easily be supposed he was in no condition to make any observation upon the time in which he had remained in an insensible state; nor did he, throughout all the remainder of the night, once recollect that criminal and detestable assignation which had before engrossed all his thoughts. He rose in a tumult of passions not to be conceived, and walked to and fro in his chamber, till he was ready to drop down, in unutterable astonishment and agony of heart, appearing to himself the vilest monster in the creation of God, who had all his lifetime been crucifying Christ afresh by his sins, and now saw, as he assuredly believed, by a miraculous vision, the horror of what he had done. With this was connected such a view both of the majesty and goodness of God, as caused him to loathe and abhor himself, and to repent as in dust and ashes. He immediately gave judgment against himself, that he was most justly worthy of eternal damnation. He was astonished that he had not been immediately struck dead in the midst of his wickedness; and (which I think deserves particular remark) though he assuredly believed that he should ere long be in hell, and settled it as a point with himself for several months, that the wisdom and justice of God did almost necessarily require that such an enormous sinner should be made an example of everlasting vengeance, and a spectacle as such both to angels and men, so that he hardly durst presume to pray for pardon; yet what he then suffered was not so much from the fear of hell, though he concluded it would soon be his portion, as from a sense of that horrible ingratitude he had shown to the God of his life, and to that blessed Redeemer who had been in so affecting a manner set forth as crucified before him."—DODDRIDGE, *Life of Col. Gardiner*, p. 45, *et seq.*

Note 13. Page 193.

" Rubor Ægyptus,"—this I take to be the leprosy; which the following account from Pliny's *Natural History* seems to confirm:—

" This disease also began, for the most part, in the face, and namely it took the nose, where it put forth a little specke, or pimple, no bigger than a small lentill; but soone after, as it spread farther, and ran over the whole bodie, a man should perceive the skin to be *painted and spotted with divers and sundrie colours*, and the same uneven, bearing out higher in one place than another, thicke here but thin there, and hard every where ; rough also, like as if a scurfe or scab over-ran it, untill, in the end, it would grow to be blackish, bearing downe the flesh flat to the bones, whiles the fingers of the hands, and toes of the feet, were puffed up and swelled againe.   A peculiar malady is this, and *natural to the Ægyptians;* but looke when any of their kings fell into it, woe worth the subjects and poore people, for there were the tubs and bathing vessels wherein they sate in the baine,[1] filled with men's blood for their cure."—P. H. T. lib. xxvi. c. 2.

The leprosy was of different kinds, and that peculiar to the Egyptians might, perhaps, wear a red appearance.

NOTE 14.   Page 194.

The romance of " Sir Isumbras " in many respects corresponds with this story, and particularly with the striking incident detailed below:—

" The knight, afflicted by Heaven in consequence of his sins, was met by a part of his household, who, with many tears, informed him that his horses and oxen had been suddenly struck dead with light-ning, and that his capons were all stung to death with adders.   He received the tidings with humble resignation, commanded his servants to abstain from murmurs against Providence, and passed on.   He was next met by a page, who related that his castle was burned to the ground; that many of his servants had lost their lives; and that his wife and children had with great difficulty escaped from the flames. Sir Isumbras, rejoiced that Heaven had yet spared those who were most dear to him, bestowed upon the astonished page his purse of gold as a reward for the intelligence.

> " A doleful sight then gan he see ;
> His wife and his children three
>   Out of the fire were fled :
> There they sat, under a thorn,
> Bare and naked as they were born,
>   Brought out of their bed.
> A woful man then was he,
> When he saw them all naked be.

[1] Bath.

> The lady said, all so blive,
> ' For nothing, sir, be ye adrad.'
> He did off his surcote of *pallade*,[1]
> And with it clad his wife.
> His scarlet mantle then shore he;
> Therein he closed his children three
> That naked before him stood.

"He then proposed to his wife that, as an expiation of their sins, they should instantly undertake a pilgrimage to Jerusalem; and, cutting with his knife a sign of the cross on his shoulder, set off with the four companions of his misery, resolved to beg his bread till he should arrive at the holy sepulchre.

"After passing through 'seven lands,' supported by the scanty alms of the charitable, they arrived at length at a forest where they wandered during three days without meeting a single habitation. Their food was reduced to the few berries which they were able to collect; and the children, unaccustomed to such hard fare, began to sink under the accumulated difficulties of their journey. In this situation they were stopped by a wide and rapid though shallow river. Sir Isumbras, taking his eldest son in his arms, carried him over to the opposite bank, and placing him under a bush of broom, directed him to dry his tears, and amuse himself by playing with the blossoms till his return with his brother. But scarcely had he left the place when a lion, starting from a neighbouring thicket, seized the child, and bore him away into the recesses of the forest. The second son became, in like manner, the prey of an enormous leopard; and the disconsolate mother, when carried over with her infant to the fatal spot, was with difficulty persuaded to survive the loss of her two elder children. Sir Isumbras, though he could not repress the tears extorted by this cruel calamity, exerted himself to console his wife, and, humbly confessing his sins, contented himself with praying that his present misery might be accepted by Heaven as a partial expiation.

> "Through forest they went days three,
> Till they came to the Greekish sea;
> They grette,[2] and were full wo!
> As they stood upon the land,
> They saw a fleet come sailand,
> Three hundred ships and mo.
> With top-castels set on-loft,
> Richly then were they wrought,
> With joy and mickle pride:
> A heathen king was therein,
> That Christendom came to win:
> His power was full wide.

"It was now seven days since the pilgrims had tasted bread or

---

[1] *Palata*, Lat., *Paletot*, O. Fr., sometimes signifying a particular stuff, and sometimes a particular dress. See Du Cange.

[2] Grieved.

meat; the soudan's galley, therefore, was no sooner moored to the beach than they hastened on board to beg for food. The soudan, under the apprehension that they were spies, ordered them to be driven back on shore: but his attendants observed to him that these could not be common beggars; that the robust limbs and tall stature of the husband proved him to be a knight in disguise; and that the delicate complexion of the wife, who was 'bright as blossom on tree,' formed a striking contrast to the ragged apparel by which she was very imperfectly covered. They were now brought into the royal presence; and the soudan, addressing Sir Isumbras, immediately offered him as much treasure as he should require, on condition that he should renounce Christianity, and consent to fight under the Saracen banners. The answer was a respectful but peremptory refusal, concluded by an earnest petition for a little food; but the soudan, having by this time turned his eyes from Sir Isumbras to the beautiful companion of his pilgrimage, paid no attention to this request.

> " The soudan beheld that lady there,
>   Him thought an angel that she were,
>   Comen a-down from heaven:
> ' Man! I will give thee gold and fee,
>   An thou that woman will sellen me,
>   More than thou can *neven*.[1]
> I will thee given an hundred pound
> Of pennies that ben whole and round,
>   And rich robes seven;
> She shall be queen of my land;
> And all men bow unto her hand;
>   And none withstand her *steven*.'[2]
> Sir Isumbras said, 'Nay!
> My wife I will nought sell away,
>   Though ye me for her sloo!
> I wedded her in Godis lay,
> To hold her to mine ending day
>   Both for weal and wo.'

" It evidently would require no small share of casuistry to construe this declaration into an acceptance of the bargain; but the Saracens, having heard the offer of their sovereign, deliberately counted out the stipulated sum on the mantle of Sir Isumbras; took possession of the lady; carried the knight with his infant son on shore; beat him till he was scarcely able to move; and then returned for further orders."— *Specimens of E. E. Rom.* v. 111.

This accordance of Sir Isumbras with the tale in the *Gesta* has not been noticed by Mr. Ellis.

The story is found in Caxton's *Golden Legend,* and in the metrical *Lives of the Saints.*

---

[1] Name.   [2] Voice.

Note 15.　Page 219.

" From this beautiful tale, of which the opening only is here given, Occleve, commonly called Chaucer's disciple, framed a poem in the octave, which was printed in the year 1614, by William Browne, in his set of Eclogues called the SHEPHEARD'S PIPE. Occleve has literally followed the book before us, and has even translated into English prose the MORALIZATION annexed. He has given no sort of embellishment to his original, and by no means deserves the praises which Browne, in the following elegant pastoral lyrics, has bestowed on his performance, and which more justly belong to the genuine Gothic, or rather Arabian, inventor.

> " Well I wot, the man that first
> Sung this lay, did quench his thirst,
> Deeply as did ever one,
> In the Muses' Helicon.
> Many times he hath been seen
> With the faëries on the green,
> And to them his pipe did sound,
> As they danced in a round ;
> Mickle solace would they make him,
> And at midnight often take him,
> And convey him from his room
> To a field of yellow broom,
> Or into the meadows where
> Mints perfume the gentle air.
> And where Flora spreads her treasure,
> There they would begin their measure.
> If it chanced night's sable shrouds
> Muffled Cynthia in her clouds,
> Safely home they then would see him,
> And from brakes and quagmires free him.
> There are few such swains as he
> Now-a-days for harmony.[1]

" The history of Darius, who gave this legacy to his three sons, is incorporated with that of Alexander, which has been decorated with innumerable fictions by the Arabian writers. There is also a separate romance on Darius, and on Philip of Macedon."—WARTON.

" The story has been very properly termed by Mr. Warton a beautiful one ; but he has not been equally accurate in his statement, that 'Occleve has literally followed the book before us (i.e. the original *Gesta*), and has even translated into English prose the moralization annexed.' Occleve's immediate model was our English *Gesta ;* nor is it improbable that he might even be the translator of it ; the moralization, also, is entirely different. Mr. Warton has omitted to notice, that this story corresponds with that of Fortunatus ; which, unless itself of oriental origin, might have been taken from it."—DOUCE.

[1] Eclogue 1.

The incident of the magic cloth may be found in "The Story of Prince Ahmed, and the Fairy Pari Banou," in the *Arabian Nights' Entertainments,* vol. iii.

———

NOTE 16   Page 227

From this story, with very beseeming alterations, Dr. Byrom wrote the following tale of

THE THREE BLACK CROWS.

"Tale!" That will raise the question, I suppose,
"What can the meaning be of three black crows?"
It is a London story, you must know,
And happened, as they say, some time ago.
The meaning of it custom would suppress,
Till to the end we come: nevertheless,
Though it may vary from the use of old,
To tell the moral ere the tale be told,
We'll give a hint for once, how to apply
The meaning first, then hang the tale thereby.

   People full oft are put into a pother
For want of understanding one another;
And strange amusing stories creep about,
That come to nothing if you trace them out;
Lies of the day, perhaps, or month, or year,
Which, having served their purpose, disappear.
From which, meanwhile, disputes of every size,
That is to say, misunderstandings rise,
The springs of ill, from bick'ring up to battle,
From wars and tumults down to tittle-tattle.
Such as, for instance (for we need not roam
Far off to find them, but come nearer home),
Such as befall, by sudden misdivining,
On cuts, on coals, on boxes, and on signing,
Or on what now,[1] in the affair of mills,
To us and you portends such serious ills.
To note how meanings, that were never meant,
By eager giving them too rash assent,
Will fly about, just like so many crows,
Of the same breed of which the story goes,—
It may, at least it should, correct a zeal,
That hurts the public, or the private weal.

   Two honest tradesmen meeting in the Strand,
One took the other briskly by the hand;

———

[1] "Some local matters were then in agitation at Manchester, particularly an application to Parliament for a Bill to abrogate the custom of grinding wheat at the school mills."

"Hark ye," said he, "'tis an odd story this
About the crows!" "*I don't know what it is,*"
Replied his friend. "No! I'm surprised at that—
Where I come from it is the common chat.
But you shall hear—an odd affair, indeed!
And that it happened, they are all agreed.
Not to detain you from a thing so strange,
A gentleman that lives not far from 'Change,
This week, in short, as all the alley knows,
Taking a puke, has thrown up three black crows!"

"Impossible!" "Nay, but indeed 'tis true;
I had it from good hands, and so may you."
"*From whose, I pray?*" So having named the man,
Straight to inquire, his curious comrade ran.
"*Sir, did you tell —— ?*" relating the affair.
"Yes, sir, I did; and if 'tis worth your care,
Ask Mr. Such-a-one—he told it me;
But, by-the-by, 'twas Two black crows, not THREE."
Resolved to trace so wondrous an event,
Whip to the third the virtuoso went.
"Sir"—and so forth—"Why, yes; the thing is fact;
Tho' in regard to number not exact:
It was not Two black crows, 'twas only *One;*
The truth of *that* you may rely upon.
The gentleman himself told me the case."
"*Where may I find him?*" "Why, in such a place.'
Away goes he, and having found him out,
"*Sir, be so good as to resolve a doubt.*"

Then to his last informant he referred,
And begged to know if true what he had heard;
"*Did you, sir, throw up a black crow?*" "Not I?"
"*Bless me! how people propagate a lie!
Black crows have been thrown up,* THREE, TWO, *and* ONE,
*And here, I find, all comes at last to none.
Did you, say nothing of a crow at all?*"
"Crow! crow! Perhaps I might, now I recall
The matter over." "*And pray, sir, what was't?*"
"Why, I was horrid sick, and at the last
I did throw up, and told my neighbour so,
Something that was as *black*, sir, as a crow!"

Misc. Poems, vol. i. p. 31.

NOTE 17. Page 227.

"This is one of the most lively stories of Macrobius," says Warton.
It is detailed *Saturnal.* lib. ii. c. 6, "*De origine ac usu prætextæ*," page
147.—"Mos antea senatoribus fuit in curiam prætextatis filiis introire.

Cum in senatu res major quœpiam consultabatur; eaque in posterum diem prolata esset: placuit ut hanc rem, super qua tractavissent, ne quis enuntiaret priusquam decreta esset. Mater Papirii pueri, qui cum parente suo in curia fuerat, percunctatur filium, quidnam in senatu egissent patres: puer respondit tacendum esse, neque id dici licere. Mulier fit audiendi cupidior, secretum rei et silentium pueri animum ejus ad inquirendum everberat. Quærit igitur compressus violentiusque; tum puer urgente matre lepidi atque festivi mendacii consilium capit; actum in senatu dixit utrum videretur utilius magisque è republica esse, unusne ut duas uxores haberet, an ut una apud duos nupta esset. Hoc illa ubi audivit, animo compavescit; domo trepidans egreditur, ad cæteras matronas affert; postridieque ad senatum copiosa matrum-familias caterva confluunt. Lacrymantes atque obsecrantes orant una potius ut duobus nupta fieret, quam ut uni duæ. Senatores ingredientes curiam, quæ illa mulierum intemperies, et quid sibi postulatio istæc vellet, mirabantur; et ut non parvæ rei prodigium illam verecundi sexus impudicam insaniam pavescebant. Puer Papirius publicum metum demit; nam in medium curiæ progressus quid ipsi mater audire institisset, quid matri ipse simulasset; sicut fuerat, enarrat. Senatus fidem atque ingenium pueri exosculatur; consultumque facit uti posthac pueri cum patribus in curiam non introëant præter illum unum Papirium; eique puero postea cognomentum honoris gratia decreto inditum, *Prætextatus;* ob tacendi loquendique in prætextæ ætate prudentiam."

Note 18. Page 244.

" Next unto which I may mention the COCKATRICE, or BASILISK; now this is the king of serpents, not for his magnitude or greatness, but for his stately pace and magnanimous mind; for the head and half part of his body he always carries upright, and hath a kind of crest like a crown upon his head. This creature is in thicknesse as big as a man's wrist, and of length proportionable to that thickness: his eyes are red in a kind of cloudy blackness, as if fire were mixed with smoke. His poison is a very hot and venomous poison, drying up and scorching the grass as if it were burned, infecting the air round about him so as no other creature can live near him: in which he is like to the *Gorgon,* whom last of all I mentioned.

" And amongst all living creatures, there is none that perisheth sooner by the poison of the Cockatrice than man; for with his sight he killeth him: which is, *because* the beams of the Cockatrice's eyes do corrupt the visible spirit of a man; as is affirmed: which being corrupted, all the other spirits of life, coming from the heart and brain, are thereby corrupted also; and *so* the man dieth. His hissing, likewise, is said to be as bad, in regard that it blasteth trees, killeth birds, &c., by poisoning the air. If any thing be slain by it, the same also proveth venomous to such as touch it: only a weasel kills it.

" That they be bred out of an egg laid by an old cock, is *scarce* credible; howbeit some affirm with great confidence, that when the cock waxeth old ... there groweth in him, of his corrupted seed, a little egg with a thin film instead of a shell, and this being hatched by the toad, or some such like creature, bringeth forth a venomous worm, although not this basilisk, that king of serpents."—SWAN's *Speculum Mundi,* chap. ix. p. 486. 1635.

NOTE 19. Page 247.

The following apologue from the Latin Æsop is probably from the *Gesta Romanorum,* the former being collected in the early part of the fifteenth century :—

" *Of the Poor Man and the Serpent.*

" He that applies himself to do other men harm, ought not to think himself secure; wherefore Æsop rehearseth this fable. There was a serpent which came into the house of a poor man, and lived of that which fell from the poor man's table, for the which thing there happened great fortune to this man, and he became rich. But on a day this man was very angrie against the serpent, and took a sword and smote at him; wherefore the serpent went out of the house, and came no more thither again. A little after, this man fell again into great poverty, and then he knew that by fortune of the serpent he was become rich; wherefore it repented him that he had driven away the serpent. Then he went and humbled himself to the serpent, saying, I pray thee that thou wilt pardon me the offence that I have done thee. And the serpent said, Seeing thou repentest thee of thy misdeed, I forgive thee; but as long as I shall live, I shall remember thy malice; for as thou hurtedst me once, so thou maiest again. *Wherefore that which was once evil, shall ever so be held; men ought therefore not to insult over him of whom they receive some benefit, nor yet to suspect their good and true friends.*"—P. 83. 1658.

There is also a fable attributed to Avian (a Latin writer of the fourth century, who imitated Phædrus), to the following purport :—

" He that seeketh to get more than he ought, oft-times getteth nothing; as saith the fable. of a man which had a goose that laid every day an egge of gold. The man, out of covetousness, commanded her that every day she should lay two eggs: and she said to him, ' Certainly, my master, I may not.' Wherefore the man was wroth with her, and slew her; by means whereof he lost his former profit, and afterwards waxed very sorrowful."—1658.

But these stories, with some of modern manufacture, have all, probably, originated from the apologue of *Gabria,* or *Babria,* a Greek poet, who put the fables of Æsop into Iambic verse. The period in which he flourished is unknown.

Περὶ ὄρνιθος ὠὸν χρυσοῦν τικτούσης,
Καὶ φιλαργύρου.

Ἔτικτε χρυσοῦν ὠὸν ὄρνις εἰσάπαξ.
Καί τις πλανηθεὶς χρυσεραστὴς τὴν φρένα,
Ἔκτεινε ταύτην, χρυσὸν ὡς λαβεῖν θέλων.
Ἐλπὶς δε μεῖζον δῶρον ὤλεκεὶ τύχης.

[This poet's name is *Babrias*, not Babria, still less Gabria.—ED.]

NOTE 20.   Page 251.

"Gower, in the CONFESSIO AMANTIS, may perhaps have copied the circumstance of the morning trumpet from this apologue.

> "It so befell, that on a day
> There was ordained by the lawe
> A trump with a stern breath,
> Which was cleped the trump of death:
> And in the court where the king was,
> A certain man this trumpe of brass
> Hath in keeping, and thereof serveth,
> That when a lord his death deserveth,
> He shall this dreadful trump-*e* blow,
> Before his gate, to make it know,
> How that the judg-*e*-ment is give
> Of death, which shall not be forgive.
> The king when it was night anon,
> This man had sent, and bade him gone,
> To trumpen at his brother's gate;
> And he, which he might do algate,[1]
> Goeth forth, and doth the king's hest.
> This lord which heard of this tempest
> That he to-fore his gate blew,
> Then wist he by the law, and knew
> That he was surely dead, &c.

"But Gower has connected with this circumstance a different story, and of an inferior cast, both in point of moral and imagination. The truth is, Gower seems to have altogether followed this story as it appeared in the SPECULUM HISTORIALE of Vincent of Beauvais, who took it from Damascenus's romance of BARLAAM AND JOSAPHAT. Part of it is thus told in Caxton's translation of that legend, fol. 393 :

"'And the kynge hadde suche a custome, that when one sholde be delyvered to deth, the kynge sholde send hys cryar wyth hys trompe that was ordeyned thereto.   And on the even he sente the cryar wyth the trompe tofore hys brother's gate, and made to soune the trompe. And whan the kyngs brother herde thys, he was in despayr of sauinge hys lyfe, and colde not slepe of all the nyght, and made hys testament.

[1] Always.

And on the morne erly, he cladde hym in blacke: and came wyth wepyng with hys wyf and chyldren to the kynges paleys. And the kynge made hym to come tofore hym, and sayd to hym, A fooll that thou art, that thou hast herde the messagere of thy brother, to whom thou knowest well thou hast not trespaced, and doubtest so mooche. Howe oughte not I then ne doute the messagures of our Lorde agaynst whom I have soo ofte synned, which signefyed unto me more clerely the deth than the trompe.'"—WARTON.

NOTE 21.　Page 265.

" *Enter* PERICLES, *with Attendants*.

" *Per*. Lord governor, for so we hear you are,
Let not our ships and number of our men
Be, like a beacon fired, to amaze your eyes.
We have heard your miseries as far as Tyre,
And seen the desolation of your streets:
Nor come we to add sorrow to your tears,
But to relieve them of their heavy load ;
And these our ships you happily may think [1]
Are, like the Trojan horse, war-stuff'd within,
With bloody views, expecting overthrow,
Are stored with corn, to make your needy bread,
And give them life, who are hunger-starved, half dead.
" *All*. The gods of Greece protect you !
And we'll pray for you.
" *Per*.　　　　　　Rise, I pray you, rise ;
We do not look for reverence, but for love,
And harbourage for ourself, our ships, and men.
" *Cle*. The which when any shall not gratify,
Or pay you with unthankfulness in thought,
Be it our wives, our children, or ourselves,
The curse of heaven and men succeed their evils !
Till when, (the which, I hope, shall ne'er be seen,)
Your grace is welcome to our town and us.
" *Per*. Which welcome we'll accept ; feast here a while,
Until our stars, that frown, lend us a smile.　　*[Exeunt.*"
SHAKESPEARE.

---

[1] This is the text of all the modern editions : it is, however, inaccurate. There are two verbs to one nominative case. I would read—

" And these our ships *which haply* you may think
Are, like the Trojan horse," &c.

" *Are* stored," &c.

The passage would then be sense.

Note 22. Page 277.

" *Enter two Sailors.*

" 1 *Sail.* What courage, sir ? God save you.

" *Per.* Courage enough : I do not fear the flaw;
It hath done to me the worst. Yet, for the love
Of this poor infant, this fresh-new seafarer,
I would it would be quiet.

" 1 *Sail.* Slack the bolins there; thou wilt not, wilt thou? Blow and
split thyself.

" 2 *Sail.* But sea-room, an the brine and cloudy billow kiss the moon,
I care not.

" 1 *Sail.* Sir, your queen must overboard; the sea works high, the wind
is loud, and will not lie till the ship be cleared of the dead.

" *Per.* That's your superstition.

" 1 *Sail.* Pardon us, sir; with us at sea it still hath been observed; and
we are strong in earnest. Therefore briefly yield her; for she must overboard straight.

" *Per.* Be it as you think meet.—Most wretched queen !

" *Lyc.* Here she lies, sir.

" *Per.* A terrible childbed hast thou had, my dear;
No light, no fire; the unfriendly elements
Forgot thee utterly; nor have I time
To give thee hallow'd to thy grave, but straight
Must cast thee, scarcely coffin'd, in the ooze;
Where, for a monument upon thy bones,
And aye-remaining lamps, the belching whale,
And humming water must o'erwhelm thy corpse,
Lying with simple shells. Lychorida,
Bid Nestor bring me spices, ink, and paper,
My casket and my jewels; and bid Nicander
Bring me the satin coffer: lay the babe
Upon the pillow; hie thee, whiles I say
A priestly farewell to her: suddenly, woman.   [*Exit Lychorida.*

" 2 *Sail.* Sir, we have a chest beneath the hatches, caulk'd and bitumed
ready.

" *Per.* I thank thee."   SHAKESPEARE.

Note 23.   Page 278.

" *Enter two Servants, with a chest.*

" *Serv.* So ; lift there.

" *Cer.*   What is that ?

" *Serv.*   Sir, even now
Did the sea toss upon our shore this chest ;
'Tis of some wreck.

" *Cer.*   Set 't down ; let's look on it.

" 2 *Gent.* 'Tis like a coffin, sir.

" *Cer.*   Whate'er it be,
'Tis wondrous heavy.   Wrench it open straight:
If the sea's stomach be o'ercharg'd with gold,
It is a good constraint of fortune, that
It belches upon us.
    " 2 *Gent.*   'Tis so, my lord.
    " *Cer.* How close 'tis caulk'd and bitumed!—
Did the sea cast it up?
    " *Serv.* I never saw so huge a billow, sir,
As toss'd it upon shore.
    " *Cer.*   Come, wrench it open;
Soft, soft!—it smells most sweetly in my sense.
    " 2 *Gent.* A delicate odouʀ.
    " *Cer.* As ever hit my nostril; so,—up with it.
O you most potent gods! what's here? a corse!
    " 1 *Gent.* Most strange!
    " *Cer.* Shrouded in cloth of state; balm'd and entreasured
With bags of spices full!"

SHAKESPEARE.

NOTE 24.   Page 278.

    " *Cer.*   She is alive; behold,
Her eyelids, cases to those heavenly jewels
Which Pericles hath lost,
Begin to part their fringes of bright gold;
The diamonds of a most praised water
Appear, to make the world twice rich.   O live,
And make us weep to hear your fate, fair creature,
Rare as you seem to be."   *Ibid.*

The original Latin text in this part ought to be preserved; and
therefore I annex it:—
    " Quod cum fecissent, medicus aperuit, vidit puellam regalibus
ornamentis decoratam et speciosam valde. Cujus pulchritudinem
omnes videntes de ea multum admirabantur quoniam verus erat
pulchritudinis radius in quo natura nihil viciosum constituit, nisi
quòd eam immortalem non formaverat. Crines namque ejus erant
nivei candoris sub quibus residerabat frontis lacteæ planicies: cujus
nulla erat *detestabilis* rugositas. Oculi enim ejus erant quasi duorum
siderum describentes orbis volubilitatem non prodigi. Aspectibus
erant modestis frenati, stabilis animi constantiam promittentes. Pal-
pebrarum etiam pili non inhonestè natura in ea collocaverat. Nasus
etiam ejus rectitudinis suæ lineam plenitudinis etiam decore possidebat
in geminas dividens maxillarum partes. Nec vergebat in supremum
nimiâ longitudine nec nimiâ brevitate correpta, sed decenti honestatis
quantitate incedebat. Cujus collum radiis solaribus candidius, spe-
ciosis ornatum clinodiis, hominum aspectibus mirabilem intulerat

animi jocunditatem. Corpus etiam non diminutum vel quantitatis mole superabundans nequaquam quibus in ea censere proposuit. Ex cujus pectore brachia pulchritudinis tanquam ex arboris trunco rami procedebant. Quorum digiti quantitatis debitam sibi assumpserant mensuram unguium fulgore non pretermisso;[1] cujus summaria speciositas nihil deformitatis sibi admisceri compatiebatur. In quâ potest notari etiam singularis animæ suæ perfectio per potentiam divinam creando sibi infusæ."—Fol. LXIV. ed. 1508.

The reader, I think, will agree with me, that this is altogether a brilliant description of female beauty; and, for the most part, as *yet* unhackneyed.

NOTE 25.   Page 284.

" *Leon.* Come, say your prayers speedily.
" *Mar.*   What mean you?
" *Leon.* If you require a little space for prayer,
I grant it: Pray! but be not tedious,
For the gods are quick of ear, and I am sworn
To do my work with haste.
" *Mar.*   Why will you kill me?
" *Leon.* To satisfy my lady.
" *Mar.* Why would she have me kill'd?
Now, as I can remember, by my troth,
I never did her hurt in all my life;
I never spake bad word, nor did ill turn
To any living creature: believe me, la,
I never kill'd a mouse, nor hurt a fly:
I trod upon a worm against my will,
But I wept for it. How have I offended,
Wherein my death might yield her profit, or
My life imply her danger?
" *Leon.*   My commission
Is not to reason of the deed, but do it.
" *Mar.* You will not do't for all the world, I hope.
You are well-favour'd, and your looks foreshow
You have a gentle heart. I saw you lately,
When you caught hurt in parting two that fought:
Good sooth, it show'd well in you; do so now:
Your lady seeks my life: come you between,
And save poor me, the weaker.
" *Leon.*   I am sworn,
And will despatch.

---

[1] " The shining of the nails not being forgotten." This has been rendered somewhat paraphrastically in the text. The nails, it should be remembered, are coloured in the East.

"*Enter Pirates, whilst Marina is struggling.*

"1 *Pir.* Hold, villain!   [*Leonine runs away.*

"2 *Pir.* A prize! a prize!

"3 *Pir.* Half-part, mates, half-part.   Come, let's have her aboard suddenly.

[*Exeunt Pirates with Marina.*"

SHAKESPEARE.

NOTE 26.   Page 294.

" *Per.* Wherefore call'd Marina?

" *Mar.*   Call'd Marina,

For I was born at sea.

" *Per.*   At sea! thy mother?

" *Mar.* My mother was the daughter of a king;

Who died the very minute I was born,

As my good nurse Lychorida hath oft

Deliver'd weeping.

" *Per.*   O, stop there a little!

This is the rarest dream that e'er dull sleep

Did mock sad fools withal: this cannot be.

My daughter's buried. (*Aside.*) Well;—where were you bred?

I'll hear you more, to the bottom of your story,

And never interrupt you.

" *Mar.* You'll scarce believe me; 'twere best I did give o'er.

" *Per.* I will believe you by the syllable

Of what you shall deliver.   Yet, give me leave—

How came you in these parts? where were you bred?

" *Mar.* The king, my father, did in Tharsus leave me;

Till cruel Cleon, with his wicked wife,

Did seek to murder me: and having woo'd

A villain to attempt it, who having drawn,

A crew of pirates came and rescued me;

Brought me to Mitylene.   But now, good sir,

Whither will you have me?   Why do you weep?   It may be

You think me an impostor; no, good faith;

I am the daughter to king Pericles,

If good king Pericles be."   *Ibid.*

NOTE 27.   Page 297.

" *Per.* Hail, Dian!   To perform thy just command,

I here confess myself the king of Tyre;

Who, frighted from my country, did wed

The fair Thaisa, at Pentapolis.

At sea in childbed died she, but brought forth
A maid-child call'd Marina; who, O goddess,
Wears yet thy silver livery.   She at Tharsus
Was nurs'd with Cleon; whom at fourteen years
He sought to murder : but her better stars
Brought her to Mitylene; against whose shore
Riding, her fortunes brought the maid aboard us,
Where, by her own most clear remembrance, she
Made known herself my daughter."

SHAKESPEARE.

George Lillo (the memorable author of *George Barnwell*) worked up this story into a drama of three acts.   Here Philoten, the daughter of Cleon, is QUEEN of Tharsus; and when Pericles arrives, he recounts his history to her in the following lines, which display very considerable poetic ability.

" But to my purpose.
'Tis more than twice seven years since I beheld thee
With my Marina; both were infants then.
Peace and security smiled on your birth;
Hers was the rudest welcome to this world
That e'er was [1] Prince's child : Born on the sea,
(Hence is she call'd *Marina*,) in a tempest,
When the high working billows kiss'd the moon,
And the shrill whistle of the boatswain's pipe
Seem'd as a whisper in the ear of death;— [2]
Born when her mother died !   That fatal hour
Must still live with me.—O you gracious gods !
Why do you make us love your goodly gifts,
And snatch them straight away?   The waves received
My queen.   A sea-mate's chest coffin'd her corpse;
In which she silent lies 'midst groves of coral,
Or in a glittering bed of shining shells. [3]
The air-fed lamps of heaven, the spouting whale,
And dashing waters that roll o'er her head,
Compose a monument to hide her bones,
Spacious as heaven, and lasting as the frame
Of universal nature."

Marina, Act II. Sc. 1.

When Pericles is informed of the death of his child, the mutability of human affairs rushes upon his mind.

" Once princes sat, like stars, about my throne,
And veil'd their crowns to my supremacy :
Then, like the sun, all paid me reverence
For what I was; and all the grateful loved me

[1] *Had*—it should be.
[2] This beautiful line is SHAKSPEARE'S—*Pericles*, Act III. Sc. I.
[3] The Peri's Song in "Lalla Rookh" may have been suggested to Mr. Moore by these lines.

> For what I did bestow: now, not a glowworm
> But in the cheerless night displays more brightness,
> And is of greater use than darken'd Pericles.
> Be not highminded, queen! be not highminded:
> TIME is omnipotent—the king of kings:
> Their parent, and their grave."   *Marina*, Act II. Sc. 1.

Lillo had much tragic power, and wrote with a pathos which is irresistible. His versification is uncommonly harmonious. He was, perhaps, the last of the old school of the drama; and there are passages in some of his plays, which would have done no discredit to his most celebrated predecessors.

NOTE 28.   Page 297.

" *Thai.* Voice and favour!—
You are—you are—O royal Pericles!   [*She faints.*
  " *Per.* What means the woman? she dies! help, gentlemen!
  " *Cer.* Noble sir,
If you have told Diana's altar true,
This is your wife.
  " *Per.*   Reverend appearer, no;
I threw her o'erboard with these very arms.
  " *Cer.* Upon this coast, I warrant you.
  " *Per.*   'Tis most certain.
  " *Cer.* Look to the lady;—O, she's but o'erjoy'd.
Early, one blust'ring morn, this lady was
Thrown on this shore.   I oped the coffin, and
Found there rich jewels; recover'd her, and placed her
Here in Diana's temple.
  " *Per.*   May we see them?
  " *Cer.* Great sir, they shall be brought you to my house,
Whither I invite you.   Look! Thaisa is
Recover'd.
  " *Thai.* O, let me look!
If he be none of mine, my sanctity
Will to my sense bend no licentious ear,
But curb it, spite of seeing.   O, my lord,
Are you not Pericles?   Like him you speak,
Like him you are: Did you not name a tempest,
A birth, and death?
  " *Per.*   The voice of dead Thaisa!
  " *Thai.* That Thaisa am I, supposed dead
And drown'd.
  " *Per.* Immortal Dian!
  " *Thai.*   Now I know you better.—
When we with tears parted Pentapolis,
The king, my father, gave you such a ring.   [*Shows a ring.*

"*Per.* This, this: no more, you gods! your present kindness
Makes my past miseries sport. You shall do well,
That on the touching of her lips I may
Melt, and no more be seen. O come, be buried
A second time within these arms.
        "*Mar.*   My heart
Leaps to be gone into my mother's bosom.   [*Kneels to Thaisa.*
        "*Per.* Look, who kneels here! Flesh of thy flesh, Thaisa ;
Thy burden at the sea, and call'd Marina,
For she was yielded there.
        "*Thai.*   Bless'd and mine own."

                                                    SHAKESPEARE.

NOTE 29. Page 299.

"This story, the longest in the book before us, and the groundwork of a favourite old romance, is known to have existed before the
year 1190.

"In the prologue to the English romance on this subject, called
KYNGE APOLYNE OF THYRE, and printed by Wynkyn de Worde, in
1510, we are told : 'My worshypfull mayster, Wynkyn de Worde, ha-
vynge a lytell boke of an auncyent hystory of a kynge sometyme
reynyne in the countree of Thyre called Appolyn, concernynge his
malfortunes and peryllous adventures right espouventables,[1] bryefly
compyled, and pyteous for to here; the which boke I, Robert Cop-
lande,[2] have me applyed for to translate out of the Frensshe language
into our maternal Englysshe tongue, at the exhortacyon of my forsayd
mayster, accordynge dyrectly to myn auctor : gladly followynge the
trace of my mayster Caxton, begynnynge with small storyes and
pamfletes and so to other.' The English romance, or the French,
which is the same thing, exactly corresponds in many passages with
the text of the GESTA. I will instance in the following one only, in
which the complication of the fable commences. King Appolyn dines
in disguise in the hall of king Altistrates. 'Came in the kynges
daughter, accompanyed with many ladyes and damoyselles, whose
splendente beaute were *too long to endyte*, for her rosacyate coloure was
medled [3] with grete favour. She dranke unto her fader, and to all the
lordes, and to all them that had ben at the play of the Shelde.[4] And
as she behelde here and there, she espyed kynge Appolyn, and then
she sayd unto her fader, syr, what is he that sytteth so hye as by you ;
it semeth by hym that he is angry or sorrowfull? The kynge sayd, I
never sawe so nimble and pleasaunt a player at the shelde, and therefore have I made hym to come and soupe with my knyghtes. And yf
ye wyll knowe what he is, demaunde hym ; for peradventure he wyll

---

[1] Fearful, terrible.—*Fr.*
[2] "The printer of that name. He also translated from the French, at the desire of
Edward duke of Buckingham, the romance of the KNYGHT OF THE SWANNE. See his
Prologue."—WARTON.
[3] Mingled.   [4] Tournament.

tell you sooner than me. Methynke that he is departed from some good place, and I thinke in my mynde that somethynge is befallen hym for which he is sory. This sayd, the noble damoysell wente unto Appolyn and sayd, Fayre sir, graunt me a boon. And he graunted her with goode herte. And she sayd unto hym, albeyt that your vysage be triste and hevy, your behaviour sheweth noblesse and facundyte, and therefore I pray you to tell me of youre affayre and estate. Appolyn answered, yf ye demaunde of my rychesses, I have lost them in the sea. The damoysell sayd, I pray you that you tell me of your adventures.'[1] But in the GESTA, the princess at entering the royal hall, kisses all the knights and lords present, except the stranger. Vossius says, that about the year 1520, one Alamanius Rinucinus, a Florentine, translated into Latin this fabulous history; and that the translation was corrected by Beroaldus. Vossius certainly cannot mean that he translated it from the Greek original."— WARTON.

" The history of APOLLONIUS, KING OF TYRE, was supposed by Mark Welser, when he printed it in 1595, to have been translated from the Greek a thousand years before [*Fabr. Bib. Gr.* v. 6, p. 821]. It certainly bears strong marks of a Greek original, though it is not (that I know) now extant in that language. The rhythmical poem, under that title, in modern Greek, was re-translated (if I may so speak) from the Latin ἀπὸ Λατινικῆς εἰς Ῥωμαϊκὴν γλῶσσαν. *Du Fresne,* Index Author. *ad. Gloss. Græc.* When Welser printed it, he probably did not know that it had been published already (perhaps more than once) among the GESTA ROMANORUM. In an edition, which I have, printed at Rouen in 1521, it makes the 154th chapter. Towards the latter end of the xiith century, *Godfrey of Viterbo,* in his *Pantheon* or Universal Chronicle, inserted this romance as part of the history of the third Antiochus, about 200 years before Christ. It begins thus [MS. *Reg.* 14, c. xi.]:—

" Filia Seleuci regis stat clara decore
Matreque defunctâ pater arsit in ejus amore.
Res habet effectum, pressâ puellâ dolet.

" The rest in the same metre, with one pentameter only to two hexameters.

" Gower, by his own acknowledgment, took his story from the *Pantheon;* as the author (whoever he was) of Pericles, prince of Tyre, professes to have followed Gower."—TYRWHITT.

" It is observable, that the hero of this tale is, in Gower's poem, as in the present play, called *prince* of Tyre; in the GESTA ROMANORUM,[2] and Copland's prose romance, he is entitled *King.* Most of the incidents of the play are found in the *Confessio Amantis,* and a few of Gower's expressions are occasionally borrowed. However, I think it is not unlikely that there may have been (though I have not met

---

[1] Cap. xi.
[2] This is not strictly true. He is frequently called PRINCEPS, and generally so in the opening of the story.

with it) an early prose translation of this popular story from the GESTA ROMANORUM, in which the name of Apollonius was changed to Pericles; to which, likewise, the author of this drama may have been indebted.

" The numerous corruptions that are found in the original edition in 1609, which have been carefully preserved and augmented in all the subsequent impressions, probably arose from its having been *frequently exhibited on the stage*. In the four quarto editions it is called *the much admired play* of PERICLES, PRINCE OF TYRE; and it is mentioned by many ancient writers as a very popular performance."— MALONE.

" There are three French translations of this story, viz. 'La chronique d'Appolin, Roy de Thyr;' 4to. Geneva, bl. l. no date; and 'Plaisante et agréable Histoire d'Appolonius Prince de Thyr en Affrique, et Roi d'Antioche; traduit par Gilles Coroset,' 8vo. Paris, 1530; and (in the seventh volume of the *Histoires Tragiques*, &c., 12mo. 1604, par François Belle-forest, &c.) 'Accidens diuers aduenus à Appollonie Roi des Tyriens: ses malheurs sur mer, ses pertes de femme et fille, et la fin heureuse de tous ensemble.'

" The popularity of this tale of Apollonius may be inferred from the very numerous MSS. in which it appears.

" Both editions of Twine's translation are now before me. Thomas Twine was the continuator of Phaer's Virgil, which was left imperfect in the year 1558."—STEEVENS.

NOTE 30. Page 302.

From this story we learn (as Warton observes), "that when a company was assembled, if a juggler or minstrel were not present, it was the custom of our ancestors to entertain themselves by relating or hearing a series of adventures. Thus the general plan of the CANTERBURY TALES, which at first sight seems to be merely an ingenious invention of the poet to serve a particular occasion, is in a great measure founded on a fashion of ancient life: and Chaucer, in supposing each of the pilgrims to tell a tale as they are travelling to Becket's shrine, only makes them adopt a mode of amusement which was common to the conversations of his age. I do not deny that Chaucer has shown his address in the use and application of this practice."

Sir Walter Scott, in his notes to the third Canto of " Marmion," cites this story immediately from Gervase of Tilbury (*Otia Imperial. ap. Script. rer. Brunsvic.* vol. i. p. 797), without knowing apparently of its existence in the GESTA ROMANORUM. The knight's name in Gervase is *Osbert*, which seems to form the only difference in the stories: Sir Walter mentions the adventure of two Bohemian knights, but not altogether as it occurs in the authority he has given. I shall transcribe the original.

" Niderius telleth this story: In the borders of the kingdome of

Bohemia lieth a valley, in which divers nights together was heard clattering of armour, and clamors of men, as if two armies had met in pitcht battell. Two knights that inhabited neere unto this prodigious place, agreed to arme themselves, and discover the secrets of this invisible army. The night was appointed, and accommodated at all assayes they rode to the place, where they might descry two battels ready ordered for present skirmish; they could easily distinguish the colours and pravant liveries of everie company: but drawing neere, the one (whose courage began to relent) told the other that he had seene sufficient for his part, and thought it good not to dally with such prodegies, wherefore further than he was he would not go. The other called him coward, and prickt on towards the armies; from one of which an horseman came forth, fought with him, and cut off his head. At which sight the other fled, and told the newes the next morning. A great confluence of people searching for the body, found it in one place, the head in another, but neither could discern the footing of horse or man; onely the print of birds feet, and those in myrie places, &c."—HEYWOOD's *Hierarchie of the Blessed Angels*, pages 554, 555. 1635.

"The most singular tale of the kind," says Sir Walter Scott, " is contained in an extract communicated to me by my friend Mr. Surtees of Mainsforth, in the Bishopric, who copied it from a MS. note in a copy of Burthogge 'On the nature of Spirits,' 8vo. 1694, which had been the property of the late Mr. Gill, attorney-general to Egerton, Bishop of Durham."—*Notes to* MARMION. This extract is in Latin; as it is certainly very curious, I annex a translation.

"It will not be tedious if I relate, upon the faith of a very worthy and noble person, a wonderful thing of this kind, which happened in our times. Ralph Bulmer, leaving the camp (at that time pitched near Norham) for the sake of recreation, and pursuing the farther bank of the Tweed with his harriers, met by accident a certain noble Scot, formerly, as he thought, well known to him. The latter commenced a furious attack; and as it was permitted amongst foes during a contest (there being but a very brief space for question), they met one another with rapid course and hostile minds. Our knight, in the first career, unable to withstand the impetuous attack of his adversary, was thrown, horse and man, to the ground; and discharged copious streams of blood from wounds in the head and breast. He resembled a dying man, which the other observing, addressed him with soothing words; and promised assistance if he would follow his instructions, and abstain from every thought of sacred things. Moreover, on condition that he offered neither prayers nor vows either to God, the Virgin Mary, or to any saint whatever, he engaged to restore him to health and strength in a short time. The condition being complied with, in consequence of the agony he suffered, the cunning knave, murmuring I know not what kind of dishonest murmur, took him by the hand; and sooner than it is said, raised him upon his feet whole, as before. But our knight, struck with the greatest terror at the unheard of novelty of the case, exclaimed, 'My Jesus!' or something like it. Looking about him immediately afterward, he saw neither his enemy nor any one else; and the steed, which but very lately had been afflicted with a grievous wound, was feeding quietly by the river-side. He returned to the camp in great astonishment; and fearful of obtaining no credit, in the first instance concealed the circumstance; but on the completion of the war he declared the whole to his confessor. There is no doubt but it was a delusion; and the vile deceit of that subtle cozener is apparent, by which he would have seduced a Christian hero to use forbidden aid. The name of this person (in other respects noble and distinguished) I forbear to mention; since there is no question but the devil, by permission of God, may assume what shape he pleases; nay, even that of an angel of light; as the hallowed eye of the Almighty observes."

The MS. Chronicle, Sir Walter adds, from which this extract was taken, cannot now be found.

NOTE 31. Page 306.

Many strange stories are related of spirits; among others, let the reader take the following. A young and beautiful girl, of a noble Scottish family, consorted with a spirit, who was discovered in her bed. "The clamour flies abroad, the neighbours come in to be spectátors of the wonderment, and amongst them the parson of the parish, who was a scholar, and a man of unblemished life and conversation: who seeing this prodigious spectacle, broke out into these words of St. John the Evangelist, *Et Verbum caro factum est*, And the Word was made flesh: which was no sooner spoke, but the devil arose, and suddenly vanished in a terrible storme, carrying with him the roofe of the chamber, and setting fire on the bed wherein he had lien, which was in a moment burned to ashes. Shee was within three days after delivered of a monster, such as the father appeared unto them, of so odible an aspect, that the midwives caused it instantly to be burnt, lest the infamy of the daughter might too much reflect upon the innocencie of the noble parents."—HEYWOOD's *Hierarchie*, lib. viii. p. 542.

" Another thing, much more admirable, hapned in the diocesse of Cullein. Diuers princes and noblemen being assembled in a beautifull and faire pallace, which was scituate upon the riuer Rhine, they beheld a boat or small barge make toward the shore, drawne by a swan in a siluer chaine, the one end fastened about her necke, the other to the vessel, and in it an unknowne souldier, a man of a comely personage, and gracefull presence, who stept upon the shore: which done, the boat, guided by the swan, left him, and floted downe the riuer. This man fell afterward in league with a faire gentlewoman, married her, and by her had many children. After some yeares, the same swanne came with the same barge unto the same place; the souldier entring into it, was caried thence the way he came, after disappeared, left wife, children, and family, and was never seen amongst them after! Now who can judge this to be other than one of those spirits that are named INCUBI."—*Ibid.*, p. 541.

This beautiful incident of the swan drawing the boat occurs, I think, in " Morte Arthur."

[Obviously we have here the story of Lohengrin in a very truncated form.—ED.]

NOTE 32. Page 315.

Scaci, Scacci, or Scachi—a *kind* of chess: *le jeu des Echecs.* Thus called, according to Du Fresne, from the Arabic or Persian word, SCACH, or king, because this is the principal piece in the game. Pseudo-Ovidius (Lib. i. *de Vetula*) furnishes the following description, which will somewhat elucidate the text :—

> "Sex species saltus exercent, sex quoque scaci,
> Miles, et Alphinus, Roccus, Rex, Virgo, Pedesque,
> In campum primum de sex istis saliunt tres,
> Rex ; Pedes, Virgo : Pedes in rectum salit, atque
> Virgo per obliquum, Rex saltu gaudet utroque,
> Ante retroque tamen tam Rex quam Virgo moventur,
> Ante Pedes solum ; capiens obliquus in ante,
> Cum tamen ad metam stadii percurrerit, extunc
> Sicut Virgo salit, in campum verò secundum
> Tres alii saliunt, in rectum Roccus, eique
> Soli concessum est ultra citraque salire.
> Obliquè salit Alphinus, sed Miles utroque
> Saltum componit."

Of the origin of this play the same worthy writer observes :—

> " Est alius ludus scacorum, *ludus Ulyssis,*
> *Ludus Trojana quem fecit in obsidione,*
> Ne vel tæderet proceres in tempore treugæ,
> Vel belli, si qui pro vulneribus remanerent
> In castris : ludus qui castris assimilatur,
> Inventor cujus jure laudandus in illo est,
> Sed caussam laudis non advertunt nisi pauci."

[To judge from **Mr.** Swan's remarks contained in the foot-notes to this Tale, it might be imagined that " Schaci" were some entirely unknown game. It is nothing more nor less than chess ; and the account of it, though rather careless, is quite clear when we take into account the way in which the game was played at the time when the *Gesta* was written. There is nothing erroneous in the description, but a good deal is omitted which ought to have been inserted, and certain statements are wanting in clearness. The description of the Rochus or Rook requires no remark. Alphinus, the Bishop, is not so easily understood. The text is probably in fault, for it is not possible to reconcile all the statements made about this piece with one another.

It should be remembered that the Bishop's move was limited to two squares, and that he could leap over an intervening man, at the time this description was written. The Knight is described correctly, and its power was then what it is now. As to the Pawns, the King's P. seems to be the Merchant, the Bishop's P. the Woolcarder, and the Rook's P. the Husbandman. The Queen's and Knight's P. are not mentioned. The Pawns *queened* as with us; but though they attacked adverse pieces diagonally as with us, on capturing them they moved straight on. The Queen was the weakest piece on the board, only commanding the four squares of the same colour adjacent to that she stood on. The King moved as with us. He was allowed once in a game to move like a Knight. Apparently the operation of Castling is obscurely alluded to in the last sentence but one of the description.—Ed.]

Note 33. Page 319.

" This fable is told in the Greek legend of Barlaam and Josaphat, written by Johannes Damascenus ; and in Caxton's Golden Legende, fol. 129. It is also found in Clericalis Disciplina of Alphonsus."—Warton.

Mr. Way has told this tale so beautifully, that no apology is necessary for its introduction here.

"THE LAY OF THE LITTLE BIRD.

" In days of yore, at least a century since,
There liv'd a carle as wealthy as a prince :
His name I wot not ; but his wide domain
Was rich with stream and forest, mead and plain ;
To crown the whole, one manor he possess'd
In choice delight so passing all the rest,
No castle, burgh, or city might compare
With the quaint beauties of that mansion rare.
The sooth to say, I fear my words may seem
Like some strange fabling, or fantastick dream,
If, unadvis'd, the portraiture I trace,
And each brave pleasure of that peerless place ;
Foreknow ye then, by necromantick might
Was rais'd this paradise of all delight ;
A good knight own'd it first ; he, bow'd with age,
Died, and his son possess'd the heritage :
But the lewd stripling, all to riot bent,
(His chattels quickly wasted and forespent,)
Was driven to see this patrimony sold
To the base carle of whom I lately told.
Ye wot right well there only needs be sought
One spendthrift heir, to bring great wealth to nought.

A lofty tower and strong, the building stood
Midst a vast plain surrounded by a flood;
And hence one pebble-paved channel stray'd,
That compass'd in a clustering orchard's shade:
'Twas a choice charming plat; abundant round
Flowers, roses, odorous spices cloth'd the ground;
Unnumber'd kinds, and all profusely shower'd
Such aromatick balsam as they flower'd,
Their fragrance might have stay'd man's parting breath,
And chas'd the hovering agony of death.
The sward one level held, and close above
Tall shapely trees their leafy mantles wove,
All equal growth, and low their branches came,
Thick set with goodliest fruits of every name.
In midst, to cheer the ravish'd gazer's view,
A gushing fount its waters upward threw,
Thence slowly on with crystal current pass'd,
And crept into the distant flood at last:
But nigh its source a pine's umbrageous head
Stretch'd far and wide in deathless verdure spread,
Met with broad shade the summer's sultry gleam,
And through the livelong year shut out the beam.
   " Such was the scene:—yet still the place was bless'd
With one rare pleasure passing all the rest:
A wondrous bird of energies divine
Had fix'd his dwelling in the tufted pine;
There still he sat, and there with amorous lay
Wak'd the dim morn, and clos'd the parting day:
Match'd with these strains of linked sweetness wrought
The violin and full-ton'd harp were nought;
Of power they were with new-born joy to move
The cheerless heart of long-desponding love;
Of power so strange, that should they cease to sound,
And the blithe songster flee the mystick ground,
That goodly orchard's scene, the pine-tree's shade,
Trees, flowers, and fount, would all like vapour fade.
            ' Listen, listen to my lay !'
            Thus the merry notes did chime,
            ' All who mighty love obey,
            Sadly wasting in your prime,
            Clerk and laick, grave and gay !
            Yet do ye, before the rest,
            Gentle maidens, mark me tell !
            Store my lesson in your breast,
            Trust me it shall profit well:
            Hear, and heed me, and be bless'd !'
So sang the bird of old: but when he spied
The carle draw near, with alter'd tone he cried—
' Back, river, to thy source; and thee, tall tower,
Thee, castle strong, may gaping earth devour !

Bend down your heads, ye gaudy flowers, and fade!
And wither'd be each fruit-tree's mantling shade!
Beneath these beauteous branches once were seen
Brave gentle knights disporting on the green,
And lovely dames; and oft, these flowers among,
Stay'd the blithe bands, and joy'd to hear my song;
Nor would they hence retire, nor quit the grove,
Till many a vow were past of mutual love;
These more would cherish, those would more deserve; ·
Cost, courtesy, and arms, and nothing swerve.
O bitter change! for master now we see
A faitour villain carle of low degree;
Foul gluttony employs his livelong day,
Nor heeds nor hears he my melodious lay.'
  "So spake the bird; and, as he ceased to sing
Indignantly he clapp'd his downy wing,
And straight was gone; but no abasement stirr'd
In the clown's breast at his reproachful word:
Bent was his wit alone by quaint device
To snare, and sell him for a passing price.
So well he wrought, so craftily he spread
In the thick foliage green his slender thread,
That when at eve the little songster sought
His wonted spray, his heedless foot was caught.
'How have I harm'd you?' straight he 'gan to cry,
'And wherefore would you do me thus to die?'—
'Nay, fear not,' quoth the clown, 'for death or wrong;
I only seek to profit by thy song;
I'll get thee a fine cage, nor shalt thou lack
Good store of kernels and of seeds to crack;
But sing thou shalt; for if thou play'st the mute,
I'll spit thee, bird, and pick thy bones to boot.'
'Ah, wo is me!' the little thrall replied,
'Who thinks of song, in prison doom'd to bide?
And, were I cook'd, my bulk might scarce afford
One scanty mouthful to my hungry lord.'
  "What may I more relate?—the captive wight
Assay'd to melt the villain all he might:
And fairly promis'd, were he once set free,
In gratitude to teach him secrets three;
Three secrets, all so marvellous and rare,
His race knew nought that might with these compare.
  "The carle prick'd up his ears amain; he loos'd
The songster thrall, by love of gain seduc'd:
Up to the summit of the pine-tree's shade
Sped the blithe bird, and there at ease he stay'd,
And trick'd his plumes full leisurely, I trow,
Till the carle claim'd his promise from below:
'Right gladly,' quoth the bird; 'now grow thee wise:
All human prudence few brief lines comprize:

First then, lest haply in the event it fail,
YIELD NOT A READY FAITH TO EVERY TALE.'—
' Is this thy secret ? ' quoth the moody elf,
' Keep then thy silly lesson for thyself;
I need it not.'—' Howbe 'tis not amiss
To prick thy memory with advice like this,
But late, meseems, thou hadst forgot the lore;
Now may'st thou hold it fast for evermore.
Mark next my second rule, and sadly know,
WHAT'S LOST, 'TIS WISE WITH PATIENCE TO FOREGO.'
  " The carle, though rude of wit, now chaf'd amain;
He felt the mockery of the songster's strain.
' Peace,' quoth the bird; ' my third is far the best;
Store thou the precious treasure in thy breast:
WHAT GOOD THOU HAST, NE'ER LIGHTLY FROM THEE CAST.'
—He spoke, and twittering fled away full fast.
Straight, sunk in earth, the gushing fountain dries,
Down fall the fruits, the wither'd pine-tree dies,
Fades all the beauteous plat, so cool, so green,
Into thin air, and never more is seen.
  " Such was the meed of avarice:—bitter cost!
The carle who all would gather, all has lost."

The same story is to be found in Lydgate, entitled " The Chorle and the Bird."

NOTE 34. Page 322.

This is compounded of two stories, apparently from the *Golden Legende*, fol. 218. " A monke that had ben a rybaude in ye worlde and a player, tempted by a wycked spyrite, wolde returne agayne to ye worlde. And as Saynt Bernarde reteyned hym, he demaunded hym wherof he sholde lyue. And he answered hym y^t he coude well playe at the dyce, and he sholde well lyue therby. And Saynt Bernarde sayd to hym. If I delyuer to the ony good wylt thou come to me agayn euery yere that I may parte halfe agayn with the. And he had grete joye therof, and promysed hym so to do. And than Saynt Bernarde said, that there sholde be delyvered to hym twenty shyllynges. And than he wente hys way therwith. And this holy man dyd this for to drawe hym agayne to the relygyon as he dyd after. And so he wente forth and lost all, and cam agayne all confused tofore ye gate. And whan Saynt Bernarde knewe hym there, he wente to hym joyously and opened hys lappe for to parte the gayne, and he sayd, Fader I have wonne no thynge, but have lost your catayle, receyue me if it please you for to be your catayle. And Saynte Bernarde answered to hym swetely, if it be so, it is better that I receyue the than lese bothe ye one and that other. ¶ On a tyme Saynt Bernarde rode upon an hors by the way, and mette a vylayne by y^e

waye whiche sayd to hym that he had not hys hert ferme and stable in prayenge. And ye vylayne or uplondysshe man had grete despyte therof, and sayd that he had hys herte ferme and stable in all hys prayers. And Saynt Bernarde which wolde vaynquysshe hym, and shewe hys foly, sayd to hym. Departe a lytell fro me, and begyn thy Pater Noster in the best entent thou canst, and if y^u canst fynysshe it without thynkyng on ony other thynge, w^tout doubte I shall gyue to the the hors that I am on. And thou shalte promyse to me by thy fayth, that if thou thynke on any other thynge, y^u shalte not hyde it fro me. And the man was gladde, and reputed that hors hys, and graunted it hym, and went aparte, and began hys Pater Noster, and he had not sayd the halfe when he remembered yf he sholde haue ye sadle withall, and therwith he returned to Saynt Bernarde, and sayd that he had thought in prayenge. And after y^t he had no more wyll to anaunt [1] hym."

Note 35. Page 333.

" The reader perceives this is the story of Guido or Guy, Earl of Warwick; and probably this is the early outline of the life and death of that renowned champion.[2]

" Many romances were at first little more than legends of devotion, containing the pilgrimage of an old warrior. At length, as chivalry came more into vogue, and the stores of invention were increased, the youthful and active part of the pilgrim's life was also written, and a long series of imaginary martial adventures was added, in which his religious was eclipsed by his heroic character, and the penitent was lost in the knight-errant. That which was the principal subject of the short and simple legend, became only the remote catastrophe of the voluminous romance. And hence, by degrees, it was almost an established rule of every romance, for the knight to end his days in a hermitage. Cervantes has ridiculed this circumstance with great pleasantry, where Don Quixote holds a grave debate with Sancho, whether he shall turn saint or archbishop.

" So reciprocal, or rather so convertible, was the pious and the military character, that even some of the APOSTLES had their romance. In the ninth century, the chivalrous and fabling spirit of the Spaniards transformed Saint James into a knight. They pretended that he appeared and fought with irresistible fury, completely armed, and mounted on a stately white horse, in most of their engagements with the Moors; and because, by his superior prowess in these bloody conflicts, he was supposed to have freed the Spaniards from paying the

[1] Boast.

[2] Mr. Ellis (*Specimens*, vol. ii. p. 5) supposes this a mistake; the original romance being written in French as early as the 13th century, and the GESTA ROMANORUM not composed till the commencement of the 14th. But the date of the *Gesta* is very uncertain, and may have been written long before.

annual tribute of a hundred Christian virgins to their infidel enemies, they represented him as a professed and powerful champion of distressed damsels. This apotheosis of chivalry in the person of their own apostle, must have ever afterwards contributed to exaggerate the characteristical romantic heroism of the Spaniards, by which it was occasioned; and to propagate, through succeeding ages, a stronger veneration for that species of military enthusiasm, to which they were naturally devoted. It is certain, that in consequence of these illustrious achievements in the Moorish wars, Saint James was constituted patron of Spain; and became the founder of one of the most magnificent shrines, and of the most opulent order of knighthood, now existing in Christendom. The legend of this invincible apostle is inserted in the Mosarabic Liturgy."—WARTON.

The following is an abstract of the romance of Sir Guy above alluded to:—

" The piety of Sir Guy was neither less capricious, nor less disastrous in its consequences, than the affection of his mistress. He had been taught that other duties were more sacred and more acceptable in the sight of heaven, than those of husband and father. But the historian shall tell his own story. At the end of forty days after the marriage, it happened that—

> " As Sir Guy came from play,
> Into a tower he went on high,
> And looked about him, far and nigh;
> Guy stood, and bethought him, tho,
> How he had done many a man wo,
> And slain many a man with his hand,
> Burnt and destroy'd many a land,
> And all was for woman's love,
> And not for God's sake above.

" Felice, who had observed his reverie, inquired the cause; and learnt, with horror and astonishment, his determination to spend the remainder of his life in a state of penance and mortification. He contented himself with directing her, whenever their child should be of proper age, if it should prove a son, to intrust his education to Sir Heraud; and quitted her without taking leave of the earl, and even without communicating to his old companion Heraud the singular resolution he had formed. Felice, unable to detain him, places on his finger a gold ring, requesting him to bestow at least a thought on her whenever he should cast his eyes on that pledge of her affection; and her husband, after promising to obey her instructions, assumes the dress of a palmer, and departs for the Holy Land.

" Felice communicates to Rohand the news of this unexpected misfortune; and the good earl is persuaded, with great appearance of probability, that Sir Guy can mean no more than to put her affection to the test, by a conduct as capricious as her own. She at first is disposed to put an end to her life, but is checked by the thoughts of her child. Sir Heraud, in hopes of diverting his friend from his resolution, takes the habit of a pilgrim, and travels in quest of him, but returns without success.

> " Guy sought *hallowes* [1] in many countrè,
>   And sithe to Jerusalem went he ;
>   And when he to Jerusalem came,
>   To Antioch his way he *name*.[2]

" Sir Guy, solely occupied with devotional pursuits, had travelled to Constantinople, and from thence into Almayne. Here he chances to meet a pilgrim who ' made semblaut sorry.' Guy enters into conversation with him, and finds him to be his old friend Sir Thierry, who had been dispossessed by the emperor of all his fiefs, and reduced to the greatest distress, in consequence of a false accusation preferred against him by Barnard, cousin of the famous Duke Otho, the felon Duke of Pavia, who had inherited the estates and the vices of that treacherous prince, and, unfortunately for the imperial vassals, possessed to the same degree the confidence of his master, together with the dignity of steward to the emperor. Sir Guy, on hearing that the death of Otho, whom he had slain, had been employed to the ruin of his friend Thierry, falls into a swoon ; a practice to which, as we have seen, he was much addicted.

> " ' Good man,' quoth Thierry, ' tell thou me
>   How long this evil hath holden thee ? '
>   ' Many a day,' quoth Sir Guy, ' it took me ore ! '
>   ' Good love ! ' quoth Thierry, ' do it no more ! '

" Thierry proceeds to lament the supposed death of Sir Guy, who, though full of compassion for his friend, and already determined to redress his injuries, continues to conceal his name. But Thierry was weak and faint with hunger ; and Sir Guy tells him, that as ' he has a penny in his purse,' it would be expedient to hasten to the nearest town, and employ that sum in the purchase of provisions. Thierry willingly accompanies him, but, feeling sleepy as well as faint, is advised to refresh himself, in the instance, with a few moments' repose ; and the famished Thierry falls asleep with his head resting on the knees of Sir Guy. During his slumber, a ' white weasel ' suddenly jumps out of his mouth ; takes refuge in the crevice of a neighbouring rock, and after a short space of time returns, and again runs down his throat. Sir Thierry, waking, informs Sir Guy that he had dreamed a dream ; that he had seen a ' fair bright sword ' and a treasure of inestimable value, and that, sleeping on his arm, he had been saved by him from a dreadful calamity. The supposed palmer interprets the dream ; goes to the spot indicated by the weasel, and finds the sword and treasure ; which he delivers to Sir Thierry, with an injunction to preserve the sword with the greatest possible care, and then takes his leave.

" Sir Guy now repairs to the emperor's palace, asks charity, and is admitted into the hall. As his habit bespeaks him a traveller, he is

---

[1] Saints.　　　　　　　　　　　　[2] Took.

on all sides assailed by inquiries after news; and the emperor, having a very proper opinion of his own importance, anxiously questions him on the reports prevailing among his subjects respecting his character. Guy boldly assures him that he is universally blamed for the flagrant injustice of his conduct towards the innocent Thierry; and, throwing down his glove, offers to prove, by force of arms, the falsehood of Barnard's accusation. The steward, though not a little surprised by the appearance of such an uncouth adversary, accepts the challenge; the battle is awarded; the palmer is presented with a suit of armour, and then repairs to Thierry for the sword which had been miraculously discovered by the white weasel. Sir Barnard, however, was so stout, that after a combat which lasted during the whole day, the victory was still undecided: but he had discovered during this trial of the palmer's prowess, that it would be much more convenient to get rid of his adversary by any other means than to abide by the issue of a second conflict. Judging therefore that the palmer would sleep soundly after his fatigue, he despatches a number of his emissaries, with orders to take him up in his bed in the middle of the night, and to throw him into the sea. Although Sir Guy was lodged in the palace, being under the immediate protection of the justice of the empire, this bold enterprise was successfully executed; and Sir Guy, when he awaked in the morning, was not a little astonished to find himself floating in his bed, at some distance from land. But Providence, who had intended that the guilt of Sir Barnard should become completely manifest, directed a fisherman to the spot, who conveyed Sir Guy in safety to the palace, and related this miraculous incident to the emperor. The monarch having determined that the punishment of the steward should be inflicted by the champion whom Heaven had thus marked out for the purpose, the battle recommences, and Sir Barnard, already half vanquished by the reproaches of his own conscience, is overpowered and slain. The victor then demands the reinstatement of Sir Thierry, and, having obtained it, goes in search of his friend, whom he finds in a church, devoutly engaged in prayer, and hastily leads him to the emperor, who weeps at the sight of his distress, and restores him to all his possessions.

> "The emperor let bathe Thierry,
> And clad him in clothes richely,
> And gave him both palfrey and steed,
> And all things that he had of need.

"Sir Thierry, who had hitherto felt little confidence in the assurances of the pilgrim, was now filled with the warmest gratitude towards his deliverer; and his gratitude was exalted to enthusiasm, when, having been invited to accompany him during a part of his journey, he discovered, in this deliverer, his old friend and benefactor. He adjured Sir Guy to share the prosperity he had bestowed; but the hero, only solicitous to become an humble instrument in the hands of Providence, and determined to fulfil his destiny, whatever it might be, tore himself from his embraces, and, pursuing his journey, arrived, without meeting any new adventures, in England.

" The disconsolate Felice, during the long interval of his absence, had passed her whole time in acts of devotion or of charity. Her husband, presenting himself at her gate in his pilgrim's weeds, was invited into the hall; was plentifully entertained; and enjoyed the pleasure of witnessing, unknown and unsuspected, her daily observance of those duties to which he had, long since, devoted the remainder of his life. Unwilling to withdraw her from these salutary pursuits, he again departed unknown, taking with him a single page as an attendant, and retired to a solitary hermitage in the forest of Ardenne, where he was advertised by an angel of his approaching dissolution. He then despatched his page to Felice with the gold ring which he had received from her at parting, and adjured her to come and give directions for his burial. She arrived; found him dying; received his last breath; and, having survived him only fifteen days, was buried in the same grave.

> " Now is the story brought to an end,
> Of Guy, the bold baron of price,
> And of the fair maid Felice,
> Fair ensamples men may lere,
> Whoso will listen and hear.
> True to love, late and early,
> As, in his life, did good Sir Guy;
> For he forsook worldly honour,
> To serve God his creatour;
> Wherefore Jesu, that was of a maid born
> To buy man's soul that was forlorn,
> And rose from death the third day,
> And led man's soul from hell away,
> On their souls have mercy!
> And ye, that have heard this story,
> God give you all his blessing,
> And of his grace to your ending;
> And joy, and bliss, that ever shall be!
> Amen, Amen, for charitè!"

" The History of Sir Guy," says Bishop Percy (*Reliques of Anc. Poetry*, vol. iii. p. 101), "though now very properly resigned to children, was once admired by all readers of wit and taste: for taste and wit had once their childhood. Although of English growth,[1] it was early a favourite with other nations; it appeared in French in 1525, and is alluded to in the old Spanish Romance TERENTE EL BLANCO, which, it is believed, was written not long after the year 1430.—See advertisement to the French translation, 2 vols. 12mo.

" The original, whence all these stories are extracted, is a very ancient romance in old English verse, which is quoted by Chaucer as a celebrated piece even in his time, viz.:—

[1] From the circumstance of the outline of the story being in the *Gesta Romanorum*, this is very disputable; and it is known to have existed in French as early as the conclusion of the 13th century. I should be inclined to give the *Gesta* the precedence.

> " Men speken of romances of price,
>   Of Horne childe and Ippotes,
>   Of Bevis and SIR GUY, etc.   R. OF THOP.

And was usually sung to the harp at Christmas dinners and brideales, as we learn from Puttenham's *Art of Poetry*, 4to. 1589."

But the *Gesta Romanorum* is most probably the origin of the tales in question, since the date is unquestionably earlier than those fixed upon by Bishop Percy.

NOTE 36.   Page 337.

" About the year 1470, a collection of Latin fables in six books, distinguished by the name of Esop, was published in Germany."—WARTON.

From a work of this kind, probably the same, the following fable has been extracted, derived, no doubt, from the *Gesta Romanorum :*—

" None ought to render evil for good ; and they that help ought not to be hurt, as this fable sheweth, of a dragon which was within a river ; and as the river was diminished of water, the dragon abode at the river, which was all dry ; and thus for lack of water he could not stir him.   A labourer, or villain, came that way, and demanded of the dragon, saying, What doest thou here ?   And the dragon said, Here I am without water, without the which I cannot move ; but if thou wilt bind me, and set me upon thy asse, and lead me into a river, I shall give thee abundance of gold and silver; and the villain, for covetousnesse bound him, and led him into a river: and when he had unbound him, he demanded of him his salary or payment.   The dragon said to him, because thou hast unbound me, thou wilt be paid; and because that I am now hungry, I will eat thee.   And the villain answered and said, for my labour wilt thou eat and devour me?   And as they strived together, the fox being within the forest, and hearing their questioning, came to them, and said in this manner: Strive ye no more together, for I will accord, and make peace betwixt you; let each of you tell me his reason, for to wit which of you have right.   And when each of them had told his tale, the fox said to the villain, shew to me how thou unboundest the dragon, that I may give thereof a lawful sentence. And the villain put the dragon upon his asse, and bound him as he did before.   Then the fox demanded of the dragon, held he thee so fast bound as thou art now ?   And the dragon answered, yea, my lord, and yet more hard.   And the fox said to the villain, bind her yet harder; for he that well bindeth, well can unbind.   And when the dragon was fast bound, the fox said to the villain, bear him again where thou didst first bind him, and there leave him bound as he is now, and so he shall not eat and devour thee."—*Æsop's Fables,* 18mo. 1658, p. 144.

Note 37. Page 337.

This allegorical race of beings is thus described in Sir John Mandevile's rare work:—

"From this isle men go to another that is called Macumeran, which is a great isle and a fair; and the men and women of this country have heads like hounds; they are *reasonable*, and *worship an ox for their God.* They are good men to fight, and they bear a great target, with which they cover all their body, and a spear in their hand. And if they take any man in battle they send him to their king, which is a great lord, and devout in his faith: for he hath about his neck, on a chain, three hundred great pearls, and as the papists say their *Pater Noster*, and other prayers, so their king saith every day three hundred prayers to his God, before he either eat or drink; and he beareth also about his neck a ruby orient, fine, and good, that is near a foot and five fingers long. For when they chuse their king, they give to him that ruby to bear in his hand, and then they lead him riding about the city, and then ever after they are subject to him, and therefore he beareth that ruby alway about his neck; for if he bear not the ruby, they would no longer hold him for their king. The great Caane of Cathay, hath much coveted this ruby; but he might never have it neither by war nor by other means. And this king is a full, true, and vertuous man, for men may go safely and surely through his land, and bear all that they will, for there is no man so hardy to let them."
—*Voyages and Travels*, p. 95.

In the *Turkish Tales* we have also some notice of this "virtuous" people:—

"The *Samsards* were monstrous anthropophagi, or men-eaters, who had the body of a man and the head of a dog."—Vol. ii. p. 349.

And Pliny (whom the Gest writer quotes), B. vii. c. 2, speaks of a country of India, "where there is a kind of men with heads like dogs, clad all over with the skins of wild beasts, who in lieu of speech used to bark."

THE END.

FOUNDERS OF THE MIDDLE AGES
by E. K. Rand

This well-known study by the late E. K. Rand, Professor of Latin at Harvard, discusses the transformation of Latin pagan culture into the first stirrings of medieval civilization. It is not only a first-rate historical study in a little-known yet very important culture period; it is also a brilliantly written, easily followed account which will interest and be of value to almost every student of philosophy, comparative literature, religion, or history.

Dr. Rand begins with an intensive study of the interrelations between the early Christian church and pagan culture in the first centuries of the Christian era. Symmachus, Gregory the Great, Prudentius, Tertullian, Minucius Felix, Lactantius and others are carefully evaluated. Chapters on St. Ambrose, St. Jerome, Boethius, St. Augustine are then followed by discussions (with extensive translations) of Latin poetry of the 4th and 5th centuries, and survey of new educational theories, as in Martianus Capella, Cassian, St. Benedict, Cassiodorus, and others. Continual reference is made to the medieval understanding of Aristotle, Plato, Porphyry, Cicero, Horace, and Virgil, and the pre-medieval cultural scene is depicted with unique charm and clarity. Later emergences from these early medieval roots are traced, and modern historians are copiously quoted and evaluated.

"Thoughtful, beautifully written . . . a work of popularization by a ripe scholar," AMERICAN HISTORICAL REVIEW. "Extraordinarily accurate," RICHARD McKEON, THE NATION. "Recommended to every student of letters," TIMES (London). "Recommended as a work of importance for its additions to our knowledge of a little-known time," YALE REVIEW.

60 pages of notes include extensive Latin quotes, and an enormous bibliography. Index. ix + 365pp. 5⅜ x 8.

T369 Paperbound **$1.75**

PRIMITIVE MAN AS PHILOSOPHER
by Paul Radin

This standard anthropological work considers aspects of primitive thought from such typical primitive peoples as the Winnebago, Oglala Sioux, Maori, Baganda, Batak, Buin of Melanesia, Polynesians of Tahiti and Hawaii, Zuni, Ewe and many others. It examines both the conditioning of thought which each society places upon the individual, and the freedom which the individual has either to deviate from group belief or to form group belief. Intensive discussion is given to such methodological problems as determining cultural standards.

It covers primitive thought on such topics as the relation of a man to his fellows, the purpose of life, marital relations, freedom of thought, death, resignation, and analyzes intensively folk wisdom from many primitive peoples. It also considers more abstract aspects of thought such as the nature of reality, the structure of the ego, human personality, the systematization of ideas, the concept of gods, belief, and similar matters.

It is not a simple compendium of traits, ripped out of context, but a brilliant interpretation of myth and symbolism in terms of the meaning assigned to them in each culture. It is factual in approach, and quotes original primitive documents extensively. It does not tear ideas from their matrix, nor does it seek far-fetched interpretations in terms of preconceived psychological theories.

Throughout most of this interesting book, primitive men are allowed to speak for themselves. Most of the supporting data were obtained at first hand, much of it by the author himself in his contacts with primitive peoples.

Bibliography. Index. xviii + 402pp. 5⅜ x 8.

T392 Paperbound **$1.95**

PRIMITIVE RELIGION
by Paul Radin

This is a thorough treatment by a noted anthropologist of the nature and origin of primitive religion, and of the influences that have shaped its expression. It takes into account comparative religions and modern psychology, and discusses in detail the role of economic factors, social factors, and religious personalities in primitive religion.

Ranging from Africa, Australia, Oceania, Asia, to the Americas, it covers religious ideology, cult, and social development among such peoples as the Arunta, Aztec, Bushmen, Crow, Dakota, and dozens of others. Of special interest is material about Winnebago religion gathered by the author himself. Throughout the book scores of primitive texts are quoted and analyzed, and such topics as shamanism, stages of religious evolution, culture levels, theories of religious experience, initiation, acculturation, diffusion vs. psychogenesis are continually subjected to penetrating criticism.

A first-rate introduction and survey volume for the anthropologist, sociologist, psychologist, historian of religion, and general reader, this book is unique in its combination of impeccable scholarship with an easily followed lively presentation.

"Excellent," NATURE (London). "A significant addition to the body of work that deals with the nature of religion," NEW REPUBLIC.

New preface by the author. Bibliographic notes. Index. x + 322pp. 5⅜ x 8.

T393 Paperbound $1.95

THE ORIGIN OF LIFE
by A. I. Oparin

This is a classic of biochemistry—the first detailed exposition of the theory that living tissue was preceded upon earth by a long and gradual evolution of nitrogen and carbon compounds. It is still one of the basic works in any science library, as is proved by repeated reference to it in later books and monography.

A historical introduction first covers theories of the origin of life from the Greeks, through the middle ages and Renaissance, to moderns. Three basic theories are examined in light of modern knowledge: that life spontaneously arises perpetually; that life has always been present in the universe as a separate basic substance; that life arose once at some distant period of the earth's past.

Techniques of modern biochemistry are then applied to the problem by Dr. Oparin, and the topic is considered afresh in the following chapters: primary forms of carbon and nitrogen compounds; origin of organic substances, primary proteins; origin of primarily colloidal systems; origin and further evolution of primary organisms.

"Easily the most scholarly authority on the question . . . it will be a landmark for discussion for a long time to come," **NEW YORK TIMES.** "Every physiologist and biochemist should call it to the attention of his students . . . chemists will want to read this volume over and over again," **AMERICAN CHEMICAL SOCIETY JOURNAL**

231-item bibliography, especially strong on Russian and Eastern European publications. 16-page introduction by the translator, S. Morgulis, University of Nebraska, considers later discoveries exemplifying Oparin's theories. Index. xxv + 270pp. 5⅜ x 8.

S213 Paperbound **$1.75**

LANGUAGE, TRUTH AND LOGIC by A. J. Ayer

First published in 1936, this first full-length presentation in English of the Logical Positivism of Carnap, Neurath, and others has gone through 10 printings to become a classic of thought and communication. It not only surveys one of the most important areas of modern thought; it also shows you how to apply analytical methods to your own field of work and dispel the confusion that arises from imperfect understanding of the uses of language. A first-rate antidote for fuzzy thought and muddled writing, this remarkable book has helped philosophers, writers, speakers, teachers, students, and general readers alike.

Mr. Ayer sets up specific tests by which you can easily evaluate statements of ideas. You will also learn how to distinguish ideas that cannot be verified by experience — those expressing religious, moral, or aesthetic experience, those expounding theological or metaphysical doctrine, and those dealing with a *priori* truth. The basic thesis of this work is that philosophy should not squander its energies upon the unknowable, but should perform its proper function in criticism and analysis.

PARTIAL CONTENTS: Elimination of metaphysics, Function of philosophy. Nature of philosophic analysis. The a priori. Truth and probability. Critique of ethics and theology. The self and the common world. Solutions of outstanding philosophical disputes.

"A delightful book... I should like to have written it myself," Bertrand Russell.

Index. 160 pp. 5⅜ x 8.   T10 Paperbound **$1.25**

A WAY OF LIFE
and Other Selected Writings
of SIR WILLIAM OSLER

Doctor, humanist, teacher of medicine at McGill University, The University of Pennsylvania, Johns Hopkins University, and Oxford University, William Osler (1849-1919) was also a curator of the Bodleian Library at Oxford and (after 1911) a baronet of the British Empire.

His work embraced many fields. But it is as a man with the gift of inspiring other men by his example, his speech, and his writings that he is most assured of immortality. A doctor deeply learned in the classics, a humanist with profound religious convictions, a devotedly thoughtful man, he—like Sir Thomas Browne, whose works were his lifelong companions—reconciled the old truths of literature, philosophy, and religion with the new science.

Here, in this selection of essays which reveal his greatness as a writer, are to be found such works as "A Way of Life" in which Osler presents his practical philosophy of everyday living in vivid and memorable language. Here also is included the brilliant address "The Student Life," which details his advice to young men. Such essays as "Creators, Transmuters, and Transmitters" and "The Collecting of a Library" reflect his deepest humanistic convictions. Included also are the incomparable "Letters to my House Physicians" in which Osler minutely describes his visits to continental hospitals and towns. "The Growth of Truth, as Illustrated by the Discovery of the Circulation of the Blood by William Harvey," is a fascinating and thought-provoking account of one of the most dramatic episodes in medicine; while the famous articles on such great physicians as Thomas Browne, Robert Burton, Gui Patin, Michael Servetus, and William Beaumont are masterpieces of medical history.

5 photographs. Introduction by G. L. Keynes, M.D., F.R.C.S. Index.
xx + 278pp. 5⅜ x 8. Paperbound $

PHILOSOPHICAL WRITINGS OF PEIRCE
Selected and Edited with an Introduction
by Justus Buchler

Charles S. Peirce was a thinker of great originality and power; and although unpublicized in his lifetime, he was recognized as an equal by such men as William James and John Dewey. Since his death in 1914, his true importance has been recognized.

This volume is a carefully balanced exposition of Peirce's complete philosophical system, as set forth in his own writings. Professor Justus Buchler has interwoven appropriate sections of Peirce's work into a brilliant selection that reveals the essence of a great American philosopher.

28 chapters cover epistemology, phenomenology, cosmology — with especially interesting sections on scientific method, logic as the theory of signs, pure chance vs. law in the universe, symbolic logic, common-sensism, pragmatism (which he called pragmaticism), ethics, and experiment in its chain of verification. The book includes much material hitherto available only in a very expensive form.

"An excellent, discerning introduction. It should prove a real boon to the student of Peirce," MODERN SCHOOLMAN. "Dr. Buchler has . . . performed a valuable service in bringing together many of Peirce's outstanding philosophical papers, and making them more generally available," John Laird, JOURNAL OF PHILOSOPHY.

Originally published as THE PHILOSOPHY OF PEIRCE: SELECTED WRITINGS. Selected and edited with an introduction by Justus Buchler. Index. xvi + 386pp. 5⅜ x 8.

T217 Paperbound **$1.95**

THE IDEA OF PROGRESS
by J. B. Bury

Written by one of the greatest historians of our generation, this unusual volume describes the birth and growth of one of the most important basic ideas of our civilization: progress, or the concept that men are advancing in a definite and desirable direction.

This idea is so much a part of our mental background that we never consider that it is purely a modern idea, and that it was not held by the Greeks or Romans or Medieval and Renaissance Europeans. It first arose in the rationalistic philosophy of the Enlightenment.

Dr. Burry does not attempt to evaluate the "truth" of the idea of progress. He does, however, demonstrate how important this idea has been as a motivating force in modern history. He relates it to the writings end actions of such men as Montesquieu, Condorcet, Darwin, Descartes, Diderot, Gibbon, Kant, Louis XIV, Malthus, Marx, Turgot, Voltaire, and Locke. He draws examples from such widely different fields as literature, philosophy, history, economics, political science, physics, biology, and music.

Unabridged reissue. Introduction by Charles A. Beard. Index. xl + 375pp. 5⅜ x 8.

T40 Paperbound **$1.95**

AND GYROSCOPIC MOTION, John Perry. A classic elementary text of the dynamics of behavior and use of rotating bodies such as gyroscopes and tops. In simple, everyday behavior and use of rotating bodies such as gyroscopes and tops. In simple, every-u are shown how quasi-rigidity is induced in discs of paper, smoke rings, chains, motions; why a gyrostat falls and why a top rises; precession; how the earth's motion and many other phenomena. Appendix on practical use of gyroscopes. 62 figures.
T416 Paperbound **$1.00**

OF SCIENTIFIC THOUGHT FROM NEWTON TO EINSTEIN, A. d'Abro. A detailed ac-olution of classical physics into modern relativistic theory and the concommitant changes hodology. The breakdown of classical physics in the face of non-Euclidean geometry magnetic equations is carefully discussed and then an exhaustive analysis of Einstein's eral theories of relativity and their implications is given. Newton, Riemann, Weyl, Maxwell, and many others are considered. "Model of semi-popular exposition,"
T2 Paperbound **$2.00**
21 diagrams. 482pp. 5⅜ x 8.

E NEW PHYSICS (formerly THE DECLINE OF MECHANISM), A. d'Abro. This authorita-hensive 2 volume exposition is unique in scientific publishing. Written for intelligent iliar with higher mathematics, it is the only thorough explanation in non-technical dern mathematical-physical theory. Combining both history and exposition, it ranges ewtonian concepts up through the electronic theories of Dirac and Heisenberg, the nics of Fermi, and Einstein's relativity theories. "A must for anyone doing serious sical sciences," THE FRANKLIN INSTITUTE. 97 illustrations. 991pp. 2 volumes.
T3 Vol. 1, Paperbound **$2.00**
T4 Vol. 2, Paperbound **$2.00**

ORY OF MATHEMATICS, D. Struik. A lucid, easily followed history of mathematical ques from the Ancient Near East up to modern times. Requires no mathematics bu excellent introduction to mathematical concepts and great mathematicians through th cal development. 60 illustrations including Egyptian papyri, Greek mss., portraits maticians. Bibliography. xix + 299pp. 5⅜ x 8.
T255 Paperbound **$1.75**

PHYSICAL THEORY, P. W. Bridgman. A Nobel Laureate's clear, non-technical lecture paradoxes connected with frontier research in the physical sciences. Concerned wit pts as thought, logic, mathematics, relativity, probability, wave mechanics, etc., ributions of such men as Newton, Einstein, Bohr, Heisenberg, and many other aining . . . recommended to anyone who wants to get some insight into curre ence," THE NEW PHILOSOPHY. Index. xi + 138pp. 5⅜ x 8. S33 Paperbound **$1.25**

VERSE, Max Born. A remarkably lucid account by a Nobel Laureate of recent theori s, behavior of gases, electrons, and ions, waves and particles, electronic structu ar physics, and similar topics. "Much more thorough and deeper than most attemp delightful," CHEMICAL AND ENGINEERING NEWS. **SPECIAL FEATURE:** 7 animate such phenomena as gas molecules in motion, the scattering of alpha particles, e s of photographs. Total of nearly 600 illustrations. 315pp. 6⅛ x 9¼.
T412 Paperbound **$2.**

?, N. Campbell. The roll of experiment and measurement, the function of math of scientific laws, the difference between laws and theories, the limitations similarly provocative topics are treated clearly and without technicalities by "Still an excellent introduction to scientific philosophy," H. Margenau in PHYSI
S43 Paperbound **$1.**
⅜ x 8.

IES IN THE NAME OF SCIENCE, Martin Gardner. Formerly entitled IN THE NA is the standard account of the various cults, quack systems, and delusions wh as science: hollow earth fanatics, Reich and orgone sex energy, dianetics, Atlan orteanism, flying saucers, medical fallacies like iridiagnosis, zone therapy, been added on Bridey Murphy, psionics, and other recent manifestations in this fie y everyone, scientist and non-scientist alike," R. T. Birge, Prof. Emeritus of Phys Former President, American Physical Society. Index. x + 365pp. 5⅜ x 8.
T394 Paperbound **$1.**

THEORY IN PHYSICS, Max Born. A Nobel Laureate examines the nature of exp theoretical physics and analyzes the advances made by the great physicists of nstein, Bohr, Planck, Dirac, and others. The actual process of creation is deta who participated. 44p. 5⅜ x 8. S308 Paperbound

RONOMY FROM THALES TO KEPLER, J. L. E. Dreyer. Formerly titled A HIST TEMS FROM THALES TO KEPLER. This is the only work in English which prov f man's cosmological views from prehistoric times up through the Renaissance onia, early Greece, Alexandria, the Middle Ages, Copernicus, Tycho Brahe, Ke Epicycles and other complex theories of positional astronomy are explained in find clear and easy to understand. "Standard reference on Greek astronomy lution," SKY AND TELESCOPE. Bibliography. 21 diagrams. Index. xvii + 43
S79 Paperbound **$**

HISTORY OF MATHEMATICS, THE STUDY OF THE HISTORY OF SCIENCE, G. Sa one. A long introduction to methods and philosophy, skills of the historian, science, psychology of idea-creation, and the purpose of history of science. ssified bibliography. Complete and unabridged. Indexed. 10 illustrations. 1
T240 Paperbound

ARISTOTLE'S THEORY OF POETRY AND THE FINE ARTS

edited by S. H. Butcher

This book contains the celebrated Butcher translation of Aristotle's POETICS, faced, page by page, with the complete Greek text (as reconstructed by Mr. Butcher from Greek, Latin and Arabic manu-scripts). The editor's 300-page exposition and interpretation follows.

In his classic commentary, Butcher discusses with insight, sympathy and great learning Aristotle's ideas and their importance in the history of thought and literature. His scholarly remarks cover art and nature, imitation as an aesthetic term, poetic truth, pleasure as the end of fine art, art and morality, the function of tragedy, the dramatic unities, the ideal tragic hero, plot and character, comedy, and poetic univer-sality. A new 35-page introductory essay, "Aristotelian Literary Criticism" by John Gassner, discusses the validity of Aristotle's ideas today and their application to contemporary literature.

"No edition with commentary can be recommended to English readers with such confidence as Butcher's," George Saintsbury. "One of the finest treatises on aesthetic theory — neither the literature nor the criticism of the past 40 years has rendered Aristotelian criticism ir-relevant or obsolete," MODERN SCHOOLMAN. "An intellectual ad-venture of the most stimulating kind," NEW YORK TIMES.

Fourth edition. Bibliography. New introduction by John Gassner. Indexes. lxxvi + 421pp. 5⅜ x 8.

T42 Paperbound **$1.95**

THE PHILOSOPHICAL WORKS OF RENE DECARTES

This is the definitive English translation and the only comprehensive English edition in print of the important writings of Rene Descartes, frequently called the Father of Modern Philosophy. His famous exposition of "Cogito Ergo Sum" and his astonishingly fruitful concept that all phenomena (except mind) could be reduced to readily formulated laws by application of the mathematical method have had enormous historical influence.

These two volumes contain all Descartes' revolutionary insights and conclusions, including such key ideas as the philosophic proof of God, and the separation of mind and matter. His views on space and matter, the nature of science, the formation of the universe, and the nature of psychology will certainly interest the modern scientific reader.

Contents, Volume One. (Each section complete). Rules for the direction of the mind. Discourse on the Method of Rightly Conducting the Reason. Meditations on First Philosophy. The Principles of Philosophy. The Search After Truth. The Passions of the Soul. Notes Directed against a Certain Program.

Contents, Volume Two. (Each section complete). Seven sets of objections propounded by contemporary philosophers and theologians to Descartes' Meditations on First Philosophy, together with Descartes' replies to each. This is a first rate source for the philosophical opinions of such men as Hobbes, Arnauld, and Gassendi, and for Descartes' defense of his own ideas. It is almost unique in classical philosophy as a symposium of philosopher and critics.

Translated by E. S. Haldane and G. R. T. Ross. Unabridged republication of the last corrected edition of 1931. Two volumes. Introductory notes. Indexes. Volume one: vi + 452pp. Volume two: iv + 380pp. 5⅜ x 8.

Paperbound. Volume One **$2.00**
Paperbound. Volume Two **$2.00**

SCIENCE THEORY AND MAN, Erwin Schrödinger. Complete unabridged reissue of SCIENCE AND THE HUMAN TEMPERAMENT plus an additional essay: "What Is an Elementary Particle?" Nobel Laureate Schrödinger discusses such topics as nature of scientific method, the nature of science, chance and determinism, science and society, conceptual models for physical entities, elementary particles and wave mechanics. Presentation is popular. "Fine practical preparation for a time when laws of nature, human institutions . . . are undergoing a critical examination without parallel," Waldemar Kaempffert, N. Y. TIMES. 192pp. 5⅜ x 8. T428 Paperbound **$1.35**

BRIDGES AND THEIR BUILDERS, D. B. Steinman & S. R. Watson. Engineers, historians, and every person who has ever been fascinated by great spans will find this book an endless source of information and interest. Greek and Roman structures, Medieval bridges, modern classics such as the Brooklyn Bridge, and the latest developments in the science are retold by one of the world's leading authorities on bridge design and construction. BRIDGES AND THEIR BUILDERS is the only comprehensive and accurate semi-popular history of these important measures of progress in print. New, greatly revised, enlarged edition. 23 photos; 26 line-drawings. Index. xvii + 401pp. 5⅜ x 8. T431 Paperbound **$1.95**

BIOLOGY, NATURAL HISTORY & TRAVEL

TREES OF THE EASTERN AND CENTRAL UNITED STATES AND CANADA, W. M. Harlow. A revised edition of a standard middle-level guide to native trees and important escapes. More than 140 trees are described in detail, and illustrated with more than 600 drawings and photographs. Supplementary keys will enable the careful reader to identify almost any tree he might encounter. xiii + 288pp. 5⅜ x 8. T395 Paperbound **$1.35**

INTRODUCTION TO THE STUDY OF EXPERIMENTAL MEDICINE, Claude Bernard. The only major work of Claude Bernard now available in English, this classical records Bernard's efforts to transform physiology into an exact science. He examines the roles of chance and error and incorrect hypothesis in leading to scientific truth and describes many classic experiments on the action of curare, carbon monoxide, and other poisons, the functions of the pancreas, the glycogenic function of the liver, and many others. Introduction. Foreword by I. B. Cohen. xxv + 266pp. 5⅜ x 8. T400 Paperbound **$1.50**

THE ORIGIN OF LIFE, A. I. Oparin. The first modern statement of the theory that life evolved from complex nitro-carbon compounds. A historical introduction covers theories of the origin of life from the Greeks to modern times and then the techniques of biochemistry as applied to the problem by Dr. Oparin. The exposition presupposes a knowledge of chemistry but can be read with profit by everyone interested in this absorbing question. Bibliography. Index. xxv + 270pp. 5⅜ x 8. S213 Paperbound **$1.75**

A SHORT HISTORY OF ANATOMY AND PHYSIOLOGY FROM THE GREEKS TO HARVEY, C. Singer. An intermediate history formerly entitled THE EVOLUTION OF ANATOMY, this work conveys the thrill of discovery as the nature of the human body is gradually clarified by hundreds of scientists from the Greeks to the Renaissance. Diogenes, Hippocrates, and other early workers, up to Leonardo da Vinci, Vesalius, Harvey, and others, with 139 illustrations from medieval manuscripts, classical sculpture, etc. Index. 221pp. 5⅜ x 8. T389 Paperbound **$1.75**

THE BEHAVIOUR AND SOCIAL LIFE OF HONEYBEES, Ronald Ribbands. The most comprehensive, lucid, and authoritative book on bees. How bees communicate, how they tell fellow workers exactly how far away stores of food are, how individual bees learn their duties in the hive, and all the complex patterns and motivations. Much of the material is the result of very recent research by Mr. Ribbands and others. "A 'MUST' for every scientist, experimenter, and educator, and a happy and valuable selection for all interested in the honeybee," AMERICAN BEE JOURNAL. 690 item bibliography. Indices. 127 illustrations; 11 photographic plates. 352pp. S410 Clothbound **$4.50**

TRAVELS OF WILLIAM BARTRAM, edited by Mark Van Doren. One of the 18th century's most delightful books; an excellent source of first-hand material on American geography, anthropology, and natural history. Many descriptions of early Indian tribes are our only source of information. "The mind of a scientist with the soul of a poet," John Livingston Lowes. 13 original illustrations and maps. Edited with an introduction by Mark Van Doren. 448pp. 5⅜ x 8. T13 Paperbound **$2.00**

SAILING ALONE AROUND THE WORLD, Captain Joshua Slocum. A great modern classic in a convenient inexpensive edition. Captain Slocum's account of his single-handed voyage around the world in a 34 foot boat which he rebuilt himself. A nearly unparalled feat of seamanship told with vigor, wit, imagination, and great descriptive power. "A nautical equivalent of Thoreau's account," Van Wyck Brooks. 67 illustrations. 308pp. 5⅜ x 8. T326 Paperbound **$1.00**

EARTH SCIENCES

THE BIRTH AND DEVELOPMENT OF THE GEOLOGICAL SCIENCES, F. D. Adams. The most complete and thorough history of the earth sciences in print. Geological thought from earliest recorded times to the end of the 19th century — covers over 300 early thinkers and systems: fossils and hypothetical explanations of them, vulcanists vs. neptunists, figured stones and paleontology, generation of stones, and similar topics. 91 illustrations, including medieval, renaissance woodcuts, etc. 632 footnotes and bibliographic notes. Index. 511pp. 5⅜ x 8. T5 Paperbound **$2.00**

URANIUM PROSPECTING, H. L. Barnes. A clear, practical book about uranium prospecting by a professional geologists with first-hand field experience. Hundreds of important facts about minerals, geological occurrence, tests, detectors, sampling, assays, claiming and developing, government regulations. Index. Glossary of technical terms. Annotated bibliography. x + 117pp. 5⅜ x 8. T309 Paperbound **$1.00**

DE RE METALLICA, Georgius Agricola. Written over 400 years ago, for 200' years the most authoritative work on production of metals; still one of the most beautiful and fascinating volumes in the history of science. 12 books, exhaustively annotated, give a wonderfully lucid and vivid picture of the history of mining, selection of sites, types of deposits, excavating pits, sinking shafts, ventilating, pumps, crushing machinery, assaying, smelting, refining metals, making salt, alum, nitre, glass, and many other topics. This definitive edition contains all 289 of the 16th century woodcuts which made the original an artistic masterpiece. A superb gift for geologists, engineers, libraries, artists, and historians. Biographical, historical introductions. Translated by Herbert & L. H. Hoover. Bibliography, survey of ancient authors. Indices. 289 illustrations. 672pp. 6¾ x 10¾. Deluxe library edition.
S6 Clothbound **$10.00**

MUSIC

A GENERAL HISTORY OF MUSIC, Charles Burney. A detailed coverage of music from the Greeks up to 1789, with full information on all types of music: sacred and secular, vocal and instrumental, operatic and symphonic. Theory, notation, forms, instruments, innovators, composers, performers, typical and important works, and much more in an easy, entertaining style. Burney travelled over much of Europe and spoke with hundreds of authorities and composers so that this work is more than a compilation of records . . . it is a living work of careful and first-hand scholarship. A recent NEW YORK TIMES review said, ''Surprisingly few of Burney's statements have been invalidated by modern research . . . still of great value.'' Edited and corrected by Frank Mercer. 35 figures. Indices. 1915pp. 5½ x 8½.
2 volumes. T36 The set, Clothbound **$12.50**

JOHANN SEBASTIAN BACH, Philipp Spitta. The complete and unabridged text of the definitive study of Bach. Written some 70 years ago, it is still unsurpassed for its coverage of nearly all aspects of Bach's life and work. There could hardly be a finer more non-technical introduction to Bach's music than the detailed, lucid analyses which Spitta provides for hundreds of individual pieces. 26 solid pages are devoted to the B minor mass, for example, and 30 pages to the glorious St. Matthew Passion. This monumental set also includes a major analysis of the music of the 18th century: Buxtehude, Pachelbel, etc. ''Unchallenged as the last word on one of the supreme geniuses of music,'' Hohn Barkham, SATURDAY REVIEW SYNDICATE. Total of 1819pp. 2 volumes. Heavy cloth binding. 5⅜ x 8.
The set, T252 Clothbound **$10.00**

A DICTIONARY OF HYMNOLOGY, John Julian. This exhaustive and scholarly work has become known as an invaluable source of hundreds of thousands of important and often difficult to obtain facts on the history and use of hymns in the western world. More than 30,000 entries on individual hymns, giving authorship, date and circumstances of composition, publication, textual variations, location of texts, translations, denominational and ritual usage, etc. Biographies of more than 9,000 hymn writers, and essays on important topics such as Christmas carols and children's hymns, and much other unusual and valuable information. A 200 page double-columned index of first lines — the largest in print. Total of 1786 pages in two reinforced clothbound volumes. 6¼ x 9¼. The set, T333 Clothbound **$15.00**

STRUCTURAL HEARING: TONAL COHERENCE IN MUSIC, Felix Salzer. Written by a pupil of the late Heinrich Schenker, this is not only the most thorough exposition in English of the Schenker method but also extends the Schenker approach to include modern music, music of the middle ages, and renaissance music. It explores the phenomenon of tonal organization by means of a detailed analysis and discussion of more than 500 musical pieces. It casts new light for the reader acquainted with harmony upon the understanding of musical compositions, problems of musical coherence, and connection between theory and composition. ''Has been the foundation on which all teaching in music theory has been based at this college,'' Leopold Mannes, President of The Mannes College of Music. 2 volumes. Total of 658pp. 6½ x 9¼. The set, S418 Clothbound **$8.00**

PUZZLES, ENTERTAINMENT, ETC.

MATHEMATICS, MAGIC AND MYSTERY, Martin Gardner. Why do card tricks work? How do magicians perform astonishing mathematical feats? How is stage mind-reading possible? This is the first book length study explaining the application of probability, set theory, theory of numbers, topology, etc., to many startling tricks. Non-technical, accurate, detailed. 115 sections discuss tricks with cards, dice, coins, knots, geometrical vanishing illusions, how a Curry square ''demonstrates'' that the sum of the parts may be greater than the whole, and dozens of others. 135 illustrations. xii + 174pp. 5⅜ x 8.
T335 Paperbound **$1.00**

MATHEMATICAL PUZZLES FOR BEGINNERS AND ENTHUSIASTS, G. Mott-Smith. 188 mathematical puzzles based on algebra, dissection of plane figures, permutations and probability, that will test and improve your powers of inference and interpretation. The Odic Force, The Spider's Cousin, Ellipse Drawing, theory and strategy of card and board games. 100 pages of detailed mathematical explanations. Appendix of primes, square roots, etc. 135 illustrations. 2nd revised edition. 248pp. 5⅜ x 8.
T198 Paperbound **$1.00**

LEARN CHESS FROM THE MASTERS, F. Reinfeld. Formerly titled CHESS BY YOURSELF, this book contains 10 games which you play against such masters as Marshall, Bronstein, Najdorf, and others, and an easy system for grading each move you make against a variety of other possible moves. Detailed annotations reveal the principles of the game through actual play. 91 diagrams. viii + 144pp. 5⅜ x 8. T362 Paperbound **$1.00**

REINFELD ON THE END GAME IN CHESS, F. Reinfeld. Formerly titled PRACTICAL END-GAME PLAY, this book contains clear, simple analyses of 62 end games by such masters as Alekhine, Tarrasch, Marshall, Morphy, Capablanca, and many others. Primary emphasis is on the general principles of transition from middle play to end play. This book is unusual in analyzing weak or incorrect moves to show how error occurs and how to avoid it. Covers king and pawn, minor piece, queen endings, weak squares, centralization, tempo moves, and many other vital factors. 62 diagrams. vi + 177pp. 5⅜ x 8. **T417 Paperbound $1.25**

101 PUZZLES IN THOUGHT AND LOGIC, C. R. Wylie, Jr. Brand new problems you need no special knowledge to solve! Take the kinks out of your mental "muscles" and enjoy solving murder problems, the detection of lying fishermen, the logical identification of color by a blindman, and dozens more. Introduction with simplified explanation of general scientific method and puzzle solving. 128pp. 5⅜ x 8. **T367 Paperbound $1.00**

THE COMPLETE NONSENSE OF EDWARD LEAR. This is the only complete edition of this master of gentle madness available at a popular price. A BOOK OF NONSENSE, NONSENSE SONGS, MORE NONSENSE SONGS AND STORIES in their entirety with all the old favorites that have delighted children and adults for years. The Dong With A Luminous Nose, The Jumblies, The Owl and the Pussycat, and hundreds of other bits of wonderful nonsense. 214 limericks, 3 sets of Nonsense Botany, 5 Nonsense Alphabets, 546 drawings by Lear himself, and much more. 320pp. 5⅜ x 8. **T167 Paperbound $1.00**

28 SCIENCE FICTION STORIES OF H. G. WELLS. Two full unabridged novels, MEN LIKE GODS and STAR BEGOTTEN, plus 26 short stories by the master science-fiction writer of all time! Stories of space, time, invention, exploration, future adventure. PARTIAL CONTENTS: Men Like Gods, The Country of the Blind, In the Abyss, The Crystal Egg, The Man Who Could Work Miracles, A Story of the Days to Come, The Valley of Spiders, and 21 more! 5⅜ x 8. **T265 Clothbound $3.95**

SEVEN SCIENCE FICTION NOVELS, H. G. Wells. Full unabridged texts of 7 science-fiction novels of the master. Ranging from biology, physics, chemistry, astronomy, to sociology and other studies, Mr. Wells extrapolates whole worlds of strange and intriguing character. "One will have to go far to match this for entertainment, excitement, and sheer pleasure," NEW YORK TIMES. Contents: THE TIME MACHINE, THE ISLAND OF DR. MOREAU, THE FIRST MEN IN THE MOON, THE INVISIBLE MAN, THE WAR OF THE WORLDS, THE FOOD OF THE GODS, IN THE DAYS OF THE COMET. 1015pp. 5⅜ x 8. **T264 Clothbound $3.95**

FIVE ADVENTURE NOVELS OF H. RIDER HAGGARD. All the mystery and adventure of darkest Africa captured accurately by a man who lived among Zulus for years, and who knew African ethnology and folkways as did few of his contemporaries. They have been regarded as examples of the very best high adventure by such critics as George Orwell, Andrew Lang and Kipling. Contents: SHE, KING SOLOMON'S MINES, ALLAN QUATERMAIN, ALLAN'S WIFE, MAIWA'S REVENGE. 821pp. 5⅜ x 8. **T108 Clothbound $3.95**

MATHEMAGIC, MAGIC PUZZLES, AND GAMES WITH NUMBERS, R. V. Heath. More than 60 new puzzles and stunts based on the properties of numbers. Easy techniques for multiplying large numbers mentally, revealing hidden numbers magically, finding the date of any day in any year, and dozens more. Edited by J. S. Meyer. 76 illustrations. 128pp. 5⅜ x 8. **T110 Paperbound $1.00**

WIN AT CHECKERS, M. Hopper. (Formerly CHECKERS.) The former World's Unrestricted Checker Champion discusses the principles of the game, expert's shots and traps, problems for the beginner, standard openings, locating your best move, the end game, opening "blitzkrieg" moves, ways to draw when you are behind your opponent, etc. More than 100 detailed questions and answers anticipate your problems. Appendix. 75 problems with solutions and diagrams. Index. 79 figures. xi + 107pp. 5⅜ x 8. **T363 Paperbound $1.00**

HOUDINI ON MAGIC, Harry Houdini. One of the greatest magicians of modern times explains his most prized secrets. How locks are picked, with illustrated picks and skeleton keys; how a girl is sawed into twins; how to walk through a brick wall — Houdini's explanations of 44 stage tricks with many diagrams. Also included is a fascinating discussion of great magicians of the past and the story of his fight against fraudulent mediums and spiritualists. Edited by W. B. Gibson and M. N. Young. Bibliography. 155 figures, photos. xv + 280pp. 5⅜ x 8. **T384 Paperbound $1.00**

THE BOOK OF MODERN PUZZLES, G. L. Kaufman. A completely new series of puzzles as fascinating as crossword and deduction puzzles but based upon different principles and techniques. Simple 2-minute teasers, word labyrinths, design and pattern puzzles, logic and observation puzzles — over 150 brainrackers. Answers to all problems. 116 illustrations. 192pp. 5⅜ x 8. **T143 Paperbound $1.00**

NEW WORD PUZZLES, G. L. Kaufman. 100 ENTIRELY NEW puzzles based on words and their combinations. Chess words, based on the moves of the chess king; design-onyms, symmetrical designs made of synonyms; rhymed double-crostics; syllable sentences; addle letter anagrams; alphagrams; linkograms; and many others all brand new. Full solutions. Space to work problems. 196 figures. vi + 122pp. 5⅜ x 8. **T344 Paperbound $1.00**

MATHEMATICAL RECREATIONS, M. Kraitchik. One of the most thorough compilations of unusual mathematical problems for beginners and advanced mathematicians. Historical problems from Greek, Medieval, Arabic, Hindu sources. 50 pages devoted to pastimes derived from figurate numbers, Mersenne numbers, Fermat numbers, primes and probability. 40 pages of magic, Euler, Latin, panmagic squares. 25 new positional and permutational games of permanent value: fairy chess, latruncles, reversi, jinx, ruma, lasca, tricolor, tetrachrome, etc. Complete rigorous solutions. Revised second edition. 181 illustrations. 330pp. 5⅜ x 8. **T163 Paperbound $1.75**

MATHEMATICAL EXCURSIONS, H. A. Merrill. Even if you hardly remember your high school math, you'll enjoy the 90 stimulating problems. Little effort. Many useful shortcuts and diversions not generally known are included: division by inspection, Russian peasant multiplication, memory systems for pi, building odd and even magic squares, square roots by geometry, dyadic systems, and many more. Solutions to difficult problems. 50 illustrations. 145pp. 5⅜ x 8.   T350 Paperbound **$1.00**

PUZZLE QUIZ AND STUNT FUN, J. Meyer. The solution to party doldrums. 238 challenging puzzles, stunts and tricks. Mathematical puzzles like The Clever Carpenter, Atom Bomb; mysteries and deductions like The Bridge of Sighs, The Nine Pearls, Dog Logic; observation puzzles like Cigarette Smokers, Telephone Dial; over 200 others including magic squares, tongue twisters, puns, anagrams, and many others. All problems solved fully. 250pp. 5⅜ x 8.   T337 Paperbound **$1.00**

MAGIC TRICKS & CARD TRICKS, W. Jonson. Two books bound as one. 52 tricks with cards, 37 tricks with coins, bills, eggs, smoke, ribbons, slates, etc. Details on presentation, misdirection, and routining will help you master such famous tricks as the Changing Card, Card in the Pocket, Four Aces, Coin Through the Hand, Bill in the Egg, Afghan Bands, and over 75 others. If you follow the lucid exposition and key diagrams carefully, you will finish these two books with an astonishing mastery of magic. 106 figures. 224pp. 5⅜ x 8.   T909 Paperbound **$1.00**

CRYPTANALYSIS, H. F. Gaines. Formerly entitled ELEMENTARY CRYPTANALYSIS. The best book in print on cryptograms and their solution. Covers all major techniques of the past, and contains much that is not generally known except to experts. Full details about concealment, substitution, and transposition ciphers; periodic mixed alphabets, multafid, Kasiski and Vignere methods, Ohaver patterns, Playfair, and scores of other topics. 6 language letter and word frequency appendix. 167 problems, now furnished with solutions. Index. 173 figures. vi + 230pp. 5⅜ x 8.
T97 Paperbound **$1.95**

FLATLAND, E. A. Abbott. A science-fiction classic of life in a 2-dimensional world that is also a first-rate introduction to such aspects of modern science as relativity and hyperspace. Political, moral, satirical, and humorous overtones have made FLATLAND fascinating reading for thousands. 7th edition. 16 illustrations. 128pp. 5⅜ x 8.   T1 Paperbound **$1.00**

PARTY GAMES, M. Moyes. Over 80 old favorites and new entertainments in this sparkling collection for adults and children. All are easy, safe, fun, and require no special equipment. Organizing the party, warming-up games, performing, games, dance games, children's games, forfeits, and others. Large and small groups, family and guest, everybody loves games! 26 illustrations. 80pp. 5 x 7¼.
T941 Paperbound **75¢**

WIN AT CHESS, F. Reinfeld. 300 practical chess situations from actual tournament play to sharpen your chess eye and test your skill. Traps, sacrifices, mates, winning combinations, subtle exchanges, show you how to WIN AT CHESS. Short notes and tables of solutions and alternative moves help you evaluate your progress. Learn to think ahead playing the 'crucial moments' of historic games. 300 diagrams. Notes and solutions. Formerly titled CHESS QUIZ. vi + 120pp. 5⅜ x 8.
T438 Paperbound **$1.00**

HOW TO FORCE CHECKMATE, F. Reinfeld. Formerly titled CHALLENGE TO CHESSPLAYERS, this is an invaluable collection of 300 lightning strokes selected from actual masters' play, which will demonstrate how to smash your opponent's game with strong decisive moves. No board needed — clear, practical diagrams and easy-to-understand solutions. Learn to plan up to three moves ahead and play a superior end game. 300 diagrams. 111pp. 5⅜ x 8.   T439 Paperbound **$1.25**

MORPHY'S GAMES OF CHESS, edited by Philip W. Sergeant. You can put boldness into your game by following the brilliant, forceful moves of the man who has been called the greatest chess player of all time. 300 of Morphy's best games, carefully annotated, reveal Morphy's principles. Unabridged reissue of the latest revised edition. Bibliography. New introduction by Fred Reinfeld. Annotations and introduction by Sergeant. Index. 235 diagrams. x + 352pp. 5⅜ x 8.
T386 Paperbound **$1.75**

THE ART OF THE STORY-TELLER, M. L. Shedlock. Regarded by librarians, story-tellers, and educators as the finest, most lucid book on the subject. The nature of the story, difficulties of communicating stories to children, artifices used in story-telling, how to obtain and maintain the effect of the story, and the elements to seek or avoid in selecting material. A 99 page selection of most effective stories. Extensive bibliography of further material. xxi + 320pp. 5⅜ x 8.   T245 Paperbound **$3.50**

CRYPTOGRAPHY, L. D. Smith. An excellent introductory work on ciphers and their solution, the history of secret writing, and actual methods and problems in such techniques as transposition and substitution. Appendices describe the enciphering of Japanese, the Baconian biliteral cipher, and contain frequency tables and a bibliography for further study. Over 150 problems with solutions. 160pp. 5⅜ x 8.   T247 Paperbound **$1.00**

LANGUAGE

NEW RUSSIAN-ENGLISH AND ENGLISH-RUSSIAN DICTIONARY, M. A. O'Brien. Over 70,000 entries in new orthography! Idiomatic uses, colloquialisms. Irregular verbs, perfective and imperfective aspects, regular and irregular sound changes, and other features. One of the few dictionaries where accent changes within the conjugation of verbs and the declension of nouns are fully indicated. "One of the best," Prof. E. J. Simmons, Cornell. First names, geographical terms, bibliography, etc. 738pp. 4½ x 6¼.   T208 Paperbound **$2.00**

MONEY CONVERTER AND TIPPING GUIDE FOR EUROPEAN TRAVEL, C. Vomacka. Currency regulations and tipping for every European country including Iron Curtain countries, Israel, Egypt, and Turkey. Complete conversion tables for every country from U.S. to foreign and vice versa. Only source of such information as phone rates, postal rates, clothing sizes, duty-free imports, and dozens of other valuable topics. 128pp. 3½ x 5¼. T260 Paperbound 65¢

MONEY CONVERTER AND TIPPING GUIDE FOR TRAVEL IN THE AMERICAS (including the United States and Canada), C. Vomacka. The information you need for informed and confident travel in North and South America. U. S. to foreign and foreign to U. S. currency conversion tables for every country. Special section covers over 250 tipping situations in the U. S. Tipping, postal and telephone rates, customs regulations, and much more is covered for all countries. 128pp. 3½ x 5¼. T261 Paperbound 65¢

DUTCH-ENGLISH AND ENGLISH-DUTCH DICTIONARY, F. G. Renier. For travel, literary, scientific or business Dutch; the most convenient, practical and comprehensive dictionary on the market. More than 60,000 entries, shades of meaning, colloquialisms, idioms, compounds and technical terms. Dutch and English·strong and irregular verbs. This is the only dictionary in its size and price range that indicates the gender of nouns. New orthography for use with older books. xviii + 571pp. 5½ x 6¼. T224 Clothbound $2.50

LEARN DUTCH!, F. G. Renier. The most satisfactory and most easily used grammar of modern Dutch. The student is gradually led from simple lessons in pronunciation, through translation, finally to a mastery of spoken and written Dutch. Grammatical principles are clearly explained while a useful, practical vocabulary is introduced in easy exercises and readings. It is used and recommended by the Fulbright Committee in the Netherlands. Phonetic appendices. Over 1200 exercises; Dutch-English, English-Dutch vocabularies. 181pp. 4¼ x 7¼. T441 Clothbound $1.75

LISTEN & LEARN

FRENCH SPANISH GERMAN ITALIAN

LISTEN & LEARN is the only language record course designed especially to meet your travel and everyday needs. It is available in separate sets for FRENCH, SPANISH, GERMAN, or ITALIAN, and each set contains 3 ten-inch 33-1/3 rpm long-playing records — 1½ hours of recorded speech by eminent native speakers who are professors at Columbia, New York University, Queens College. Check the following special features found only in LISTEN & LEARN:

- **Dual-language recording. 812 selected phrases and sentences,** over 3200 words, spoken first in English, then in their foreign language equivalents. A suitable pause follows each foreign phrase, allowing you time to repeat the expression. You learn by unconscious assimilation.

- **128-page manual** contains everything on the records, plus a simple phonetic pronunciation guide.

- **Indexed for convenience. The only set on the market** that is completely indexed. No more puzzling over where to find the phrase you need. Just look in the rear of the manual.

- **Practical.** No time wasted on material you can find in any grammar. LISTEN & LEARN covers central core material with phrase approach. Ideal for the person with limited learning time.

- **Living, modern expressions,** not found in other courses. Hygienic products, modern equipment, shopping — expressions used every day, like "nylon" and "air-conditioned."

- **Limited objective.** Everything you learn, no matter where you stop, is immediately useful. You have to finish other courses, wade through grammar and vocabulary drill, before they help you.

- **High-fidelity recording.** LISTEN & LEARN records equal in clarity and surface-silence any record on the market costing up to $6 per record.

41 different categories covering all your travel wants — Greetings, introductions, social conversations . . . Making yourself understood . . . Useful words, phrases, sentences . . . Passing customs, checking baggage . . . Buying travel tickets . . . Flying, train travel, boats, buses, streetcars, taxis, subways . . . Automobile travel, repairs, parts . . . At a nightclub, restaurant . . . Menus: breakfast, soups, entrees, vegetables, salads, fruits, drinks, desserts . . . Sports, sightseeing, concerts, dancing . . . Cashing checks . . . Cameras, photography, films . . . Drugstores, doctors, dentists, medicines . . . Barber shops, beauty parlors, laundries, dry cleaning . . . Telephoning, postal services . . . Time, numbers, dates, months, seasons . . . and many more, including the largest collection of street and shop signs in print anywhere.

"Excellent . . . the spoken records . . . impress me as being among the very best on the market," **Prof. Mario Pei,** Dept. of Romance Languages, Columbia University. "Inexpensive and well-done . . . it would make an ideal present," CHICAGO SUNDAY TRIBUNE. "More genuinely helpful than anything of its kind which I have previously encountered," **Sidney Clark,** well-known author of "ALL THE BEST" travel books.

UNCONDITIONAL GUARANTEE. Try LISTEN & LEARN, then return it within 10 days for full refund if you are not satisfied. The only course on the market guaranteed after you actually use it.

LISTEN & LEARN comes in 4 useful modern languages — FRENCH, SPANISH, GERMAN, or ITALIAN — one language to each set of 3 ten-inch records, (33-1/3 rpm). 128 page manual. Album.

Spanish	the set **$4.95**	German	the set **$4.95**
French	the set **$4.95**	Italian	the set **$4.95**

SAY IT language phrase books

These handy phrase books (128 to 196 pages each) make grammatical drills unnecessary for an elementary knowledge of a spoken foreign language. Covering most matters of travel and everyday life each volume contains:

> Over 1000 phrases and sentences in immediately useful forms — foreign language plus English. Modern usage designed for Americans. Specific phrases like, "Give me small change," and "Please call a taxi."
> Simplified phonetic transcription you will be able to read at sight.
> The only completely indexed phrase books on the market.
> Covers scores of important situations: — Greetings, restaurants, sightseeing, useful expressions, etc.

These books are prepared by native linguists who are professors at Columbia, N.Y.U., Fordham and other great universities. Use them independently or with any other book or record course. They provide a supplementary living element that most other courses lack. Individual volumes in:

French 60¢	**German 60¢**	**Italian 60¢**
Russian 60¢	**Portuguese 75¢**	**Spanish 60¢**
Hebrew 60¢	**Norwegian 75¢**	**Swedish 60¢**
Japanese 60¢	**Polish 75¢**	**Modern Greek 60¢**
Dutch 75¢	**Esperanto 75¢**	**Yiddish 75¢**
English for Spanish-speaking people 60¢		
English for Italian-speaking people 60¢		
English for German-speaking people 60¢		
Turkish 75¢		

Large clear type. 128-196 pages each. 3½ x 5¼.
Sturdy paper binding.

LITERATURE

WORLD DRAMA, B. H. Clark. 46 plays from Ancient Greece, Rome, Medieval Europe, France, Germany, Italy, England, Russia, Scandinavia, India, China. Japan, etc. — including classic authors like Aeschylus, Sophocles, Euripides, Aristophanes, Plautus, Marlowe, Jonson, Farquhar, Goldsmith, Cervantes, Moliere, Dumas, Goethe, Schiller, Ibsen, and many others. This creative collection avoids hackneyed material. Over 1/3 of this material is unavailable in any other current edition! "The most comprehensive collection of important plays from all literature available in English," SAT. REV. OF LITERATURE. Introduction. Reading lists. 2 volumes. 1364pp. 5⅜ x 8.
Vol. 1, T57 Paperbound **$2.00**
Vol. 2, T59 Paperbound **$2.00**

MASTERS OF THE DRAMA, John Gassner. The most comprehensive history of the drama in print, covering drama in every important tradition from the Greeks to the Near East, China, Japan, Medieval Europe, England, Russia, Italy, Spain, Germany, and dozens of other drama producing nations. This unsurpassed reading and reference work encompasses more than 800 dramatists and over 2000 plays, with biographical material, plot summaries, theatre history, etc. "Best of its kind in English," NEW REPUBLIC. Exhaustive 35 page bibliography. 77 photographs and drawings. Deluxe edition with reinforced cloth binding, headbands, stained top. xxii + 890pp. 5⅜ x 8.
T100 Clothbound **$5.95**

THE DRAMA OF LUIGI PIRANDELLO, D. Vittorini. All 38 of Pirandello's plays written between 1918 and 1935 are summarized and analyzed in this authorized study. Their cultural background, place in European dramaturgy, symbolic techniques, and plot structure are carefully examined. Foreword by Pirandello. Biography. Bibliography. xiii + 350pp. 5⅜ x 8.
T435 Paperbound **$1.98**

ARISTOTLE'S THEORY OF POETRY AND THE FINE ARTS, edited by S. H. Butcher. The celebrated Butcher translation of this great classic faced, page by page, with the complete Greek text. A 300 page introduction discussing Aristole's ideas and their influence in the history of thought and literature, and covering art and nature, imitation as an aesthetic form, poetic truth, art and morality, tragedy, comedy, and similar topics. Modern Aristotelian criticism discussed by John Gassner. lxxvi + 421pp. 5⅜ x 8.
T41 Clothbound **$3.95**
T42 Paperbound **$2.00**

EUGENE O'NEILL: THE MAN AND HIS PLAYS, B. H. Clark. No source-book has previously been published on O'Neill's life and work. Clark analyzes each play from the early THE WEB to the recently produced MOON FOR THE MISBEGOTTEN and THE ICEMAN COMETH, revealing the environmental and dramatic influences necessary for a complete understanding of these important works. Bibliography. Appendices. Index. ix + 182pp. 5⅜ x 8.
T379 Paperbound **$1.25**

EPIC AND ROMANCE, W. P. Ker. Written by one of the foremost authorities on medieval literature, this is the standard survey of medieval epic and romance. It covers Teutonic epics, Icelandic sagas, Beowulf, French chansons de geste, the Roman de Troi, and many other important works of literature. It is an excellent account of a body of literature whose beauty and value has only recently come to be recognized. Index. xxiv + 398pp. 5⅜ x 8.
T355 Paperbound **$1.95**

FOUNDERS OF THE MIDDLE AGES, E. K. Rand. The best non-technical discussion of the transformation of Latin pagan culture into medieval civilization. Tertullian, Gregory, Jerome, Boethius, Augustine, the Neoplatonists, and many other literary men, educators, classicists, and humanists. A storehouse of information presented clearly and simply for the intelligent non-specialist. "Thoughtful, beautifully written," AMERICAN HISTORICAL REVIEW. "Extraordinarily accurate," Richard McKeon, THE NATION. ix + 365pp. 5⅜ x 8.
T369 Paperbound **$1.85**

ORIENTALIA

CHRISTIAN AND ORIENTAL PHILOSOPHY OF ART, A. K. Coomaraswamy. A unique fusion of philosopher, orientalist, art historian, and linguist discusses the true function of aesthetics in art, symbolism, intellectual and philosophic backgrounds, the role of traditional culture in enriching art, the nature of medieval art, the nature of folklore, the beauty of mathematics, and similar topics. 2 illustrations. Bibliography. 148pp. 5⅜ x 8.   T378 Paperbound **$1.25**

TRANSFORMATION OF NATURE IN ART, A. K. Coomaraswamy. Unabridged reissue of a basic work upon Asiatic religious art and philosophy of religion. The theory of religious art in Asia and Medieval Europe (exemplified by Meister Eckhart) is analyzed and developed. Indian Medieval aesthetic manuals, symbolic language in philosophy, the origin and use of images in India, and many other fascinating and little known topics. Glossaries of Sanskrit and Chinese terms. Bibliography. 41pp of notes. 245pp. 5⅜ x 8.   T368 Paperbound **$1.75**

ORIENTAL RELIGIONS IN ROMAN PAGANISM, F. Cumont. A study of the cultural meeting of east and west in the Early Roman Empire. Important eastern religions from their first appearance in Rome, 204 B.C., when the Great Mother of the Gods was first brought over from Syria. The ecstatic cults of Syria and Phrygia — Cybele, Attis, Adonis, their orgies and mutilatory rites; the mysteries of Egypt — Serapis, Isis, Osiris; the dualism of Persia, the elevation of cosmic evil to equal stature with the deity, Mithra; worship of Hermes Trismegistus; Ishtar, Astarte; the magic of the ancient Near East, etc. Introduction. 55pp. of notes; extensive bibliography. Index. xxiv + 298pp. 5⅜ x 8.
T321 Paperbound **$1.75**

THE MYSTERIES OF MITHRA, F. Cumont. The definitive coverage of a great ideological struggle between the west and the orient in the first centuries of the Christian era. The origin of Mithraism, a Persian mystery religion, and its associaion with the Roman army is discussed in detail. Then utilizing fragmentary monuments and texts, in one of the greatest feats of scholarly detection, Dr. Cumont reconstructs the mystery teachings and secret doctrines, the hidden organization and cult of Mithra. Mithraic art is discussed, analyzed, and depicted in 70 illustrations. 239pp. 5⅜ x 8.
T323 Paperbound **$1.85**

YOGA, H. P. Shastri. A disciple of the Indian saint Shri Dada, and founder of an important center of classical Yoga, the author gives a lucid, comprehensive account of yoga as practised according to Shankara's Ideal Monism. This is neither an occult book nor a shallow popularization; it is a careful introduction to one of the most important Indian philosophic methods of achieving self-discipline and self-understanding through mental and physical exercise. Glossary. Passages from yoga literature. 6 figures. 96pp. 5 x 7¼.   T975 Paperbound **75¢**

ANTHROPOLOGY, SOCIAL SCIENCES, ETC.

THE IDEA OF PROGRESS, J. B. Bury. Practically unknown before the Reformation, the idea of progress has since become one of the central concepts of western civilization. Prof. Bury analyzes its evolution in the thought of Greece, Rome, the Middle Ages, the Renaissance, to its flowering in all branches of science, religion, philosophy, industry, art, and literature, during and following the 16th century. Introduction by Charles Beard. Index. xl + 357pp. 5⅜ x 8.   T39 Clothbound **$3.95**
T40 Paperbound **$1.95**

PRIMITIVE MAN AS PHILOSOPHER, P. Radin. A standard anthropological work covering primitive thought on such topics as the purpose of life, marital relations, freedom of thought, symbolism, death, resignation, the nature of reality, personality, gods, and many others. Drawn from factual material gathered from the Winnebago, Oglala Sioux, Maori, Baganda, Batak, Zuni, among others, it interprets strictly within the original framework. Extensive selections of original primitive documents. Bibliography. Index. xviii + 402pp. 5⅜ x 8.   T392 Paperbound **$2.00**

PRIMITIVE RELIGION, P. Radin. A thorough treatment of the supernatural and the influences that have shaped religious expression in primitive societies. Ranging over Arunta, Ashanti, Aztec, Bushman, Crow, Fijian, etc., Africa, Australia, Pacific Islands, the Arctic, North and South America, Prof. Radin integrates modern psychology, comparative religion, and economic thought with first-hand accounts gathered by himself and other scholars of primitive initiations, training of the shaman, and other fascinating topics. "Excellent," NATURE (London). New author's preface. Bibliographic notes. Index. x + 322pp. 5⅜ x 8.   T393 Paperbound **$1.85**

THE GIFT OF LANGUAGE, M. Schlauch. Formerly titled THE GIFT OF TONGUES, this is a middle-level survey that avoids both superficiality and pedantry. It covers such topics as linguistic families, word histories, grammatical processes in such foreign languages as Aztec, Ewe, and Bantu, semantics, language taboos, and dozens of other fascinating and important topics. Especially interesting is an analysis of the word-coinings of Joyce, Cummings, Stein and others in terms of linguistics. 232 bibliographic notes. Index. viii + 342pp. 5⅜ x 8.   T243 Paperbound **$1.85**

PHILOSOPHY

GUIDE TO PHILOSOPHY, C. E. M. Joad. Does free will exist? Is there plan in the universe? How do we know and validate our knowledge? Such opposed solutions as subjective idealism and realism, chance and teleology, vitalism and logical positivism, are evaluated and the contributions of the great philosophers from the Greeks to moderns like Russell, Whitehead, and others, are considered in the context of each problem. "The finest introduction," BOSTON TRANSCRIPT. Index. Classified bibliography. 592pp. 5⅜ x 8.   T297 Paperbound **$2.00**

THE PHILOSOPHY OF HEGEL, W. T. Stace. The first detailed analysis of Hegel's thought in English, this is especially valuable since so many of Hegel's works are out of print. Dr. Stace examines Hegel's debt to Greek idealists and the 18th century and then proceeds to a careful description and analysis of Hegel's first principles, categories, reason, dialectic method, his logic, philosophy of nature and spirit, etc. Index. Special 14 x 20 chart of Hegelian system. x + 526pp. 5⅜ x 8.
T253 Clothbound **$3.95**
T254 Paperbound **$2.00**

ARISTOTLE, A. E. Taylor. A brilliant, searching non-technical account of Aristotle and his thought written by a foremost Platonist. It covers the life and works of Aristotle; classification of the sciences; logic, first philosophy, matter and form; causes; motion and eternity; God; physics; metaphysics; and similar topics. Bibliography. New index compiled for this edition. 128pp. 5⅜ x 8.
T279 Clothbound **$2.75**
T280 Paperbound **$1.00**

HISTORY OF ANCIENT PHILOSOPHY, W. Windelband. Perhaps the clearest survey of Greek and Roman philosophy. Discusses ancient philosophy in general, intellectual life in Greece in the 7th and 6th centuries B.C., Thales, Anaximander, Anaximenes, Heraclitus, the Eleatics, Empedocles, Anaxagoras, Leucippus, the Pythagoreans, the Sophists, Socrates, Democritus (20 pages), Plato (50 pages), Aristotle (70 pages), the Peripatetics, Stoics, Epicureans, Sceptics, Neo-platonists, Christian Apologists, etc. 2nd German edition translated by H. E. Cushman. xv + 393pp. 5⅜ x 8.   T357 Paperbound **$1.75**

LANGUAGE AND MYTH, E. Cassirer. Analyzing the non-rational elements in culture, Cassirer demonstrates that beneath both language and myth lies an unconscious "grammar" of experience whose categories and canons are not those of logical thought. His analyses of seemingly diverse phenomena such as Indian metaphysics, the Melanesian "mana," the Naturphilosophie of Schelling, modern poetry, etc., are profound without being pedantic. Introduction and translation by Susanne Langer. Index. x + 103pp. 5⅜ x 8.   T51 Paperbound **$1.25**

SUBSTANCE AND FUNCTION, EINSTEIN'S THEORY OF RELATIVITY, E. Cassirer. In this double-volume, Cassirer develops a philosophy of the exact sciences that is historically sound, philosophically mature, and scientifically impeccable. Such topics as the concept of number, space and geometry, non-Euclidean geometry, traditional logic and scientific method, mechanism and motion, energy, relational concepts, degrees of objectivity, the ego, Einstein's relativity, and many others are treated in detail. Authorized translation by W.C. and M. C. Swabey. xii + 465pp. 5⅜ x 8.   T50 Paperbound **$2.00**

THE PHILOSOPHICAL WORKS OF DESCARTES. Definitive English edition of all major philosophical works and letters of René Descartes. All of his revolutionary insights, from his famous "Cogito ergo sum" to his detailed account of contemporary science and his astonishingly fruitful concept that all phenomena of the universe (except mind) could be reduced to clear laws by the use of mathematics. An excellent source for the thought of men like Hobbes, Arnauld, Gassendi, etc. Translated by E. S. Haldane and G. Ross. Introductory notes. Index. Total of 842pp. 5⅜ x 8.
T71 Vol. 1, Paperbound **$2.00**
T72 Vol. 2, Paperbound **$2.00**

ESSAYS IN EXPERIMENTAL LOGIC, J. Dewey. Based upon the theory that knowledge implies a judgement, which in turn implies an inquiry, these papers consider the inquiry stage in terms of: the relationship of thought and subject matter, antecedents of thought, data and meanings. 3 papers examine Bertrand Russell's thought, while 2 others discuss pragmatism and a final essay presents a new theory of the logic of values. Index. viii + 444pp. 5⅜ x 8.   T73 Paperbound **$1.95**

THE PHILOSOPHY OF HISTORY, G. W. F. Hegel. One of the great classics of western thought which reveals Hegel's basic principle: that history is not chance but a rational process, the realization of the Spirit of Freedom. Ranges from the oriental cultures of subjective thought to the classical subjective cultures, to the modern absolute synthesis where spiritual and secular may be reconciled. Translation and introduction by J. Sibree. Introduction by C. Hegel. Special introduction for this edition by Prof. Carl Friedrich. xxxix + 447pp. 5⅜ x 8.   T112 Paperbound **$1.85**

THE WILL TO BELIEVE and HUMAN IMMORTALITY, W. James. Two complete books bound as one. THE WILL TO BELIEVE discusses the interrelations of belief, will, and intellect in man; chance vs. determinism, free will vs. fate, pluralism vs. monism; the philosophies of Hegel and Spencer, and more. HUMAN IMMORTALITY examines the question of survival after death and develops an unusual and powerful argument for immortality. Two prefaces. Index. Total of 429pp. 5⅜ x 8.
T294 Clothbound **$3.75**
T291 Paperbound **$1.75**

INTRODUCTION TO SYMBOLIC LOGIC, S. Langer. No special knowledge of math required. You start with simple symbols and advance to a knowledge of the Boole-Schroeder and Russell-Whitehead systems. Forms, logical structure, classes, the calculus of propositions, logic of the syllogism, etc., are all covered. "One of the clearest and simplest introductions," MATHEMATICS GAZETTE. Second enlarged, revised edition. 368pp. 5⅜ x 8. S164 Paperbound **$1.75**

MIND AND THE WORLD-ORDER, C. I. Lewis. Building upon the work of Peirce, James, and Dewey, Professor Lewis outlines a theory of knowledge in terms of "conceptual pragmatism." Dividing truth into abstract mathematical certainty and empirical truth, the author demonstrates that the traditional understanding of the a priori must be abandoned. Detailed analyses of philosophy, metaphysics, method, the "given" in experience, knowledge of objects, nature of the a priori, experience and order, and many others. Appendices. xiv + 446pp. 5⅜ x 8. T359 Paperbound **$1.95**

THE GUIDE FOR THE PERPLEXED, Maimonides. One of the great philosophical works of all time and a necessity for everyone interested in the philosophy of the Middle Ages in the Jewish, Christian, and Moslem traditions. Maimonides develops a common meeting-point for the Old Testament and the Aristotelian thought which pervaded the medieval world. 2nd revised edition. Complete unabridged Friedländer translation. 55 page introduction to Maimonides' life, period, etc., with an important summary of the GUIDE. Index. lix + 414pp. 5⅜ x 8. T351 Paperbound **$1.85**

THE PHILOSOPHICAL WRITINGS OF PEIRCE, edited by J. Buchler. Formerly THE PHILOSOPHY OF PEIRCE), a carefully integrated exposition of Peirce's complete system composed of selections from his own work. Symbolic logic, scientific method, theory of signs, pragmatism, epistemology, chance, cosmology, ethics, and many other topics are treated by one of the greatest philosophers of modern times. xvi + 386pp. 5⅜ x 8. T216 Clothbound **$5.00**
T217 Paperbound **$1.95**

SCEPTICISM AND ANIMAL FAITH, G. Santayana. To eliminate difficulties in the traditional theory of knowledge, Santayana distinguishes between the independent existence of objects and the essence our mind attributes to them. Scepticism is thereby established as a form of belief, and animal faith is shown to be a necessary condition of knowledge. Belief, classical idealism, intuition, memory, symbols, literary psychology, and much more, discussed with unusual clarity and depth. Index. xii + 314pp. 5⅜ x 8. T235 Clothbound **$3.50**
T236 Paperbound **$1.50**

THE ANALYSIS OF MATTER, B. Russell. Logical analysis of physics, prerelativity physics, causality, scientific inference, Weyl's theory, tensors, invariants and physical interpretations, periodicity, and much more is treated with Russell's usual brilliance. "Masterly piece of clear thinking and clear writing," NATION AND ATHENAEUM. "Most thorough treatment of the subject," THE NATION. Introduction. Index. 8 figures. viii + 408pp. 5⅜ x 8. T231 Paperbound **$1.95**

THE SENSE OF BEAUTY, G. Santayana. A revelation of the beauty of language as well as an important philosophic treatise, this work studies the "why, when, and how beauty appears, what conditions an object must fulfill to be beautiful, what elements of our nature make us sensible of beauty, and what the relation is between the constitution of the object and the excitement of our susceptibility." "It is doubtful if a better treatment of the subject has since been published," PEABODY JOURNAL. Index. ix + 275pp. 5⅜ x 8. T237 Clothbound **$2.85**
T238 Paperbound **$1.00**

THE CHIEF WORKS OF SPINOZA. Spinoza's most important philosophical works. Vol. I: The Theologico-Political Treatise and the Political Treatise. Vol. II: On The Improvement Of Understanding, The Ethics, Selected Letters. Profound and enduring ideas on God, the universe, pantheism, society, religion, the state, democracy, the mind, emotions, freedom, and the nature of man, which influenced Goethe, Hegel, Schelling, Coleridge, Whitehead, and many others. Introduction. 2 volumes. 862pp. 5⅜ x 8.
T249 Vol. I, Paperbound **$1.50**
T250 Vol. II, Paperbound **$1.50**

TRAGIC SENSE OF LIFE, M. de Unamuno. The acknowledged masterpiece of one of Spain's most influential thinkers. Between the despair at the inevitable death of man and all his works and the desire for something better, Unamuno finds that "saving incertitude" that alone can console us. This dynamic appraisal of man's faith in God and in himself has been called, "A masterpiece," by the ENCYCLOPAEDIA BRITANNICA. xxx + 332pp. 5⅜ x 8. T257 Paperbound **$1.95**

PHILOSOPHY AND CIVILIZATION IN THE MIDDLE AGES, M. de Wulf. This semi-popular survey covers aspects of medieval intellectual life such as religion, philosophy, science, the arts, etc. It also covers feudalism vs. Catholicism, rise of the universities, mendicant orders, monastic centers, and similar topics. Unabridged. Bibliography. Index. viii + 320pp. 5⅜ x 8. T284 Paperbound **$1.75**

AN INTRODUCTION TO SCHOLASTIC PHILOSOPHY, Prof. M. de Wulf. Formerly entitled SCHOLASTICISM OLD AND NEW, this examines the central scholastic tradition from St. Anslem, Albertus Magnus, Thomas Aquinas, up to Suarez in the 17th century. The relation of scholasticism to ancient and medieval philosophy and science is clear and easily followed. The second part of the book considers the modern revival of scholasticism, the Louvain position, relations with Kantianism and Positivism. Unabridged. xvi + 271pp. 5⅜ x 8. T296 Clothbound **$3.50**
T283 Paperbound **$1.75**

HISTORY OF MEDIAEVAL PHILOSOPHY, M. de Wulf. An unabridged reproduction of this standard history of medieval philosophy from the 4th to 12th centuries A.D. Covers St. Augustine, Boethius, John Scotus Erigena, St. Anselm, the school of Chartres, Abelard, Hugh of St. Victor, John of Salisbury, Peter Lombard, and scores of others including dualists, canonists, jurists, mystics like Dionysius Areopagitica, St. Bernard, Joachim of Flores, and others. Byzantine, Arabic and Jewish philosophy, and the scholastic tradition covered in detail. Classified bibliography of thousands of items. "The best treatment of the subject in English," Richard McKeon. Recommended by SHAW'S LIST OF BOOKS FOR COLLEGE LIBRARIES; STANDARD CATALOG FOR PUBLIC LIBRARIES. Indexed. xviii + 317pp. Volume 1 only.
　　　　　　　　　　　　　　　　　　　　　　　　　　　　　　　　T285 Clothbound **$4.00**

A HISTORY OF MODERN PHILOSOPHY, H. Höffding. An exceptionally clear and detailed coverage of western philosophy from the Renaissance to the end of the 19th century. Major and minor men such as Pomponazzi, Bodin, Boehme, Telesius, Bruno, Copernicus, da Vinci, Kepler, Galileo, Bacon, Descartes, Hobbes, Spinoza, Leibniz, Wolff, Locke, Newton, Berkeley, Hume, Erasmus, Montesquieu, Voltaire, Diderot, Rousseau, Lessing, Kant, Herder, Fichte, Schelling, Hegel, Schopenhauer, Comte, Mill, Darwin, Spencer, Hartmann, Lange and many others are discussed in terms of theory of knowledge, logic, cosmology, and psychology. Index. 2 volumes, total of 1159pp. 5⅜ x 8.　　　　　T117 Vol. 1, Paperbound **$2.00**
　　　　　　　　　　　　　　　　　　　　　　　　　　　　　　　T118 Vol. 2, Paperbound **$2.00**

LANGUAGE, TRUTH AND LOGIC, A. J. Ayer. A clear, careful analysis of the basic ideas of Logical Positivism. Building on the work of Schlick, Russell, Carnap, and the Viennese School, Mr. Ayer develops a detailed exposition of the nature of philosophy, science, and metaphysics; the Self and the World; logic and common sense, and other philosophic concepts. An aid to clarity of thought as well as the first full-length development of Logical Positivism in English. Introduction by Bertrand Russell. Index. 160pp. 5⅜ x 8.　　　　　　　　　　　　　　　　　　　　　　　　　T10 Paperbound **$1.25**

PSYCHOLOGY

SEX IN PSYCHO-ANALYSIS (formerly CONTRIBUTIONS TO PSYCHO-ANALYSIS), S. Ferenczi. Written by an associate of Freud, this volume presents countless insights on such topics as impotence, transference, analysis and children, dreams, symbols, obscene words, masturbation and male homosexuality, paranoia and psycho-analysis, the sense of reality, hypnotism and therapy, and many others. Also includes full text of THE DEVELOPMENT OF PYSCHO-ANALYSIS by Ferenczi and Otto Rank. Two books bound as one. Total of 406pp. 5⅜ x 8.　　　　　　　　　　　　　　　　　　　　T324 Paperbound **$1.85**

THE PRINCIPLES OF PSYCHOLOGY, William James. The full long course, unabridged, of one of the great classics of Western literature and science. Wonderfully lucid descriptions of mental activity, the stream of thought, consciousness, time perception, memory, imagination, emotions, reason, abnormal phenomena, and similiar topics. Original contributions are integrated with the work of such men as Berkeley, Binet, Mills, Darwin, Hume, Kant, Royce, Schopenhauer, Spinoza, Locke, Descartes, Galton, Wundt, Lotse, Herbart, Fechner and scores of others. All contrasting interpretations of mental phenomena are examined in detail — introspective analysis, philosophical interpretation, and experimental research. "A classic," JOURNAL OF CONSULTING PSYCHOLOGY. "The main lines are as valid as ever," PSYCHOANALYTICAL QUARTERLY. "Standard reading . . . a classic of interpretation," PSYCHIATRIC QUARTERLY. 94 illustrations. 1408pp. 2 volumes. 5⅜ x 8.　　　　　　　　　　　　Vol. 1, T381 Paperbound **$2.00**
　　　　　　　　　　　　　　　　　　　　　　　　　　　　　　Vol. 2, T382 Paperbound **$2.00**

ARTS AND CRAFTS

STICKS AND STONES, Louis Mumford. A survey of forces that have conditioned American architecture and altered its forms. The medieval tradition in early New England villages; the Renaissance influence and rise of the merchant class; the classical influence of Jefferson's time; the "Mechanicsvilles" of Poe's generation; the Brown Decades; the philosophy of the Imperial facade; and finally the modern machine age "A truly remarkable book," SAT. REV. OF LITERATURE. 2nd revised edition. 21 illustrations. xvii + 228pp. 5⅜ xx 8.　　　　　　　　　　　　　　　　　　　　　T202 Paperbound **$1.60**

THE AUTOBIOGRAPHY OF AN IDEA, Louis Sullivan. The pioneer architect whom Frank Lloyd Wright called "the master" records the crystallization of his opinions and theories, the growth of his organic theory of architecture that still influences American designers and architects. This volume contains 34 full-page plates of his finest architecture. Unabridged reissue of 1924 edition. New introduction by R. M. Line. Index. xiv + 335pp. 5⅜ x 8.　　　　　　　　　　　　　　　　　T281 Paperbound **$1.85**

THE MATERIALS AND TECHNIQUES OF MEDIEVAL PAINTING, D. V. Thompson. Based on years of study of medieval manuscripts and laboratory analysis of medieval paintings, this book discusses carriers and grounds, binding media, pigments, metals used in painting, etc. Considers relative merits of painting al fresco and al secco, the processing of coloring materials, burnishing, and many other matters. Preface by Bernard Berenson. Index. 239pp. 5⅜ x 8.　　　　　　　　　　T327 Paperbound **$1.85**

WILD FOWL DECOYS, J. Barber. The standard work on this fascinating branch of folk art, this book describes duck decoys of all sorts ranging from Indian mud and grass devices to the realistic carved wooden decoys invented in Revolutionary days and still in use. Collectors information about styles, types, and periods as well as detailed information on producing your own decoys is given in a lucid and entertaining style. Seven decoy paintings and sets of plans (14 new plates) have been added, making a total of 140 unusual and valuable illustrations (4 in color) for handycrafters, artists, hunters, and students of folk art. 281pp. 7⅞ x 10¾. Deluxe edition.　　　　　　　　　　　T11 Clothbound **$8.50**

METALWORK AND ENAMELLING, H. Maryon. Probably the best book ever written on the subject. Prepared by Herbert Maryon, F.S.A., of the British Museum, it tells everything necessary for home manufacture of jewelry, rings, ear pendants, bowls, and dozens of other objects. Clearly written chapters provide precise information on such topics as materials, tools, soldering, filigree, setting stones, raising patterns, spinning metal, repoussé work, hinges and joints, metal inlaying, damascening, overlaying, niello, Japanese alloys, enamelling, cloisonné, painted enamels, casting, polishing coloring, assaying, and dozens of other techniques. This is the next best thing to apprenticeship to a master metalworker. 363 photographs and figures. 374pp. 5½ x 8½.   T183 Clothbound **$7.50**

PRINCIPLES OF ART HISTORY, H. Wölfflin. Analyzing such terms as "baroque," "classic," "neoclassic," "primitive," "picturesque," and 164 different works by artists like Botticelli, van Cleve, Dürer, Hobbema, Holbein, Hals, Rembrandt, Titian, Brueghel, Vermeer, and many others, the author shows what really occurred between the 14th century primitives and the sophistication of the 18th century in terms of basic attitudes and philosophies. "A remarkable lesson in the art of seeing," SAT. REV. OF LITERATURE. Translated from the 7th German edition. 150 illustrations. 254pp. 6⅛ x 9¼.   T276 Paperbound **$2.00**

SHAKER FURNITURE, E. D. and F. Andrews. Far and away the most illuminating study of Shaker furniture and the principles of Shaker craftsmanship ever written. The results of 15 years of research in Shaker communities, archives, and collections, Chronology, craftsmanship, furniture, houses, shops, etc., of Shaker culture. Over 200 chairs, tables, desks, clocks, beds, benches, are illustrated by clear photographs. For everyone interested in Americana, antiques, art, American culture of fine arts. "Mr. & Mrs. Andrews knows all there is to know about Shaker furniture," MARK VAN DOREN, NATION. 48 full page plates. 192pp. Deluxe cloth binding. 7⅞ x 10¾.   T7 Clothbound **$6.00**

HANDBOOK OF ORNAMENT, F. S. Meyer. One of the largest collections of copyright-free traditional art. Over 3300 line cuts of Greek, Roman, Medieval, Islamic, Renaissance, Baroque, 18th and 19th century objects. 180 plates illustrate networks, Gothic tracery, geometric elements, flower and animal motifs, etc., while 100 plates illustrate decorative objects: chairs, thrones, cabinets, crowns, weapons, utensils, vases, jewelry, armor, heraldry, bottles, altars, and scores of other objects. Full text. 3300 illustrations. xiv + 548pp. 5⅜ x 8.   T302 Paperbound **$2.00**

THREE CLASSICS OF ITALIAN CALLIGRAPHY, edited by Oscar Ogg. Complete reproductions of three famous calligraphic works by the greatest writing masters of the Renaissance: Arrighi's OPERINA and IL MODO, Tagliente's LO PRESENTE LIBRO, and Palatino's LIBRO NUOVO. These books present more than 200 complete alphabets and thousands of lettered specimens. The basic hand is Papal Chancery, but scores of other alphabets are also given: European and Asiatic local alphabets, foliated and "art" alphabets, scrolls, cartouches, borders, etc. Text is in Italian. Introduction. 245 plates. x + 272pp. 6⅛ x 9¼.   T212 Paperbound **$1.95**

THE HISTORY AND TECHNIQUES OF LETTERING, A. Nesbitt. The only thorough inexpensive history of letter froms from the point of view of the artist. Mr. Nesbitt covers every major development in lettering from the ancient Egyptians to the present and illustrates each development with a complete alphabet. Such masters as Baskerville, Bell, Bodoni, Caslon, Koch, Kilian, Morris, Garamont, Jenson, and dozens of others are analyzed in terms of artistry and historical development. The author also presents a 65 page practical course in lettering, besides the full historical text. 89 complete alphabets; 165 additional lettered specimens. xvii + 300pp. 5⅜ x 8.   T427 Paperbound **$2.00**

LETTERING AND ALPHABETS, J. A. Cavanagh. This unabridged reissue of LETTERING offers a full discussion, analysis, illustration of 89 basic hand lettering styles — styles derived from Caslons, Bodonis, Garamonds, Gothic, Black Letter, Oriental and many others. Upper and lower cases, numerals and common signs pictured. Hundreds of technical hints on make-up, construction, artistic validity, strokes, pens, brushes, white areas, etc. May be reproduced without permission! 89 complete alphabets; 72 lettered specimens. 121pp. 9¾ x 8.   T53 Paperbound **$1.25**

THE HUMAN FIGURE IN MOTION, Eadweard Muybridge. The largest selection in print of Muybridge's famous high-speed action photos of the human figure in motion. 4789 photographs illustrate 162 different actions: men, women, children — mostly undraped — are shown walking, running, carrying various objects, sitting, lying down, climbing, throwing, arising, and performing over 150 other actions. Some actions are shown in as many as 120 photographs each. More than 500 action strips at shutter speeds as high as 1/6000th of a second! These are not posed shots, but true stopped motion. They show bone and muscles in situations that the human eye is not fast enough to capture. Earlier, smaller editions of these prints have brought $40 and more on the out-of-print market. "A must for artists," ART IN FOCUS. "An unparalled dictionary of action for all artists," AMERICAN ARTIST. 390 full-page plates, with 4789 photographs. Printed on heavy glossy stock. Reinforced binding with headbands. 7⅞ x 10⅝. T204 Clothbound **$10.00**

ANIMALS IN MOTION, Eadweard Muybridge. This is the largest collection of animal action photos in print. 34 different animals (horses, mules, oxen, goats, camels, pigs, cats, guanacos, lions, gnus, deer, monkeys, eagles — and 21 others) in 132 characteristic actions. The horse alone is shown in more than 40 different actions. All 3919 photographs are taken in series at speeds up to 1/6000th of a second. You will see exactly how a lion sets his foot down; how an elephant's knees are like a human's — and how they differ; the position of a kangaroo's legs in mid-leap; how an ostrich's head bobs; details of the flight of birds — and thousands of facts of motion only the fastest cameras can catch. Neither semiposed artificial shots nor distorted telephoto shots taken under adverse conditions. Artists, biologists, cartoonists, will find this book indispensable for understanding animals in motion. "A really marvelous series of plates," NATURE (London). "The dry plate's most spectacular early use was by Eadweard Muybridge," LIFE. 3919 photographs; 380 full pages of plates. 440pp. Printed on heavy glossy paper. Deluxe binding with headbands. 7⅞ x 10⅝.   T203 Clothbound **$10.00**

THE BOOK OF SIGNS, Rudolf Koch. 493 symbols from ancient manuscripts, medieval cathedrals, coins, catacombs, pottery, etc. Crosses, monograms of Roman emperors, astrological, chemical, botanical, runes, housemarks, and 7 other categories. Invaluable for handycraft workers, illustrators, scholars, etc., this material may be reproduced without permission. 493 illustrations by Fritz Kredel. 104pp. 6⅛ x 9¼. Sewn binding. T162 Paperbound **$1.00**

A HANDBOOK OF EARLY ADVERTISING ART, C. P. Hornung. The largest collection of copyright-free early advertising art ever compiled. Vol. I contains some 2,000 illustrations of agricultural devices, animals, old automobiles, birds, buildings, Christmas decorations (with 7 Santa Clauses by Nast), allegorical figures, fire engines, horses and vehicles, Indians, portraits, sailing ships, trains, sports, trade cuts — and 30 other categories! Vol. II, devoted to typography, has over 4000 specimens: 600 different Roman, Gothic, Barnum, Old English faces; 630 ornamental type faces; 1115 initials, hundreds of scrolls, flourishes, etc. This third edition is enlarged by 78 additional plates containing all new material. "A remarkable collection," PRINTERS' INK. "A rich contribution to the history of American design," GRAPHIS.
Volume 1, Pictorial Volume. Over 2000 illustrations. xlv + 242pp. 9 x 12. T122 Clothbound **$10.00**
Volume II, Typographical Volume. Over 4000 specimens. vii + 312pp. 9 x 12. T123 Clothbound **$10.00**
Two volume set, Clothbound, only **$18.50**

DESIGN FOR ARTISTS AND CRAFTSMEN, L. Wolchonok. The most thorough course on the creation of art motifs and designs. Create your own designs out of things around you — from geometric patterns, plants, birds, animals, humans, landscapes, and man-made objects. It leads you step by step through the creation of more than 1300 designs, ranging from near representationalism to the most advanced forms of abstraction. The material in this book is entirely new, and combines full awareness of traditional design with the work of such men as Miro, Leger, Picasso, Moore, and others. 113 detailed exercises, with instruction hints, diagrams, and details to enable you to apply Wolchonok's methods to your own work. "A great contribution to the field of design and crafts," N. Y. SOCIETY OF CRAFTSMEN. More than 1300 illustrations. xv + 207pp. 7⅞ x 10¾. T274 Clothbound **$4.95**

HANDBOOK OF DESIGNS AND DEVICES, C. P. Hornung. Indispensable to the designer, commercial artist, and hobbyist. It is not a text-book but a working collection of 1836 basic designs and variations, which may be used without permission. Variations of circle, line, band, triangle, square, cross, diamond, swastika, pentagon, octagon, hexagon, star, scroll, interlacement, shields, etc. Supplementary notes on the background and symbolism. "A necessity to every designer who would be original without having to labor heavily," ARTIST AND ADVERTISER. 204 plates. 240pp. 5⅜ x 8. T124 Clothbound **$3.95**
T125 Paperbound **$1.90**

THE UNIVERSAL PENMAN, George Bickham. This beautiful book, which first appeared in 1743 contains 212 full-page plates drawn from the work of such 18th century masters of English roundhand as Dove, Champion, and Bland. They contain 22 complete alphabets, over 2,000 flourishes, and 122 illustrations, each drawn with a stylistic grace impossible to describe. This book is invaluable to anyone interested in the beauties of calligraphy, or to any artist, hobbyist, or craftsman who wishes to use the very best ornamental handwriting and flourishes for decorative purposes. Commercial artists, advertising artists, have found it unexcelled as a source of material suggesting quality. "An essential part of any art library, and a book of permanent value," AMERICAN ARTIST. 212 plates. 224pp. 9 x 13¾.
T20 Clothbound **$10.00**

AN ATLAS OF ANATOMY FOR ARTISTS, F. Schider. A new 3rd edition of this standard text enlarged by 52 new illustrations of hands, anatomical studies by Cloquet, and expressive life studies of the body by Barcsay. 29 plates show all aspects of the skeleton, with closeups of special areas, while 54 full-page plates, mostly in two colors, give human musculature as seen from four different points of view, with cutaways for important portions of the body. 14 full-page plates provide photographs of hand forms, eyelids, female breasts, and indicate the location of muscles upon models. 59 additional plates show how great artists of the past utilized human anatomy! Michelangelo, Leonardo da Vinci, Goya, and 15 others. This is a lifetime reference work which will be one of the most important books in any artist's library. "The standard reference tool," AMERICAN LIBRARY ASSOCIATION. "Excellent," AMERICAN ARTIST. Third enlarged edition. 189 plates, 647 illustrations. xxvi + 192pp. 7⅞ x 10⅝.
T241 Clothbound **$6.00**

FOUNDATIONS OF MODERN ART, A. Ozenfant. An illuminating discussion of the interrelationship of all forms of human creativity, from painting to science, writing to religion. The creative process is explored in all facets of art, from paleolithic cave painting to modern French painting and architecture, and the great universals of art are isolated. Expressing its countless insights in aphorisms accompanied by carefully selected illustrations, this book is itself an embodiment in prose of the creative process. Enlarged by 4 new chapters. 226 illustrations. 368pp. 6⅛ x 9¼. T215 Paperbound **$1.95**

AN ATLAS OF ANIMAL ANATOMY FOR ARTISTS, W. Ellenberger, H. Baum, H. Dittrich. The largest, richest animal anatomy for artists available in English. 99 detailed anatomical plates of such animals as the horse, dog, cat, lion, dear, seal, kangaroo, flying squirrel, cow, bull, goat, monkey, hare, and bat. Surface features are clearly indicated, while progressive beneath-the-skin pictures show musculature, tendons, and bone structure. Detailed cross-sections are given for heads and important features. The animals chosen are representative of specific families so that a study of these anatomies will provide knowledge of hundreds of related species. "Highly recommended as one of the very few books on the subject worthy of being used as an authoritative guide," DESIGN. Second revised, enlarged edition with new plates from Cuvier, Stubbs, etc. 288 illustrations. 153pp. 11⅜ x 9.
T82 Clothbound **$6.00**

ANIMAL ANATOMY AND PSYCHOLOGY, C. R. Knight. 158 studies of the artistic aspects and individual traits which characterize a wide variety of vertebrates and invertebrates. The author, a noted animal artist, provides detailed and fascinating insights into the personality of such animals as the gorilla, mandrill, bear, bison, dromedary, camel, peccary, kangaroo, vulture, pelican, hornbill, iguana, shark, crab, and many others. Distinctive features such as eye movements, lip contour under various emotions such as fear, curiosity, or hunger, positional differences during attack and defense, horn formation, stride, and hundreds of other characteristics are clearly described and illustrated. "An excellent reference work," SAN FRANCISCO CHRONICLE. 158 illustrations. vii + 149pp. 10½ x 8¼. T426 Paperbound **$1.75**

PRIMITIVE ART, Franz Boas. A great American anthropologist covers the entire gamut of primitive art. Pottery, leatherwork, metal work, stone work, wood, basketry, etc. Theories of primitive art, historical depth in art history, technical virtuosity, unconscious levels of patterning, symbolism, styles, literature, music, dance, etc. For laymen, the anthropologist, artist, handycrafter (hundreds of unusual motifs), and the historian. Over 900 illustrations (50 ceramic vessels, 12 totem poles, etc., etc.). 376pp. 5⅜ x 8. T25 Paperbound **$1.95**

ON THE LAWS OF JAPANESE PAINTING, H. Bowie. Based on 9 years of profound study-experience in the late Kano art of Japan; the most authentic guide to the spirit and technique of Japanese painting. A wealth of data on control of the brush; practice exercises; manufacture of ink, brushes, colors; the use of various lines and dots to express moods. Best possible substitute for lessons from a great oriental master. 66 plates with 220 illustrations. Index. xv + 117pp. 6⅛ x 9¼. T30 Paperbound **$1.95**

THE CRAFTSMAN'S HANDBOOK, Cennino Cennini. The finest English translation of IL LIBRO DELL' ARTE, a 15th century Florentine introduction to art technique. It is both fascinating reading and a wonderful mirror of another culture for artists, art students, historians, social scientists, or anyone interested in details of life some 500 years ago. While it is not an exact recipe book, it gives direction for such matters as tinting papers, gilding stone, preparation of various hues of black, and many other useful but nearly forgotten facets of the painter's art. 4 illustrations. xxvii + 142pp. D. V. Thompson translator. 6⅛ x 9¼. T54 Paperbound **$3.50**

THE BROWN DECADES, Lewis Mumford. The "buried renaissance" of the post-Civil War period. He demonstrates that it contained the seeds of a new integrity and power and documents his study with detailed accounts of the founding of modern architecture in the work of Sullivan, Richardson, Root, Roebling; landscape development of Marsh, Olmsted, and Eliot; the graphic arts of Homer, Eakins, and Ryder. 2nd revised enlarged edition. Bibliography. 12 illustrations. Index. xiv + 266pp. 5⅜ x 8. T200 Paperbound **$1.65**

STIEGEL GLASS, F. W. Hunter. Acclaimed and treasured by librarians, collectors, dealers and manufacturers, this volume is a clear and entertaining account of the life, early experiments, and final achievements in early American glassware of "Baron" Stiegel. An 18th century German adventurer and industrialist, Stiegel founded an empire and produced much of the most highly esteemed early American glassware. His career and varied glassware is set forth in great detail by Mr. Hunter and a new introduction by Helen McKearin provides details revealed by later research. "This pioneer work is reprinted in an edition even more beautiful than the original," ANTIQUES DEALER. "Well worth reading," MARYLAND HISTORICAL MAGAZINE. Introduction. 171 illustrations; 12 in full color. xxii + 338pp. 7⅞ x 10¾. T128 Clothbound **$10.00**

THE HUMAN FIGURE, J. H. Vanderpoel. Every important artistic element of the human figure is pointed out in minutely detailed word descriptions in this classic text and illustrated as well in 430 pencil and charcoal drawings. Thus the text of this book directs your attention to all the characteristic features and subtle differences of the male and female (adults, children, and aged persons), as though a master artist were telling you what to look for at each stage. 2nd edition, carefully revised and enlarged by George Bridgman. Foreword. 430 illustrations. 143pp. 6⅛ x 9¼. T432 Paperbound **$1.45**

PINE FURNITURE OF EARLY NEW ENGLAND, R. H. Kettell. A rich understanding of one of America's most original folk arts. 413 illustrations of more than 300 chairs, benches, racks, beds, cupboards, mirrors, shelves, tables, and other furniture show all the simple beauty and character of early New England furniture. 55 detailed drawings carefully analyze outstanding pieces. "With its rich store of illustrations, this book emphasizes the individuality and varied design of early American pine furniture. It should be welcomed," ANTIQUES. 413 illustrations and 55 working drawings. 475pp. 8 x 10¾. T145 Clothbound **$10.00**

MASTERPIECES OF FURNITURE IN PHOTOGRAPHS AND MEASURED DRAWINGS, V. C. Salomonsky. Collectors of antiques and craftsmen know that the best possible aids to intelligent and successful furniture collecting and building are careful photographs plus detailed measured drawings. Photographs and drawings (accurate to 1/16th of an inch) of 101 exceptional pieces of furniture. Renaissance chairs and tables; Chippendale chairs, stools, etc.; Louis XV arm chairs; Queen Anne settee; Sheraton style of window seat and chairs; Hepplewhite card tables, dressing tables, sideboards; chests, secretaries, highboys, mirrors, clocks, etc., from the Jacobean to Louis XVI, Duncan Phyfe, Pembroke, and other styles. Complete information on traditions, materials, characteristics, history, etc., of each piece. "Invaluable as a reference book for students or as a guide to craftsmen," CRAFT HORIZONS. 102 photographs, over 500 drawings. Bibliography. 224pp. 7⅞ x 10¾. T234 Clothbound **$6.00**

BASIC BOOKBINDING, A. W. Lewis. Enables the beginner and the expert to apply the latest and most simplified techniques to rebinding old favorites and binding new paperback books. Complete lists of all necessary materials and guides to the selection of proper tools, paper, glue, boards, cloth, leather, or sheepskin covering fabrics, lettering inks and pigments, etc. You are shown how to collate a book, sew it, back it, trim it, make boards and attach them in easy step-by-step stages. Author's preface. 261 illustrations with appendix. Index. xi + 144pp. 5⅜ x 8. T169 Paperbound **$1.35**

DESIGN MOTIFS OF ANCIENT MEXICO, J. Enciso. 766 superb designs from Aztec, Olmec, Totonac, Maya, and Toltec origins. Plumed serpents, calendrical elements, wind gods, animals, flowers, demons, dancers, monsters, abstract ornament, and other designs. More than 90% of these illustrations are completely unobtainable elsewhere. Use this work to bring new barbaric beauty into your crafts or drawing. Originally $17.50. 766 illustrations, thousands of motifs. 192pp. 7⅞ x 10¾.   T84 Paperbound **$1.85**

AFRICAN SCULPTURE, Ladislas Segy. First publication of a new book by the author of critically acclaimed AFRICAN SCULPTURE SPEAKS. 163 full-page plates illustrating masks, fertility figures, ceremonial objects, etc., representing the culture of 50 tribes of West and Central Africa. Over 95% of these works of art have never been illustrated before. A 34 page introduction explains the anthropological, psychological, and artistic values of African sculpture. "Mr. Segy is one of its top authorities," NEW YORKER. 164 full-page photographic plates. Bibliography. 244pp. 6 x 9.   T396 Paperbound **$2.00**

PETS

THE CARE AND BREEDING OF GOLDFISH, Anthony Evans. Hundreds of important details about indoor and outdoor pools and aquariums; the history, physical features and varieties of goldfish; selection, care, feeding, health and breeding — with a special appendix that shows you how to build your own goldfish pond. Enlarged edition, newly revised. Bibliography. 22 full-page plates; 4 figures. 128pp. 5 x 7¼.   T920 Paperbound **75¢**

THE CARE OF CATS, K. Wilson and A. Webb. Practical advice on housebreaking, feeding, grooming, breeding, breaking cats of furniture scratching, collars, grass, many other subjects. From Abyssinians to Siamese, cats in art and folklore are discussed. 3 chapters on neutering, lice, worms, distemper, bad breath, colds, rabies, etc. Bibliography. 55 illustrations, some by famous artists. 105pp. 5 x 7¼.
T912 Paperbound **65¢**

OBEDIENCE TRAINING FOR YOUR DOG, C. Wimhurst. You can teach your dog to heel, retrieve, sit, jump, track, climb, refuse food, etc. Covers house training, developing a watchdog, obedience tests, working trials, police dogs. "Proud to recommend this book to every dog owner who is attempting to train his dog," says Blanche Saunders, noted American trainer, in her Introduction. Index. 34 photographs. 122pp. 5 x 7¼.   T938 Paperbound **75¢**

AQUARIUMS, A. Evans. Instructions on building aquariums at home: glass and cement, aerating, heating, electric wiring, etc. How to stock with waterplants; the care, breeding, diseases and difficulties of fish rearing; fish communities, and other topics. Covers tropical fish (including seahorses), goldfish, coldwater fish, and how to build, stock and maintain outdoor garden ponds. "The best small book in English on aquariums and general aquarium care," AQUARIUM JOURNAL. 115 illustrations. Bibliography. Index. 115pp. 5 x 7¼.   T900 Paperbound **65¢**